GEMSTONE
& MINERAL
DATA BOOK

GEMSTONE & MINERAL DATA BOOK

A COMPILATION OF DATA, RECIPES, FORMULAS
AND INSTRUCTIONS FOR THE MINERALOGIST,
GEMOLOGIST, LAPIDARY, JEWELER,
CRAFTSMAN AND COLLECTOR

JOHN SINKANKAS

VNR VAN NOSTRAND REINHOLD COMPANY
NEW YORK   CINCINNATI   TORONTO   LONDON   MELBOURNE

First published by Van Nostrand Reinhold in 1981
Copyright © 1972 by John Sinkankas
Library of Congress Catalog Card Number 80-52974
ISBN 0-442-24709-5

Van Nostrand Reinhold Company
A division of Litton Educational Publishing, Inc.
135 West 50th Street, New York, NY 10020

Van Nostrand Reinhold Ltd.
1410 Birchmount Road, Scarborough, Ontario M1P 2E7

Van Nostrand Reinhold Australia Pty. Ltd.
17 Queen Street, Mitcham, Victoria 3132

Van Nostrand Reinhold Company Ltd.
Molly Millars Lane, Wokingham, Berkshire, England RG11 2PY

Cloth edition published 1972 by Winchester Press
First paperback edition published 1974 by Collier Books

16 15 14 13 12 11 10 9 8 7 6 5 4 3 2 1

To Don MacLachlan
Editor and Publisher of **Gems and Minerals**
For a career devoted to
promoting the interests of the amateur
in geology, mineralogy, lapidary and the allied arts

Preface

This book is a compilation of data, recipes, formulas and instructions designed specifically for use by mineralogists, gemologists, jewelers and lapidaries. Aside from providing a readily available source book it also saves each reader the tedious task of ferreting out the information for himself from among the many dozens of references used by the author.

Work on this project began several years ago upon the urging of friends and correspondents who stated that a text dealing extensively with cleaning mineral specimens was needed. During the search for information it became apparent that equally important subject matter should be included with the result that the book expanded to its present size and scope. While most of the information is derived from the sources referenced throughout the text, much is original, reflecting the personal experiences of the author in testing materials and techniques used in lapidary and mineralogical work.

In addition, the extensive lists of properties of gemstones and minerals for example, are believed to be the most complete in existence. The list of minerals for which solubilities and/or cleaning instructions are given includes over 1400 entries and again is believed to be the most extensive compilation available. Aside from the unique nature of such data, the variety and completeness of subject matter elsewhere in the book should do much to eliminate the frustration and waste of time that all of us have experienced at one time or another in seeking the odd fact or obscure formula that we know exists yet cannot readily find in texts at hand.

In the course of research, other interesting data had to be regretfully put aside because of its marginal value as compared to space limitations imposed on the book itself. Perhaps readers may want such information included in succeeding editions. If this is the case, suggestions for enlargement or improvement will be most seriously considered.

John Sinkankas

San Diego, California
June, 1972

Contents

GEMSTONE
& MINERAL
DATA BOOK

Part 1 / *Weights, Measures, Conversions, and Mathematical Formulas*

WEIGHTS AND MEASURES:
METRIC SYSTEM

with appropriate equivalents in other systems.

Length

1 kilometer (km)	= 1,000 meters (m)
	= 100 dekameters (dkm)
	= 10 hectometers (hm)
	= 0.621372 statute mile
1 meter (m)	= 1,000 millimeters (mm)
	= 100 centimeters (cm)
	= 10 decimeters (dm)
	= 1.0936 yards
	= 3.2808 feet
	= 39.37 inches
1 centimeter (cm)	= 10 millimeters
	= 0.032808 foot
	= 0.39370 inch
1 millimeter (mm)	= 1,000 microns (μ)
	= 0.03937 inch
1 micron (μ)	= 1/10,000 centimeter
	= 1/1,000 millimeter
1 angstrom (A)	= 1/100,000,000 centimeter
	= 1/10,000 micron

Volume

1 cubic meter (m^3)	= 35.3144 cu. ft.
	= 1.3079 cu. yd.
1 cubic cm (cm^3)	= 0.0610 cu. inch

Capacity

1 liter (l)	= volume of pure water which weighs 1 kg at standard pressure and temperature
	= 10 deciliters (dl)
	= 100 centiliters (cl)
	= 1,000 milliliters (ml)
	= 1.0567 liquid quarts
	= 0.2641 gallon

1 milliliter (ml)	= 1 cubic centimeter
	= 0.0610 cu. in.

Weight

1 metric ton	= 1,000 kilograms (kg)
	= 2,204.622 lb. avoir.
	= 0.9842 long ton
	= 1.1023 short tons
1 kilogram (kg)	= 10 hectograms (hg)
	= 100 dekagrams (dkg)
	= 1,000 grams (g or gm)
	= 2.2046 lb. avoir.
	= 2.6792 lb. troy
	= 32.15076 oz. troy
	= 35.2739 oz. avoir.
	= 643.01 pennyweights (dwt.)
	= 15,432.3563 grains (gr.)
1 gram (gm)	= 1,000 milligrams (mg)
	= 5 metric carats (ct)
	= 0.00220 lb. avoir.
	= 0.03527 oz. avoir.
	= 0.03215 oz. troy
	= 0.6430 pennyweight
	= 15.4324 grains
1 milligram (mg)	= 0.005 carat
	= 0.015432 grain
1 metric carat	= 200 milligrams
	= 1/5 gram
	= 0.0070548 oz. avoir.
	= 3.08647 grains
	= 4 pearl grains
	= 0.1286 pennyweight

WEIGHTS AND MEASURES:
U.S. SYSTEM

with appropriate equivalents in other systems.

Length

1 mile (mi.)	= 320 rods (rd.)
	= 1,760 yards (yd.)

1 rod (rd.)	= 5,280 feet (ft.)
	= 1.60935 kilometers
	= 5.5 yards
	= 16.5 feet
	= 198 inches (in.)
	= 5.0292 meters
1 yard (yd.)	= 3 feet
	= 36 inches
	= 0.9144 meter
1 inch (in.)	= 1,000 mils
	= 2.54001 centimeters
	= 25.4001 millimeters
1 mil	= 25.4001 microns
	= 0.0254001 millimeter

Volume

1 cubic yard (cu. yd.)	= 27 cubic feet (cu. ft.)
	= 46,656 cubic inches (cu. in.)
	= 0.76456 cubic meter
1 cubic foot (cu. ft.)	= 1,728 cubic inches
	= 0.02832 cubic meter
	= 7.481 U.S. gallons
1 cubic inch (cu. in.)	= 16.3872 cubic centimeters

Capacity

1 gallon (gal.)	= 4 quarts (qt.)
	= 8 pints (pt.)
	= 32 gills (gi.)
	= 128 fluid ounces (fl. oz.)
	= 231 cubic inches
	= 3.7853 liters
	= about 8.337 lb. avoir. weight of water
	= 3.7820 kg of water
	= 0.83268 British gallon
1 quart (qt.)	= 2 pints
	= 8 gills
	= 32 fluid ounces
	= 57.749 cubic inches
	= 0.94633 liter
1 pint (pt.)	= 4 gills
	= 16 fluid ounces
	= 28.875 cubic inches
	= 0.47317 liter

Apothecaries' Fluid Measure

1 pint (pt.)	= the capacity pint above
	= 16 fluid ounces (fl. oz.)
	= 128 fluid drams (fl. dr.)
	= 7,680 minims (min.)
	= 0.47317 liter

1 fluid ounce (fl. oz.)	= 8 fluid drams
	= 480 minims
	= 1.80469 cubic inches
	= 29.5729 milliliters
1 fluid dram (fl. dr.)	= 60 minims
	= 3.6966 milliliters

Avoirdupois Weight

1 short ton (tn.)	= 2,000 pounds (lb.)
	= 32,000 ounces (oz.)
	= 907.18486 kilograms
	= 2,430.56 troy pounds
	= 0.89286 long ton
1 pound (lb.)	= 16 ounces (oz. avoir.)
	= 256 drams (dr. avoir.)
	= 7,000 grains (gr.)
	= 0.45359 kilogram
	= 453.5924 grams
	= 27.692 cubic inches of water
	= 1.21528 troy pounds
	= 14.5833 troy ounces
	= 291.667 pennyweights
	= 1 British pound
1 ounce (oz. avoir.)	= 16 drams
	= 437.5 grains
	= 28.34953 grams
	= 0.91146 troy ounce
	= 18.22917 pennyweights
	= 141.75 carats

Troy Weight

1 pound (lb. t.)	= 12 ounces (oz. t.)
	= 240 pennyweights (dwt.)
	= 5,760 grains (gr.)
	= 0.82286 pound avoir.
	= 13.1657 ounces avoir.
	= 373.24177 grams
	= 0.373242 kilogram
	= 1,866.12 carats
1 ounce (oz. t.)	= 20 pennyweights
	= 480 grains
	= 1.09714 ounces avoir.
	= 31.1075 grams
	= 155.51 carats
1 pennyweight (dwt.)	= 24 grains
	= 0.003429 pound avoir.
	= 0.05486 ounce avoir.
	= 1.5517 grams
	= 7.77 carats
1 grain (gn. t.)	= 1 grain avoir.
	= 0.041667 pennyweight
	= 0.0648 gram
	= 0.3240 carat
	= 64.7989 milligrams

United States—Great Britain Equivalents

U.S.	Great Britain

1 yard = 1.000003 imperial yards
      = 0.914359 meter
1 pound = 1 imperial pound almost exactly
1 gallon = 0.83267 imperial gallon
       = 4.5459631 liters

Great Britain	U.S.

1 imperial yard = 0.999997 yard
1 imperial pound = 1 pound
1 imperial gallon = 1.20095 gallons
              = 10.0 pounds avoir. of water
1 imperial quart = 1.201 quarts
1 imperial pint = 1.201 pints
1 fluid ounce = 0.961 fluid ounce

Pearl grain = 1/4 carat
Quintal, metric = 100 kilograms
              = 220.46 pounds avoir.
Stere = 1 cubic meter
Tael, Japan = 10 mommes
Tael, Hong Kong = 1.333 ounces avoir.
Tael, Thailand = 936.25 grains
Tola, India = 180 grains
Township, U.S. = 36 square miles

Weight per gallon of liquids: Multiply the specific gravity of the liquid by 8.337.

Capacities of tanks in gallons: Compute volume in cubic inches and divide result by 231.

Standard U.S. drum contents (55 gallons), lying on the side: Insert dipstick through bunghole to touch bottom, withdraw, and note inches wetted.

MISCELLANEOUS WEIGHTS AND MEASURES

Acre, U.S. = 4,840 square yards
Angstrom unit = 10^{-10} meter, or 1/10,000 micron
Arroba, Sp., Port. = 14.68-15 kilograms
Assay ton, U.S. = 29.167 grams
Bat, baht, tical = 15 grams
Catty, Orient = 1.333 pounds avoir.
Chain, U.S., G.B. = 66 feet
Cubic foot of water = 62.29 pounds avoir.
Cubic inch of water = 0.576 ounce avoir. ($22°$ C., $71.6°$ F.)
Gallon, U.S., of water = 8.337 pounds avoir.
Hectare = 2.471 acres
Hundredweight, G.B. = 112 pounds avoir.
Micron = 0.00004 inch
Mile, nautical, U.S. = 6,076.103 feet
Mile, nautical, G.B. = 6,080 feet
Mile, square = 640 acres
Mile, statute, U.S. = 5,280 feet
Momme, Japan = 1/1000 kwan
           = 3.75 grams

Inches wetted	Gallons	Inches wetted	Gallons
3	4.4	12	31.6
4	6.8	13	34.9
5	9.5	14	38.1
6	12.3	15	41.2
7	15.3	16	44.3
8	18.4	17	47.1
9	21.6	18	49.7
10	25.0	19	52.1
11	28.3	20	54.3

BARREL VOLUME. For barrels with circularly curved staves.

Approx. volume = $1/12 \times 3.1416 \times$ height $\times$ (twice the largest diameter squared + once the smallest diameter squared)

Approx. gallons = $0.0034 \times$ inches in the average diameter $\times$ height

Average diameter = 1/2 (largest diam. + smallest diam.)

BULK WEIGHTS OF VARIOUS LIQUIDS AND SOLIDS

Liquids

Substance	lb./gal.	lb./ft.^{3}	Substance	lb./gal.	lb./ft.^{3}
Acetone	6.59	49	Alcohol, methyl (100%)	6.66	50
Alcohol, ethyl (100%)	6.59	49	Benzene	7.50	56

Liquids (*Continued*)

Substance	lb./gal.	lb./ft.^{3}	Substance	lb./gal.	lb./ft.^{3}
Carbon disulfide	10.76	81	Mercury	113.4	549
Carbon tetrachloride	13.01	100	Mineral oils	7.5	57
Gasoline	6.0	45	Nitric acid		
Glycerine	10.51	79	(91%)	12.51	94
Hydrochloric	10	75	Olive oil	7.67	57
acid (40%)	6.67	50	Sulfuric acid		
Kerosene			(87%)	15.01	112
			Water	8.34	62.29
			Water, sea	8.55	63.99

Solids

Substance	lb./ft.^{3}	Substance	lb./ft.^{3}
Agate	156-168	Limestone	167-171
Alabaster (gypsum)	141-145	Magnetite	306-324
Amber	66-69	Malachite	231-256
Barite	281	Marble	160-177
Basalt	150-190	Meerschaum	62-80
Beryl	168-169	Mica	165-200
Borax	109	Opal	137
Cinnabar	507	Porphyry	162-181
Dolomite	181	Pumice	40
Emery	250	Pyrite	309-318
Feldspar	159-172	Quartz	165
Flint	164	Salt, rock	136
Fluorite	198	Sandstone	134-147
Galena	460-470	Serpentine	156-165
Garnet	197-268	Slag	125-240
Glass, common	150-175	Slate	162-205
Glass, flint	180-370	Soapstone	162-175
Gneiss	175	Syenite	165
Granite	165-172	Talc	168-174
Gypsum	144-145	Topaz	219-223
Hematite	306-330	Tourmaline	190-200

BRAZILIAN WEIGHTS AND MEASURES

Length

Legoa = 4.10 U.S. miles	= 6.6 kilometers
Milha = 1.21 U.S. miles	= 2.2 km
Braca (2 varas)	= 2.20 meters
Vara (5 palmos)	= 1.10 m
Pe (12 pollegadas)	= 0.33 m
Palmo (8 pollegadas)	= 0.22 m
Pollegada (12 linhas)	= 0.275 m
Linha (12 pontos)	= 0.0023 m
Covado	= 0.66 m
Passo geometrico	= 1.65 m

Capacity

Tonel (2 pipas)	= 253.2 U.S. gallons = 958.32 liters
Pipa (15 almudes)	= 479.16 liters
Almude (12 canadas)	= 31.944 liters
Canada (4 quartilhos)	= 2.662 liters
Quartilho (4 martellos)	= 0.6655 liter
Martello	= 0.166 liter

Weight

Tonelada (13.5 quintaes)	= 793.2384 kilograms

Quintal (4 arrobas)	= 58.7584 kg	Barrels, U.S. liq.,	
Arroba (32 libras)	= 14.6896 kg	to cu. ft.	X 4.2109
Arroba, metric	= 15 kg	to gal., U.S. liq.	X 31.5
Libra (2 marcos)	= 459.050 grams	to liters	X 0.9869
Marco (8 oncas)	= 229.525 gm	Carats to grains	X 3.0865
Onca (8 oitavas)	= 28.691 gm	to grams	X 0.2
Oitava (3 escropulos)	= 3.586 gm	to milligrams	X 200
Escropulo (6 quilates)	= 1.195 gm	Centimeters to angstroms	X 10^8
Quilate (gràos)	= 0.199 gm	to feet	X 0.0328
Quilate, metric	= 0.20 gm, or	to inches	X 0.3937
	1 carat	to microns	X 10,000
Grào	= 0.049 gm	to mils	X 393.701

WEIGHTS OF CARATS (IN MILLIGRAMS) BEFORE STANDARDIZATION ON THE METRIC CARAT OF 200 MG

Alexandria	191.7 mg
Amsterdam	205.1
Antwerp	205.3
Arabia	194.4
Austria-Hungary	206.1
Berlin	205.5
Bologna	188.5
Brazil	192.2
Constantinople	205.5
East Indies	196.9-205.5
Florence	196.5
France	205-205.5
Frankfurt	205.8
Hamburg	205.8
Lisbon	205.8
London	205.3-205.5
Madras	205.5
Persia	213.5
Russia	205.1
Spain	199.9
Turin	213.5
Venice	207.0
Vienna	206.1
Pearl carat	207.3

USEFUL CONVERSIONS

Multiply left unit by factor to obtain desired unit.

Acres to sq. ft.	X 43,560
to sq. yd.	X 4,840
Angstroms to cm	X 1×10^{-8}
to in.	X 3.937×10^{-9}
Barrels, Brit.	
to bbl., U.S. liq.	X 1.3725
to cu. ft.	X 5.7796
to gal., Brit.	X 36
to liters	X 163.655

Cubic cm to cu. inches	X 0.06102
to gal., Brit.	X 0.00022
to gal., U.S. liq.	X 0.000264
to oz., U.S. fl.	X 0.0338
to qt., U.S. liq.	X 0.00106
Cubic feet to cu. cm	X 28, 316.847
to cu. meters	X 0.028317
to gal., U.S. liq.	X 7.4805
to liters	X 28.3161
to qt., U.S. liq.	X 29.92208
Cu. ft. of water	
to lb., avoir.	X 62.4262
Cubic inches	
to cu. cm	X 16.38706
to gal., U.S. liq.	X 0.004329
to liters	X 0.01639
to oz., U.S. fl.	X 0.55411
to pt., U.S. liq.	X 0.03463
to qt., U.S. liq.	X 0.01732
Cubic meters	
to cu. ft.	X 35.3147
to cu. in.	X 61,023.74
to cu. yd.	X 1.30795
to gal., U.S. liq.	X 264.17205
to qt., U.S. liq.	X 1,056.688
Cubic yards	
to cu. meters	X 0.76455
to gal., U.S. liq.	X 201.974
to liters	X 764.5335
to qt., U.S. liq.	X 807.8961
Feet to centimeters	X 30.48
to meters	X 0.3048
Ft./min. to cm/sec.	X 0.508
to km/hr.	X 0.01829
to m/sec.	X 0.00508
to mph	X 0.011364
Gallons, Brit.,	
to cu. cm	X 4,546.087
to cu. ft.	X 0.160544
to cu. in.	X 277.4193
to gal., U.S. liq.	X 1.20095
to liters	X 4.54596
to oz., U.S. liq.	X 153.7215
to lbs. water	X 10

Gallons, U.S. liq.,
to cu. cm   X 3,785.412
to cu. ft.   X 0.13368
to cu. in.   X 231
to cu. m   X 0.0037854
to cu. yd.   X 0.004951
to gal., Brit.   X 0.83267
to liters   X 3.7853
to lb. water   X 8.34517

Grains to carats   X 0.324
to grams   X 0.0648
to milligrams   X 64.799
to oz., avoir.   X 0.002286
to oz., troy   X 0.00208
to dwt.   X 0.04167

Grams to carats   X 5
to grains   X 15.4324
to oz., avoir.   X 0.03527
to oz., troy   X 0.03215
to dwt.   X 0.64301
Hectares to acres   X 2.47105
Inches to centimeters   X 2.54
to meters   X 0.0254

Kilograms to grains   X 15,432.358
to oz., avoir.   X 35.274
to oz., troy   X 32.15074
to dwt.   X 643.015
to lb., avoir.   X 2.20462
to lb., troy   X 2.6792

Kilometers to feet   X 3,280.84
to mi., statute   X 0.62137
to yards   X 1,093.6133
Liters to cu. centimeters   X 1,000.028
to cu. feet   X 0.03532
to cu. inches   X 61.0255
to cu. yards   X 0.001308
to gal., Brit.   X 0.21998
to gal., U.S. liq.   X 0.26418
to oz., U.S. fl.   X 33.815
to pt., U.S. liq.   X 2.11344
to qt., Brit.   X 0.8799
to qt., U.S. liq.   X 1.0567

Meters to feet   X 3.28084
to inches   X 29.37008
to yards   X 1.0936133
Microns to angstroms   X 10,000
to inches   X 3.937 X 10^{-5}
Miles, statute to km   X 1.609344
to m   X 1,609.344
Milligrams to grains   X 0.015432
Milliliters to cu. cm   X 1.000028
to cu. inches   X 0.061025
to oz., Brit. fl.   X 0.035196
to oz., U.S. fl.   X 0.03381
Millimeters to angstroms   X 10^7
to feet   X 0.00328

to inches   X 0.03937
to mils   X 39.37
Ounces, avoir., to grains   X 437.5
to grams   X 28.3495
to oz., troy   X 0.91146
to dwt.   X 18.2291
to lb., troy   X 0.07595

Ounces, Brit. fl.,
to cu. cm   X 28.413
to cu. in.   X 1.73387
to ml   X 28.41225
to oz., U.S. fl.   X 0.96076

Ounces, troy, to grains   X 480
to grams   X 31.1035
to oz., avoir.   X 1.0971
to dwt.   X 20
to lb., avoir.   X 0.06857

Ounces, U.S. fl.,
to cu. cm   X 29.5737
to cu. in.   X 1.80469
to liters   X 0.02957
to oz., Brit. fl.   X 1.0408

Pennyweights to grains   X 24
to grams   X 1.5551
to oz., avoir.   X 0.05486
Pounds, avoir., to grains   X 7,000
to grams   X 453.592
to kg   X 0.4536
to oz., troy   X 14.58333
Pounds, troy, to grams   X 373.24172
to kg   X 0.37324
to oz., avoir.   X 13.1657
to lb., avoir.   X 0.82286

Quarts, Brit.,
to cu. cm   X 1,136.522
to cu. inches   X 69.3548
to gal., U.S. liq.   X 0.30024
to qt., U.S. liq.   X 1.20095
Quarts, U.S. liq.,
to cu. cm   X 946.353
to cu. ft.   X 0.033420
to cu. in.   X 57.75
to liters   X 0.94633
to qt., Brit.   X 0.83267
Sq. cm to sq. feet   X 0.001076
to sq. inches   X 0.1550
Sq. feet to sq. centimeters   X 929.03
to sq. meters   X 0.09290
Sq. inches to sq. cm   X 6.4516
to sq. meters   X 0.000645
Sq. meters to sq. feet   X 10.76391
to sq. inches   X 1,550.003
to sq. yards   X 1.19599
Sq. millimeters to sq. in.   X 0.00155
Sq. yards to sq. cm   X 8,361.2736
to sq. inches   X 1,296

to sq. meters	× 0.83613	Tons, short, to kilograms	× 907.185
Tons, long, to kilograms	× 1,016.047	to tons, long	× 0.89286
to lb., avoir.	× 2,240	to tons, metric	× 0.90719
to tons, metric	× 1.01605	Townships, U.S.,	
to tons, short	× 1.12	to acres	× 23,040
Tons, metric,		to sections	× 36
to lb., avoir.	× 2,204.6226	to sq. miles	× 36
to tons, long	× 0.9842	Yards to centimeters	× 91.44
to tons, short	× 1.10231	to meters	× 0.9144

FRACTIONS AND DECIMALS: INCHES TO MILLIMETERS

Fractions	Decimals	Millimeters	Fractions	Decimals	Millimeters
1/64	0.15625	0.3969	33/64	0.515625	13.0968
1/32	0.03125	0.7937	17/32	0.53125	13.4936
3/64	0.046875	1.1906	35/64	0.546875	13.8905
1/16	0.0625	1.5875	9/16	0.5625	14.2874
5/64	0.078125	1.9843	37/64	0.578125	14.6842
3/32	0.09375	2.3812	19/32	0.59375	15.0811
7/64	0.109375	2.7781	39/64	0.609375	15.4780
1/8	0.125	3.1750	5/8	0.625	15.8749
9/64	0.140625	3.5718	41/64	0.640625	16.2717
5/32	0.15625	3.9687	21/32	0.65625	16.6686
11/64	0.171875	4.3656	43/64	0.671875	17.0655
3/16	0.1875	4.7624	11/16	0.6875	17.4623
13/64	0.203125	5.1593	45/64	0.703125	17.8592
7/32	0.21875	5.5562	23/32	0.71875	18.2561
15/64	0.234375	5.9530	47/64	0.734375	18.6529
1/4	0.25	6.3499	3/4	0.75	19.0498
17/64	0.265625	6.7468	49/64	0.765625	19.4467
9/32	0.28125	7.1437	25/32	0.78125	19.8436
19/64	0.29875	7.5405	51/64	0.796875	20.2404
5/16	0.3125	7.9374	13/16	0.8125	20.6373
21/64	0.328125	8.3343	53/64	0.828125	21.0342
11/32	0.34375	8.7312	27/32	0.84375	21.4311
23/64	0.359375	9.1280	55/64	0.859375	21.8279
3/8	0.375	9.5249	7/8	0.875	22.2248
25/64	0.390625	9.9217	57/64	0.890625	22.6216
13/32	0.40625	10.3186	29/32	0.90625	23.0185
27/64	0.421875	10.7155	59/64	0.921875	23.4154
7/16	0.4375	11.1124	15/16	0.9375	23.8123
29/64	0.453125	11.5092	61/64	0.933125	24.2091
15/32	0.46875	11.9061	31/32	0.96875	24.6060
31/64	0.484375	12.3030	63/64	0.984375	25.0029
1/2	0.5	12.6999	1	1.0	25.4001

Integers: Inches to Millimeters

Inches	Millimeters	Inches	Millimeters
1	25.40	7	177.80
2	50.80	8	203.20
3	76.20	9	228.60
4	101.60	10	254.00
5	127.00	11	279.40
6	152.40	12	304.80

Millimeters	Inches	Millimeters	Inches
1	0.03937	34	1.3386
2	0.07874	35	1.3780
3	0.11811	36	1.4173
4	0.15748	37	1.4567
5	0.19685	38	1.4961
6	0.23622	39	1.5354
7	0.27559	40	1.5748
8	0.31496	41	1.6142
9	0.35433	42	1.6535
10	0.39370	43	1.6929
11	0.43307	44	1.7323
12	0.47244	45	1.7717
13	0.51181	46	1.8110
14	0.55118	47	1.8504
15	0.59055	48	1.8898
16	0.62992	49	1.9291
17	0.66929	50	1.9685
18	0.70866	51	2.0079
19	0.74803	52	2.0472
20	0.78740	53	2.0866
21	0.82677	54	2.1260
22	0.86614	55	2.1654
23	0.90551	60	2.3622
24	0.94488	65	2.5591
25	0.98425	70	2.7559
26	1.0236	75	2.9528
27	1.0630	80	3.1496
28	1.1024	85	3.3465
29	1.1417	90	3.5433
30	1.1811	95	3.7402
31	1.2205	100	3.9370
32	1.2598	105	4.1339
33	1.2992	110	4.3307

LENGTHS AND AREAS OF PLANE FIGURES

SQUARE. Four sides of equal length; 4 angles, each = $90°$. Angle subtended by each side = $90°$.

Area = length of a side squared
Diagonal length = 1.414 $\times$ side

CIRCLE INSCRIBED IN SQUARE. The diameter is the same as the length of a side.

Radius = 1/2 side
Area = 0.7854 $\times$ area of the square
Circumference = 3.1416 $\times$ side

CIRCLE CIRCUMSCRIBED AROUND SQUARE. The diameter is equal to the diagonal of the square.

Radius = 0.7071 $\times$ side
Area = 1.5708 $\times$ side squared
Circumference = 3.1416 $\times$ diagonal of square, or
= 3.1416 $\times$ 1.414 $\times$ side of square

RECTANGLE. A distorted square in which the angles remain $90°$ but only opposite pairs of sides are equal in length.

Area = height $\times$ base (one side $\times$ adjacent side)
Diagonal = square root of (height squared + base squared)

PARALLELOGRAM. A diagonally distorted rectangle with no angles equal to $90°$ but with two pairs of sides, each of equal length.

Area = height X base, or one side X the perpendicular distance between the adjacent pair of faces

RHOMBUS. A special form of the parallelogram in which all sides are of equal length; a lozenge.

Area = 1/2 of (larger diagonal X shorter diagonal)

TRAPEZOID. Four-sided figure in which two sides are parallel but the others are not.

Area = 1/2 of the total length of the two parallel sides X the perpendicular distance between them

Circle

Area = 3.1416 X the square of the radius

Circumference = 3.1416 X the diameter, or
= 3.1416 X twice the radius, or
= 0.7854 X the diameter squared

Sector (pie-shaped section) area
= 1/2 radius X the length along the circumference

Circular Ring

Area = area of the larger circle minus the area of the smaller, or
= 3.1416 X (larger radius squared – smaller radius squared), or
= 3.1416 X (large radius + small radius) X (large radius– small radius)

Ellipse

Area = 1.5708 X longest diameter X smallest diameter

TRIANGLE. The sum of the interior angles for any triangle always equals $180°$.

RIGHT TRIANGLE. The angle between the two shorter sides is $90°$. The longest side is called the hypotenuse.

Hypotenuse = square root of the sum of the squares of the other two sides, that is,
hyp = $\sqrt{\text{side } a^2 + \text{side } b^2}$

Area = 1/2 side a X side b

CIRCLE CIRCUMSCRIBED AROUND A RIGHT TRIANGLE. The diameter is always equal to the hypotenuse.

Circumference = 3.1416 X hypotenuse

Area = 0.7854 x (side a squared + side b squared)

AREA OF ANY TRIANGLE, with sides a, b, and c.

Area = 1/2 of (base X height), or

$$\text{Area} = \sqrt{s \times (s - a) \times (s - b) \times (s - c)},$$

where $s = \frac{1}{2}(a + b + c)$.

EQUILATERAL TRIANGLE. All sides equal in length, the interior angles are all equal to $60°$.

Area = 1/2 base X height, or
Area = 0.43301 X one side squared

Circle Circumscribed Around an Equilateral Triangle

Radius = 0.57774 X side
Circumference = 3.1416 X 1.1555 X side
Area = 3.1416 X the square of (1.1555 X side)

Circle Inscribed in Equilateral Triangle

Radius = 0.2887 X side
Circumference = 3.1416 X 5.7774 X side
Area = 3.1416 X square of (0.2887 X side)

RADIUS OF CIRCLE CIRCUMSCRIBED AROUND ANY TRIANGLE, with sides a, b, and c.

$$\text{Radius} = \frac{a \times b \times c}{4\sqrt{s(s - a)(s - b)(s - c)}}$$

where $s = \frac{1}{2}(a + b + c)$.

RADIUS OF CIRCLE INSCRIBED IN ANY TRIANGLE, with sides a, b, and c.

$$\text{Radius} = \sqrt{\frac{s(s - a)(s - b)(s - c)}{s}}$$

REGULAR POLYGON. All sides are of equal length and all the angles between the sides are the same value.

REGULAR PENTAGON. Five sides, angles between sides = $108°$; the angle subtended by each side is $72°$.

Radius of circumscribed circle = 0.85065 X side

Radius of inscribed circle
= 0.68819 X side

Area = 1.72048 X one side squared

REGULAR HEXAGON. Six sides, angles between sides = 120°; subtended angle of each side is 60°.

Radius of circumscribed circle = length of side

Radius of inscribed circle = 0.86602 X side

Area = 2.59808 X one side squared

REGULAR OCTAGON. Eight sides, angles between sides = 135°; subtended angle of each side is 45°.

Radius of circumscribed circle = 1.3065 X side

Radius of inscribed circle = 1.2071 X side

Area = 4.82843 X one side squared

REGULAR DECAGON. Ten sides, angles between sides = 144°; subtended angle of each side is 36°.

Radius of circumscribed circle = 1.6180 X side

Radius of inscribed circle = 1.5388 X side

Area = 7.6942 X one side squared

REGULAR DODECAGON. Twelve sides, angles between sides = 150°; subtended angle of each side is 30°.

Radius of circumscribed circle = 1.9318 X side

Radius of inscribed circle = 1.8660 X side

Area = 11.19615 X one side squared

VOLUMES AND AREAS OF SOLIDS

Sphere

Volume = 0.523599 X cube of diameter

= 4.188790 X cube of radius

= 2/3 the volume of the circumscribed cylinder

Area = 4 X 3.1416 X square of radius

= 3.1416 X square of diameter

= lateral area of circumscribed cylinder.

CYLINDER. Formulas apply to any type of cylinder.

Volume = area of cross-section X height

Lateral area = perimeter (or circumference) of cross-section X height

CONE. Formula applies to any type of cone.

Volume = 1/3 base area X height

RIGHT CIRCULAR CONE. The apex is perpendicularly above the center of the circular base.

Volume = 1.0472 X radius of base squared X height

Lateral area = 3.1416 X radius X slant height

Slant height = square root of (radius squared + height squared)

PRISM. The formulas below apply to all types.

Volume = area of base X height

Lateral area = perimeter of base X height

PYRAMID. The formula below applies to all types.

Volume = 1/3 area of base X height

Regular Pyramid

Volume = 1/3 base area X height

Lateral area = 1/2 slant height X perimeter of base

Slant height = distance from the center of any bottom edge to the vertex = square root of (radius of inscribed circle squared + height squared)

ELLIPSOID. A solid formed by revolving an ellipse about a major or minor axis. The values *a*, *b*, and *c* represent *one-half* the length of each of the three axes.

Volume = 4/3 X 3.1416 X *a* X *b* X *c*

REGULAR TETRAHEDRON. Bounded by 4 equilateral triangles.

Area = 1.7321 X edge squared

Volume = 0.1179 X edge squared

Cube

Area = 6 X edge squared

Volume = edge cubed

REGULAR OCTAHEDRON. Bounded by 8 equilateral triangles.

Area = 3.4641 X edge squared

Volume = 0.4714 X edge cubed

REGULAR PENTAGONAL DODECA-
HEDRON. Bounded by 12 regular penta-
gons.

Area = 20.6457 × edge squared
Volume = 7.6631 × edge cubed

REGULAR ICOSAHEDRON. Bounded
by 20 equilateral triangles.

Area = 8.6603 × edge squared
Volume = 2.817 × edge cubed

SPEEDS AND DISTANCES, CONVERSIONS FOR TOURING

KILOMETERS TO MILES. Conversion
factor: 1 kilometer = 0.621 mile. For
rough conversion use the following
method:

Step 1. Multiply km by 6,

Step 2. Drop last zero, the result is
miles.

Example: 60 km × 6 = 360; drop last
zero, = 36 miles.

HANDY CAR TABLE. To be posted
on a strip of paper readily visible to the
motorist. See table A.

You may add the figures to obtain values
not given in the table. See table B.

MILES TO KILOMETERS. Conversion
factor: 1 mile = 1.609 kilometers. For
rough conversion *add* 6 km to each 10
miles as follows:

Example: 60 miles, add 6 × 6 = 36, or
60 + 36 = 96 kilometers. See tables C and D.

GASOLINE VOLUME EQUIVALENTS

Gasoline (petrol) is sold by the *gallon* in
the U.S., by the *imperial gallon* in Canada
and the United Kingdom, and by the *liter*
in Mexico and elsewhere. These measures
are considerably different in volume, hence
also in price. Conversion factors are:

U.S. gallon   = 0.833 imp. gal.
                = 3.785 liters
Imperial gallon = 1.201 U.S. gal.
                = 4.546 liters
Liter   = 0.264 U.S. gal.
                = 0.22 imp. gal.

For very rough conversion, the U.S.
gallon = 4 liters and the imperial gallon =
1-1/5 U.S. gallon. See tables E and F.

A

Kilometers:	1	5	8	10	25	40	60	100
Miles:	5/8	3.1	5	6.2	15.5	25	37	62

B

Kilometers to Miles

Kilometers	Miles	Kilometers	Miles	Kilometers	Miles
1	0.621	15	9.321	65	40.389
2	1.242	20	12.427	70	43.496
3	1.864	25	15.534	75	46.603
4	2.486	30	18.641	80	49.710
5	3.107	35	21.748	85	52.816
6	3.728	40	24.855	90	55.923
7	4.350	45	27.962	95	59.030
8	4.971	50	31.069	100	62.137
9	5.592	55	34.175		
10	6.214	60	37.282		

C

Miles:	1	5	10	25	40	50	60	100
Kilometers:	1.6	8	16	40	65	80	97	161

Miles to Kilometers

Miles	Kilometers	Miles	Kilometers	Miles	Kilometers
1	1.609	15	24.14	65	104.60
2	3.219	20	32.18	70	112.65
3	4.828	25	40.23	75	120.69
4	6.437	30	48.28	80	128.74
5	8.047	35	56.32	85	136.78
6	9.656	40	64.37	90	144.84
7	11.265	45	72.42	95	152.88
8	12.874	50	80.05	100	160.94
9	14.484	55	88.09		
10	16.094	60	96.56		

E

U.S. gallons	1	3	5	7	9	11	13	15
Imp. gallon	0.83	2.5	4.2	5.8	7.5	9.2	10.8	12.5
Liters	3.8	11.4	18.9	26.5	33.9	41.6	49.2	56.8

F

US to Imp		US to L		Imp to US		Imp to L		L to US		L to Imp	
1 =	0.83	1 =	3.79	1 =	1.20	1 =	4.55	1 =	0.26	1 =	0.22
2	1.67	2	7.57	2	2.40	2	9.09	2	0.53	2	0.44
3	2.5	3	11.36	3	3.60	3	13.64	3	0.79	3	0.66
4	3.33	4	15.14	4	4.80	4	18.18	4	1.06	4	0.88
5	4.17	5	18.93	5	6.00	5	22.73	5	1.32	5	1.10
6	5.0	6	22.71	6	7.21	6	27.28	6	1.58	6	1.32
7	5.83	7	26.5	7	8.41	7	31.82	7	1.85	7	1.54
8	6.66	8	30.28	8	9.61	8	36.37	8	2.11	8	1.76
9	7.5	9	34.07	9	10.81	9	40.91	9	2.38	9	1.98
10	8.33	10	37.85	10	12.01	10	45.5	10	2.64	10	2.2
11	9.16	11	41.64	11	13.21	11	50.0	11	2.9	11	2.42
12	10.0	12	45.42	12	14.41	12	54.55	12	3.17	12	2.64
13	10.83	13	49.21	13	15.61	13	59.1	13	3.43	13	2.86
14	11.66	14	52.99	14	16.81	14	63.64	14	3.7	14	3.08
15	12.5	15	56.78	15	18.02	15	68.19	15	3.96	15	3.30

WORLD WEATHER SUMMARY

Maximum and minimum daily temperatures and number of days per month with precipitation are given for selected cities of the world to assist in planning of trips, especially field trips to rural areas.

AUSTRALIA. *Sydney:* pleasant temperate. Jan. 78°-65° F. (25°-18° C.), 14 days. July. 60°-46° F. (15°-8° C.), 12 days. Rain very evenly distributed throughout the year. *Melbourne:* similar. Interior of Australia: very dry, sunny, cold to hot desert climate. New Zealand, *Auckland:* cool temperate. Jan.-Feb. 73°-60° F. (23°-15° C.), 10 days. July. 56°-46° F. (13°-8° C.), 21 days. Rain occurs in every month.

AUSTRIA. *Vienna:* cool temperate.

Jul. 75°-59° F. (24°-14° C.), 9 days. Jan. 34°-26° F. (1°- -4° C.), 8 days. Precipitation evenly distributed throughout year.

BELGIUM. *Brussels:* cool temperate. Jul. 73°-54° F. (23°-12° C.), 11 days. Jan. 43°-31° F. (6°-0° C.), 12 days. Even distribution of precipitation during year.

BRAZIL. *Rio de Janeiro:* warm, humid all year. Jul. driest month, 75°-63° F. (24°-17° C.), 7 days. Jan. 84°-73° F. (29°-23° C.), 13 days. Rainiest period Dec.-Feb. *Sao Paulo:* like Rio. Feb. 82°-64° F. (27°-18° C.), 17 days. Jun.-Jul., 71°-49° F. (21°-10° C.), 6-8 days. Driest in Jun.-Aug., wettest Jan.-Feb. Driest months and easiest accessibility to *mining areas of interior* in May-Aug.; Sept. or April marginal with considerable rain. *Belo Horizonte:* pleasant temperate. Feb. (rainy season) 72° F. (22° C.) to 63° F. (17° C.) in July dry season. *Teofilo Ottoni:* driest in July, about 1″ (22 mm) rain; June-Sept. nearly as dry, but by October rain sharply increases and remains at a high level to June with the monthly average at 4″ (100 mm) to 9.7″ (244 mm).

BRITISH ISLES. *Edinburgh:* cool temperate. Jul. 65°-52° F. (18°-11° C.), 17 days. Jan.-Feb. 43°-35° F. (6°-2° C.), 15-18 days. Rain rather evenly distributed throughout the year with an average of about 15-18 days per month. *London:* cool temperate. Jul. 73°-55° F. (23°-13° C.), 13 days. Jan. 44°-35° F. (7°-2° C.), 17 days. Rain usually distributed rather evenly over year, but "dry" spells are most likely to occur in Jul.-Aug.; average of 11-17 days per month rainfall.

BURMA. *Rangoon:* warm to hot, humid. April 97°-76° F. (36°-24° C.), 2 days. Aug. 85°-76° F. (30°-24° C.), 25 days. Dry season Nov.-April; wettest months Jun.-Sept. with 20-26 days per month.

CEYLON. *Colombo:* very uniform warm, humid climate. Mar.-April 88°-74° F. (31°-23° C.), 8-14 rainy days per month. Dec. 85°-72° F. (29°-22° C.), 10 days. Driest during Jan.-March, 6-8 days per month. Gem areas in interior essentially same.

COLOMBIA. *Bogota:* mild to cool temperate. Feb. 68°-49° F. (20°-10° C.), 7 days. Jul. 64°-50° F. (18°-10° C.), 18 days. Jan.-Feb. driest months; all others average 13-20 days per month.

CZECHOSLOVAKIA. *Prague:* cool temperate. Jul. 74°-58° F. (23°-14° C.), 14 days. Jan. 34°-25° F. (1°- -5° C.), 12 days. Uniform monthly precipitation throughout the year.

DENMARK. *Copenhagen:* cool temperate. Jul. 72°-55° F. (22°-13° C.), 9 days. Jan.-Feb. 36°-28° F. (2°- -3° C.), 7-9 days. Uniform monthly precipitation during the year.

FRANCE. *Paris:* temperate. Jul. 76°-55° F. (24°-13° C.), 12 days. Jan. 42°-32° F. (5°-0° C.), 15 days. Fairly uniform rain distribution throughout the months.

GERMANY. *Bonn:* cool temperate. Jul. 73°-56° F. (23°-13° C.), 16 days. Feb. 37°-26° F. (3°- -3° C.), 6 days. April-Dec. averages 13-19 rainy days per month. *Munich* and other cities similar.

GREECE. *Athens:* dry temperate to warm. Jul.-Aug. 90°-72° F. (32°-22° C.), less than one day rain. Jan. 54°-42° F. (12°-5° C.), 7 days. *Laurion* climate same.

HONG KONG. Pleasant moderate to warm, low rainfall. Jul.-Aug. 87°-78° F. (30°-26° C.), 15-17 days. Jan. 63°-55° F. (17°-12° C.), 5 days. Driest during Oct.-April, 2-8 days rain per month average.

ICELAND. *Reykjavik:* cold, disagreeable windy and rainy climate. Jul. 58°-48° F. (14°-9° C.), 16 days. Jan. 36°-28° F. (2°- -2° C.), 20 days. Average rainy days 16-20 throughout year. There is no "dry" season although Jul.-Aug.-Sept. are slightly better.

INDIA. *Bombay:* warm to hot, dry to wet. May 91°-80° F. (33°-27° C.), 1 day. Jan.-Feb. 83°-67° F. (28°-19° C.) less than one day. Driest months Oct.-May; wettest, during the monsoon, Jun.-Sept., 13-19 days per month. Climate at *Poona* similar. In the interior the climate becomes drier with greater temperature variations as one goes north away from the Indian Ocean.

ITALY. *Milan:* moderate temperate. Jul. 84°-64° F. (29°-18° C.), 6 days. Jan. 40°-29° F. (4°- -2° C.), 7 days. Uniform distribution of 6-7 rainy days per month throughout year. *Cagliari* (Sardinia): pleasant temperate. Jul. 86°-56° F. (30°-13° C.), 1 day. Jan. 57°-42° F. (14°-6° C.), 9 days. Maximum rain during Dec.-Jan.; driest months Jun.-Sept. *Rome:* temperate to warm. Jul.-Aug. 88°-64° F. (31°-18° C.), 2-3 days. Jan. 54°-39° F. (12°-4° C.), 8 days. Maximum rainfall during Feb. 11

days. Summer months dry. *Naples:* mild to warm. Jul.-Aug. 86°-67° F. (30°-19° C.), 1-3 days. Jan. 54°-42° F. (12°-6° C.), 11 days. Rainy season Nov.-Feb., 11 days per month.

JAPAN. *Tokyo:* temperate. Aug. 86°-72° F. (30°-22° C.), 9 days. Jan. 47°-29° F. (8°- -2° C.), 5 days. Maximum rainfall Sept. 12 days. *Nagasaki:* Aug. 88°-74° F. (31°-23° C.), 9 days. Jan. 49°-36° F. (10°-2° C.), 11 days. Rainfall uniformly 6-11 days per month throughout the year.

MADAGASCAR. *Tananarive:* pleasant to warm. Nov. 81°-58° F. (27°-14° C.), 13 days. Jul. 68°-48° F. (20°-9° C.), 10 days. Wettest period during Dec.-March, 17-21 days per month; driest during May-Oct. 7-11 days per month.

MEXICO. *Mexico City:* mild, uniform temperate. May 78°-54° F. (25°-12° C.), 17 days. Jan. 66°-42° F. (19°-5° C.), 4 days. Wettest during June-Sept., 21-27 days per month. Much drier climate over most of northern Mexico and Baja California, becoming hotter and more humid along Pacific and Caribbean coasts southward.

MOZAMBIQUE. *Beira:* warm to hot, fairly dry. Jan.-Feb. 89°-75° F. (32°-24° C.), 11-12 days. Jul. 77°-61° F. (25°-16° C.), 4 days. Driest during Jul.-Aug., 3-4 days per month.

NETHERLANDS. *Amsterdam:* cool temperate. Jul. 69°-59° F. (21°-15° C.), 11 days. Jan. 40°-34° F. (4°-1° C.), 19 days. Driest months May-June, 12 days per month.

NORWAY. *Oslo:* cool temperate. Jul. 73°-56° F. (23°-13° C.), 10 days. Jan. 30°-20° F. (-1°- -6° C.), 8 days. Rainier in July-Dec.

RHODESIA. *Salisbury:* pleasant, warm climate. Oct. 83°-58° F. (28°-14° C.), 4 days. Jun.-Jul. 70°-44° F. (21°-7° C.), 1 day. Driest May-Sept. Wet season Nov.-March, maximum 18 days with rain per month.

SOUTH AFRICA. *'Cape Town:* temperate. Feb. 79°-60° F. (26°-16° C.), 2 days. Jul. 63°-45° F. (17°-7° C.), 10 days. *Johannesburg:* moderate temperate. Jan. 78°-58° F. (26°-14° C.), 12 days. Jun. 62°-39° F. (17°-4° C.), 1 day. Driest June-Sept., less than 2 days per month.

SOUTH VIET NAM. *Saigon:* warm to hot, humid. April 95°-76° F. (35°-24° C.),

4 days. Dec. 87°-71° F. (31° -22° C.), 7 days. Wet season May-Oct., 16-23 days per month.

SOUTH WEST AFRICA. *Windhuk:* average annual temp. 67° F. (19° C.) with Nov. 74° F. (23° C.) and July 56° F. (13° C.). Very dry climate as a whole, with the coastal area cool and with practically no rainfall; 12 inches of annual rainfall occur in the central portion, and 22 inches in the northern portion.

SPAIN. *Madrid:* moderate to warm temperate. Jul. 87°-62° F. (31°-17° C.), 3 days. Jan. 47°-33° F. (8°-1° C.), 9 days. Rainfall peaks in Mar. *Barcelona:* temperate to pleasantly warm. Aug. 82°-69° F. (28°-20° C.), 3 days. Jan. 47°-33° F. (8°-0° C.), 5 days. Maximum precipitation any month 8 days.

SWEDEN. *Stockholm:* cool temperate. Jul. 70°-55° F. (21°-13° C.), 9 days. Jan.-Feb. 31°-22° F. (0°- -5° C.), 8 days. Rainy days uniformly distributed over the year.

TANZANIA. *Dar Es Salaam:* warm to hot. Feb. 88°-77° F. (31°-25° C.), 6 days. Jul. 83°-66° F. (28°-19° C.), 6 days. Driest June-Nov.; wettest Dec.-May, with April having 19 rainy days.

U.S.S.R. *Moscow:* cold temperate. Jul. 76°-55° F. (24°-13° C.), 12 days. Jan 21°-9° F. (-6°- -13° C.), 11 days. Driest Feb.-July, 8-10 days. *Leningrad:* similar.

YUGOSLAVIA. *Belgrade:* temperate. Jul. 84°-61° F. (29°-16° C.), 6 days. Jan. 37°-27° F. (3°- -3° C.), 8 days. Rainy days 6-9 per month evenly distributed over the year.

ROMAN NUMERALS

May be expressed in capital or lowercase letters. Commonly used in preliminaries of books with lowercase used in U.S. and England, and capitals in Europe.

I = 1	XX = 20	CC = 200
II = 2	XXX = 30	CCC = 300
III = 3	XL = 40	CD = 400
IV = 4	L = 50	D = 500
V = 5	LX = 60	DC = 600
VI = 6	LXX = 70	DCC = 700
VII = 7	LXXX = 80	DCCC = 800
VIII = 8	XC = 90	CM = 900
IX = 9	IC = 99	XM = 990
X = 10	C = 100	M = 1,000

TEMPERATURE SCALES
AND CONVERSIONS

The commonly used scales are fahrenheit ($^{\circ}$F.) and centigrade ($^{\circ}$C.). They are related at several points expressing the properties of pure water, that is, at the freezing point the centigrade thermometer reads 0° while the fahrenheit reads 32°; at the boiling point of water the centigrade thermometer reads 100° while the fahrenheit reads 212°. From these relationships are derived the formulas for conversions from one scale to the other:

C. = 5/9 (F.-32°) and F. = 9/5C. + 32°

FAHRENHEIT TO CENTIGRADE. Subtract 32° from the F. temperature, multiply by 5, and then divide by 9.

Example: Given 120° F., what is the temperature in C.?

Step 1. Subtract 32° from F.
$$120 - 32 = 88$$

Step 2. Multiply by 5
$$88 \times 5 = 440$$

Step 3. Divide by 9
$$\frac{440}{9} = 48.8^{\circ} \text{ C. answer.}$$

Alternatively, one may subtract 32 from the F. temperature and divide by 1.8.

CENTIGRADE TO FAHRENHEIT. Multiply C. temperature by 9, divide by 5, and then add 32°.

Example: Given 100° C. what is the temperature in F.?

Step 1. Multiply C. by 9
$$100 \times 9 = 900$$

Step 2. Divide by 5
$$\frac{900}{5} = 180$$

Step 3. Add 32°
$$180 + 32 = 212^{\circ} \text{ F. answer.}$$

Alternative: Multiply C. by 1.8 and add 32.

Centigrade-Fahrenheit Conversion Table

C.	F.	C.	F.	C.	F.	C.	F.
0	32.0	26	78.8	52	125.6	78	172.4
1	33.8	27	80.6	53	127.4	79	174.2
2	35.6	28	82.4	54	129.2	80	176.0
3	37.4	29	84.2	55	131.0	81	177.8
4	39.2	30	86.0	56	132.8	82	179.6
5	41.0	31	87.8	57	134.6	83	181.4
6	42.8	32	89.6	58	136.4	84	183.2
7	44.6	33	91.4	59	138.2	85	185.0
8	46.4	34	93.2	60	140.0	86	186.8
9	48.2	35	95.0	61	141.8	87	188.6
10	50.0	36	96.8	62	143.6	88	190.4
11	51.8	37	98.6	63	145.4	89	192.2
12	53.6	38	100.4	64	147.2	90	194.0
13	55.4	39	102.2	65	149.0	91	195.8
14	57.2	40	104.0	66	150.8	92	197.6
15	59.9	41	105.8	67	152.6	93	199.4
16	60.8	42	107.6	68	154.4	94	201.2
17	62.6	43	109.4	69	156.2	95	203.0
18	64.4	44	111.2	70	158.0	96	204.8
19	66.2	45	113.0	71	159.8	97	206.6
20	68.0	46	114.8	72	161.6	98	208.4
21	69.8	47	116.6	73	163.4	99	210.2
22	71.6	48	118.4	74	165.2	100	212
23	73.4	49	120.2	75	167.0	110	230
24	75.2	50	122.0	76	168.8	120	248
25	77.0	51	123.8	77	170.6	130	266

C.	F.	C.	F.	C.	F.		
140	284	410	770	1,500	2,732		
150	302	420	788	1,600	2,912		
160	320	430	806	1,700	3,092		
170	338	440	824	1,800	3,272		
180	356	450	842	1,900	3,452		
190	374	460	860	2,000	3,632		
200	392	470	878	2,100	3,812		
210	410	480	896	2,200	3,992		
220	428	490	914	2,300	4,172		
230	446	500	932	2,400	4,352		
240	464	550	1,022				
250	482	600	1,112				
260	500	650	1,202				
270	518	700	1,292				
280	536	750	1,382				
290	554	800	1,472				
300	572	850	1,562				
310	590	900	1,652				
320	608	950	1,742				
330	626	1,000	1,832				
340	644	1,050	1,922				
350	662	1,100	2,012				
360	680	1,150	2,102				
370	698	1,200	2,192				
380	716	1,250	2,282				
390	735	1,300	2,372				
400	752	1,400	2,552				

USEFUL TEMPERATURE REFERENCE POINTS

	C.	F.		C.	F.
Water freezes	0°	32°	Sulfur MP	235°	455°
Glycerine freezes	18	64	Boric acid MP	236	457
Glycerine MP	20	68	Diethyl. glycol BP	245	473
Carb. disulfide BP	46	115	Bismuth MP	271	519
Acetone BP	56	133	Solder		
Methyl alcohol BP	65	148	(67% Pb, 33% Sn) MP	275	527
Wood's metal MP	70	158	Glycerine BP	290	554
Carb. tetrachlor. BP	77	170	Molten lead freezes	327	621
Ethyl alcohol BP	79	174	Mercury BP	357	675
Benzene BP	80	176	Molten zinc freezes	419	787
Isopropyl alc. BP	82	180	Sulfur BP	445	832
Water boils	100	212	Stibnite MP	525	977
Toluene BP	111	231	Borax MP	560	1,040
Bromobenzene BP	156	313	Molt. antimony freezes	630	1,166
Aniline BP	184	363	Chalcopyrite fuses	800	1,472
Glycol BP	198	388	Salt (halite, NaCl) MP	801	1,474
Naphthalene BP	218	424	Anhydr. Na-carbonate MP	851	1,562
Solder 50/50 Pb-Sn MP	225	437	Silver, U.S. coin MP	890	1,634
Molt. tin freezes	232	449	Zinc BP	907	1,665

Silver, sterling MP	920° C.	1,688° F.	Bunsen burner flame	1,870° C.	3,398° F.
Silver, pure MP	961	1,761	Oxy-hydrogen flame	2,800	5,072
Gold, pure MP	1,063	1,946	Oxy-acetylene flame	3,500	6,332
Molt. copper freezes	1,083	1,981			

Note: For other melting and boiling points see "Chemicals List" (p. 23) and "Waxes, Gums, . . ." (p. 39).

Part 2 / Chemicals, Useful Miscellaneous Materials, and Formulations

COMMON NAMES AND SYNONYMS

Name	Synonym
Acetic ether	Ethyl acetate
Acid of sugar	Oxalic acid
Aloxite	Aluminum oxide; abrasive
Alum	See "Alums" in "Chemicals List" (p. 24)
Alumina	Aluminum oxide; abrasive
Alumina, levigated	Aluminum oxide; abrasive
Alundum	Aluminum oxide; abrasive
Ammonia water	Ammonia gas diss. in water
Antifreeze	Diethylene glycol
Aqua ammonia	Same as ammonia water
Aqua fortis	Nitric acid
Aqua regia	Mix of HNO_3 + HCl
Bakelite	Phenolic resin
Baking soda	Sodium bicarbonate
Banana oil	Amyl acetate
Barnesite	Rare-earth polishing agent
Bentonite	Absorbent smectite clay
Benzene	Petroleum distillate
Benzine	Mix of petrol. distillates
Benzol	Benzene
Bichrome	Potassium dichromate
Bitter salt	Magnesium sulfate
Black ash	Impure sodium carbonate
Bleaching powder	Calcium hypochlorite
Blue copperas	Copper sulfate
Blue salts	Nickel sulfate
Blue stone	Copper sulfate
Blue verditer	Basic copper carbonate
Blue vitriol	Copper sulfate
Boart, bort	Industrial diamond
Bole	A nonplastic clay
Bone ash	Impure Ca-phosphate from bones
Bone black	Charcoal from animal matter

Name	Synonym
Boracic acid	Boric acid
Borax	Sodium tetraborate
Borazon	Boron nitride
Brimstone	Sulfur
Burnt lime	Ca-oxide, unslaked lime
Burnt ocher	Ferric oxide; a pigment
Burnt ore	Ferric oxide; a pigment
Butter of — —	Chloride of — —
Calcothar	Ferric oxide or rouge
Caliche	Crude Na-nitrate (or gypsum)
Calomel	Mercurous chloride
Canada turpentine	Canada balsam
Canadol	Benzine
Cane sugar	Sucrose
Carbolic acid	Phenol
Carbona	Cleaning fluid contain. CCl_4
Carbonado	Gray cryptocrystalline diamond
Carbonic acid	Carbon dioxide
Carbonic anhydride	Carbon dioxide
Carborundum	Silicon carbide
Castile soap	Pure soap
Caustic — —	Hydroxide of — —
Cellosolve	Solvent for cellulose
Celluloid	Cellulose nitrate plastic
Cerium	Cerium oxide polishing agent
Chalk	Natural porous Ca-carbonate, calcite
Chile niter	Sodium nitrate
Chile saltpeter	Sodium nitrate
Chloride of lime	Ca-chloro-hypochlorite
Chloride of soda	Na-hypochlorite sol.
Chrome alum	K-Cr-sulfate
Chrome green	Chromium oxide pigment
Chromic acid	Chromium trioxide
Colophony	Rosin
Common salt	Sodium chloride
Copperas	Ferrous sulfate

Name	Synonym	Name	Synonym
Copper vitriol	Copper sulfate	Hartshorn salt	Ammonium carbonate carbamate
Corn sugar	Glucose	Hexamine	Hexamethylene teramine
Corrosive sublimate	Mercuric chloride	Hypo	Sodium thiosulfate
Cream of tartar	Potassium hydrogen tartrate	Indian red	Ferric oxide pigment (rouge)
Crocus	Rouge	Jewelers rouge	Ferric oxide polishing agent
Crocus martis	Rouge	Kieselguhr	Diatomaceous earth
Dental spar	Microcline feldspar	Lac	Shellac
Dextrose	Glucose	Lampblack	Soot from oil flame
Diakon	Acrylic resin plastic	Lanolin	Sheep wool fat
Diamond paste	Diamond powder in thick paste	Laughing gas	Nitrous oxide
Diamontine, diamantine	Sized synthetic ruby abrasive	Levulose	Fructose
Dimethylketone	Acetone	Lighter fluid	Petroleum distillate
Dry ice	Solid carbon dioxide	Lime	Calcium oxide, burnt lime
Eau-de-Javelle	K-hypochlorite sol.	Linde A, Linde B	Alumina polishing agents
Emery	Impure natural corundum abrasive	Litharge	Lead monoxide pigment
Epsom salts	Magnesium sulfate	Lithopone	Zn-sulfide and Ba-sulfate pigment
Essence of bitter almonds	Benzaldehyde	Liver of sulfur	Potassium sulfides
Ethanol	Ethyl alcohol	London rouge	Rouge
Ethyl ether	Ether	Lucite	Acrylic resin plastic
Ferro prussiate	Potassium ferrocyanide	Lunar caustic	Silver nitrate
Flaxseed oil	Linseed oil	Lye	Na or K hydroxide
Flowers of sulfur	Sulfur in fine powder	Magnesia	Magnesium oxide
Flowers of——	Oxide of——	Marsh gas	Methane
Flushing oil	Light petroleum distillate	Methanol	Methyl alcohol
Formalin	Formaldehyde in water sol.	Methylated spirits	Ethyl alcohol + methyl alcohol
Freezing salt	Crude sodium chloride	Methyl benzol	Toluene
French chalk	Hydrated magnesium silicate	Microcosmic salt	Sodium ammonium hydrogen phosphate
French verdigris	Basic copper acetate	Milk of barium	Barium hydroxide
Fruit sugar	Fructose	Milk of lime	Calcium hydroxide
Fuller's earth	Absorbent clay	Milk of magnesia	Magnesium hydroxide
Fulminate of mercury	Mercury fulminate explosive	Milk of sulfur	Sulfur precipitated in sol.
Fusel oil	Mix of amyl alcohols	Mineral oil	Colorless, refined petroleum
Gasoline	Mix of petroleum distillates	Mohr's salt	Ferrous ammonium sulfate
Glacial acetic acid	Almost water-free acetic acid	Mothballs, flakes	Napthalene
Glauber's salt	Sodium sulfate	Muriate of——	Chloride of——
Glucose	Dextrose	Muriatic acid	Hydrochloric acid
Glycerine	Glycerol	Naphtha	Petroleum or coal tar distillate
Grain alcohol	Ethyl alcohol	Niter	Potassium nitrate
Grape sugar	Glucose	Nitro-lime	Calcium cyanamide
Green rouge	Chrome oxide polishing agent	Nitrous ether	Ethyl nitrite
Green vitriol	Ferrous sulfate	Norbide	Boron carbide
		Nordhausen acid	Fuming sulfuric acid
		Ocher	Iron oxide pigment earths

Name	Synonym	Name	Synonym
Oil of bitter almonds	Benzaldehyde	Salt of lemon	Potassium acid oxalate
Oil of vitriol	Conc. sulfuric acid	Salt of phosphorus	Sodium ammonium acid phosphate
Oil of winter-green	Methyl salicylate	Salt of sorrel	Potassium acid oxalate
Oleum	Fuming sulfuric acid	Salt of tartar	Potassium carbonate
Pearl ash	Potassium carbonate	Salt of wormwood	Potassium carbonate
Pearl essence	Pearly fish scale pigment	Saltpeter	Potassium nitrate
Pellon	Fibrous plastic fabric	Sal volatile	Ammonium sesquicarbonate
Perspex	Acrylic resin plastic		
Petrolatum	Petroleum grease; vaseline	Silicones	See "Chemical List" (p. 36)
Petroleum ether	Petroleum distillates		
Petroleum naptha	Benzine	Slaked lime	Calcium hydroxide
		Soda ash	Sodium carbonate
Phenic acid	Phenol	Soda lime	Sodium hydroxide + calcium oxide
Plaster of Paris	Dehydrated gypsum; calcium sulfate		
		Soda lye	Sodium hydroxide
Plasticine	Modeling clay	Soda niter	Sodium nitrate
Plexiglas	Acrylic resin plastic	Sodium hyposulfite	Sodium thiosulfate
Plumbago	Graphite		
Polystyrene	Vinyl group plastic	Soft soap	Potash soap
Porcelain	Fused feldspar-quartz mix	Soluble glass	Sodium silicate
Potash lye	Potassium hydroxide	Soluble tartar	Potassium tartrate
Precipitated chalk	Purified chalk powder	Spirit of hartshorn	Ammonia in water
Prussian blue	Ferric ferrocyanide	Spirit of salt	Hydrochloric acid
Prussic acid	Hydrocyanic acid	Spirit of wine	Ethyl alcohol
Pumice	Volcanic ash	Sugar of lead	Lead acetate
Putty powder	Tin and lead oxides mix	Sulfuric ether	Ethyl ether, ether
Pyro	Pyrogallic acid	Superphosphate	Crude calcium acid phosphate
Pyroligneous acid	Crude acetic acid		
		Table salt	Sodium chloride
Pyroligneous spirit	Methyl alcohol	Talcum powder	Very pure talc
		Tartar	Crude potassium bitartrate
Quicklime	Ca-oxide; unslaked lime		
Quicksilver	Mercury	Tartar emetic	Potassium antimonyl tartrate
Quinol	Hydroquinone		
Rectified spirit	Redistilled alcohol	Tin ash	Tin oxide, stannic oxide
Red lead	Minium, lead tetroxide	Tincture of--	Solution in alcohol of--
Red prussiate of potash	Potassium ferricyanide	Tin crystals	Tin chloride, stannous chloride
Rochelle salt	Potassium sodium tartrate	TNT	Trinitrotoluene explosive
Rock salt	Sodium chloride, halite	Toluol	Toluene
Rottenstone	Siliceous abrasive	Tripoli	Siliceous earth abrasive
Rouge	Ferric oxide polishing agent	Unslaked lime	Calcium oxide
		Venetian red	Ferric oxide, rouge
Rubbing alcohol	Isopropyl alcohol	Verdigris	Basic copper acetate
Rutile	Titanium dioxide pigment	Vermilion	Red mercuric sulfide pigment
Sal ammoniac	Ammonium chloride		
Salol	Phenylsalicylate	Vinegar	Dilute, flavored acetic acid
Salt	Sodium chloride		
Salt cake	Crude sodium sulfate	Vitriol	Sulfuric acid
Salt of amber	Succinic acid	Vitriolate of---	Sulfate of---
Salt of hartshorn	Ammonium carbonate	Washing soda	Sodium carbonate

Name	Synonym	Name	Synonym
Water glass	Sodium silicate sol.	Whiting	Powdered calcite
White acid	HF + ammonium bi-fluoride	Wood alcohol	Methyl alcohol
		Wood naphtha	Methyl alcohol
White arsenic	Arsenic trioxide	Wood spirit	Methyl alcohol
White copperas	Zinc sulfate; goslarite	Xylol	Xylene
White lead	Basic lead carbonate	Yellow prussiate of potash	Potassium ferrocyanide
White oil	Light petroleum oil		
White vitriol	Zinc sulfate	Zinc vitriol	Zinc sulfate
Whitewash	Powdered lime	Zinc white	Zinc oxide

ATOMIC TABLE OF THE ELEMENTS

Element	Symbol	Atomic Number	Atomic Weight	Atomic Radius (Angstroms)	Ion	Ionic Radius (Angstroms)
Actinium	Ac	89				
Aluminum	Al	13	26.98	1.48	Al^{+3}	0.50
Americium	Am	95				
Antimony	Sb	51	121.75	1.439	Sb^{+5}, Sb^{-3}	0.62, 2.45
Argon	Ar	18	39.95	1.91		
Arsenic	As	33	74.92	1.25	As^{+5}, As^{-3}	0.47, 2.22
Astatine	At	85				
Barium	Ba	56	137.34	2.17	Ba^{+2}	1.34
Berkelium	Bk	97				
Beryllium	Be	4	9.01	1.11	Be^{+2}	0.31
Bismuth	Bi	83	208.98	1.55	Bi^{+5}	0.74
Boron	B	5	10.81	0.7	B^{+3}	0.20
Bromine	Br	35	79.90	1.13	Br^{-1}	1.95
Cadmium	Cd	48	112.40	1.486	Cd^{+2}	0.97
Calcium	Ca	20	40.08	1.97	Ca^{+2}	0.99
Californium	Cf	98				
Carbon	C	6	12.01	0.77	C^{+4}	0.15
Cerium	Ce	58	140.12	1.81	Ce^{+4}	1.01
Cesium	Cs	55	132.90	2.62	Cs^{+1}	1.69
Chlorine	Cl	17	35.45	0.97	Cl^{-1}	1.81
Chromium	Cr	24	51.99	1.35	Cr^{+3}, Cr^{+6}	0.63, 0.52
Cobalt	Co	27	58.93	1.25	Co^{+2}, Co^{+3}	0.72, 0.63
Copper	Cu	29	63.54	1.275	Cu^{+1}, Cu^{+2}	0.96, 0.72
Curium	Cm	96				
Dysprosium	Dy	66	162.50			
Einsteinium	Es	99				
Erbium	Er	68	167.26			
Europium	Eu	63	151.96			
Fermium	Fm	100				
Fluorine	F	9	18.99	0.68	F^{-1}	1.36
Francium	Fr	87				
Gadolinium	Gd	64	157.25			
Gallium	Ga	31	69.72	1.22	Ga^{+2}	0.62
Germanium	Ge	32	72.59	1.32	Ge^{+4}	0.53
Gold	Au	79	196.96	1.439	Au^{+1}	1.37
Hafnium	Hf	72	178.49		Hf^{+4}	0.78
Helium	He	2	4.00			
Holmium	Ho	67	164.93			

Element	Symbol	Atomic Number	Atomic Weight	Radius (Angstroms)	Ion	Ionic Radius (Angstroms)
Hydrogen	H	1	1.00	0.37	H^{-1}	2.08
Indium	In	49	114.82	1.62	In^{+3}	0.81
Iodine	I	53	126.90	1.35	I^{-1}	2.16
Iridium	Ir	77	192.2		Ir^{+4}	0.68
Iron	Fe	26	55.84	1.26	Fe^{+2}, Fe^{+3}	0.74, 0.64
Krypton	Kr	36	83.80			
Lanthanum	La	57	138.91	1.86	La^{+3}	1.14
Lawrencium	Lr	103				
Lead	Pb	82	207.19	1.746	Pb^{+2}, Pb^{+4}	1.20, 0.84
Lithium	Li	3	6.94	1.50	Li^{+1}	0.68
Lutetium	Lu	71	174.97		Lu^{+3}	0.85
Magnesium	Mg	12	24.31	1.595	Mg^{+2}	0.66
Manganese	Mn	25	54.93	1.26	Mn^{+2}, Mn^{+4}	0.80, 0.60
Mendelevium	Md	101				
Mercury	Hg	80	200.59	1.50	Hg^{+2}	1.10
Molybdenum	Mo	42	95.94	1.36	Mo^{+6}	0.62
Neodymium	Nd	60	144.24	1.81		
Neon	Ne	10	20.18			
Neptunium	Np	93				
Nickel	Ni	28	58.71	1.243	Ni^{+2}	0.69
Niobium	Nb	41	92.90	1.426	Nb^{+5}	0.69
Nitrogen	N	7	14.00	0.53	N^{+5}	0.13
Nobelium	No	102				
Osmium	Os	76	190.2		Os^{+6}	0.69
Oxygen	O	8	15.99	0.60	O^{-2}	1.40
Palladium	Pd	46	106.4	1.372	Pd^{+2}	0.80
Phosphorus	P	15	30.97	1.08	P^{+5}	0.35
Platinum	Pt	78	195.09		Pt^{+2}	0.80
Plutonium	Pu	94				
Polonium	Po	84				
Potassium	K	19	39.10	2.27	K^{+1}	1.33
Praseodymium	Pr	59	140.90			
Promethium	Pm	61				
Protactinium	Pa	91				
Radium	Ra	88				
Radon	Rn	86				
Rhenium	Re	75	186.2		Re^{+4}	0.72
Rhodium	Rh	45	102.90	1.342	Rh^{+3}	0.68
Rubidium	Rb	37	85.47	2.43	Rb^{+1}	1.47
Ruthenium	Ru	44	101.07	1.322	Ru^{+4}	0.67
Samarium	Sm	62	150.35			
Scandium	Sc	21	44.95	1.51	Sc^{+3}	0.81
Selenium	Se	34	78.96	1.16	Se^{+6}	0.42
Silicon	Si	14	28.08	1.172	Si^{+4}	0.42
Silver	Ag	47	107.86	1.441	Ag^{+1}	1.26
Sodium	Na	11	22.98	1.86	Na^{+1}	0.97
Strontium	Sr	38	87.62	2.14	Sr^{+2}	1.12
Sulfur	S	16	32.06	1.06	S^{-2}, S^{+6}	1.84, 0.30
Tantalum	Ta	73	180.94		Ta^{+5}	0.68
Technetium	Tc	43				

Element	Symbol	Atomic Number	Atomic Weight	Radius (Angstroms)	Ion	Ionic Radius (Angstroms)
Tellurium	Te	52	127.60	1.44	Te^{+6}	0.56
Terbium	Tb	65	158.92			
Thallium	Tl	81	204.37	1.70	Tl^{+1}	1.47
Thorium	Th	90	232.03	1.79	Th^{+4}	1.02
Thulium	Tm	69	168.93			
Tin	Sn	50	118.69	1.508	Sn^{+4}	0.71
Titanium	Ti	22	47.90	1.45	Ti^{+4}	0.68
Tungsten	W	74	183.85		W^{+6}	0.62
Uranium	U	92	238.03	1.41	U^{+4}	0.97
Vanadium	V	23	50.94	1.313	V^{+3}, V^{+5}	0.74, 0.59
Xenon	Xe	54	131.30			
Ytterbium	Yb	70	173.04			
Yttrium	Y	39	88.90	1.79	Y^{+3}	0.92
Zinc	Zn	30	65.37	1.329	Zn^{+2}	0.74
Zirconium	Zr	40	91.22	1.58	Zr^{+4}	0.79

CHEMICALS LIST

The data and nomenclature in the following list were compiled from a number of sources and checked against data in the *Handbook of Chemistry and Physics*, 51st ed. (Cleveland: Chemical Rubber Company, 1970-71). Each substance is described under the name most likely to be recognized by the reader and not necessarily the scientifically accepted name. In brackets [ ] are given the common or trivial names, and synonyms.

Abbreviations: BP = boiling point; C. = centigrade; conc. = concentrated; F. = fahrenheit; G = specific gravity; insol. = insoluble; MP = melting point; pt., pts. = part(s); sol. = soluble; v. = very; wgt. = weight; xls = crystals.

ACETIC ACID–CH_3CO_2H. [Ethanoic acid]. Glacial acet. acid colorless liquid at ordinary room temp. but solidifies near freezing to a semisolid; G = 1.05, BP = 118° C. (244° F.), n = 1.370 (25° C.). Strong vinegar odor, slowly evaporates. Mixes freely with acetone, water, alcohol, benzol, ether. Diss. acetate (celluloid, pyroxylin) plastics and used as cementing agent by softening of same to sticky consistency: typical formula 2 pts. by wgt. glacial acid to 1 pt. acetone. Diss. gums, vegetable oils, gelatin. A 28% sol. acid is 3 pts. by vol. glacial acid to 8 pts. dist. water. Conc. acid causes painful skin burns. Vinegar, obtained by nat. fermentation, contains c. 4% acid + water, esters, sugars, etc. Used as a substitute mild acid for HCl in treating minerals.

ACETONE–CH_3COCH_3. [Dimethyl ketone; 2-propanone]. Colorless, v. volatile liquid, mobile and penetrating, with characteristic pleasant odor; very flammable, easily creates explosive atmosphere. G = 0.79 (20° C.), BP = 55°-57° C. (131°-135° F.), n = 1.539 (20° C.), 1.537 (25° C.). Mixes with acetic acid, amyl or butyl acetates, oils, mineral oil distillates; dissolves in water, alcohols. ether. Readily diss. rosin, camphor, gums, fats, waxes, rayon, acetate films. Slower evaporating solvent is 3 pts. by vol. acetone, 1 pt. amyl acetate ("nail-polish remover").

ACETYLENE–C_2H_2. Colorless, odorless gas (when pure) but ordinarily with disagreeable odor when generated from calcium carbide. Extremely flammable, easily creating wide range explosive mixtures with air. Burning flame (carbide lamps) brilliant yellow due to incandescent carbon particles; used with oxygen in welding, and in jewelers' torches with air.

ACETYLENE DIBROMIDE = DIBROMOETHYLENE.

ALUMINA–Al_2O_3. [Aluminum oxide; corundum]. Manufactured in large quantities for abrasive purposes in wheels and for lapping powders; chemically prepared alumina used for fine polishing (Linde A, Linde B, etc.); also melted into boules (Verneuil method) and rods (Czochralski method) for use as gemstones, optical and electronic parts, etc. Emery is an impure natural abrasive containing corundum, magnetite, and other minerals.

ALUMS. Water-sol. sulfates, principally potassium alum: $KAl(SO_4)_2 \cdot 12H_2O$; sodium alum, $NaAl...$; ammonium alum, $NH_4Al...$; ferric (iron) alum, $NaFe...$; chrome alum, $KCr(SO_4)_2 \cdot 12H_2O$. Bitter, astringent taste; v. rapidly sol. water. Used in starch pastes as preservative. Eminently suitable for xl-growing experiments from water sol.

AMMONIA–NH_3. Colorless, choking gas, lighter than air. Diss. very rapidly in water to form the hydroxide (aqua ammonia). "Household ammonia" commonly contains detergents and other contaminants which make it unfit for use in the laboratory. Attacks and diss. greases, oils; excessive contact leads to rawness of skin. Aqua ammonia diss. silver chloride and precipitates Al, Be, Bi, Cr^{+3}, Fe^{+3}, Pb, rare-earth salts as hydroxides.

AMMONIUM ACETATE– $NH_4C_2H_3O_2$. White xls or powder. G = 1.07, MP = $114°$ C. $(237°$ F.), but decomposes at higher temp. Sol. water, decomposes in hot water; sol. alcohol, slightly sol. acetone. Reagent in mineral testing.

AMMONIUM BIFLUORIDE–NH_4HF_2. [Ammonium hydrogen fluoride]. White xls; G = 1.50, MP = $126°$ C. $(259°$ F.). Sol. water; deliquescent. In hot aqueous sol. etches and diss. silicates, glass, but more slowly than HF; used to etch piezoelectric quartz slabs to reveal twinning boundaries. Cleans metals, including native, much like HF but far less dangerous to use.

AMMONIUM CARBAMATE ACID CARBONATE–$NH_4NH_2CO_2 \cdot NH_4HCO_3$. [Sal volatile; hartshorn salt]. White xls; sol. water, glycerine; decomposes in alcohol, readily decomposes when heated. Used in the green dyeing of agate.

AMMONIUM CARBONATE– $(NH_4)_2CO_3 \cdot H_2O$. White xls or powder; ordinary commercial salt contains a mixture of carbonates but is satisfactory to use in mineral testing where this chemical is called for. Sol. water, decomposed hot water; insol. alcohol. Precipitates Ca, Sr, Ba carbonates from aqueous sols. previously treated with ammonia.

AMMONIUM CHLORIDE–NH_4Cl. [Sal ammoniac]. White powder or xls. G = 1.527; sublimes $340°$ C. $(644°$ F.), melts $520°$ C. $(968°$ F.). Ingredient soldering pastes. Forms as dense white cloud when ammonia vapors contact vapors from conc. HCl, and then useful for coating brilliant mineral xls with a nonreflective layer to reduce or eliminate strong highlights for purposes of photography. V. readily sol. water.

AMMONIUM DICHROMATE– $(NH_4)_2Cr_2O_7$. Orange xls. G = 2.15; decomposes at $170°$ C. $(338°$ F.). Sol. water, alcohol. Used in green dyeing of agate.

AMMONIUM HYDROXIDE–NH_4OH. The active ingredient in aqua ammonia, and formed by leading ammonia gas into dist. water; a mild alkali, degreasing agent, etc. Reagent for chemical testing of minerals.

AMMONIUM MOLYBDATE– $(NH_4)_2MoO_4$. White powder; G = 2.27; decomposes when heated; sol. with decomposition in water, acids; insol. alcohol, acetone. Reagent in mineral testing.

AMMONIUM NITRATE–NH_4NO_3. White xls or pellets manufactured in large quantities for agricultural fertilizer. G = 1.725, MP = $170°$ C. $(338°$ F.) but inclined to be unstable and explode when heated, especially in presence of combustible material; commonly used as an explosive when pellets mixed with fuel oil. V. readily sol. water; sol. acetone, acids. Mineral test reagent.

AMMONIUM OXALATE– $(NH_4)_2C_2O_4 \cdot H_2O$. White or colorless xls. G = 1.50; decomposes when heated; sol. water. Precipitates Ca-oxalates from aqueous sols. previously treated with ammonia; also precipitates Ba, Sr. Reagent for mineral testing. Aqueous sol. removes ink stains.

AMMONIUM PHOSPHATES. Sol. water and used to fireproof paper, wood, fabrics, etc. Mineral test reagent.

AMMONIUM SULFATE–$(NH_4)_2SO_4$. Formed in water by adding sulfuric acid to aqua ammonia; mineral test reagent.

AMMONIUM SULFIDE (mono)–

$(NH_4)_2S$. White to yellowish powder or xls; decompose in hot water or when heated; sol. cold water, alcohol. Mineral test reagent.

AMMONIUM TARTRATE– $(NH_4)_2C_4H_4O_6$. White powder; G = 1.60; decomposes in hot water or when heated; sol. cold water. Mineral test reagent.

AMMONIUM THIOCYANATE– NH_4SCN. [Ammon. sulfocyanate]. White xls or powder; G = 1.31, MP = $150°$ C. ($302°$ F.); decomposes $170°$ C. ($338°$ F.); sol. water, alcohol, ether. Mineral test reagent.

AMYL ACETATE–$CH_3CO_2C_5H_{11}$. [Amyl acetic ether; "banana oil," "pear oil"]. Colorless, somewhat oily, slowly evaporating liquid with fruity odor. G = 0.88, BP = $138°$-$142°$ C. ($280°$-$288°$ F.), n = 1.400 ($25°$ C.). Sol. alcohol, ether, acetone; diss. celluloids (acetates or nitrates), camphor. Flammable, explosive vapors sink to floor. Used for cements, lacquers, etc.

AMYL ALCOHOL – $(CH_3)_2CHCH_2CH_2OH$. [Isoamyl or isopentyl alcohol, 3-methyl, 1-butanol]. Colorless flammable liquid; G = 0.81, BP = $129°$ C. ($264°$ F.), n = 1.408 ($20°$ C.). Solvent; antifoaming agent; sol. ether, acetone.

AMYL ALCOHOL–$CH_3(CH_2)_4OH$. [1-Pentanol; butyl carbinol; n-amyl alcohol]. Colorless flammable liquid; G = 0.814, BP = $137°$ C. ($279°$ F.), n = 1.410 ($20°$ C.). Sol. methyl alc., ether, acetone, benzene, gasoline, etc. General solvent; lacquer formulations.

ANILINE–$C_6H_5NH_2$. [Aminobenzene; phenylamine]. Colorless, oily liquid, highly poisonous; G = 1.02, BP = $184°$ C. ($363°$ F.), n = 1.583 ($25°$ C.). Refractive index fluid.

ANTIMONY TRIIODIDE–SbI_3. Reddish xls; G = 4.77, MP = $167°$ C. ($333°$ F.). Sol. HCl, alcohol, acetone, carbon disulfide; decomposed in water. Additive to refractive index fluids (corrosive to glass!).

AQUA REGIA–Any mixture of hydrochloric and nitric acids; typical sol. for diss. gold is 3 pts. by vol. HCl, 1 pt. HNO_3; for platinum, 9 pts. HCl, 2 pts. HNO_3.

ARSENIC IODIDE–AsI_2. Red xls; decomposes at $136°$ C. ($277°$ F.). Sol. ether, chloroform, carbon disulfide.

Poisonous additive to refractive index fluids; corrosive to glass!

ARSENIC TRIBROMIDE–$AsBr_3$. Yellowish xls or powder; G = 3.54, MP = $33°$ C. ($91°$ F.), n = 1.78. Sol. HCl, carbon disulfide; decomposes in water. Refractive index fluid additive, poisonous, corrosive to glass!

ARSENIC TRISELENIDE–As_2Se_3. Brown xls; G = 4.75, MP = $360°$ C. ($680°$ F.). Sol. alkaline sols.; decomposes in hot water; additive to refractive index fluids; corrosive to glass; poisonous!

ARSENIC TRISULFIDE–AsS. [Realgar]. Red powder; G = 3.50, MP = $267°$ C. ($513°$ F.). Sol. alcohol, methylene iodide. Refractive index fluid additive; corrosive to glass; poisonous!

BARIUM CHLORIDE–$BaCl_2 \cdot 2H_2O$. Colorless xls, powder; G = 3.1; sol. water, acids; insol. alcohol. Reagent in mineral testing; precipitates Ba-sulfate from acidified sols.

BARIUM HYDROXIDE – $Ba(OH)_2 \cdot 8H_2O$. Colorless xls; G = 2.18, MP = $78°$ C. ($172°$ F.). Sol. water, slightly sol. alcohol. Reagent in testing minerals.

BENZALDEHYDE–C_6H_5CHO. [Oil of bitter almonds; benzenecarbonal]. Colorless liquid; G = 1.04, BP = $178°$ C. ($352°$ F.), n = 1.544 ($25°$ C.). Refractive index fluid.

BENZENE–C_6H_6. [Benzol, formerly "benzine"; phene]. Colorless, mobile fluid with agreeable odor; volatile, highly flammable, explosive vapor danger. G = 0.88, MP = $5.5°$ C. ($42°$ F.), BP = $80°$ C. ($176°$ F.), n = 1.498 ($25°$ C.). Sol. ether, alcohol, acetone, chloroform, toluene, acetic acid; dissolves resins, fats, greases, waxes, rubber. General solvent; diluent of refractive index fluids; cleaning agent. Prolonged inhalation fumes dangerous.

BENZINE. [Petroleum ether, nezoline, petroleum naphtha, canadol]. Colorless, mobile liquid, a mixture of "light" hydrocarbons derived from distillation of petroleum and virtually identical to gasoline. In general, G = 0.73-0.75, BP = $80°$-$130°$ C. ($176°$-$266°$ F.); pharmaceutical G = 0.625-0.660, BP = $35°$-$80°$ C. ($127°$-$176°$ F.). Sol. alcohol, chloroform, ether, other petroleum distillates; insol. water. Very flammable, like gasoline. Cleaning agent for greases, waxes, oils, etc.; paint thinner.

BENZYL ACETATE – $CH_3CO_2CH_2C_6H_5$. [Benzyl ester, acetic acid, benzyl ethanoate]. Colorless liquid, G = 1.055, BP = $216°$ C. ($421°$ F.), n = 1.518 ($25°$ C.). Sol. acetone, ether, alcohol; diss. celluloids. General solvent.

BENZYL BENZOATE – $C_6H_5CO_2CH_2C_6H_5$. [Benzyl ester, benzoic acid]. Colorless oily liquid; G = 1.11, MP = $21°$ C. ($67°$ F.), BP = $323°$ C. ($613°$ F.), n = 1.568 ($25°$ C.). Sol. ether, chloroform; insol. cold water, glycerine. Refractive index fluid.

BORAX–$Na_2B_4O_7 \cdot 10H_2O$. [Sodium tetraborate]. White powder or lumps; G = 1.73, MP = $75°$ C. ($167°$ F.); begins to lose water and melts to glass at about $320°$ C. ($640°$ F.) or higher. Poorly sol. cold water, but more rapidly in hot water; sol. glycerine. Mixed with water or sprinkled as powder for soldering at higher temps. (silver, gold, etc.). Used in making beads for mineral identification tests.

BORIC ACID–H_3BO_3. [Orthoboric acid]. White powder; G = 1.435, MP = $185°$ C. ($365°$ F.) decomposing. Slowly sol. cold water, more rapidly in hot; slightly sol. glycerine, alcohol, acetone. Used as soldering flux in lieu of borax and for making mineral identification test beads.

BORON CARBIDE–B_6C. ["Norbide"]. Black, extremely hard, brittle synthetic compound used for abrasive purposes; H = 9.3.

BROMOBENZENE–C_6H_5Br. [Phenyl bromide]. Colorless oily liquid; G = 1.495, BP = $156°$ C. ($313°$ F.), n = 1.557 ($25°$ C.). Sol. alcohol, ether, benzene. Refractive index fluid.

BROMOETHANE–C_2H_5Br. [Ethyl bromide]. Colorless liquid; G = 1.46, BP = $38°$ C. ($100°$ F.), n = 1.424 ($20°$ C.). Sol. ether, chloroform, alcohol. Refractive index fluid.

BROMOFORM–$CHBr_3$. [Tribromomethane]. Colorless liquid with sweetish odor; G = 2.89 ($20°$ C.), BP = $150°$ C. ($302°$ F.), n = 1.5976 ($20°$ C.), 1.595 ($24°$ C.), 1.587 ($25°$ C.). Sol. benzene, alcohol, ether, chloroform, petroleum ether, gasoline, oils; slightly sol. water. Refractive index and density fluid.

1-BROMONAPHTHALENE $C_{10}H_7Br$. [Monobromonaphthalene]. Colorless, oily liquid; G = 1.483 ($20°$ C.), BP = $281°$ C.

($538°$ F.), n = 1.658 ($20°$ C.). Sol. benzene, chloroform, acetone, ether, alcohol. Refractive index fluid.

2-BROMOTOLUENE – C_7H_7Br. [Bromtoluene; o-tolyl bromide]. Colorless liquid; G = 1.42, BP $\cdot$ $182°$ C. ($360°$ F.), n = 1.557 ($20°$ C.). Sol. benzene, carbon tetrachloride, alcohol. Refractive index fluid.

3-BROMOTOLUENE – C_7H_7Br. [Bromtoluene; m-tolyl bromide]. Colorless liquid; G = 1.41, BP = $184°$ C. ($363°$ F.), n = 1.551 ($20°$ C.). Sol. benzene, carbon tetrachloride, alcohol. Refractive index fluid.

BUTANE–$CH_3(CH_2)_2CH_3$. Colorless liquid or gas, flammable. G = 0.58 (liq.), BP = $-0.5°$ C. ($31°$ F.). Used for heating and cooking, and for jewelers' torches.

BUTYL ACETATE – $CH_3CO_2(CH_2)_3CH_3$. [Butyl ester acetic acid]. Colorless, slowly evaporating liquid; G = 0.88, BP = $127°$ C. ($261°$ F.), n = 1.392 ($25°$ C.). Sol. alcohol, ether, acetone; dissolves acetate and nitrate films; cement for cellulose acetate and nitrate when mixed with ethyl acetate.

BUTYL ALCOHOL – $CH_3CH_2CH_2CH_2OH$. [1-Butanol]. Colorless liquid, G = 0.81, BP = $117°$ C. ($242°$ F.), n = 1.397 ($25°$ C.). Sol. acetone, ether, alcohol, benzene; diss. resins, plastics, gums; does not diss. celluloid.

BUTYL ALCOHOL – $CH_3CH_2CHOHCH_3$. [2-Butanol; sec.-butyl alcohol]. Colorless liquid; G = 0.81, BP = $100°$ C. ($212°$ F.), n = 1.395 ($25°$ C.). Sol. acetone, benzene, ether, alcohol; diss. waxes, gums, resins, oils, etc.

CACOTHELINE–$C_{21}H_{21}N_3O_7$. A poisonous base compound in orange-yellow xls, sometimes used as a chemical reagent in testing minerals.

CADMIUM BOROTUNGSTATE–$Cd_5(BW_{12}O_{40})_2 \cdot xH_2O$. Yellow xls; MP = $75°$ C. ($167°$ F.); sol. water. Used as reagent in testing minerals.

CALCIUM CARBIDE–CaC_2. Gray or brown pea-size lumps with characteristic foul odor are supplied commercially for generating acetylene gas for illumination purposes (miners' lamps, camp lamps, etc.). G = 2.22; decomposes rapidly in water to form C_2H_2 (acetylene) and $Ca(OH)_2$ (calcium hydroxide), with generation of considerable heat.

CALCIUM CHLORIDE–$CaCl_2$. White granules; G = 2.512, MP = 772° C. (1,422° F.). V. sol. water; sol. alcohol, acetic acid, acetone. Used to melt ice and extract water from air (desiccant). Mineral testing reagent.

CALCIUM HYDROXIDE–$Ca(OH)_2$. [Slaked lime]. White solid; G = 2.34. Upon exposure to air, gradually converts to the carbonate and forms cement. Sol. water, ammonium chloride sol. Reagent in mineral testing.

CALCIUM OXIDE–CaO. [Quicklime, lime, unslaked lime]. White powder, G = 3.40, reacting quickly with water and with much generation of heat to form calcium hydroxide (slaked lime). Burns the skin. Used in cements.

CARBOLIC ACID = PHENOL.

CARBON DIOXIDE–CO_2. [Carbonic acid gas; "dry ice" when solid]. Colorless, odorless gas generated by the attack of acids on carbonates. Solid at −56.7° C. (−134° F.) and usually sold in form of white cakes. Used for cooling. At atmospheric pressure and 15° C. (60° F.) water takes up an equal vol. of the gas in sol.

CARBON DISULFIDE–CS_2. Colorless to slightly yellowish mobile liquid with agreeable odor if pure, sometimes with "rotten egg" odor if impure; G = 1.26 (20° C.), BP = 46° C. (115° F.), n = 1.628 (25° C.), 1.632 (20° C.). Sol. alcohol, ether, benzene, chloroform. Very volatile, with heavy fumes settling to floor and presenting explosive vapor hazards; extremely flammable. Refractive index fluid or diluent; dissolves rubber.

CARBON TETRACHLORIDE–CCl_4. [Tetrachlormethane, perchlormethane, bencinoform, "carbon tet," "Carbona" (in part)]. Highly mobile, colorless liquid with agreeable odor. G = 1.594 (20° C.), BP = 77° C. (170° F.), n = 1.460 (20° C.), 1.459 (25° C.). Sol. benzene, ether, alcohol, chloroform, acetone; insol. water. Effective degreaser. Incombustible. Prolonged breathing of fumes dangerous. Typical cleaning fluids contain about 60% CCl_4 by wgt., and 40% benzene, and are incombustible. Solvent; diluent to refractive index fluids; density fluid.

CHLOROBENZENE–C_6H_5Cl. [Phenyl chloride]. Colorless liquid, G = 1.106 (20° C.), BP = 132° C. (270° F.), n = 1.524 (20° C.), 1.523 (24° C.). Sol. alcohol, ether, benzene, chloroform, carbon tetrachloride, carbon disulfide. Refractive index fluid.

CHLOROFORM–$CHCl_3$. [Trichloromethane]. Colorless liquid, with agreeable odor; G = 1.483 (20° C.), BP = 62° C. (144° F.), n = 1.446 (20° C.), 1.444 (25° C.). Sol. benzene, ether, alcohol, carbon disulfide. Diluent and refractive index or density fluid. Outmoded anesthetic.

1-CHLORONAPHTHALENE–$C_{10}H_7Cl$. [Monochloronaphthalene]. Colorless liquid, G = 1.194 (20° C.), BP = 259° C. (498° F.), n = 1.633 (20° C.), 1.633 (24° C.). Sol. carbon disulfide, alcohol, ether, benzene. Refractive index fluid and diluent.

CHLOROPLATINIC ACID–$H_2PtCl_6 \cdot 6H_2O$. Red-brown powder; G = 2.43, MP = 60° C. (140° F.). Sol. water, alcohol, ether. Reagent in mineral testing.

CHROMIC OXIDE–Cr_2O_3. [Chrome oxide; "green rouge"]. Green powder prepared by calcining chrome alum. G = 5.21. Insol. acids, alkalies, water. Polishing agent, especially for jade; paint pigment.

CHROMIUM TRIOXIDE–CrO_3. [Chromic acid, chromic anhydride]. Red xls. G = 2.70, MP = 196° C. (385° F.). Decomposes at higher temperatures. Sol. water, alcohol, ether, acids. Melts to black globules, then ca. 25° C. (482° F.) suddenly puffs up into froth of green chromic oxide (Cr_2O_3). Used in green dyeing of agate.

CINEOLE–$C_{10}H_{18}O$. [1,8-Cineole; cajeputol; eucalyptol]. Colorless aromatic liquid; G = 0.927, BP = 176° C. (349° F.), n = 1.459 (20° C.), 1.456 (24° C.). Sol. chloroform, glac. acetic acid, oils, ether, benzene, alcohol. Refractive index fluid.

CINNAMALDEHYDE–$C_6H_5CHCHCHO$. [Cinnamic aldehyde]. Colorless aromatic liquid; G = 1.05, BP = 253° C. (487° F.), n = 1.62 (20° C.). Sol. alcohol, ether, chloroform; v. slightly sol. water. Refractive index fluid.

CITRIC ACID–$HOC(CH_2CO_2H)_2CO_2H$. [2-Hydroxy-1,2-propanetricarboxylic acid]. White xls; odorless, but sharp biting taste, made from fruits. G = 1.542. Sol. water. Used as a mild mineral cleaning acid.

COBALT NITRATE–$Co(NO_3)_2 \cdot 6H_2O$. Red xls; G = 1.87, MP = c. 100° C. (212° F.). V. sol. water; sol. alcohol, acetone. Reagent for identification of minerals.

COPPER OXIDE–CuO. [Tenorite]. Black powder; G = 6.4. Insol. water; sol. ammonium chloride sol., potassium chloride sol. Reagent used in mineral identification.

COPPER SULFATE–$CuSO_4 \cdot 5H_2O$. ["Blue stone," blue vitriol, copper vitriol]. G = 2.284. Insol. alcohol; partly sol. methyl alcohol; v. readily sol. water. Forms beautiful blue triclinic xls when conc. sol. evaporated, sometimes deliberately upon natural mineral matrices and then sold as genuine.

CYCLOHEXANOL–$C_6H_{11}OH$. [Hexahydrophenol; hexalin]. Colorless liquid at warm temp.; G = 0.96, MP = 25° C. (77° F.), BP = 161° C. (322° F.), n = 1.465 (25° C.). Sol. water, benzene, alcohol, ether, carbon disulfide, turpentine. Refractive index fluid additive.

DECALIN–$C_{10}H_{18}$. [Decahydronaphthalene; naphthane; cis-decalin]. Colorless liquid; G = 0.896, BP = 196° C. (385° F.), n = 1.481 (20° C.), 1.479 (25° C.). Sol. benzene, alcohol, acetone, ether, bromoform. Refractive index fluid.

DECALIN (trans)–$C_{10}H_{18}$. Colorless liquid; G = 0.87, BP = 187° C. (369° F.), n = 1.469 (20° C.). Refractive index fluid, like preceding entry.

1,1-DIBROMOETHANE–CH_3CHBr_2. [Ethylidene bromide]. Colorless liquid; G = 2.06 (20° C.), BP = 108° C. (226° F.), n = 1.513 (20° C.). Sol. acetone, benzene, ether, alcohol. Refractive index and density fluid.

1,2-DIBROMOETHANE–$BrCH_2CH_2Br$. [Ethylene bromide or dibromide]. Colorless liquid; G = 2.18 (20° C.), BP = 131° C. (268° F.), n = 1.539 (20° C.), 1.538 (25° C.). Sol. alcohol, ether, acetone, benzene. Refractive index and density fluid.

1,2-DIBROMOETHANOL–BrCH:CHBr. [sym-Dibromoethylene]. Colorless liquid; G = 2.246 (20° C.), BP = 113° C. (235° F.), n = 1.543 (20° C.). Sol. alcohol, ether, benzene, acetone. Refractive index and density fluid.

1,2-DIBROMOETHANOL (trans)–BrCH:CHBr. [Dibromoethylene]. Colorless liquid; G = 2.231 (20° C.), BP = 108° C. (226° F.), n = 1.551 (18° C.). Sol. alcohol, ether, acetone, benzene, chloroform. Refractive index and density fluid.

DIBROMOMETHANE–CH_2Br_2. [Methylene bromide]. Colorless liquid; G = 2.497 (20° C.), BP = 97° C. (207° F.), n = 1.542 (20° C.). Sol. acetone, ether, alcohol. Refractive index and density fluid.

1,3-DIBROMOPROPANE–$BrCH_2CH_2CH_2Br$. [Trimethylene bromide]. Colorless liquid; G = 1.98 (20° C.), BP = 167° C. (333° F.), n = 1.523 (20° C.), 1.514 (24° C.). Sol. chloroform, ether, alcohol. Refractive index and density fluid.

1,1-DICHLOROETHANE–CH_3CHCl_2. [Ethylidene chloride]. Colorless liquid; G = 1.176 (20° C.), BP = 57° C. (135° F.), n = 1.416 (20° C.). Sol. benzene, alcohol, acetone, ether. Refractive index fluid.

1,2-DICHLOROETHANE–$ClCH_2CH_2Cl$. [Ethylene chloride or dichloride]. Colorless liquid; G = 1.235, BP = 83° C. (181° F.), n = 1.445 (20° C.). Sol. acetone, benzene, ether, chloroform; efficient degreaser, diss. fats, greases, oils, waxes, etc. Brushed on acrylic resins (Lucite, Plexiglas), creates sticky surfaces for cementing together.

DICHLOROMETHANE–CH_2Cl_2. [Methylene chloride]. Colorless liquid; G = 1.327 (20° C.), BP = 40° C. (104° F.), n = 1.424 (20° C.). Sol. ether, alcohol, benzene, chloroform. Refractive index fluid.

1,3-DICHLOROPROPANE–$ClCH_2CH_2CH_2Cl$. [Trimethylene chloride]. Colorless liquid; G = 1.188 (20° C.), BP = 120° C. (248° F.), n = 1.449 (20° C.), 1.446 (24° C.). Sol. benzene, alcohol, ether. Refractive index fluid.

DIETHYLENE GLYCOL–$HO(CH_2)_2O(CH_2)_2OH$. ["Antifreeze"]. Colorless, somewhat oily liquid with characteristic not unpleasing odor; G = 1.12, BP = 245° C. (473° F.), n = 1.447 (20° C.). Sol. readily water, alcohol, ether, also acetone, benzene, carbon tetrachloride. Used to depress freezing point of water; additive to stone sawing liquids or alternative sawing liquid.

DIIODOMETHANE = METHYLENE IODIDE.

N,N-DIMETHYLFORMAMIDE–$HCON(CH_3)_2$. G = 0.9345 (25° C.), n = 1.427 (25° C.). Readily sol. water. Diluent of bromoform and methylene iodide.

DIMETHYLGLYOXIME–$CH_3C(:NOH)C(:NOH)CH_3$. [2,3-Butanedione dioxime]. White xls, MP = 235° C. (455° F.). Insol. water; sol.

alcohol, ether. Reagent in mineral identification testing; sensitive test for Ni.

DIMETHYL KETONE = ACETONE.

DIMETHYL SULFOXIDE – CH_3SOCH_3. [Methyl sulfoxide]. Oily liquid, G = 1.10, MP = $18°$ C. ($64°$ F.), BP = $189°$ C. ($372°$ F.), n = 1.477 ($20°$ C.). Sol. acetone, ether, alcohol, water. Recommended as alternate diluent for bromoform.

EPSOM SALTS–$MgSO_4 \cdot 7H_2O$. [Magnesium sulfate hydrate; epsomite.] Commonly present in small but upsetting quantities in drinking water taken from serpentine rock areas.

ETHANOL = ETHYL ALCOHOL.

ETHER–$CH_3CH_2OCH_2CH_3$. [Diethyl ether; ethyl ether; vinic ether; sulfuric ether; ethoxyethane]. Colorless, extremely mobile and evaporative liquid with characteristic penetrating odor; G = 0.71, BP = $34°$ C. ($93°$ F.), n = 1.353. Extremely flammable; very high rate of evaporation, quickly forms dangerously explosive atmosphere. Sol. chloroform, acetone, alcohol, benzene; v. rapidly diss. oils, fats, greases, waxes, etc. Used to test amber.

ETHYL ACETATE–$CH_3CO_2CH_2CH_3$. [Ethyl ester acetic acid; acetic ether]. Colorless, rapidly evaporating liquid with pleasing odor; G = 0.90, BP = $77°$ C. ($171°$ F.), n = 1.372 ($20°$ C.), 1.370 ($25°$ C.). Sol. benzene, alcohol, acetone, ether, carbon tetrachloride, chloroform; efficient sol. for oils, greases, waxes, etc.; diss. cellulose acetate or nitrate and commonly used in cements utilizing these plastics.

ETHYL ALCOHOL–CH_3CH_2OH. [Ethanol; grain alcohol; spirit of wine]. Colorless, rapidly evaporating liquid with pleasing odor and the basis of alcoholic beverages when more or less diluted with water and flavoring additives. G = 0.79, BP = $76°$ C. ($169°$ F.), n = 1.361 ($20°$ C.), 1.359 ($25°$ C.). Sol. water, other alcohols, ether, acetone, benzene, chloroform, acetic acid. Highly flammable, burning with an almost invisible blue flame; explosive vapor hazard. Ordinary conc. of "pure" liquid is 95% by wgt., with remainder water. "Neutral spirits" are essentially pure grain alcohol. Used as a solvent, cleanser, additive to various formulations, but potable grain alcohol is unobtainable without special license and the liquid sold in drugstores is denatured, i.e., made unpalatable because of small quantities of additives which, however, do not seriously affect its usefulness in the arts. "Proof" refers to relative wgt. % of alcohol present, "100 proof" = 50% by wgt., remainder water. Drugstore "pure" alcohol is useful for gentle washing of mineral specimens, particularly those with thin films of grease or oil.

ETHYL BROMIDE = BROMOETHANE.

ETHYL BUTYRATE – $CH_3CH_2CH_2CO_2C_2H_5$. [Ethyl ester butanoic acid]. Colorless liquid; G = 0.88, BP = $121°$ C. ($250°$ F.), n = 1.400 ($20°$ C.), 1.393 ($24°$ C.). Sol. alcohol, ether, acetone, etc. Used as solvent in lacquers.

ETHYLENE BROMIDE (DIBROMIDE) = 1,2-DIBROMOETHANE.

ETHYLENE CHLORIDE = 1,2-DICHLOROETHANE.

ETHYLENE GLYCOL = GLYCOL.

ETHYL ETHER = ETHER.

ETHYLIDENE BROMIDE = DIBROMOETHANE.

ETHYLIDENE CHLORIDE = DICHLOROETHANE.

ETHYL IODIDE – CH_3CH_2I. [Iodoethane]. Colorless liquid; G = 1.936 ($20°$ C.), BP = $72°$ C. ($162°$ F.), n = 1.513 ($20°$ C.). Sol. benzene, chloroform, ether, alcohol, and other organic solvents. Refractive index or density fluid.

ETHYL METHYL KETONE – $CH_3COC_2H_5$. [2-Butanone]. Colorless liquid; disagreeable odor; G = 0.805, BP = $80°$ C. ($176°$ F.), n = 1.379 ($20°$ C.), 1.377 ($25°$ C.). Sol. benzene, ether, alcohol, acetone, and other organic solvents. Efficient degreaser; diss. waxes, oils, resins, nitrocellulose; rapidly softens or diss. paints, lacquers.

ETHYL VALERATE – $CH_3(CH_2)_3CO_2C_2H_5$. [Ethyl ester pentanoic acid]. Colorless liquid; G = 0.88, BP = $145°$ C. ($293°$ F.), n = 1.412 ($20°$ C.). Sol. ether, alcohol, refractive index fluid.

GASOLINES. Colorless, rapidly evaporating liquids representing light fractions of petroleum distillation. Generally G = 0.73-0.76, BP = $40°$-$225°$ C. ($104°$-$437°$ F.). Very flammable and use indoors commonly creates dangerous explosion hazard, especially in presence of open flames (hot-water heaters), electrical switches (sparks), etc. "White" gasoline contains no lead additives.

GLYCERINE–$C_3H_5(OH)_3$. [Glycerin; glycerol; 1,2,3-propanetriol]. Colorless, odorless, syrupy fluid with sweetish taste; rapidly absorbs water from atmosphere. G = 1.26, MP = 20° C. (68° F.), BP = 290° C. (554° F.), n = 1.475 (20° C.), 1.473 (25° C.). Sol. water, alcohol, chloroform, carbon tetrachloride, carbon disulfide; insol. acetone. The elevated BP makes glycerine desirable for use in double boilers where higher temperatures are required than can be obtained with water. Deliquescent nature makes glycerine useful in various gum cements to prevent drying out. Used to immerse chips of opal ("floating opals") because of viscosity and near-match of refractive indices.

GLYCOL – $HOCH_2CH_2OH$. [1,2-Ethanediol; ethylene glycol; dihydroxyethane]. Colorless liquid; G = 1.11, BP = 198° C. (388° F.), n = 1.432 (20° C.), 1.429 (25° C.). Sol. water, alcohol, acetone, acetic acid, chloroform.

HALAZONE–$C_6H_4(SO_2NCl_2)$.COOH. [4(N,N-dichlorosulfamyl) benzoic acid]. White powder; soluble in water and sometimes used to disinfect same.

HEPTANE–$CH_3(CH_2)_5CH_3$. Colorless liquid, pleasant odor, mobile, moderately evaporative. G = 0.68, BP = 98° C. (208° F.), n = 1.388 (20° C.), 1.385 (25° C.). Sol. benzene, acetone, ether, alcohol, chloroform, petroleum distillates. Flammable. Solvent, degreaser, additive to refractive index fluids; less dangerous to use than benzene with solvent powers being about equal.

HERAPATHITE = QUININE IODO-SULFATE.

HEXACHLORO-1,3-BUTADIENE–CCl_2:CClCCl:CCl_2. Col. liquid; G = 1.682 (20° C.), 1.671 (25° C.), BP = 215° C. (419° F.), n = 1.554 (20° C.). Insol. water; readily sol. in many organic heavy liquids and recommended as diluent for same.

HEXAHYDROPHENOL = CYCLO-HEXANOL.

HEXANE – $CH_3(CH_2)_4CH_3$ [Dipropyl]. Colorless liquid with pleasing odor; G = 0.66, BP = 69° C. (156° F.), n = 1.375 (20° C.), 1.372 (25° C.). Sol. like heptane and similar properties and uses.

HYDRIODIC ACID–HI. A water sol. reagent sometimes used in mineral identification testing. Unstable when pure; strong reducing agent.

HYDROBROMIC ACID–HBr. [Hydrogen bromide]. Pale yellow liquid; G = 3.50, BP = –67° C. (when pure) but made indirectly in a dil. water sol. as needed for reagent purposes in mineral testing.

HYDROCHLORIC ACID–HCl. [Hydrogen chloride; muriatic acid]. The pure compound is a colorless, incombustible acrid gas while the ordinary chemical reagent is the gas dissolved in water (1 vol. water at 0° C. (32° F.) dissolves 507 equal vols. of gas). Typical sols. are 20% by wgt. G = 1.1, BP = 110° C. (262° F.), 31% by wgt. G = c.1.16, and 35% by wgt. G = c.1.18. Chem. pure conc. acid is colorless; the usual "commercial" acid is supplied in plastic jugs and is faint to pale yellow due to diss. iron compounds but this has little if any effect on its usefulness in mineral cleaning work. Unless plastic jugs are coated with an impervious lacquer (not always the case), the acid slowly diffuses through the sides and corrodes metals in the vicinity; recommend decanting into glass jugs where possible. Conc. acid fumes readily; transfer into water should be accomplished with due speed. Rapidly attacks and diss. carbonates; more slowly, phosphates, certain silicates (esp. zeolites). Precipitates Ag, Pb, Hg chlorides from nitric acid sols. Fumes react immediately with fumes of aqua ammonia to form dense white clouds of ammonium chloride useful for masking reflective surfaces on xls for photographic purposes.

HYDROCHLORPLATINIC ACID = CHLOROPLATINIC ACID.

HYDROCYANIC ACID–HCN. [Prussic acid; hydrogen cyanide; formonitrile]. Colorless liquid, extremely poisonous upon ingestion or inhalation, causing death within minutes; mobile, evaporative. G = 0.69, BP = 26° C. (78° F.). Sol. water, alcohol, ether. Sometimes accidentally generated by pouring acid into an aqueous sol. of a cyanide salt, especially in electroplating shops.

HYDROFLUORIC ACID–HF. [Hydrogen fluoride]. Colorless gas or colorless, fuming, highly mobile liquid emitting pungent suffocating odor; also colorless penetrating liquid when diluted with dist. water to 36%-38% in the usual reagent grade; the latter has G = 1.25. Infinitely sol. in water. Produced by reacting 80% H_2SO_4 with very pure fluorite, a technique which has been used to etch glass by applying a paste of fluorite moistened with concentrated acid. Attacks silicates and glass, forming with Si the volatile compound silicon tetrafluoride, SiF_4. Sold in polyethylene plastic bottles or jugs but inevitably some HF gas escapes through the sides and causes etching of adjacent glass objects and corrosion of metal objects. While this uniquely useful acid finds greatest use in dissolving silicate minerals, it does not always dissolve them cleanly, perhaps owing to the formation of complex F-metallic ion-Si salts which remain as white incrustations or spongy layers upon the minerals being dissolved. Such are not easily removed except mechanically, although treatment with warm oxalic acid is said to dissolve such crusts (see discussion under "Alexandrite Chrysoberyl" in the "Minerals Treatment" section).

In summarizing experiments involving the use of 9% conc. HF, Hunt gives the following observations on its effectiveness:

Silicates not visibly etched: Diopside, enstatite, danburite, garnet, epidote, zoisite, axinite, tourmaline, staurolite, spodumene, beryl, topaz, andalusite, kyanite, zircon, talc, muscovite, lepidolite, ripidolite, margarite.

Silicates more or less attacked: Tremolite, amphibole, augite, chrysolite, fayalite, datolite, prehnite, idocrase, phlogopite, biotite.

Silicates visibly etched: Wollastonite, willemite, rhodonite, apophyllite, pectolite, hemimorphite, heulandite, stilbite, harmotome, chabazite, analcime, natrolite, albite, oligoclase, labradorite, anorthite, petalite, iolite, wernerite, orthoclase, leucite, jefferisite, serpentine, halloysite, titanite.

Source: T. Sterry Hunt, Systematic Mineralogy (New York, 1891), p. 95.

HF is extremely dangerous to use and no precautions are too great to ensure that fumes or liquid cannot in any manner contact the skin or be ingested. Damage to throat and lung tissues results from inhalation of vapors, while even a small droplet on the skin results in severe lesions and excruciating pain. Dilutions down to about 5% are much less harmful and where such will serve the purpose they should be used in preference to the concentrated acid. Immediate and continued washing with water to one-half hour is recommended where acid contacts the skin, followed by application of dil. ammonia sol. to the affected parts. Massive contacts call for immediate treatment by a doctor.

HYDROGEN PEROXIDE–H_2O_2. Colorless aqueous sol. 3% by wgt. obtainable from drugstores; used as chemical reagent in mineral testing.

HYDROGEN SULFIDE–H_2S. Colorless gas with typical "rotten egg" odor generated by acids in contact with sulfides or sulfide minerals. Extremely poisonous gas but seldom generated in dangerous quantities during normal mineral testing; the gas quickly disables the olfactory mechanism and after a few moments of exposure it cannot be smelled. Sol. water, carbon disulfide, alcohol. Generated in the laboratory by treating ferrous sulfide, FeS, with conc. HCl. The gas introduced into aqueous sols. of HCl or H_2SO_4 precipitates Ag, Pb, Hg, Cu, Bi, Cd, As, Sb, or Sn as sulfides.

HYDROXYLAMINE HYDROSULFATE–$(NH_2OH)_2 \cdot H_2SO_4$. Colorless xls or white powder; decomposes $170°$ C. ($338°$ F.); sol. water, ether; slightly sol. alcohol. Strong reducing agent; may be used to remove manganese oxides from mineral specimens.

IODINE–I_2. Violet-black tabular xls; G = 4.93, MP = $114°$ C. ($237°$ F.); slowly sublimes in air; dangerous burns to skin when in contact. Sol. alcohol, the ordinary sol. containing 3% by wgt. (tincture of iodine), also sol. ether, chloroform, glycerine, carbon disulfide. Reagent in mineral testing; antiseptic ("tincture").

IODOBENZENE–C_6H_5I. [Monoiodobenzene; phenyl iodide]. Colorless liquid; G = 1.83, BP = $188°$c. ($370°$ F.), $n = 1.620$ ($20°$ C.). Sol. benzene, acetone, ether, alcohol, carbon tetrachloride, chloroform. Refractive index and density fluid.

IODOETHANE = ETHYL IODIDE.

IODOFORM–CHI_3. [Triiodomethane]. Yellowish xls; G = 4.00, MP = $123°$ C. ($253°$ F.). Rapid, possibly explosive decomposition c. $210°$ C. ($410°$ F.)! Sublimes; store in brown glass bottles to avoid light decomposition. Sol. alcohol, ether, chloroform, glycerine, carbon disulfide, methylene iodide, and other organic liquids and used to raise refractive index of same.

1-IODONAPHTHALENE—$C_{10}H_7I$. [Monoiodonaphthalene]. Colorless oily liquid; $G = 1.74$, $MP = 4°$ C. ($39°$ F.), $BP = 302°$ C. ($576°$ F.), $n = 1.703$ ($20°$ C.). Refractive index and density fluid.

IRON OXIDE, FERRIC—Fe_2O_3. [Ferric oxide; rouge, jewelers' rouge, crocus (coarse grains), calcothar, turkey red, etc.]. The natural equivalent is hematite; the synthetic compound is made by strongly calcining ferric hydroxide or ferrous sulfate. Deep somewhat purplish red in powder form; black in grains (crocus) or when massive. $G = 5.24$. Slowly sol. conc. warm HCl, more rapidly when in fine powder form or thin coatings.

IRON OXIDE, FERROSOFERRIC— Fe_3O_4. [Ferrosoferric oxide; "black rouge"]. Natural equivalent is magnetite. $G = 5.18$. Sometimes used as polishing or fine abrasive agent.

ISOAMYL ALCOHOL = AMYL ALCOHOL.

ISOPROPYL ALCOHOL— $CH_3CH(OH)CH_3$. [2—Propanol; isopropanol]. Colorless liquid, with not unpleasant odor; $G = 0.79$, $BP = 82°$ C. ($179°$ F.), $n = 1.378$ ($20°$ C.). Sol. alcohols, acetone, benzene, ether, water. Diss. gums, resins, oils. Burns with smoky, luminous flame and hence not as suited for lamps as either ethyl or methyl alcohol. The so-called "rubbing" alcohol is 91% by wgt. isopropyl alcohol with remainder water, but some brands may contain considerably less alcohol and also scenting agents. May be used for cleaning slightly greasy or oily mineral specimens; used to rinse off glassware to prevent formation of stains.

KEROSENE. Mixture of various lighter petroleum distillates but far less combustible and evaporative than the gasoline fractions. Generally $G = 0.80$-0.84, $BP = 175°$-$300°$ C. ($347°$-$572°$ F.), $n = $ c. 1.45. Colorless but characteristically odoriferous liquid unless carefully redistilled to eliminate certain compounds causing odor ("deodorized petroleum distillate") or mixed with amyl acetate to disguise odor (typical formula 1.5 fl. oz. amyl acetate/gal.). Degreasing agent; diluent; paint thinner; sometimes used for sawing stone

or adding to light sawing oil to reduce viscosity.

LEAD ACETATE— $Pb(C_2H_3O_2)_2 \cdot 3H_2O$. White xls; $G = 2.55$, $MP = 75°$ C. ($167°$ F.). Sol. water; insol. alcohol. Sometimes used as reagent in mineral testing.

LITHARGE—PbO. [Lead oxide]. Yellowish powder added to linseed oil to hasten oxidation ("drier"). $G = 9.35$.

LITHIUM FLUORIDE—LiF. White powder or xls; $G = 2.60$, $MP = 870°$ C. ($1,598°$ F.). Sol. acids; insol. alcohol, acetone. Sometimes used in making flame beads for testing minerals.

MAGNESIA—MgO. White, impalpable powder; $G = 3.20$. Used as a mild polishing agent, especially for very soft minerals as the sulfides, but must be stored in sealed containers to prevent absorbing moisture from atmosphere and altering to $Mg(OH)_2$. Made by calcining magnesium carbonate (magnesite) between $600°$-$800°$ C. ($1,112°$-$1,472°$ F.).

MALIC ACID—$C_4H_6O_5$. [l-Hydroxybutanedioic acid; 1-hydroxysuccinic acid]. White acicular xls; $G = 1.6$; $MP = 100°$ C. ($212°$ F.). V. sol. water. Used as a mild acid in lieu of oxalic, HCl, etc., in mineral cleaning.

MANGANESE DIOXIDE—MnO_2. Black powder; $G = 5.03$; heated to $535°$ C. ($995°$ F.) decomposes, liberating oxygen; treated with conc. HCl liberates chlorine gas. Used as an oxidant or "drier" in oil-based paints. The mineral pyrolusite is a common source.

MERCURY—Hg. [Quicksilver]. Silvery white metal, liquid at room temp.; $G = 13.55$, $BP = 357°$ C. ($675°$ F.); freezes at $-39°$ C. ($-102°$ F.). Readily sol. nitric acid, hot sulfuric; insol. hydrochloric acid. Mercury vapor is invisible, odorless, tasteless, but very poisonous. Forms amalgams with many metals. The quartz shortwave UV lamp contains mercury which when incandescent emits several wavelength bands in the UV.

METHANOL = METHYL ALCOHOL.

2-METHOXY ETHYL ACETATE— $CH_3 \cdot COOCH_2 \cdot CH_2OCH_3$. Liquid, $G = 1.009$ ($20°$ C.). Readily sol. water. Used as a diluent for heavy fluids.

METHYL ACETATE—$CH_3CO_2CH_3$. [Methyl ester acetic acid]. Colorless aromatic liquid; $G = 0.93$, $BP = 57°$ C.

(135° F.), n = 1.359 (20° C.), 1.360 (25° C.). Sol. benzene, acetone, ether, alcohol, chloroform and other organic solvents. Diss. cellulose acetate (celluloid) or cellulose nitrate; degreaser; rapidly diss. fats, oils, waxes, etc. Cementing solvent for plastics.

METHYL ALCOHOL – CH_3OH. [Methanol; wood alcohol; carbinol]. Colorless aromatic liquid; G = 0.79, BP = 65° C. (149° F.), n = 1.329 (20°C.), 1.326 (25° C.). Sol. water, alcohols, acetone, benzene, ether, chloroform. Mobile, flammable (burns with almost invisible blue flame), rapidly evaporative. Much more poisonous than ethyl alcohol which it closely resembles in all respects; ingestion or excessive inhalation can lead to serious nervous disorders, blindness, and even death. Useful fuel for lamps; effective solvent for greases, oils, waxes, shellac. Can be used for cleaning mineral specimens. Commercially available in sealed metal cans at c. 95% by wgt. alcohol, the remainder water.

METHYLBENZENE = TOLUENE.

METHYL BUTYRATE – $CH_3CH_2CH_2CO_2CH_3$. [Methyl ester butanoic acid]. Colorless liquid; G = 0.898, BP = 102° C. (215° F.), n = 1.388 (20° C.). Sol. ether, alcohol. Lacquer solvent.

METHYLENE BROMIDE = DIBROMO-METHANE.

METHYLENE CHLORIDE = DICHLOROMETHANE.

METHYLENE IODIDE – CH_2I_2. [Diiodomethane]. Yellowish liquid, somewhat oily in consistency, with penetrating odor; G = 3.325 (20° C.), BP = 182° C. (360° F.), n = 1.7407 (20° C.), 1.738 (24° C.) Sol. water, alcohol, benzene, ether, bromoform, chloroform, carbon tetrachloride. Very useful for refractive index and density fluids, store in dark or in brown bottles to prevent decomposition; discoloration can be removed by inserting bright copper wires or filings.

METHYL SALICYLATE – $C_8H_8O_3$. [2-Hydroxymethyl ester of benzoic acid; methyl ester of salicylic acid; oil of wintergreen]. Colorless liquid; pleasant mint odor; G = 1.17, BP = 223° C. (433° F.), n = 1.537. Sol. alcohol, ether, glacial acetic acid, carbon disulfide. Refractive index fluid.

MICROCOSMIC SALT = SODIUM AMMONIUM PHOSPHATE.

MINERAL OIL. Thick, tasteless, odorless, and colorless oil, refined from petroleum; G = c. 0.84, n = 1.47-1.48. Lubricant; refractive index fluid.

MONOBROMOBENZENE = BROMO-BENZENE.

MONOBROMONAPHTHALENE = 1-BROMONAPHTHALENE.

MONOCHLORONAPHTHALENE = 1-CHLORNAPHTHALENE.

MONOIODOBENZENE = IODO-BENZENE.

MONOIODONAPHTHALENE = 1-IODONAPHTHALENE.

MORIN – $C_{15}H_{10}O_7$. [2',3,4',5,7,8-pentahydroxyflavone]. Red-yellow xls. MP = 303° C. (577° F.). Sol. alcohol, benzene, carbon disulfide; slightly sol. water. Reagent used in mineral identification testing.

NAPHTHALENE – $C_{10}H_8$. ["Mothballs," "moth flakes"]. White platy xls or compressed solid forms; G = 1.03, MP = 81° C. (178° F.), BP = 218° C. (424° F.), n = 1.400 (20° C.). Sol. alcohol, ether, chloroform, carbon disulfide, benzene, carbon tetrachloride. Sometimes used in mineral cabinets to prevent tarnish on certain minerals and native metals.

NAPHTHAS. Colorless, highly mobile light fluid fractions distilled from petroleum; G = 0.66-0.80, BP = 40°-225° C. (104°-437° F.). Equivalent to gasolines in general.

NITRIC ACID – HNO_3. [Aqua fortis]. Colorless mobile liquid when pure but commonly with brownish vapors of NO_2 over surface of liquid when stored in jars; fumes readily. G = 1.50 (pure), BP = 83° C. (181° F.); usually supplied conc. 68%-70% by wgt. acid, remainder water, with G = c. 1.42. Sol. water, ether, alcohol. Powerful oxidizer, capable of starting fire when spilled upon finely divided carbonaceous materials. Store in brown glass jugs to avoid decomposition due to light. Severe skin burns; fumes dangerous. Much used in mineral testing and other purposes.

NITROBENZENE – $C_6H_5NO_2$. Yellowish liquid; G = 1.20, MP = 6° C. (43° F.), BP = 211° C. (412° F.), n = 1.556 (20° C.), 1.550 (25° C.). Sol. benzene, oils, ether, alcohol, acetone. Refractive index fluid.

2-NITROTOLUENE – $C_7H_7NO_2$. [o- or Orthotoluene]. Yellowish liquid; G = 1.16,

BP = $220°$ C. ($428°$ F.), n = 1.545 ($20°$ C.), 1.544 ($25°$ C.). Sol. benzene, petrol. distillates, chloroform, ether, alcohol. Refractive index fluid.

OXALIC ACID–HO_2CCO_2H. [Ethanedioic acid]. White xls; G = 1.90, MP = $190°$ C. ($374°$ F.) but sublimes beginning c. $157°$ C. ($325°$ F.). Sol. water, alcohol, chloroform. Poisonous, but usual dil. aqueous sols. not dangerous providing liquid not ingested. Bleaches inks, organic dyes, and some coloring matter in minerals, notably in black petrified wood, or in some tigereye. Mild acid; diss. iron oxide stains. Precipitates gold from aqueous sols. containing salts of gold. Avoid use of this acid with any calcium-bearing mineral soluble in acids, e.g., calcite, certain zeolites, etc. because nearly insol. calcium oxalates form which can precipitate in crevices on the specimen and create unsightly stains; use of distilled water for specimen cleaning strongly recommended when preparing this acid.

PENTACHLOROETHANE – Cl_3CCHCl_2. [Pentalin]. Colorless liquid; G = 1.680, BP = $162°$ C. ($323°$ F.), n = 1.503 ($20°$ C.), 1.501 ($25°$ C.). Sol. alcohol, ether. Refractive index, density fluid.

PERCHLORIC ACID–$HClO_4$. Colorless liquid; G = 1.76, BP = $39°$ C. ($102°$ F.). Sol. water; unstable; powerful oxidizer (see remarks under NITRIC ACID); sometimes used in mineral testing.

PETROLATUM ["Vaseline"]. Purified petroleum grease, yellowish to white (bleached), without taste or odor. G = 0.84, MP = c. $42°$-$45°$ C. ($108°$-$113°$ F.); can be melted repeatedly without harm. Lubricant; protective coating. Sol. petroleum distillates, benzene, etc.

PETROLEUM ETHER. Colorless, light fluid fractions from petroleum distillation. Generally, G = 0.65-0.67, BP = $35°$-$80°$ C. ($95°$-$176°$ F.). Sol. napthas, gasolines, lighter fluids, benzene, etc., and similar in properties and behavior to same. Very flammable; dangerous explosion hazard from vapors in confined places. General solvent, diluent, degreaser.

PHENOL–C_6H_5OH. [Carbolic acid; benzenol; hydroxybenzene]. Colorless or white xls; G = 1.07, MP = $43°$ C. ($109°$ F.), BP = $182°$ C. ($360°$ F.), n = 1.551 ($21°$ C.). Sol. water, alcohol, ether, chloroform, glycerine, carbon disulfide, carbon tetra-chloride. Caustic poison, readily burning skin. Sometimes used as an acid in treatment of minerals and in mineral testing.

PHOSPHOMOLYBDIC ACID– $H_3PMo_{12}O_{40} \cdot xH_2O$. Yellowish xls, sol. in water, alcohol, ether, and used as reagent in mineral testing.

PHOSPHORIC ACID–H_3PO_4. [Orthophosphoric acid]. Colorless sirupy liquid, usually supplied in 85% by wgt. conc. liquid. G = 1.725. Sol. water, alcohol. Alternative acid in mineral cleaning; testing reagent.

PHOSPHORUS (White or Yellow)–P_4. White to yellowish waxlike solid; G = 1.82, MP = $44°$ C. ($111°$ F.), *ignites in air* $35°$-$45°$ C. ($95°$-$113°$ F.) after first oxidizing and warming to ignition temp.; n = 2.144. Extremely poisonous. Sold in stick form and kept under water to exclude oxygen. Sol. carbon disulfide, benzene, chloroform, turpentine. Sometimes used as a reagent in mineral identification and additive to refractive index fluids.

PIPERINE–$C_{17}H_{19}NO_3$. [1-Piperyl-piperidine]. White xls or powder; G = 1.193, MP = $128°$ C. ($262°$ F.). Sol. chloroform, benzene, ether, alcohol. Sometimes used as a solvent for iodides in high index refractive index liquids (melts).

POTASSIUM ACID CARBONATE– $KHCO_3$. [Potassium bicarbonate]. White powder; G = 2.04. Sol. water. Reagent in mineral testing.

POTASSIUM ACID SULFATE– $HKSO_4$. [Potassium bisulfate]. White powder; G = 2.25, MP = $210°$ C. ($410°$ F.). Sol. water. Reagent in mineral testing.

POTASSIUM ALUM. See ALUMS.

POTASSIUM CHLORATE–$KClO_3$. White xls; G = 2.32, MP = $368°$ C. ($694°$ F.), but decomposes beginning c. $400°$ C. ($752°$ F.) liberating oxygen which can explosively combine with any oxidizable material in contact. Sol. water, alcohol, alkaline sols. Reagent in mineral testing.

POTASSIUM CHLORIDE–KCl. White powder; G = 1.98, MP = $776°$ C. ($1,493°$ F.). Sol. water, ether, glycerine. Reagent sometimes used in mineral testing.

POTASSIUM CYANIDE–KCN. White xls; G = 1.52, MP = $635°$ C. ($1,175°$ F.). Sol. water, glycerine, methyl alcohol. Used in electroplating and removing gold from ores. Deadly poison; accidental pouring of acid into cyanide sol. creates equally deadly hydrocyanic acid gas.

POTASSIUM DICHROMATE– $K_2Cr_2O_7$. Orange-red xls, sometimes grown from aqueous sol. and sold as the mineral "realgar." G = 2.69, MP = 398° C. (748° F.); decomposes c. 500° C. (932° F.). Readily sol. water. Powerful oxidizing agent; used in electroplating; reagent for testing minerals.

POTASSIUM FERRICYANIDE– $K_3Fe(CN)_6$. Red xls; G = 1.89. Sol. water, acetone; insol. alcohol. Tends to decompose in water and sols., should be made up only as needed. Reagent for testing minerals and for blue dyeing of agate.

POTASSIUM FERROCYANIDE– $K_4Fe(CN)_6 \cdot 3H_2O$. Lemon yellow xls; G = 1.85. Sol. water, acetone; insol. alcohol. Reagent used in mineral testing and for blue dyeing of agate.

POTASSIUM FLUORIDE–KF. White powder or xls; G = 2.48, MP = 880° C. (1,616° F.). Sol. water, HF or ammonia sol.; insol. alcohol. Reagent in mineral testing.

POTASSIUM HYDROXIDE–KOH. [Caustic potash, potash lye, lye]. White massive, in sticks; G = 2.04, MP = 360° C. (680° F.). Sol. water with liberation much heat; also sol. alcohol, ether; insol. aqua ammonia. Deliquescent and must be stored in sealed containers. Reacts with oils, greases, etc., to form soap. Severe burns to skin. Melts capable of decomposing silicates.

POTASSIUM IODATE–KIO_3. Colorless xls; G = 3.89, MP = 560° C. (1,040° F.), decomposing when heated. Sol. water. Reagent in mineral testing.

POTASSIUM IODIDE–KI. White xls; G = 3.13, MP = 723° C. (1,333° F.). Very sol. water; sol. alcohol, ammonia sol. Reagent in testing minerals.

POTASSIUM MERCURIC IODIDE–KI, HgI_2. Decomposes in water; sol. alcohol, ether, acetic acid. Painful skin burns! Reagent used in mineral testing.

POTASSIUM NITRATE–KNO_3. [Saltpeter, niter]. White xls; G = 2.11, MP = 337° C. (639° F.), decomposing 400° C. (720° F.) liberating oxygen and readily exploding when in presence oxidizable matter. Sol. water, insol. alcohol. Deposits of carbon on metals, diamond xls, etc., can be removed by heating with pot. nitrate which burns off carbon.

POTASSIUM NITRITE–KNO_2. White xls; G = 1.92, MP = 387° C. (729° F.). Sol. water, aqua ammonia. Reagent in mineral testing.

POTASSIUM PERMANGANATE– $KMnO_4$. Purple xls; G = 2.70, decomposes c. 240° C. (464° F.). Sol. water; decomposes in alcohol; sol. sulfuric acid; readily sol. alcohols, acetone. Reagent in mineral testing. Disinfectant.

POTASSIUM PYROSULFATE– $K_2S_2O_7$. White powder, G = 2.27, MP = 300° C. (540° F.), decomposing at higher temp. Sol. water. Reagent in chemical testing of minerals.

POTASSIUM SODIUM TARTRATE– $KNaC_4H_4O_6 \cdot 4H_2O$. [Rochelle salt]. White xls. G = 1.79, MP = 70°-80° C. (158°-176° F.). Readily loses water of crystallization c. 215° C. (419° F.). Sol. water. Used in cleaning of native copper specimens; chemical reagent in mineral identification testing.

POTASSIUM THIOCYANATE–KNCS. Colorless xls. G = 1.89, MP = 173° C. (343° F.); decomposes c. 500° C. (932° F.). Sol. water, alcohol, acetone, amyl alcohol. Used in red dyeing of agate.

PROPANE–$CH_3CH_2CH_3$. Colorless flammable gas; liquid: G = 0.50, BP = –42° C. (–44° F.). Fuel for heaters, cookstoves, and torches.

PRUSSIC ACID = HYDROCYANIC ACID.

QUINALDINE–$C_{10}H_9N$. [2-Methyl-quinoline]. Colorless liquid; G = 1.06, BP = 248° C. (478° F.). n = 1.612 (20° C.). Sol. chloroform, benzene, alcohol, ether. Refractive index fluid.

QUINALIZARIN–$C_{14}H_8O_6$. [9,10-Anthraquinone, 1,2,5,8-tetrahydroxy-]. Red powder; MP over 275° C. (527° F.). Insol. water; slightly sol. acetone, benzene, alcohol, ether. Reagent in mineral testing.

QUININE IODOSULFATE– $4C_{20}H_{24}N_2O_2 \cdot 3H_2SO_4 \cdot 2HI \cdot I_4 \cdot 6H_2O$. ["Herapathite"]. Strongly dichroic olive-green platy xls; decomposes in water. Used in making polarizing plastic films.

QUINOLINE–C_9H_7N. [1-Benzazine; benzopyridine]. Colorless liquid; G = 1.09, BP = 238° C. (460° F.), n = 1.627 (20° C.), 1.622 (24° C.). Sol. carbon disulfide, ether, alcohol, acetone, benzene, Refractive index fluid.

ROCHELLE SALT = POTASSIUM SODIUM TARTRATE.

SELENIUM—Se. Red powder; G = 4.26, MP = $40°$-$50°$ C. ($104°$-$122°$ F.). Sol. sulfuric acid, carbon disulfide, benzene; insol. water. Burns in air with bluish flame. Additive to refractive index fluids.

SILICONES. Organic-type compounds in which silicon has been substituted for certain positions normally occupied by carbon in the molecular structures, thus conferring unusual resistance to chemical attack and decomposition due to heat. Among silicone compounds are colorless oils used as lubricants, hydraulic fluids, etc., and "rubbers" which retain flexibility from about $-180°$ C. ($-292°$ F.) to nearly $450°$ C. ($842°$ F.). The latter are strongly adhesive and find wide use as sealing compounds but are also useful for making flexible molds for casting resins, including epoxies and low-melt alloys.

SILVER NITRATE—$AgNO_3$. [Lunar caustic]. White xls or pressed forms; G = 4.35, MP = $212°$ C. ($414°$ F.); decomposes c. $440°$ C. ($824°$ F.). Sol. water, ether, glycerine. Sols. used as reagents in testing minerals. Precipitates silver chlorides, bromides, or iodides from aqueous or acidic sols.

SODA LYE = SODIUM HYDROXIDE.

SODIUM AMMONIUM PHOSPHATE— $NaHN_4HPO_4 \cdot 4H_2O$. [Microcosmic salt]. White xls; G = 1.55, decomposes c. $79°$ C. ($174°$ F.). Sol. water; insol. alcohol. Used for fusion tests in mineral testing; upon fusion becomes sodium metaphosphate, $NaPO_3$.

SODIUM BICARBONATE—$NaHCO_3$. [Baking soda; sodium acid carbonate]. White powder; sol. water; slightly sol. alcohol. G = 2.2; MP = $270°$ C. ($518°$ F.). Flux in mineral fusions.

SODIUM CARBONATE (Anhydrous)— Na_2CO_3. [Soda ash; soda]. White xls; G = 2.51, MP = $851°$ C. ($1,562°$ F.). Sol. water; slightly sol. absolute alcohol. Flux for mineral testing, assaying ores.

SODIUM CARBONATE (Hydrous)— $Na_2CO_3 \cdot 10H_2O$. [Washing soda; sal soda]. White xls; G = 1.44, MP = $33°$ C. ($91°$ F.), rapidly losing water of crystallization, which also is slowly lost upon exposure to air. Rapidly sol. water; insol. alcohol.

Effective degreaser in warm sols. but milder than sols. of sodium hydroxide. Precipitates Fe, Zn, Mn, Co, Ni, Cu, Mg as carbonates from aqueous sols. of their salts. Flux for mineral fusions.

SODIUM CHLORIDE—NaCl. [Table salt]. White xls; rapidly sol. water; sol. glycerine; insol. alcohol. G = 2.165, MP = $801°$ C. ($1,474°$ F.). Table salt usually contains small amounts of magnesium chlorides to prevent caking due to absorption of atmospheric water. Reagent in mineral testing.

SODIUM CYANIDE—NaCN. White xls; G = 1.5; MP = $564°$ C. ($1,047°$ F.). Sol. water; slightly sol. alcohol. Reacts readily with acids to produce hydrocyanic acid gas which is an even deadlier poison than the cyanide. Used in electroplating baths, cleaning of metals, reagent in mineral testing, and solvent for sulfides as on silver.

SODIUM DITHIONATE— $Na_2S_2O_6 \cdot 2H_2O$. White or colorless xls; G = 2.189; loses water when heated to about $110°$ C. ($230°$ F.); evolves SO_2 gas when heated to about $267°$ C. ($513°$ F.). Readily sol. water; sol. HCl; insol. alcohol. Mild acid in aqueous sol. used for removal of iron oxide films from carbonates, phosphates, and others likely to be attacked by other acids; sol. 1 teaspoon in 1 pint water.

SODIUM FLUOBORATE—$NaBF_4$. White xls; G = 2.47. Sol. water. Used as flux to decompose silicate minerals for analysis or other purposes. Decomposes in H_2SO_4; sol. in HF.

SODIUM FLUORIDE—NaF. White xls; G = 2.79; MP = $990°$ C. ($1,814°$ F.). Sol. water. Flux used to make certain fluorescent beads in mineral testing.

SODIUM HYDROXIDE—NaOH. [Caustic soda; lye; soda lye]. White xline sticks; G = 2.13, MP = $318°$ C. ($604°$ F.). Rapidly absorbs water from atmosphere; store in sealed containers. Sol. water liberating much heat. Attacks and forms water-sol. compounds with greases, oils, other organic matter. Sols. with even slight traces of sodium hydroxide possess a very bitter taste and feel soapy; conc. sols. cause serious burns to skin. Also sol. alcohol, glycerine; insol. acetone. Melts used to decompose silicates; precipitates Fe, Mn, Co, Ni, Cu, Bi, Cd, Mg, and rare earths as hydroxides from aqueous sols.

SODIUM HYPOCHLORITE—NaClO.

Available in aqueous sol. only and used as a reagent in mineral testing.

SODIUM HYPOPHOSPHATE – $Na_4 P_2 O_6 \cdot 10H_2 O$. Colorless xls; G = 1.82, decomposes when heated; sol. water. Reagent in testing minerals and commonly used to detect Mg.

SODIUM METAPHOSPHATE – $NaPO_3$. White powder; G = 2.47, MP = $628°$ C. (1,162° F.). Sol. water. Easily derived from fusion of sodium ammonium phosphate. Used in testing minerals.

SODIUM NITRATE – $NaNO_3$. [Chile saltpeter; soda niter]. White deliquescent powder which must be stored in sealed containers. G = 2.26, MP = $307°$ C. ($585°$ F.); decomposes c. $380°$ C. ($716°$ F.) releasing oxygen which can explosively combine with organic matter present. Sol. water; slightly sol. glycerine, acetone. Reagent in testing minerals.

SODIUM PEROXIDE – $Na_2 O_2$. [Sodium dioxide]. Yellowish white powder; G = 2.805; decomposes c. $460°$ C. ($860°$ F.). Sol. water; decomposes in hot water; insol. alcohol. Reagent used in mineral testing.

SODIUM PYROSULFITE – $Na_2 S_2 O_5$. [Sodium bisulfite, sod. metabisulfite]. White powder; G = 1.4; decomposes above $150°$ C. ($302°$ F.). Sol. water; sol. glycerine; slightly sol. alcohol. Used in aqueous sol. for removing manganese dioxide stains from mineral specimens; a mild acid.

SODIUM SILICATE – $Na_2 Si_4 O_9$. [Water glass; sodium tetrasilicate]. Easily sol. water to form thick to syrupy liquid of considerable adhesive power and drying to a glassy gel. Sold in lumps or as thick conc. fluid. Used as cement, sealing agent, stiffener for felt, cloth, etc.

SODIUM SULFATE – $Na_2 SO_4$. White xls; G = 2.7, MP = $884°$ C. (1,623° F.). Sol. water, glycerine; insoluble alcohol. Reagent in mineral testing.

SODIUM SULFIDE – $Na_2 S$. [Sodium monosulfide]. Yellowish pink to whitish powder; G = 1.86, MP = c. $920°$ C. (1,688° F.). Sol. water and decomposed in acid sols. Reagent in mineral testing.

SODIUM SULFITE – $Na_2 SO_3$. White powder; G = 2.63. Sol. water. Reagent in testing minerals.

SODIUM THIOSULFATE – $Na_2 S_2 O_3 \cdot 5H_2 O$. [Sodium hyposulfite; hypo]. White powder; G = 1.729; sol. water, ammonia sol; insol. alcohol. A 20% by wgt. sol. in water diss. silver bromides (100 parts of the sol. diss. 6 parts by wgt. of the bromide). Slightly diss. silver. Reagent in mineral testing.

STANNIC OXIDE = TIN OXIDE.

SULFAMIC ACID – $NH_2 SO_3 H$. White crystals; G = 2.13; decomposes c. $200°$ C. ($392°$ F.). Sol. water, more readily in hot water. Used in boiler-cleaning compounds because of its very low rate of attack against metals and therefore recommended by some authorities for use in cleaning native copper specimens where it is desired to remove enclosing carbonates.

SULFUR – S. [Flowers of sulfur = chemically precipitated pure sulfur]. Yellow solid or powder; G = 2.07, MP = $113°$ C. ($235°$ F.), BP = $445°$ C. ($833°$ F.), liquefies readily but commonly catches fire and burns with an almost invisible blue flame and formation of choking fumes of sulfur dioxide. Readily sol. carbon disulfide; sol. toluene, methylene iodide; slightly sol. alcohol, benzene, ether, carbon tetrachloride. With fillers used as a cement; fumes of burning S sometimes used as a disinfectant or bleach.

SULFURIC ACID – $H_2 SO_4$. [Oil of vitriol; vitriol; oleum; hydrogen sulfate]. Colorless syrupy fluid when conc. with noticeable heaviness. G = 1.84 c. 96%-98% conc.; BP = $338°$ C. ($640°$ F.) reaching c. 96% conc. in the process of heating and driving off of water. Conc. acid rapidly attracts water from the atmosphere until the resulting sol. reaches 52% by wgt. conc., and conversely, dil. acid loses water until the same conc. is eventually reached. Sol. water with evolution of much heat which may cause part of the water to flash into steam with resulting spattering and danger to operator; the usual technique is to dilute by dribbling acid via glass rod into container of water. Sol. alcohol. Removes water from many organic compounds causing their carbonization. Precipitates Pb, Ba, Sr, Ca sulfates from aqueous sols. Pickling acid in jewelry work; diss. carbonates; attacks and diss. certain metals; used in dyeing agate.

TANNIC ACID – $C_{76} H_{52} O_{46}$. [Tannin; gallotannic acid]. Pale yellowish brown powder; MP = c. $210°$ C. ($410°$ F.). Sol. water, acetone, alcohol, chloroform, carbon disulfide. Reagent sometimes used in mineral testing.

TARTARIC ACID–$C_4H_6O_6$. [*l*-2,3-Dihydroxybutanedioic acid; *d*-2,3-dihydroxysuccinic acid]. White xls; G = 1.76, MP = c. 171° C. (340° F.). Sol. water, alcohol, acetone. Mild acid sometimes used for dissolving carbonates.

TETRABROMOETHANE–Br_3CCH_2Br. [1,1,1,2-Tetrabromoethane; unsymmetrical tetrabromoethane]. Colorless liquid; G = 2.87 (20° C.), MP = 0° C. (32° F.), BP-112° C. (234° F.), n = 1.628 (20° C.). Sol. acetone, benzene, chloroform, aniline, ether, alcohol. Refractive index and density fluid.

TETRABROMOETHANE–$Br_2CHCHBr_2$. [1,1,2,2-Tetrabromoethane; symmetrical tetrabromoethane; acetylene tetrabromide]. Yellowish liquid; G = 2.967 (20° C.), MP = 0° C. (32° F.), BP = 244° C. (471° F.), n = 1.638 (20° C.). Sol. alcohol, ether, acetone, benzene, chloroform, carbon tetrachloride. Refractive index and density fluid.

TETRACHLORETHANE–Cl_3CCH_2Cl. [Unsymmetrical tetrachlorethane]. Yellowish red liquid; G = 1.541 (20° C.), BP = 131° C. (268° F.), n = 1.482 (20° C., 1.481 (24° C.). Sol. alcohol, ether, acetone, benzene, chloroform, carbon tetrachloride. Refractive index and density fluid but less satisfactory than symm. tetrachlorethane.

TETRACHLORETHANE–$Cl_2CHCHCl_2$. [Acetylene tetrachloride; symmetrical tetrachlorethane]. Colorless liquid; G = 1.595 (20° C.), BP = 146° C. (295° F.), n = 1.494 (20° C.), 1.492 (24° C.). Sol. alcohol, ether, acetone, benzene, chloroform, carbon tetrachloride. Refractive index and density fluid. Diss. cellulose acetate.

TETRACHLORMETHANE = CARBON TETRACHLORIDE.

TETRAIODOETHYLENE–$I_2C:CI_2$ or C_2I_4. [Tetraiodoethene; periodoethylene]. Yellow xls; G = 2.98, MP = 192° C. (378° F.), subliming with increase in temp. Sol. carbon disulfide, benzene, toluene, ether, alcohol, chloroform, methylene iodide. Additive to methylene iodide to increase refractive index.

THALLIUM FORMATE–$TlHCO_2$. White xls; G = 4.97; conc. aqueous sol. G = 3.5; MP = 101° C. (214° F.); sol. water.

Extremely poisonous density fluid additive.

THALLIUM MALONATE–$CH_2(CO_2Tl)_2$. Used in conjunction with thallium formate to provide density liquids up to G = 4.9. Sol. water and as dangerously poisonous as the formate.

THALLIUM SILVER NITRATE–$TlNO_3 \cdot AgNO_3$. White xls; MP = 75° C. (167° F.). Sol. water and sometimes employed in density fluids. Extremely poisonous.

TIN CHLORIDE–$SnCl_2$. [Stannous chloride]. White xls; G = 3.95, MP = 246° C. (475° F.). Sol. water, alcohol, ether, acetone, ethyl acetate, methyl acetate. Reagent used in mineral testing.

TIN IODIDE–SnI_2. Yellow-red xls; G = 5.28, MP = 320° C. (608° F.). Sol. water, benzene, carbon disulfide, carbon tetrachloride. Reagent used in testing minerals.

TIN OXIDE–SnO_2. [Stannic oxide; cassiterite]. White powder; G = 6.95, MP = 1,127° C. (2,061° F.); sublimes at higher temp. Dissolves in KOH or NaOH melts; insol. acids incl. A.R. The impalpable artificially prepared powder is extensively used for polishing glass and gemstones.

TITANIUM DIOXIDE–TiO_2. [Rutile]. White powder; G = 4.26, MP = c. 1,840° C. (3,344° F.). Sol. sulfuric acid (hot), strong hydroxide sols. (hot); insol. water. The artificially prepared impalpable powder is used as a paint pigment and sometimes as a polishing agent.

TOLUENE–$C_6H_5CH_3$. [Toluol; methylbenzene; phenylmethane]. Colorless aromatic liquid; G = 0.867 (20° C.), BP = 111° C. (232° F.), n = 1.496 (20° C.), 1.494 (24° C.). Sol. ether, chloroform, benzene, carbon disulfide, acetone, and other organic solvents. Effective degreaser and solvent for oils, waxes, fats. Additive to density fluids; refractive index fluid.

o-TOLUIDINE–C_7H_9N. [2-Amino-toluene; methylaniline]. Colorless liquid; G = 0.998 (20° C.), BP = 200° C. (392° F.), n = 1.573 (20° C.), 1.570 (25° C.). Sol. carbon tetrachloride, alcohol, ether, other organic solvents. Refractive index and density fluid additive.

TRIBROMOMETHANE = BROMOFORM.

TRICHLOROETHANOL–$ClCH:CCl_2$. [Trichlorethylene; chlorylene; perchlorethylene]. Colorless mobile liquid; G =

1.464, BP = $87°$ C. ($189°$ F.), n = 1.477 ($20°$ C.). Sol. alcohol, ether, chloroform, other organic solvents. Degreaser; additive to refractive index or density fluids.

TRIETHYL ESTER PHOSPHORIC ACID—$(C_2H_5O)_3PO$, also $(C_2H_5)_3PO_4$. [Triethyl orthophosphate]. Col. liquid; G = 1.0695 ($20°$ C.), n = 1.405 ($20°$ C.); MP = $-56°$ C. ($-69°$ F.), BP = $215°$ C. ($419°$ F.). Sol. in water with decomposition; sol. alcohol, slightly sol. acetone, benzene, sol. in and diluent for methylene iodide or bromoform.

TRIIODOMETHANE = IODOFORM.

TRIMETHYLENE BROMIDE = 1,3-DIBROMOPROPANE.

TRIMETHYLENE CHLORIDE = 1,3-DICHLOROPROPANE.

UREA—H_2NCONH_2. [Carbamide]. White powder; G = 1.32, MP = $135°$ C. ($275°$ F.). Sol. water, alcohol; insol. chloroform, benzene, ether. Reagent used in chemical testing of minerals.

VASELINE = PETROLATUM.

WATER GLASS = SODIUM SILICATE.

o-XYLENE—C_8H_{10}. [1,2-Dimethyl xylene; $ortho$ xylene]. Colorless liquid with characteristic odor; G = 0.88 ($20°$ C.), BP = $144°$ C. ($291°$ F.), n = 1.506 ($20°$ C.). Sol. alcohol, ether, acetone, benzene, petroleum distillates, carbon tetrachloride; insol. water. Degreasing agent; refractive index fluid and diluent. Also related compounds 1,3-dimethyl benzene, and 1,4-dimethyl benzene, with the common name "xylene" and with somewhat lower properties may be substituted.

XYLIDINE—$C_6H_5N(CH_3)_2$. [N,N-dimethylaniline]. Colorless liquid; G = 0.956 ($20°$ C.), BP = $194°$ C. ($381°$ F.), n = 1.558 ($20°$ C.). Sol. benzene, acetone, ether, alcohol, chloroform. Refractive index fluid.

ZINC OXIDE—ZnO. [Zincite]. White impalpable powder; G = 5.61, MP = $1,975°$ C. ($3,587°$ F.). Sol. acids, strong alkaline sols. Sometimes used in formulation of cements.

WAXES, GUMS, RESINS, AND SIMILAR ORGANIC COMPOUNDS

ACACIA GUM = GUM ARABIC.

AGAR-AGAR. Translucent white gelatinous substance obtained from seaweeds, especially kelps; used as a stiffener in foods and jellies, and as a biological culture medium.

ALMOND OIL. Pressed from the kernels of almonds; pale yellowish oily fluid, nearly odorless and nondrying; n = 1.45-1.47.

AMBER OIL. Obtained from dry distillation of amber; colorless to yellowish-brown fluid with characteristic odor and acrid taste; n = 1.45-1.48; rectified oil n = 1.51.

ANISE OIL. Pressed from the fruit or leaves of the plant *Illicium verum* of the Far East; pungent, aromatic oil; G = 0.98-0.99; n = 1.55-1.556.

ANISE SEED OIL. Pressed from seeds of the shrub *Pimpinella anisum* of the Near East; colorless, thin oily fluid with characteristic "anise" odor; G = 0.86-0.91; n = 1.55-1.556.

ASPHALT, ASPHALTUM. Black semisolid mineral pitch fracturing with glasslike conchoidal fracture. Obtained from distillation of coal. G = 0.93-1.10, MP = c. $150°$ C. ($302°$ F.). Readily sol. all petroleum distillates such as gasoline, benzene, lighter fluid. Acid resistant and waterproof; used for caulking, waterproofing, surfacing, etc. May be used for pitch polishing laps although the pine-tree pitches are preferred.

BALSAM PERU. Sticky semisolid or syrupy substance obtained from the tropical American tree *Myroxylon pereirae;* reddish-brown; n = 1.593.

BEESWAX. Obtained from honeycombs; ordinary purified wax is yellowish or brownish, the white is bleached. G = 0.96-0.967, MP = $62°$-$66°$ C. ($144°$-$151°$ F.), melting to transparent fairly mobile liquid; n = 1.44-1.46. Supplied in small blocks or cakes. Used as wax for cementing slabs to base plates for lapping and polishing and as a constituent of dopping waxes. Sol. petroleum derivatives such as gasoline, benzene, lighter fluid.

BONE OIL. Pale yellowish foul-smelling oil obtained by distillation of fats from bones; n = 1.47.

BURGUNDY PITCH. Yellow-brown hard resin from the exudate of the Norway spruce (*Picea abies*). G = 1.09. Used as a resin in cements, pitch laps.

CAMPHOR. Translucent white, slowly

volatile resin of waxy texture obtained from the camphor tree of Taiwan ("Formosa camphor") and used as a plasticizer in plastics, particularly in celluloids.

CANADA BALSAM [Canada turpentine]. Yellow, sticky semisolid, perfectly transparent, obtained from the exudate of the balsam fir (*Abies balsamica*). It slowly solidifies, rapidly when heated during which time volatiles escape. When solidified by heat or "cooked" it becomes brittle. G = 0.98-0.99, n = 1.52-1.53. Sol. turpentine, acetone, chloroform, benzene, ether; insol. water. Used as cement for glass slides in microscopy and for other cementing purposes.

CARNAUBA WAX. A hard, semibrittle wax from the leaves of the Brazilian palm *Copernica cerifera*. G = 0.990-0.999, MP = 83°-93° C. (181°-199° F.), n = 1.45-1.47. The crude wax is brownish and contains many impurities and is refined by melting and passing through filter paper or cloth. Sol. petroleum distillates. Much used for floor and shoe waxes, car waxes, and as a constituent of dopping waxes or wax polishing laps.

CASEIN. White phospho-protein obtained from milk and used in making plastics and glues (casein mixed with hydrated lime, to which water is added as needed).

CASSIA OIL. Yellowish to brownish oil obtained from the leaves and twigs of the tree *Cinnamomum cassia*. G = 1.01-1.07, n = 1.58-1.60. Used as a refractive index fluid.

CASTOR OIL. Yellowish or colorless thick oil obtained from seeds of the castor plant *Ricinis communis*. G = 0.961, n = 1.47-1.48. Sol. in 90% alcohol and petroleum derivatives. Used as a lubricant and as a substitute for olive oil.

CEDARWOOD OIL. Obtained from distillation of the wood of the cedar tree, e.g., *Juniperus virginiana*. Colorless and fragrant with typical odor. G = 0.94-0.96, n = 1.50-1.51. Used as a refractive index fluid.

CELLULOSE –$(C_6H_{10}O_5)_x$. The basic solid material of wood and other vegetation, and seen in more or less purified form in filter and blotting papers. It is inert but is dissolved by certain organic solvents and can be treated with acids to form celluloid

plastics as the nitrate or acetate.Insol. water, alcohol, ether, dil. acids.

CINNAMON OIL [Cinnamon bark oil; Ceylon cinnamon oil; note that CASSIA OIL is Chinese cinnamon oil]. Any oil from the trees of the genus *Cinnamomum*, but specifically a light yellow oil from *C. zeylanica* of Asia of which one type is from the bark and the other from the leaves. G = 1.00-1.04 (bark), 1.04-1.07 (leaf), n = 1.59-1.60. Aromatic oil used for refractive index determinations. Sol. benzene.

CITRONELLA OIL. A yellowish, light oil derived from citronella grass, *Cymbopogon nardus*, of southern Asia. G = 0.89-0.92, n = 1.48. Mainly used as an insect repellant but also useful as a refractive index fluid. Sharp, penetrating odor. Sol. petroleum distillates; rather readily washes off with soap and water.

CLOVE OIL. Very pale yellow oil obtained from the buds of the East Indian tree *Eugenia aromatica*, with typical sharp aroma. G = 1.04-1.07, n = 1.53. Used in flavoring, medicine, and sometimes as a refractive index fluid.

COCONUT OIL [Coco butter]. Colorless oil extracted from the seed kernel of the coconut palm, *Cocos nucifera*. G = 0.924, MP = 25° C. (77° F.), n = 1.45.

COD LIVER OIL. Oil obtained from the liver of the codfish *Gadus morhua;* G = 0.925, n = 1.481.

COPAL. Resin exuded by various tropical trees; colorless, yellowish or reddish, and fairly hard. G = 1.06-1.08, MP = 120°-166° C. (248°-331° F.), n = 1.528. Insol. acetone or alcohol; partly sol. benzene, chloroform, ether, turpentine. Used in varnishes, cements, sealing compounds.

CORN (MAIZE) OIL. Pale yellow oil expressed from seeds of the corn plant *Zea mays*, and used primarily in cooking or for making soap. G = 0.917, n = 1.47-1.48. Gradually oxidizes and becomes gummy. A convenient immersion fluid.

COTTONSEED OIL. Pale yellow oil expressed from the seeds of the cotton plant *Gossypium hirsutum;* G = 0.917, n = 1.45-1.48. Used in food mainly, but is also used in paints, varnishes, etc. Gradually oxidizes and becomes gummy. A convenient immersion fluid.

DAMMAR. A resin obtained from trees of the genus *Agathis* of Australia and New

Zealand, specifically the kauri tree *Agathis australis*. G = 1.00-1.08, MP = 95°-190° C. (203°-374° F.). Pale to medium yellow or brownish. Sol. benzene, chloroform, carbon disulfide; partly sol. alcohol, ether, acetone, amyl alcohol. The kauri gum has sometimes been used as a substitute for amber. Used in varnishes and cement preparations.

DEXTRINS. Produced by heating starches to 170°-270° C. (338°-518° F.) and resulting in water-sol. gums much used for stamp and stationery adhesives.

DRAGON'S BLOOD. Dark red resin from fruit of the Malayan rattan palm *Calamus draco*. Primarily used to impart color to varnishes. G = 1.2, MP = 120° C. (248° F.). Acid resistant; sol. alcohol, ether, benzene; partly sol. acetone, chloroform.

EUCALYPTUS OIL. Colorless oil obtained from leaves of any eucalyptus tree, but specifically from *E. globulus* of Australia. Highly aromatic. G = 0.86-0.96, n = 1.46-1.47. Used in ore flotation and is also used to some extent as a refractive index fluid.

GELATIN. Colloidal organic material extracted from the cartilages of animals and from the air bladders of fishes ("isinglass"). Colorless to white, and furnished in sheets, threads, and other forms. G = 1.27, n = 1.51-1.53. Used as an ingredient in cements and glues. Absorbs water and becomes jellylike.

GUM ARABIC. White to very pale yellow transparent gum obtained from various trees of the *Acacia* genus of southeast Asia. G less than 1.00; n = 1.48-1.51. Used in water-based cements and glues.

GUM MASTIC. Semihard resin obtained from the mastic tree *Pistacia lentiscus* of southern Europe and Asia. G = 1.04-1.28, MP = 105°-120° C. (221°-248° F.). Sol. amyl alcohol, benzene, ether; partly sol. ethyl alcohol, acetone, methyl alcohol, ethyl acetate, turpentine. Waterproof. Used in caulking compounds, cements.

GUM TRAGACANTH. A water soluble gum from the plant *Astragalus gummifer*. Furnished in sticks, or plates, and nearly colorless. Swells in water and forms an adhesive much used for cementing paper.

GUTTA PERCHA. Semisolid resin, similar to rubber in properties, obtained from the latex of the Malaysian trees of genera *Payena* and *Palaquium*. Pure gutta percha is colorless, tasteless, and odorless, but crude is white to brown. Softens when heated and is vulcanizable. G = 0.96-0.98, MP = 120° C. (248° F.), softening at about 37° C. (99° F.), and molded at about 90° C. (195° F.); above 130° C. (265° F.) melts to a colorless oil. Sol. toluene, chloroform, carbon disulfide; slightly sol. turpentine, alcohol, benzene; insol. water. Used in many formulations where some degree of flexibility and elasticity is required.

ISINGLASS. The semitransparent, whitish, and very pure gelatin obtained from the air bladders of fish ("fish glue") and used in cement or glue formulations. The term "isinglass" is also applied to muscovite mica.

KAURI GUM. See DAMMAR.

LANOLIN. The grease or fat removed from sheep's wool and used in leather pastes and waxes, book leather preservatives, etc.

LEMON OIL. Thin, colorless oil squeezed from the rinds of lemons. G = 0.86, n = 1.47-1.48. Can be used as a refractive index fluid.

LINSEED (FLAXSEED) OIL. Fairly thick, yellowish oil expressed from the seeds of the flax (linen) plant of Europe and elsewhere. Slowly oxidizes and changes to a gum and eventually to a semihard resin. Oxidation or "drying" is accelerated by addition of driers as manganese oxides or litharge (lead oxides). G = 0.934, n = 1.47-1.49. Used in paints and varnishes.

LITMUS. A blue dye obtained from lichens and used to stain papers which then serve to indicate acidity (turn red) or alkalinity (turn blue) when immersed in solutions.

MASTIC = GUM MASTIC.

NEATSFOOT OIL. Pale yellow, odoriferous oil obtained from the feet and shinbones of oxen. G = 0.92, n = 1.47. Used to preserve and soften leather in footwear and in bookbindings.

OLIVE OIL. Yellowish oil of fairly thick consistency expressed from the flesh of the olive-tree fruit. G = 0.91, solidifies about $-9°$ C. (16° F.); n = 1.44-1.47. "Virgin" oil is the first pressing and is used primarily in cooking; it is free of acid. Used also for suspending diamond powders in abrasive and polishing operations.

PALM OIL. Yellow or reddish semi-solid from the flesh of the fruit of *Elaeis guineensis* palm. G = 0.92, MP = 35° C. (95° F.), n = 1.44-1.46. Used in soaps, candles, and greases.

PARAFFIN WAX. White tasteless and odorless soft wax obtained as a byproduct of petroleum distillation. G = 0.79-0.94, MP = 32°-80° C. (90°-176° F.), n = 1.42-1.45. The name "paraffin" in England is applied to kerosene or similar liquid petroleum distillate. Used in cements, sealing compounds, etc.

PEPPERMINT OIL. Colorless aromatic and volatile oil obtained from distilling leaves and stems of the peppermint plant *Mentha peperita*. G = 0.90-0.93, n = 1.46-1.47. Refractive index fluid.

PINE OIL. Oils obtained either from distillation of pine needles or from distillation of turpentine. G = 0.85-0.92, n = 1.47-1.49. Pine oil is used in ore flotation.

PITCH. Dark brown to black resin obtained by destructive distillation of wood (and also from coal or oil). Natural pitch is asphalt. Wood pitch is black, hard, and brittle with typical "piny" odor but that from coal or oil is variable in properties and generally disagreeable in odor. G = 1.11 (pine pitch), 1.25 (coal pitch). Melts at low temperature and runs readily as a thick fluid; softens appreciably and very slowly flows at ordinary room temperatures. Sol. petroleum distillates such as benzene, gasolines, kerosene, also carbon disulfide. Waterproof. Used as a stop (acid resist) in etching, for cement and caulking compounds, and as lap material for polishing (pine pitch).

RAPE SEED OIL. Light yellow oil obtained from pressing of rape seeds (*Brassica campestris*) or turnip seeds. May be oxidizable or nonoxidizable. G = 0.91-0.92, n = 1.47-1.48. Edible oil used as substitute for olive oil, and may be so used in lapidary work.

ROSIN [Colophony, pine resin, yellow resin]. Amberlike solid, brittle, obtained from distillation of pine-tree exudates. G = 1.07-1.09, MP = 100°-150° C. (212°-248° F.), n = 1.548. Sol. acetone, ethyl alcohol, methyl alcohol, amyl alcohol, benzene, ethyl acetate, turpentine, and many petroleum distillates. Used in dopping and other cements.

RUBBER. Made from the latex of the rubber tree *Hevea*, principally species in southeast Asia. Uncured rubber is translucent, yellowish, and readily sticks to itself when freshly cut surfaces are placed in contact. Begins to melt 182°-240° C. (360°-400° F.), losing elasticity and becoming sticky. Preserved indefinitely in cold water but rapidly deteriorates when exposed to sun and air, then becoming hard and brittle. Sol. carbon disulfide, benzene, petroleum ether, turpentine. Used in many compounds and cements.

SAFFLOWER OIL. Pale yellow oil prepared from the seeds of the safflower plant *Carthamus tinctorius*. G = 0.93, n = 1.47-1.48. Edible oil used like olive oil.

SANDALWOOD OIL. An oil distilled from the wood of the tree *Santalum album* of India-Asia. G = 0.96-0.98, n = 1.50-1.51. Fragrant. Sometimes used as a refractive index fluid.

SESAME OIL. A pale yellowish oil expressed from the seeds of the East Indian plant *Sesamum indicum*. G = 0.92, n = 1.47. Edible oil, used for salads, cooking, etc., and as a substitute for olive oil.

SHELLAC [Lac, gum lac, garnet lac]. Resin exuded by trees of the genus *Ficus*, and *Tachardia lacca* of Asia. Naturally transparent yellowish or orangeish, but nearly colorless when bleached and then less strong; also dyed in many colors. G = 1.08-1.13, MP = 78°-80° C. (172°-176° F.), flows readily about 180°-196° C. (230°-248° F.), then hardens about 180°-196° C. (356°-384° F.) and begins to carbonize. Sol. alcohols, acetic acid, benzene, ether, turpentine, acetone, ethyl acetate; also sol. hot aqueous sols. of K-carbonates, lyes, borax. Insol. isopropyl alcohol. Used extensively in varnishes and lacquers, but also as binder in abrasive-grit wheels, in cements, dopping cement, sealing wax, etc. Unique in its adhesive powers but requires that both cement and objects being cemented be warmed to same degree.

SOYBEAN OIL. Expressed from seeds of the leguminous plant *Glycine soja*, now grown extensively in many parts of the world. Pale yellow, medium viscosity, semidrying oil; G = 0.92-0.93, n =

1.47-1.48. Used in paints, soaps, and as an edible oil.

STARCH. A vegetable substance with the basic composition $C_6H_{10}O_5$. Amorphous solid, swelling in water and then used for pastes.

TUNG OIL. Oil extracted from seeds of the tung tree *Aleurites fordi*. G = 0.93-0.95, *n* = 1.49-1.52. Oxidizes rapidly. Used as a substitute for linseed oil in paints, varnishes; also used as a sealer.

TURMERIC. Aromatic powder of the East Indian herb *Curcuma longa*. Used to impregnate paper for acidity-alkalinity indicators; such a paper immersed in an alkaline solution turns from yellow to brown, and in acid to red-brown.

TURPENTINE. Colorless, mobile aromatic liquid distilled from the exudates of pine trees. G = 0.85-0.91, BP = $155°$-$165°$ C. ($311°$-$329°$ F.), *n* = 1.45-1.49. Sol. ether, chloroform, carbon disulfide, various petroleum distillates. Dissolves rosin, waxes, oils, gums. Rags soaked in turpentine are prone to spontaneously combust. Used in paints, for cleaning, as a solvent, etc.

TURPENTINE RESIN. Thick exudate of pine trees, also the balsam firs, larches, and other conifers, and the raw material from which turpentine is distilled with one of the byproducts being rosin. Sol. alcohol, benzene, ether, chloroform, ethyl acetate, petroleum distillates.

VENICE TURPENTINE. A turpentine distilled from the exudate of the larch tree.

WINTERGREEN OIL. Colorless aromatic oil obtained from distillation of leaves of the low shrub *Gaultheria procumbens* ("checkerberry" of the U.S.), but also from related species and from certain tree barks. G = 1.17, *n* = 1.53-1.537. The oil consists mostly of methyl salicylate (see "Chemicals List," p. 33). Sol. alcohol, ether, carbon disulfide. Used as a refractive index fluid.

SOME COMMON PLASTICS

These are some of the plastics that the mineral and gem collector may work with in the workshop or laboratory. *Thermosetting* plastics are those which harden or *cure* when heat is applied and generally cannot be molded afterward by the reapplication of heat (e.g., bakelite). The *Thermoplastics,* on the other hand, are those which require heat to soften and mold, and can generally be reheated and remolded a number of times without suffering decomposition. A final type of plastic compound is a mixture of plastic in water or plastic dissolved in some suitable solvent, either of which hardens by the evaporation of the water or solvent.

CELLULOID. General name for plastics made by treating cellulose, usually cotton, with mixtures of glacial acetic acid and sulfuric acid (acetates), or nitric acid and sulfuric acid (nitrates). Plasticizers may be added to impart flexibility and reduce brittleness.

CELLULOSE ACETATE (Lumarith, Plastacele, Rayon). Transparent colorless thermoplastic, resistant to burning ("safety film"). G = 1.27-1.60; RI = 1.46-1.50. Distorts $41°$-$100°$ C. ($106°$-$212°$ F.), softens $60°$-$130°$ C. ($140°$-$284°$ F.). Hot water swells and softens. Sol. alcohols, ketones, esters, especially ethyl acetate, glacial acetic acid, or acetone. Disagreeable acidy smell when scorched. Common ingredient quick-drying household cements sold in tubes.

CELLULOSE NITRATE (Celluloid, Pyroxlin, Pyralin). Transparent colorless thermoplastic, which burns furiously and dangerously, emitting poisonous fumes and capable of smoldering even in atmospheres virtually deprived of oxygen. Once used extensively in photographic films but now entirely replaced by acetate. Emits distinctive camphor odor when warmed or rubbed. G = 1.35-1.60; RI = 1.46-1.58. Distorts $43°$-$66°$ C. ($111°$-$151°$ F.), softens $60°$-$90°$ C. ($140°$-$194°$ F.). Sol. alcohols, ketones, esters; especially sol. in amyl acetate and methyl alcohol, in butyl acetate, or in mixture of alcohol and ether; sol. acetone. Resists most acids and alkalies.

EPOXIES. Thermosetting, two-part mixtures of resin and catalytic agent which usually must be mixed in exact proportions specified by manufacturer; may require heat to cure rapidly and thoroughly. Large variety available. G about 1.1; RI about 1.58. From colorless or nearly so to dark red or brown. Very resistant to most chemicals; resistant to heat and tending not to distort. Some types slowly dissolved by ketones but most must be regarded as permanent once prepared and used. Very low shrinkage upon curing.

METHACRYLATES (Lucite, Plexiglas, Perspex). Transparent colorless thermoplastics. G = 1.16; RI = 1.48-1.50 (when pure). Distorts $50°$-$85°$ C. ($122°$-$185°$ F.), softens $66°$-$123°$ C. ($151°$-$253°$ F.); hot water softens and permits twisting, bending, etc. At about $149°$ C. ($300°$ F.) softens in from 5-6 minutes. Slowly burns. Transmits much UV. Poor resistance to strong mineral acids or alkalies; swells or dissolves in alcohols; dissolves in ketones or esters; softens in aromatic hydrocarbons; softens and becomes sticky with ethylene chloride which can be used to join pieces. Typical flower-perfume odor when scorched.

NYLON. Translucent thermoplastic much used in making fabric fibers but also used for quiet-running gears, bearings, and other mechanical parts. G = 1.13-1.15; RI = 1.53.

PHENOL-FORMALDEHYDES (Bakelite, Formica, Catalin, Micarta). Thermosetting plastics which are generally hard, tough, and heat and chemical resistant, but not resistant to strong acids or alkalies. G about 1.31, but higher (to 1.55) when filled. A phenol-formaldehyde does not burn by itself. A cellulose-fiber filled type has been used for lapidary lap bases and fine-grinding and polishing laps and buffs. Much used for counter and tabletop coverings. When charred, emits very disagreeable acrid fumes.

POLYETHYLENE. Translucent whitish thermoplastic much used for bottles and containers. G = 0.91-0.965; RI = 1.50-1.54. Distorts about $40°$ C. ($104°$ F.). Slowly burns. Degrades when exposed to sunlight, due to UV. Sol. in aromatic hydrocarbons and less so in aliphatic; very resistant to acids and oils. Commonly used in acid containers, e.g., hydrochloric (muriatic) and hydrofluoric acids.

Caution: Most of these containers are porous and acids or hydrocarbons stored in them escape through the sides, allowing fumes to attack neighboring objects. If possible, transfer such fluids to glass bottles.

POLYPROPYLENE. Transparent colorless thermoplastic. G = 0.90; RI = 1.49.

Burns. Resists acids and alkalies and most solvents. Used for containers.

POLYSTYRENE. Transparent thermoplastic; in foamed form known as "styrofoam." G = 1.04-1.07; RI = 1.592-1.597. Slowly burns. Distorts $72°$-$90°$ C. ($162°$-$194°$ F.), softens $88°$-$121°$ C. ($190°$-$250°$ F.) Sol. ketones and swells in aliphatic hydrocarbons or esters. Resists acids and alkalies, but affected by oils and petroleum products. Styrofoam is very quickly attacked and slumps when touched with any of the quick-drying acetate household cements; may be cemented with water-sol. glues as the "white" glues furnished in squeeze bottles. Pleasant fruity aroma when burnt.

POLYVINYL CHLORIDE ACETATE. Transparent colorless thermoplastic. G = 1.36-1.4; RI = 1.54. Does not burn by itself. Resists acids and alkalies; swells in ketones and esters or aromatic hydrocarbons. Special emulsions in water are sold as "white" glues in squeeze bottles.

SILICONE RUBBERS (Silastic). Translucent to white or black (pigmented) when cured. Cures by emitting acetic acid (typical vinegary smell) and absorbing water from the atmosphere; maximum cure depth less than 2.5 cm ($1''$). G = 1.1-1.2. Burns very slowly and poorly. Softens about $316°$ C. ($600°$ F.), possessing excellent heat resistance and therefore valuable in making molds which must be warmed. Waterproof, acidproof. Adheres tenaciously to smooth surfaces.

TEFLON (Polytetrafluorethylene). White waxy-feeling thermoplastic. G = 2.1-2.3; RI = 1.30-1.40. Does not burn; decomposes at high temperatures emitting poisonous fumes. Distorts $132°$ C. ($270°$ F.). Almost perfectly resistant to any common chemical, oil, resin, etc. Extremely friction-free and unwettable by water, oil, etc. Useful mold material for casting epoxies.

VINYLIDENE CHLORIDE ("Saran"). Thermoplastic. G = 1.68-1.75; RI = 1.60-1.63. Does not burn by itself. Distorts $66°$-$82°$ C. ($151°$-$180°$ F.); softens $116°$-$138°$ C. ($241°$-$280°$ F.). Good to excellent resistance to most chemicals including acids and alkalies.

VINYLS. Resistant to oils, alkalies, alcohols. Sol. methyl isobutyl ketone.

Notes on Plexiglas (Methacrylate) Plastic Use

The following notes are taken from a pamphlet provided by the Rohm and Haas Company, makers of the methacrylate plastic known as Plexiglas.

Chemical Attack: Unaffected by mineral acids such as hydrochloric, sulfuric, nitric, or by strong alkalies or kerosene. Affected by ethyl and leaded gasolines, concentrated alcohols, benzene, acetone, lacquer thinners, carbon tetrachloride, and many window-spray-type cleaning fluids.

To clean: Use mild soap and water; avoid any solvents or sprays.

Softening for bending: Easily bent between 290° and 340° F. (143°-171° C.); do not exceed latter temperature.

Thermal expansion clearances: For large sheets set in rigid frames allow 1/8" per 24" of length of sheet, and 3/16" per 48" of sheet length.

Cementing: Make joints to fit as closely as possible; by fine eyedropper or other applicator which will prevent touching plastic other than at the joint, apply one of the following fluids: methylene chloride ("MDC"), ethylene dichloride ("EDC"), or 1-1-2-trichlorethane.

USEFUL ADHESIVES FOR THE MINERAL COLLECTOR AND LAPIDARY

A large number of cements, glues, and other adhesives are now available, some generally useful for a variety of jobs but others uniquely suited to just one kind of application. Adhesives can be divided into two broad classes, those that contain a solvent that evaporates to leave a hard residue and those that harden by cooling or by a chemical reaction. Solvent glues naturally shrink as the volatile escapes and such shrinkage may be very useful for certain applications but disastrous in others. Furthermore, for any adhesive solvent to escape, the surfaces being cemented together must be porous. Thus it is feasible to use polyvinyl or "white" glue on wood because the water solvent escapes through the wood itself. On the other hand, to use it between two pieces of stone could result in an extremely long drying period because so little of the water can

escape through the stone. For applications such as the last mentioned, other adhesives, notably the epoxies, are much better.

Abbreviations: pt(s) = part(s); wgt. = weight; / = by.

Dopping Cements

SEALING WAX. Red sealing wax 3 pts./wgt., flake shellac, 1 pt.; melt. Adjust stiffness of cold wax by remelting and adding plaster of Paris powder (harder) or shellac (softer).

GENERAL SHELLAC-BASED. Shellac flakes 2 pts./wgt., rosin 1 pt.; melt cautiously on hot plate (avoid open flame). When fluid, stir in 1 pt./wgt. turpentine, stir, now add finely powdered clay or plaster of Paris powder by dusting into container while stirring constantly. When mixture becomes stiff, pour into cold water. Increase strength by slightly reducing rosin and adding more clay or plaster. To reduce chances of scratching soft gemstones, use plaster only.

LOW MELT. Melt 6 pts./wgt. rosin, now add 4 pts./wgt. plaster of Paris. Can be made harder by increasing the plaster.

LOW MELT SHELLAC. Melt shellac flakes 2 pts./wgt. and rosin 1 pt./wgt. Now add beeswax 1 pt./wgt. Carnauba wax may be substituted for the beeswax to make a somewhat stiffer cement with slightly higher melting point.

COLD SHELLAC CEMENT. Dissolve flake shellac in methyl (wood) alcohol until a thick syrupy mixture is obtained. Clean off surface to be cemented with fresh alcohol, e.g., a faceted gem; avoid thereafter touching with the fingers. Apply cement and let dry. Any gem coated with this mixture adheres better to a dop and at the same time requires less heating to make a good bond.

SHELLAC CEMENT, THICKENED. Melt shellac flakes in a shallow pan; when thoroughly fluid ignite surface. Snuff out flames when surface begins to bubble. The liquid underneath is poured into a suitable container and used as a cement.

CHASING CEMENT. A brownish cement used by silversmiths and jewelers; melts at a lower temperature than stick shellac. Can be bought from jewelry supply houses.

COLORING SHELLAC MIXTURES.

Can be dyed any color using alcohol-soluble aniline dyes or by addition of dragon's blood (red), chrome oxide (green), talc (whitish), or lampblack, etc.

COLD DOPPING CEMENT. Mix stiff paste of household quick-drying cement (acetate type, in tube) with plaster of Paris, talcum powder, or cornstarch, using ratio of about 1 drop glue to 4 times that volume of powder. Dissolves in acetone or ethyl acetate. Apply, let dry at least 24 hours.

COLD DOPPING CEMENT. Take 1 drop thick water-glass solution, add plaster of Paris powder, talcum, or cornstarch to make a stiff paste. May take two days to set thoroughly. Dissolves in tepid water.

COLD DOPPING CEMENT. Same as above, but use thick solution of fish glue (isinglass).

Hint: All of the above cold dopping cements shrink as water or solvent evaporates; after thorough drying test stone to see that it resists being pulled off the dop. If the stone comes off, apply a thin film of the COLD SHELLAC CEMENT described above to both the dop and the stone; let dry until shellac is tacky; now join stone to dop and place in dopping jig until shellac is dry. To remove, soak in wood alcohol with or without water.

SOFTENING DOPPING WAXES. Melt the wax, add 1 pt./wgt. dental wax to 3 pts./wgt. dopping cement.

Dopping Cements for Flatwork

BEESWAX. Can be used to make a fairly strong bond between flats, e.g., between stone wafers on a steel plate for gang-lapping, thin-section work, etc. Merely heat all parts cautiously on a hot plate over which an asbestos cloth has been laid; touch parts frequently with beeswax to see if melting temperature has been reached or place on one of the parts a small bit of wax and observe when it begins to melt. Rub beeswax in thin film over all areas. Join parts while wax still fluid. Let cool. Excess beeswax removable with lighter fluid, gasoline, benzene, etc.

SHELLAC. Use in same manner as above; melts at considerably higher temperature. Clean up excess shellac by chipping away and then washing with acetone or methyl (wood) alcohol.

CANADA BALSAM. Used as above, but it is necessary to "cook" the balsam for some minutes to drive off excess volatiles in the resin. To test if balsam has been cooked enough, touch melted surface with pin, draw out thin thread of resin and note if it is brittle; if so, the balsam is ready to apply to the parts. Use sliding action to join all parts in order to exclude air bubbles.

LAKESIDE CEMENT. A resin in stick form which is used in the same manner as balsam but does not require cooking.

PARAFFIN WAX. A very low-melting-point join can also be made using ordinary white household paraffin wax in lieu of any of the cements mentioned above. For lapping thin sections of large size it is strong enough to hold work securely.

CONTACT CEMENTS. Generally not recommended because of difficulties in applying a uniformly thin layer and in later separation of parts.

DOUBLE-STICK TAPES. Sold in rolls, with adhesive on both sides. Apply to clean base plate in strips avoiding excessive touching with the fingers; now apply the work from above at which moment a good join is made. Soak in gasoline, lighter fluid, heptane, benzene, or other petroleum distillate to soften the adhesive and permit separation and clean up of work.

Jewelers Cements

DIAMOND CEMENT. Dissolve isinglass (very pure fish glue) in water to make thick paste; dilute with ethyl (grain) alcohol. Dissolve mastic resin in ethyl alcohol to form thick paste. Mix the two pastes thoroughly while warming the container gently. Used for cementing pearls or small stones into recesses in jewelry.

ENGRAVERS AND STONE SETTERS CEMENT. Melt together burgundy pitch 2 pts./wgt., rosin 1.5 pts./wgt., beeswax 1.5 pts./wgt. and plaster of Paris powder 1 pt./wgt. to be added after the other ingredients have been melted and blended. Pour into cold water to solidify. Used for repoussé work.

ROSIN CEMENT. Melt rosin 6 pts./wgt., then dust in plaster of Paris powder 4 pts./wgt., stirring until thoroughly blended. Adjust stiffness by adding more plaster as needed.

PITCH BOWL FILLING. Melt and blend pitch 2 pts./wgt., powdered rosin 1.5 pts./wgt., and tallow 1.5 pts./wgt.; when thoroughly blended dust in plaster of Paris 1 pt./wgt.

MODELING WAX. Melt together beeswax 4 pts./wgt., burgundy pitch 1 pt./wgt.; heat until near boiling. Dust in venetian red 2 pts./wgt. and whiting 1 pt./wgt. Be sure both powder ingredients are thoroughly dry beforehand. Now add about 1/8 pt./wgt. tallow. Pour in water to cool and solidify.

Water-Glass Cements

HARD CEMENT. Make stiff paste by spatulating talcum powder into water-glass solution.

STANDARD CEMENT. Use directly from the bottle, or if too fluid, thicken by gentle warming or evaporation. Usually requires overnight setting time to become strong enough. Excellent emergency cement for cardboard boxes.

FAST SETTING CEMENT. Take 25 pts./wgt. water glass, 5 pts./wgt. slaked lime, 5 pts./wgt. powdered white lead, and 1 pt./wgt. chalk powder, blend thoroughly. Add water to make a smearable paste; use immediately.

BULKY CEMENT. Mix water glass with sawdust or other bulky light powder.

Vinyl Acetate ("White Glue") Cements

These cements are sold extensively in plastic "squeeze" bottles for many household and arts purposes and consist of polyvinyl acetates dissolved in water. They dry by evaporating water to produce a strong colorless translucent resin. Because evaporation of the water is necessary they cannot be used in airtight joints as between pieces of stone, metal, or glass. In storage, they tend to settle and form thick films along the sides of the containers and upon the bottoms. Shake before using. May be diluted with water in any proportion. Excellent for cementing all manner of porous materials; useful with styrofoam.

PAPER PASTING CEMENT. Dilute cement with about 10% by volume water; stir very thoroughly. Apply with 1" bristle brush, working quickly.

FLEXIBLE BINDING CEMENT. Some of the companies producing polyvinyl cements also sell a type that dries to a flexible film; this cement is used to repair weak book hinges or other parts that require a tough flexible joint.

SPECIMEN REPAIR CEMENT. Dilute cement with about 50% by volume of water to form a runny liquid; add a pinch of household detergent or a drop of liquid detergent; stir thoroughly. First brush cracks in specimen with water to which a little detergent has been added; allow water to creep into cracks. Wait until cracks appear dry (several minutes) and then brush on the thinned cement. As the cement creeps into the cracks, add a little more until the crack is filled. Wipe off excess; let dry at least several days.

SPECIMEN SOAKING CEMENT. Dilute the cement with 6 to 10 times its own volume with water to which a drop of liquid detergent has been added. This forms a milky liquid in which the entire specimen may be submerged to fill minute cracks. Allow to soak for about 1/2 hr. Remove specimen from solution, rinse off surface cement quickly and dry in cloth or paper towel. Dry for at least several days. A very useful preservative technique for crumbling materials such as clays containing crystals, masses of laumontite crystals. When properly carried out, scarcely any trace of the cement is visible from the exterior but the interior is greatly strengthened.

COLORATION. Polyvinyl cements can be colored by any of the water-soluble dyes, e.g., vegetable dyes, or by water-soluble inks.

Epoxy Cements

These are two-part liquid cements, one part resin, the other a catalyst. They must be *carefully* mixed in the exact proportions specified by the manufacturer to obtain satisfactory results. In general, the kinds in which the parts are squeezed out of tubes are subject to measuring errors for obvious reasons and it is usually better to use a balance to weigh out the parts for greater accuracy. Other types use resin plus drops of catalyst and these are much more satisfactory on the whole. Despite the exaggerated claims that have been made for epoxies they cannot correct carelessness on the part of the user in cleaning the parts to be joined before application of the mixed resin. Epoxies will not cement well to any surface that is dirty, oily, or greasy, or even one that has been touched by the fingers. However, when used correctly, they provide great strength and the enormous advantage that the resin shrinks but little during hardening.

Most epoxies can be cleaned up quickly with acetone before setting. To some extent, all are toxic and some are irritating to the skin causing dermatitis in sensitive individuals. In any case, study instructions provided by the manufacturer before using.

After setting, many epoxies are untouched by any commonly available solvent, although methyl ethyl ketone soaking will slowly soften them. Some manufacturers sell solvents which work with their products but may not soften or dissolve other types of epoxy. It is therefore best to assume that correcting mistakes is going to be impossible and to plan and execute the cementing task on this basis.

COMMON CAUSES OF FAILURE. The most common source of failure is improper mixing of the epoxy components; most users simply do not mix the ingredients long enough or fail to reach all parts of the mixture during stirring because they use a flat-bottomed container and/or a poor stirrer. If possible, use a round-bottomed container and a round-edged spatula (laboratory stainless steel or artist's palette knife). Never mix in cold atmosphere, and if needed, hold the container in the hands to warm up the mix or warm gently on a hot plate or stove. Avoid excessive warming because this accelerates setting and may reduce pot life to the point where the epoxy sets before it can be applied. Gentle stirring avoids entrapment of air bubbles. The other common source of error is failure to measure out the ingredients in the *exact* proportions specified. The use of a gram or even a carat balance is recommended to avoid this mistake. The last source of error is failure to clean off the parts to be cemented as thoroughly as they should. The parts must not have the slightest trace of any oily or greasy substance and to ensure this, it is a good idea to rinse them in acetone. Any trace of wax is also disastrous because it

dissolves in the epoxy and causes it to become sticky and resilient rather than clean and hard. Finally, if heat treatment is required for curing, it *must be done* to ensure that the epoxy dries hard and smooth.

MOLDS FOR EPOXIES. Epoxies will not stick to smooth teflon surfaces and this material can be used for making molds or serve as a base upon which the epoxy can rest while curing. Silicone rubber also makes excellent molds for epoxy castings, especially for small shapes that must be cast in number. The model for the silicone rubber mold or recess is made from teflon and the silicone rubber cast around it. When dry, the mold is rubbery and can be bent to release the model, leaving a recess exactly the correct size and shape. Mixed epoxy, and/or any enclosure, is poured in the silicone rubber mold and allowed to cure. Since silicone rubber is highly resistant to heat, heat curing is perfectly feasible if called for. Silicone rubber is available in hardware stores in tube form.

CRACK FILLING WITH EPOXY. Fissures in rough gem materials, slabs, and preforms can be filled with epoxy providing the crevices are not too narrow and the following precautions are taken. Thoroughly clean material to be impregnated, being especially careful to remove oils, greases, waxes, or soaps. Place in warm oven to dry and to preheat, maintaining temperature of about 120° F. (38° C.) or just uncomfortably warm to the touch. When the stone is warm, mix epoxy according to directions, then warm along with the stone and stir again. Apply to crevices with a toothpick or other convenient tool. Always apply at one end of the crevice in order to allow the now thoroughly fluid epoxy to creep inside and displace the air which would otherwise be trapped if the entire crevice were coated at once. Continue application until all crevices are filled to overflowing. Cure.

VACUUM IMPREGNATION. Where a bell jar and vacuum pump are available, a better impregnation can be obtained by heavily coating the specimen with epoxy to cover all crevices, or even better, to immerse the specimen in a container filled with epoxy. Drawing a vacuum will cause air inside to expand and escape. Several cyclings are best to obtain optimum filling.

The epoxy and stone must be warm as noted above.

HIGH-PRESSURE IMPREGNATION. Excellent epoxy impregnation of even very narrow crevices is obtainable by use of pressures applied to the specimen suspended completely within epoxy in a rubber bag compressed between two steel plungers within a suitable steel cylinder. Pressures up to 15,000 lb./in.^{2} have been employed.

Reference: For details see J. Sinkankas, *Amer. Mineralogist* 53 (1968): 339-42.

MISCELLANEOUS CEMENTS

OPAL DOUBLET. Melt flake shellac, stir in lampblack to color.

BEESWAX CEMENT. A good temporary cement made by melting together 1 pt./wgt. beeswax to 2, 3, or 4 pts./wgt. powdered rosin, with cement stiffness increasing as rosin is added. Melt in double boiler and avoid open flames. Dissolved with turpentine or any petroleum distillate.

PITCH CEMENT. Melt 70 pts./wgt. pine pitch, 2 pts./wgt. rosin, and dust in 28 pts./wgt. plaster of Paris to melt. Semirigid, waterproof sealing cement.

MASTIC CEMENT. Melt asphalt, bring nearly to boil, now add lime powder, clay, or other inert powder to achieve desired degree of stiffness. A good sticky waterproof sealant for tanks, plumbing, gutters, etc.

SULFUR CEMENT. Melt 3 pts./wgt. sulfur in iron ladle, dust in 1 pt./wgt. portland cement. Great care needed to prevent ignition of sulfur; keep iron cover handy to snuff out flames if sulfur burns. When fluid, pour into holes in rock or concrete to secure iron rods or similar metal objects which require firm support.

CEMENT FOR GLASS. To 3 fluid oz. glycerine add enough litharge to make 1 lb.; stir and spatulate into thick creamy paste. The glycerine must be pure (without water). Sets in about 1 hr., forming a good cement for glass and metal to glass.

GLASS TO METAL CEMENT. To 5 pts./wgt. water add 3 pts./wgt. plaster of Paris, 3 pts./wgt. rosin, and 1 pt./wgt. soda lye in stick form. Mix mechanically, then boil. Apply while warm.

CEMENT FOR STONE. Water glass 25 pts./wgt., unslaked lime 5 pts./wgt., powdered white lead 5 pts./wgt., and powdered chalk 1 pt./wgt. Add water a little at a time and stir into thick paste. Apply immediately.

CEMENT FOR MARBLE. Mastic resin 5 pts./wgt., beeswax 1 pt./wgt. Warm the marble pieces, then melt, stir, and apply the cement immediately.

RUBBER CEMENT. Dissolve bits of unvulcanized or "crepe" rubber (or rubber bands) in a solution of equal parts by volume of benzine and carbon tetrachloride. Let stand several days for mixture to homogenize. Useful for quick "paste-up" jobs, but *caution:* Must not be used for permanent files of clippings, photographs, etc., because the rubber eventually strikes through, decomposes, and discolors the papers.

CELLULOID CEMENT. Made from either cellulose acetate or nitrate by placing shavings of the plastic in a small bottle filled with a solution of equal parts by volume of amyl acetate and acetone. Dries very quickly. The nitrate solution is highly flammable as is the nitrate plastic itself. Cellulose nitrate cement dissolves in ethylene glycol monoethyl ether ("cellusolve") and in this form is used as a lacquer. Household quick-drying cements sold in tubes can be dissolved readily in amyl acetate or acetone.

COLLODION. Same as above, but also the plastic may be dissolved in a solution of ether, pure alcohol, acetone, etc., or combinations of these solvents. Forms a thin transparent coating.

ACETATE PLASTIC CEMENT. Take 1 pt./volume glacial acetic acid, 2 pts./volume acetone, mix. Brush on both surfaces of acetate plastic parts that are to be cemented together; repeat as necessary until surfaces are soft; press together and secure in position until dry.

ACRYLIC RESIN CEMENT ("Plexiglas" or "Lucite," "Perspex," etc.). Brush ethylene chloride on joints to soften; press parts together and let dry.

QUICKMOUNT. A proprietary plastic casting material consisting of a powder of minute clear beads of plastic and a colorless solvent. Mix 2 pts./volume plastic to 1 pt./vol. of liquid, stir and when fluid, pour in mold or over object to be cemented. Sets rapidly with evolution of heat. Produces strong and tough plastic which polishes readily. Dissolves in acetone.

ANIMAL GLUES (hide glues). May be melted in double boiler with a little water or purchased in liquid form and used hot or cold. Not moisture resistant; remains fairly flexible in thin films for many years. Used for woodworking and cementing backs of books during their manufacture.

VEGETABLE OR STARCH PASTES. Used for cementing paper. Not waterproof.

CASEIN GLUES. Made from a milk protein and mixed with water to form a runny paste. Used for general woodworking and pasting paper or cardboard. Poor moisture resistance.

UREA RESIN GLUES. Powders mixed with water and used like casein. Not waterproof.

RESORCINOL GLUES. Two-part adhesives consisting of a liquid and curing agent. Form strong bonds and much used where waterproof glues are needed.

Silicone Rubber Cements

These are sold in hardware stores in small to large tubes in colorless, white, or black compounds. They cure by absorbing water from the atmosphere and releasing acetic acid which gives off a vinegary smell during the curing period. Cannot be used in single-cast sections of over about 1/2 inch but thicker sections can be built up by repeated castings. Produces a strong rubbery material which is highly resistant to temperature (well above boiling point of water), and most ordinary chemicals including acids and alkalies. It is almost impossible to remove chemically and is usually removed by mechanical means. Unusually adhesive to even the smoothest surfaces, e.g., glass, porcelain, polished metal, etc., providing such surfaces are carefully cleaned beforehand to remove any traces of grease, oil, or wax. Used for waterproof seals, shockmounts, flexible seals, and molds for casting epoxies (see "Epoxy Cements," p. 47).

Acid-Resistant Artificial Stone

Thoroughly mix about 1 pt./volume powdered sulfur with about 6 pts./volume powdered coke, asbestos, or other suitable acidproof material. Place in iron container and apply heat to melt; when melted cast into desired form.

Adhesive Tapes

A large variety of adhesive tapes are available on the market, some of which are extremely useful for laboratory use as well as for packaging.

WATER SOLUBLE GLUE ON PAPER OR CLOTH. Provide good strength if applied correctly. A uniform wetting with water is essential to success and is best done by means of sponging or using applicators specially designed for the purpose. A rectangular viscose sponge of about 6" x 3" x 1", placed half-immersed in a shallow plastic tray filled with water, provides an excellent uniform wetter. Pass tape over top of sponge pressing downward slightly with the fingertips to ensure uniform contact. In any method of wetting, the tape should be allowed to soak up the water to moisten the glue; this takes but a few seconds and is signaled by flattening of the tape; now apply to the work. If tape is wetted and applied too soon, the water merely soaks into the object being taped and the glue is not wetted enough for a good bond. If too much water has been applied, wait until it partially dries off before applying. This type of tape is useless on very smooth surfaces like glass or polished metal. Remove by placing wet blotter over tape.

CONTACT CEMENT TAPES. All of these tapes depend for adhesion on a sticky coating which stays tacky for a long time but eventually hardens and becomes brittle. The cement is readily soluble in gasoline, lighter fluid, benzine, etc.; it is not soluble in acetone but the tape itself usually is. The worst kind are paper "masking" tapes which harden and embrittle rather rapidly and cannot be peeled off surfaces without leaving a residue, especially after a few months after application. About as poor are the transparent cellophane tapes which are so commonly applied to torn pages in books and which soon become hard and brittle. The residue left is almost impossible to clean up and many books have been ruined by indiscriminate use of this material. Other types of contact cement tapes include those made from thin stretchable plastic films and from cloth; neither is good for permanent repair of any kind.

DANGEROUS FLAMMABLE OR EXPLOSIVE SUBSTANCES

A large variety of easily available and commonly used substances are highly flammable and/or capable of quickly creating an explosive gas concentration due to evaporation. Sources of gas ignition are hot-water heaters (pilot lights), electrical switches (sparking at contacts), abrasion of steel against stone, etc. As a general rule, as little as one cupful of the more rapidly evaporating liquids in an average-size unventilated room may create an explosive atmosphere. Many such liquids are also highly toxic but are so familiar to all that constant use breeds contempt for their dangers and carelessness in handling.

Particularly to be avoided are any liquids poured in flat pans which expose maximum surface for evaporation, and even more particularly, accidental spills of large quantities of liquid (usually as a result of breaking glass containers!). Store all liquids in metal or plastic containers, with *narrow* mouths. Attempt to accomplish all tasks requiring a cupful or more liquid out of doors or under a hood with adequate ventilation. Operations should be conducted away from all open flames.

ACETONE. Very flammable, rapidly evaporating, quickly creates explosive atmosphere. Mildly toxic, but not dangerously so if used in small quantities.

ALCOHOLS. Concentrated methyl or wood alcohol is the most common form and is sold in tin cans; highly flammable, toxic when inhaled or ingested; avoid prolonged use.

CARBON DISULFIDE. Very flammable, toxic, quickly forms an explosive atmosphere.

CEMENT SOLVENTS. Many of these are highly flammable and toxic; consult container label before use.

ETHER. Extremely rapid rate of evaporation and creation of explosive atmosphere; very easily ignited; toxic (anesthetic).

GASOLINES. Highly flammable and rapidly evaporate to create explosive atmospheres; cause many home accidents because used so often for "dry" cleaning.

LACQUER SOLVENTS. Invariably highly flammable, evaporative.

PAINT THINNERS. Many are petroleum distillates, very flammable, rapidly evaporative.

SPRAY PAINT SOLVENTS. These may be particularly dangerous if flammable solvents are involved because ideal explosive atmospheres are created almost instantly.

TURPENTINE. Highly flammable but considerably slower to evaporate and hence safer to use than other common solvents.

Spontaneous Combustion

Caused by the rapid absorption of oxygen from the atmosphere by rapidly "drying" oils, usually those employed in conventional paint and varnish formulations, and the rise in temperature of the wiping rags used to clean up after paint work. If the rags are spread out in a single layer little chance of combustion occurs because heat is dissipated as fast as it is generated, but if rags are piled together, especially in a box or container, heat cannot escape and may easily build to the point where actual combusion occurs. As a general rule, all rags used for wiping up any oily liquids or paints should be removed from the inside of any building immediately after use.

STORAGE PRECAUTIONS FOR CHEMICALS AND COMBUSTIBLES

PAINTS, VARNISHES. Preferably stored outside; small containers must always be very tightly sealed if stored inside. Breakable containers must be stored outside.

PAINT THINNERS, TURPENTINE, ETC. Always purchase or transfer to metal cans; never store in glass bottles. Most preferable to store outside. Extreme fire and explosive atmosphere hazards.

GASOLINES, CHARCOAL LIGHTER FLUIDS, ETC. Always store in metal cans and always outside.

HIGHLY VOLATILE FLUIDS. As a general rule, these either present a breathing poison or explosive atmosphere hazard and should be kept in nonbreakable containers as metal or plastic and never in bottles unless in very small quantities as needed for frequent use.

ACIDS. Never store with or near any kind of metal or paper, wood, or other organic material that can be chemically attacked by the acid. Plastic containers possess the advantage of being unbreakable but porosity of the plastic permits acids to slowly evaporate through the sides and contaminate the atmosphere; severe rusting of steel tools commonly results when plastic acid bottles are stored in the same room. Certain acids, notably nitric and sulfuric, attack organic materials very rapidly and may cause combustion.

POISONS. Must be marked conspicuously and stored in such a manner that persons ignorant of their danger cannot have access.

HYGROSCOPIC SUBSTANCES. Store in dry atmosphere and in any case, store with a dish or plastic receptacle beneath to trap any exudate.

EVAPORATIVE LIQUIDS IN GLASS CONTAINERS. Reduce evaporation hazards by covering top with sheet of plastic tied tightly around the neck.

RADIOACTIVITY HAZARDS FROM MINERAL SPECIMENS

Uranium and thorium minerals emit the gases radon and thoron and introduce them into the atmosphere around the mineral cabinet. As little as a "few" ounces of minerals bearing substantial quantities of these radioactive elements may result in lung doses on the same order as the internationally accepted radiation limit. "It is therefore preferable not to include radioactive minerals in the home collection."

Source: J. E. Cook (A.A.E.C. Research Establishment, Lucas Heights, New South Wales), Australian Lapidary Magazine 8, no. 3 (October 1971): 28-29.

WORKSHOP ELECTRICAL HAZARDS

Under ordinary circumstances only a nasty shock is the result of touching a bare "live" wire with the hands or some other part of the body. Normally the skin is protected by a thin film of oil which acts as an effective insulator but when thoroughly wet, the skin permits current to pass within the body and the resulting shock to the nervous system may easily cause death. Even greater danger exists when voltages are higher, such as those supplied to heavy-duty appliances as clothes driers and stoves.

Unfortunately, many lapidary operations call for the use of abundant water in the immediate vicinity of electric motors. Such water may spray over the hands, dribble to floor where it puddles and soaks through shoes, or otherwise establish a potential path for electrical current. Thus the first precaution is to avoid excess water by carefully shielding water supplies to prevent spray, piping off water to basins or sewers to prevent floor accumulations, and keeping all wires or motors hooded or elevated where water cannot reach them. Observe the following precautions.

GROUND WIRES. Be sure these are connected either to a proper 3-hole receptacle or by separate wire to a metal "ground"; if in doubt call in an electrician for advice.

LEAD WIRES. For wet work these should be led to the equipment from above and not from below. They must not rest on tables or floors where water puddles may form.

SWITCHES. Avoid any metal toggle switches; use plastic toggles if possible. Where metal toggles are installed, obtain plastic tubing, cut off short sections, and force over toggles to cover the metal completely. For push-button switches, cover with a sheet of plastic or thin rubber so that no water can enter between the button and button housing. If possible, arrange switches above the equipment, with plastic pull-cord to actuate.

FLOOR DAMPNESS. If wet floors cannot be avoided, consider use of rubber-link mats on which to stand, or other forms of racks which will elevate the soles of the shoes well above the floor.

CHAFED WIRING. Inspect frequently and discard or replace wires which are chafed or cracked (aging). Heavy duty wires should always be used, not lampcord wire.

ELECTRICAL FIRES. Caused generally by failure to use wire of sufficient diameter (increased resistance and overheating) or wire which is cracked or chafed and lying in contact with metal. Marginally satisfactory wire feels warm to the touch after use, and may be quite warm at the wall receptacle where plugged in; it should be replaced with heavier wire.

HAND MOTORS. Small hand motor tools are perfectly safe when used dry but may cause severe shock if used in wet work or if accidentally laid in a water puddle on the bench.

WATERPROOF MOTORS. These are available but cost considerably more than ordinary motors.

REMOVAL OF STAINS AND INKS

BLOOD. Laundry bleach removes hemoglobin from cotton and linen; hydrogen peroxide removes from wool and silk.

GRASS. Removed from fabrics by liquid laundry bleach solution.

GUM OR RESIN. One or more of the following solvents may be used, depending upon the specific nature of the gum or resin: turpentine, benzene, carbon tetrachloride, chloroform, 95% ethyl alcohol, ethyl ether, kerosene, gasoline, carbon disulfide.

GUM, CHEWING. Removed best by carbon tetrachloride.

INK, ANILINE, COLORED. Mostly removed from cotton and linen by bleach solution followed by ordinary washing; for wool and silk the ink may dye directly but it is removed with potassium permanganate solution (1 oz. xls in 1 gal. water) or sodium bisulfite solution saturated.

INK, BLACK ANILINE. Not removable with any common agent that is harmless to fabrics.

INK, BLACK PRINTING. Treat like INDIA INK.

INK, INDELIBLE PENCIL. Removed from cotton or linen by washing, with persistent remainders removed by bleach solution or by potassium permanganate solution followed by treatment with dilute oxalic acid solution. Remove from wool or silk by scrubbing in 95% ethyl alcohol or potassium permanganate solution followed by weak oxalic acid solution.

INK, INDIA. Difficult to remove but usually disappears in ordinary washing; deep stains may be loosened beforehand by dabbing with lard to loosen particles, then washing.

INK, IRON, ORDINARY WRITING. Warm oxalic-acetic acid solution.

INK, SILVER NITRATE. Soak in sodium thiosulfate solution, or in laundry bleach solution, then soak in weak solution of ammonia to remove the silver chloride which forms. For wool and silk the stains may be removed by solutions of potassium cyanide (poison!).

MILDEW. Usually removed in ordinary laundering but persistent stains should be treated alternately with laundry liquid bleach and mild oxalic acid solution.

OILS, GREASES. Light stains removed in standard washing process; thick stains should be treated first by an organic solvent or with carbon tetrachloride; the latter is preferred as it is incombustible. Or treat heavy stains, especially of grease, by rubbing in a mixture of 2 parts of oleic acid to 98 parts of lard, and then launder.

PAINT, VARNISH. Most easily removed by organic solvent before hardening or drying occurs, then launder immediately; or rub oleic acid into stained areas, followed by washing with 1% sol. oleic acid in kerosene (2 ounces oleic acid per gallon kerosene); wash with warm solution of anhydrous sodium carbonate (soda ash; 6 ounces per gallon of water). For wool and silk straight paint and varnish solvents are preferred.

TARS, ASPHALTS. Usually removed by dissolving with an organic solvent such as turpentine or gasoline, followed by normal washing.

VASELINE. Treat like OILS, GREASES.

WAXES. Excess removed in fabrics by pressing with a hot iron applied to a sandwich of blotting paper which absorbs most of the wax after it becomes liquefied through heat; traces removed by gasoline, lighter fluid, carbon tetrachloride, or other organic solvents of greases.

Standard Solutions

AMMONIA. Ordinary household ammonia may be too strong to use directly; dilute with 10 times its volume with water.

ACETIC ACID. Take commercial acetic acid solution and dilute to half strength by adding an equal volume of water. Evaporate after use but rinsing still advisable.

OXALIC ACID. Usual solution is 1 ounce of crystals to 1 gallon of water; more effective when used warm. Must be washed generously, several times, with warm water after use to prevent formation of chemically active residue.

HYDROGEN PEROXIDE. Use pure solution purchased in drugstore; no dilution is required.

POTASSIUM PERMANGANATE. Use 1 ounce of crystals to 1 gallon of water; must not be used in greater strength because it will "burn" fibers.

SODIUM PERBORATE. Mix powder with water into a paste and work into stained areas; rinse with water to remove.

SODIUM BISULFITE. Used as a saturated solution.

OLEIC ACID. Purchase from drugstore.

SODIUM THIOSULFATE. Also used as stain remover; prepare saturated solution.

POTASSIUM CYANIDE. Extremely poisonous and great care must be employed to remove all traces after use and the solution discarded after use. Standard solution is 1 ounce in 1 gallon of water.

Part 3 / Lapidary Equipment

LAPIDARY EQUIPMENT OPERATIONAL SPEEDS

The following data and recommendations have been compiled from instructional brochures supplied by a number of manufacturers of lapidary machines and replaceable components. See table A.

SHAFTING FOR SAWS. To 10″ diameter blades, at least 5/8″ diameter; 12″ and 14″ blades, 3/4″; 16″, 18″, and 20″ blades, 1″; 24″ blades, at least 1¼″ diameter, and preferably larger.

SAW BLADE COLLARS OR FLANGES. At least 1/4 of the blade diameter although this provision is commonly ignored in order to obtain greatest depth of cut. However, for small blades where very accurate cutting is required with least sideplay or wobble in the blade, flanges may be as much as 3/4 the diameter of the blade.

Grinding Wheels

Grinding wheels are tested at a speed higher than that expected to be used and are so labeled upon the blotting paper disks cemented to the sides of the wheel; under no circumstances should this speed be reached in practice. See table B.

VITRIFIED AND SILICATE WHEELS. Do not exceed 6,500 SFPM.

RESINOID AND RUBBER WHEELS. Do not exceed 9,500 SFPM.

A

Diameter (inches)	Surface feet per minute (SFPM)	Revolutions per minute (RPM)
4	6,000	4,200
5	4,500	3,600
6	—	1,600; 2,500; 2,600; 3,450
8	3,150*	1,250; 1,450; 1,725; 2,000
10	3,150	925; 1,500; 1,725
12	3,150	800; 1,100; 1,200
14	3,150	700; 950; 1,100
16	3,150	600; 800; 850
18	3,150	540; 800
20	3,150	500; 660; 800
24	3,150	540
36	3,150	420

* A general SFPM recommendation for satisfactory cutting of agate.

Note: For "mud" saws, or plain metal circular blades charged with loose abrasive grit, RPM producing 1,500 SFPM for 8″ and 630 SFPM for 12″ blades have been recommended.

B

Table of Grinding Wheel Speeds

Diameter	Flange Size	Shaft Size	Max. RPM	SFPM
4″	1-1/2″	1/2″	4,300	4,510
6″	2″	5/8″	2,900	5,660
8″	3″	3/4″	2,300	4,820
10″	3-1/2″	1″	1,800	4,710

PREINSTALLATION TEST. Suspend wheel by inserting pencil through center hole, tap lightly along periphery with a piece of wood; a clear ringing note indicates the wheel is sound but a dull note indicates that the wheel is cracked and it should not be used. This test does not apply to resinoid or rubber wheels.

Sanding Wheels

The data below are for wheels to which fixed silicon carbide abrasive cloth disks or belts are attached. Considerable differences exist in recommendations made by various manufacturers but it may be noted that generally SFPM range between 2,000 and 4,000. Lower SFPM are recommended for sanders which utilize a spring clamp around the periphery to seize the sanding cloth or for those sanding wheels in which dynamic balance is poor at high RPM. See table C.

COOLANT. Practically all sanding is done wet with tap water as the coolant, but very high RPM tend to prevent water contact with the sanding surface and may require either high-pressure spray jets to force water to the surface or reductions in RPM.

Loose Grit Lapping

Because of problems in keeping loose grits from flying off while lapping, operational RPM of standard horizontal lapping wheels are kept low with the SFPM of the rim held between 700 and 800. See table D.

Polishing Buff Speeds

Peripheral speeds are kept low to prevent overheating of gems due to accidental drying and slinging off of polishing agent slurry. Higher speeds may be employed where polishing compounds are formulated with a wax or soap that provides better retention on the buff. See table E.

Faceting Lap Speeds

Low speeds are used to avoid loss of polishing agent and to minimize shock to

C

Table of Sanding Speeds

Diameter (inches)	SFPM = 2,000	SFPM = 3,000	SFPM = 4,000
4	RPM = 1,910	RPM = 2,865	RPM = 3,820
6	1,270	1,910	2,550
8	980	1,430	1,910
10	760	1,145	1,530
12	635	955	1,275

D

Table of Lapping Speeds

Diameter (inches)	SFPM = 700	SFPM = 800
10	RPM = 270	RPM = 300
12	220	250
14	190	220
16	165	190
18	150	170
20	130	150
24	110	130

E

Table of Polishing Buff Speeds

Diameter (inches)	SFPM = 1,200	SFPM = 1,400
6	RPM = 760	RPM = 890
8	570	670
10	460	540
12	380	450

Note: SFPM = 1,200 is better suited for leather and harder surfaced buffs while SFPM = 1,400 is satisfactory for rock hard felt buffs using a water-polishing agent slurry.

gemstones. Much higher speeds may be used in polishing the very hard gemstones, particularly chrysoberyl, corundum, and diamond. Variable speeds, down to zero and into the reverse direction, are desirable for many gemstones in which softness and pronounced directional differences in physical properties require experimentation to determine best polishing direction and speed. The general rule in polishing is the harder the gemstone, the higher the speed, and vice versa. See table F.

Drilling and Coring Speeds

For extremely small holes of the kind placed in jewel bearings for watches and instruments, solid steel tapered needles are employed with loose diamond abrasive and spin at from 24,000 to 50,000 RPM. For ordinary lapidary shops the special machinery required to obtain such high RPM is not available and much lower speeds are used. For example, in order to obtain the optimum SFPM speed of 3,100, as previously recommended for hard materials like agate, a 1/4" tube drill would have to

spin at close to 50,000 RPM. In practice, such tube drills are operated at RPM in the range from ordinary motor speed, or 1,725 RPM, to about 3,000 RPM. While cutting rates are much slower, it is much easier to keep the abrasive slurry within the hole being drilled than would be the case if much higher RPM were employed. The following recommendations therefore are based on what is practical in the ordinary lapidary workshop with either homemade equipment or that currently available to amateur lapidary workers. See table G.

Sphere Making

Low speeds are generally used, with the cups driven by motor rotating at about 150 RPM for spheres of several inches diameter or more. An RPM of about 750 can be used for spheres of about 2" in diameter, to ordinary motor speed of 1,725 RPM for spheres of smaller size.

Tumbler Drum Speeds

The efficiency of any tumbler depends on a series of variables and much art is

F

Table of Faceting Lap Speeds

Diameter (inches)	SFPM = 315	SFPM = 525	SFPM = 6,500*	SFPM = 7,500*
6	RPM = 200	RPM = 335	RPM = 4,130	RPM = 4,770
8	150	250	3,100	3,580
10	120	200	2,480	2,860
12	100	165	2,065	2,385
14	85	140	1,770	2,045

* Diamond polishing.

G

General Drilling Speed Recommendations

Drill		RPM
Extremely fine solid steel drills		24,000-50,000
Diamond crystal pointed drills,	about 2-3 mm	3,000-4,000
Solid point, sintered diamond,	about 2-3 mm	4,000-5,000
Tube drills, loose abrasive,	about 3-10 mm	3,000-4,000
	about 20-25 mm	2,000-3,000
	about 25-75 mm	1,200-2,000
Larger tube drills, loose abrasive		500-1,725

involved in hitting upon the correct combination of type and quantity of charge, abrasives, fluids, fillers, etc., not to mention the RPM of the barrel for any given drum diameter. However, experience has shown that for any diameter drum, a SFPM peripheral speed of about 100 appears to be satisfactory.

Formula for Conversion SFPM (100) into RPM

$$RPM = \frac{1,200}{C}$$

C = circumference of drum
  = π × diameter in inches
  = 3.14 × diameter in inches

Example: What is RPM for a 10″ diameter drum to produce 100 SFPM?

Step 1: C = 3.14 × 10
           = 31.4

Step 2: Divide 31.4 into 1,200 = 38 RPM, answer. See table H.

RPM TO SURFACE SPEED IN FEET (PERIPHERAL FEET) PER MINUTE

To obtain the surface feet per minute traveled by any wheel use the following formula:

SFPM = 0.262 × RPM × diameter of wheel in inches (See tables I, J. K.)

H

Table of RPMs for Tumbler Drums

Drum diameter (inches)

	6	8	10	12	14	16	18	20	24	36
Tumbler Drum	62	47	38	32	27	24	21	19	16	10
Round Drum	54	48	42	38	35		31		27	
Hexagonal Drum	32	29	25	23	21		19		16	

Source: Round and hexagonal drums, recommendations by Jack R. Cox, *Specialized Gem Cutting* (Mentone, Calif., Gembooks, 1970).

I

Short Conversion Table

Diameter (inches)	SFPM = 1,000	SFPM = 2,000	SFPM = 3,000
4	RPM = 955	RPM = 1,910	RPM = 2,865
5	764	1,528	2,292
6	637	1,273	1,910
7	546	1,091	1,637
8	478	955	1,433
9	424	849	1,273
10	382	764	1,146
12	318	637	955
14	273	546	819
16	239	477	716
18	212	424	637
20	191	382	573
24	159	318	478
30	127	255	382
36	106	212	318

Extended Conversion Table

Diameter (inches)	4,000	4,500	5,000	5,500	6,000	6,500	7,000	7,500	8,000	8,500	9,000	9,500	10,000	12,000	14,000	16,000
1	15,279	17,189	19,098	21,008	22,918	24,828	26,737	28,647	30,558	32,467	34,377	36,287	38,196	45,836	53,474	61,116
2	7,639	8,594	9,549	10,504	11,459	12,414	13,368	14,328	15,278	16,238	17,188	18,143	19,098	22,918	26,737	30,558
3	5,093	5,729	6,366	7,003	7,639	8,276	8,913	9,549	10,186	10,822	11,459	12,096	12,732	15,278	17,826	20,372
4	3,820	4,297	4,775	5,252	5,729	6,207	6,685	7,162	7,640	8,116	8,595	9,072	9,549	11,459	13,368	15,278
5	3,056	3,438	3,820	4,202	4,584	4,966	5,348	5,730	6,112	6,494	6,876	7,258	7,640	9,168	10,696	12,224
6	2,546	2,865	3,183	3,501	3,820	4,138	4,456	4,775	5,092	5,411	5,729	6,048	6,366	7,639	8,913	10,186
7	2,183	2,455	2,728	3,001	3,274	3,547	3,820	4,092	4,366	4,638	4,911	5,183	5,456	6,548	7,640	8,732
8	1,910	2,148	2,387	2,626	2,865	3,103	3,342	3,580	3,820	4,058	4,297	4,535	4,775	5,729	6,685	7,640
9	1,698	1,910	2,122	2,334	2,546	2,758	2,970	3,182	3,396	3,606	3,820	4,032	4,244	5,092	5,940	6,792
10	1,528	1,719	1,910	2,101	2,292	2,483	2,674	2,865	3,056	3,247	3,438	3,629	3,820	4,584	5,348	6,112
12	1,273	1,432	1,591	1,751	1,910	2,069	2,228	2,386	2,546	2,705	2,864	3,023	3,183	3,820	4,456	5,092
14	1,091	1,228	1,364	1,500	1,637	1,773	1,910	2,046	2,182	2,319	2,455	2,592	2,728	3,274	3,820	4,366
16	955	1,074	1,194	1,313	1,432	1,552	1,672	1,791	1,910	2,029	2,149	2,268	2,387	2,865	3,342	3,820
18	849	955	1,061	1,167	1,273	1,379	1,485	1,591	1,698	1,803	1,910	2,016	2,122	2,546	2,970	3,396
20	764	859	955	1,050	1,146	1,241	1,337	1,432	1,528	1,623	1,719	1,814	1,910	2,292	2,674	3,056
22	694	781	868	955	1,042	1,128	1,215	1,302	1,388	1,476	1,562	1,649	1,736	2,084	2,430	2,776
24	637	716	796	875	955	1,034	1,115	1,194	1,274	1,353	1,433	1,512	1,591	1,910	2,228	2,546
26	588	661	734	808	881	955	1,028	1,101	1,176	1,248	1,322	1,395	1,468	1,762	2,056	2,352
28	546	614	682	750	818	887	955	1,023	1,092	1,159	1,228	1,296	1,364	1,637	1,910	2,182
30	509	573	637	700	764	828	891	955	1,018	1,082	1,146	1,210	1,274	1,528	1,782	2,036
32	477	537	597	656	716	776	836	895	954	1,014	1,074	1,134	1,194	1,432	1,672	1,910
34	449	505	562	618	674	730	786	843	898	955	1,011	1,067	1,124	1,348	1,572	1,796
36	424	477	530	583	637	690	742	795	848	902	954	1,007	1,061	1,273	1,484	1,698
38	402	452	503	553	603	653	704	754	804	854	904	955	1,006	1,206	1,408	1,608
40	382	430	478	525	573	620	669	716	764	812	860	908	956	1,146	1,338	1,528
42	366	409	454	500	545	591	636	682	732	775	818	863	908	1,090	1,272	1,464
44	347	390	434	478	521	564	608	651	694	737	780	824	868	1,042	1,216	1,388
46	333	375	416	458	500	541	582	624	666	708	750	791	832	1,000	1,164	1,332
48	318	358	398	438	478	517	558	597	636	676	716	756	796	956	1,116	1,272
53	288	324	360	395	432	468	503	539	576	612	648	683	720	864	1,006	1,152
60	255	287	319	350	387	414	446	478	510	542	574	606	638	774	892	1,020
72	212	239	265	291	318	345	371	398	424	451	477	504	530	637	742	849

Short Conversion Table:

RPM to SFPM for Wheels of Given Diameter

Diameter (Inches)

RPM	2	4	6	8	10	12	14
				SFPM			
1,000	525	1,050	1,575	2,100	2,600	3,100	3,600
1,200	630	1,260	1,950	2,550	3,200	3,750	4,400
1,400	730	1,470	2,250	2,950	3,650	4,400	5,100
1,600	840	1,680	2,550	3,400	4,200	5,000	5,900
1,800	940	1,890	2,900	3,800	4,750	5,650	6,600
2,000	1,050	2,100	3,200	4,200	5,250	6,250	7,300
2,200	1,150	2,300	3,450	4,550	5,750	6,900	8,000
2,400	1,260	2,500	3,750	5,000	6,300	7,500	8,800
2,600	1,360	2,700	4,100	5,450	6,800	8,200	9,600
2,800	1,470	2,950	4,400	5,900	7,400	8,900	10,400
3,000	1,570	3,140	4,700	6,250	7,900	9,400	11,200
3,200	1,680	3,350	5,000	6,650	8,400	10,000	11,900
3,400	1,780	3,560	5,250	7,000	8,900	10,600	12,600
3,600	1,880	3,780	5,600	7,500	9,500	11,300	13,300

PULLEY AND BELT COMBINATIONS

Pulley Diameter Formulas

Motor pulley diameter =

$$\frac{\text{drive pulley RPM} \times \text{drive pulley diameter}}{\text{motor pulley RPM}}$$

Drive pulley diameter =

$$\frac{\text{motor pulley RPM} \times \text{motor pulley diameter}}{\text{drive pulley diameter}}$$

or: MPD × MP-RPM = DPD × DP-RPM
See table L.

Length of Endless Belt Connecting Two Pulleys

Uncrossed belt formula: Length of belt
= $1.57 (D + d) + 2C$

Crossed belt formula: Length of belt =
$1.625 (D + d) + 2C$

Where: D = diameter of larger pulley wheel

d = diameter of smaller pulley wheel

C = distance between centers of pulley wheels

L
RPM VERSUS PULLEY COMBINATIONS

(1,725 RPM electric motor)

Motor Pulley	Drive Pulley													
	1-1/2	1-3/4	2	2-1/4	2-1/2	3	4	5	5-1/2	6	8	10	12	14
1-1/2	1,725	1,478	1,293	1,149	1,034	862	647	517	470	431	323	259	216	185
1-3/4	2,013	1,725	1,510	1,342	1,208	1,006	755	604	549	503	377	302	252	216
2	2,300	1,971	1,725	1,533	1,380	1,150	863	690	627	575	431	345	286	246
2-1/4	2,587	2,218	1,941	1,725	1,552	1,294	970	776	706	647	485	388	323	277
2-1/2	2,875	2,465	2,157	1,917	1,725	1,438	1,078	863	784	719	539	431	359	308
2-3/4	3,163	2,711	2,372	2,108	1,898	1,581	1,186	949	863	791	593	474	395	339
3	3,450	2,957	2,588	2,300	2,070	1,725	1,294	1,035	941	863	647	518	431	370
4	4,600	3,943	3,450	3,067	2,760	2,300	1,725	1,380	1,255	1,150	863	680	575	493
5	5,750	4,929	4,313	3,833	3,450	2,875	2,156	1,725	1,568	1,438	1,078	863	719	616

Part 4 / Abrasives, Polishing Agents, Buffs and Laps, and Their Uses

ABRASIVE GRAIN SIZES COMPARED IN INCHES AND MICRONS (0.001 mm)

Size number	Average diameter (inches)	Average diameter (microns)	Size range (microns)
4	–	–	5,100-4,000
5	–	–	4,000-3,500
6	–	–	3,500-2,830
8	0.1817	4,620	2,830-2,380
10	0.1366	3,460	2,380-2,000
12	0.1003	2,550	2,000-1,680
14	0.0830	2,100	1,680-1,410
16	0.0655	1,660	1,410-1,190
20	0.0528	1,340	1,190-1,000
24	0.0408	1,035	840-710
30	0.0365	930	710-590
36	0.0280	710	590-500
40			500-420
46	0.0200	508	420-350
50			350-297
54	0.0170	430	
60	0.0160	406	297-250
70	0.0131	328	250-210
80	0.0105	266	210-177
90	0.0085	216	177-149
100	0.0068	173	149-125
120	0.0056	142	125-105
150	0.0048	122	105-88
180	0.0034	86	88-74
200			74-62
220	0.0026	66	62-53
240	0.00248	63	53-45
280	0.00175	44	45-37
320	0.00128	32	37-31
400	0.00090	23	31-27
500	0.00065	16	27-22
600	0.00033	8	22-18
700	–	–	18-15
800	–	–	15-11
1,000	–	–	11-8
2,000	–	–	8-5
3,000	–	–	5-0

Sources: Norton Company; last column from W. Burkart (1956), p. 68, representing sizes in use in Europe and with consistent differences as noted.

Common Sizes Available in the United States

Alumina (Norton): Screened sizes: 4, 6, 8, 10, 12, 14, 16, 20, 24, 30, 36, 46, 54, 60, 70, 80, 90, 100, 120, 150, 180, 220, 240. Unclassified flours: F, 2F, 3F, 4F, XF. Classified flours: 280, 320, 400, 500, 600.

Silicon carbide (Norton): Screened sizes: 8, 10, 12, 14, 16, 20, 24, 30, 36, 46, 60, 70, 80, 90, 100, 120, 150, 180, 220, 240. Unclassified flours: F, 2F, 3F, 4F, XF. Classified flours: 280, 320, 400, 500, 600. See table A.

GRINDING WHEEL CODES

The codes explained herein appear upon the blotters supplied with all grinding wheels and when deciphered describe the characteristics of each wheel. See table B.

Grade (Strength of Intergranular Bond)

Norton Company: Very soft (A, B, C, D, E, F, G), soft (H, I, J, K), medium (L, M, N, O), hard (P, Q, R, S), very hard (T, U, W, Z).
Carborundum Company: Very soft (A) to very hard (Z).

Bond (Nature of Intergranular Bonding Material)

The letter
V = vitrified bond
S = silicate bond
R = rubber bond
B = resinoid bond
E = shellac bond
O = magnesite bond (Norton Company only)

A

MICRON SIZE VERSUS MESH NUMBER

Microns	ASTM mesh	Microns	ASTM Mesh
2,000	10	297	50
1,680	12	250	60
1,410	14	210	70
1,190	16	177	80
1,000	18	149	100
840	20	125	120
710	25	105	140
590	30	88	170
500	35	74	200
420	40	63	230
350	45	53	270
		44	325
		37	400

Source: De Beers booklet, *Diamond Abrasives for Industry* (n.d., c. 1969).

B

Grain Size

	Very coarse	Coarse	Medium	Fine	Very fine	Flours
Norton Company	8, 10	12, 14, 16, 20, 24	30, 36, 46, 60	70, 80, 90, 100, 120	150, 180, 220, 240	280, 320 400, 500 600
Carborundum Company	6, 8, 10, 12	14, 16, 20, 24	30, 36, 46, 54, 60	70, 80, 90, 100, 120	150, 180, 220, 240	280, 320 400, 500 600

In addition, the Carborundum Company uses an oxychloride bond.

Structure (Intergranular Pore Space)

Norton Company: Close spacing (0, 1, 2, 3), medium spacing (4, 5, 6), wide spacing (7, 8, 9, 10, 11, 12)
Carborundum Company: Dense (1) to open (12).

Code Markings and Interpretation

Norton example: 37C90-L8V, or:
37C = silicon carbide
90 = grain size
L = grade (medium)
8 = pore spacing (wide)
V = vitrified bond
Carborundum example: GA 461-H6-V10, or:
G = grain type (company identification)
A = alumina
46 = grain size
1 = grain combination
H = grade (soft)
6 = pore spacing (medium)
V = vitrified bond
10 = manufacturing record

LAPIDARY GRINDING WHEELS

In general, most wheels supplied to amateur lapidaries are silicon carbide, 80- to 400-grain size, in medium soft (K) to medium (L, M, N) grades, medium wide pore spacing (6, 7, 8), vitrified bond. The tendency is to supply harder grades of wheels under the assumption that they will wear less rapidly but all too commonly such wheels glaze and refuse to cut except with excessive pressure and the danger of burning the gemstones. At such times they must be diamond-dressed, with loss of material, and it therefore seems doubtful that much is gained. Much faster and smoother cutting is obtained with the medium soft bonds (e.g., I or K), but wheel wear is somewhat more rapid. It is usually impractical to grind gemstones in excess of H.8, such as chrysoberyl and corundum, because of excessive wheel wear, and diamond abrasives should be used instead.

DIAMOND GRINDING WHEELS

Seven parts are used in the code designations of diamond grinding wheels, reading from left to right:

1. Abrasive type: D = natural, SD or MD = manufactured diamond.
2. Grain size: ranges from 16 to 2,000 mesh.
3. Grade: A (soft) to Z (hard).
4. Diamond concentration: low = 25, medium = 50-75, high = 100, and extra high = 150. See note below.
5. Bond: B = resinoid, M = metal, V = vitrified.
6. Bond modification: a letter, numeral, or combination used to indicate a variation from standard bond.
7. Depth of diamond section, in inches. Absence of depth figure indicates the diamond appears in the entire useful portion of the tool.

DIAMOND CONCENTRATION

Quantity of diamond in the abrasive portion of the tool is based on a standard concentration of 72 carats per cubic inch, but variations occur among manufacturers. A concentration of 100 indicates 72 carats of diamond to the cubic inch; 75 concentration is 54 carats, 50 concentration is 36 carats, and 25 concentration is 18 carats; a 150 concentration indicates a higher than standard concentration, presumably about 100 carats to the cubic inch. See table C.

U.S. Mesh Sizes of Natural and Synthetic Diamond Particles Available in the Trade

COARSER SIZES. Generally used for saws, hard matrix tools, and other operations calling for rapid material removal:

16-20	40-50	70-80
20-30	50-60	
30-40	60-70	

FINER SIZES. Generally used for grinding wheels in various types of bond, slitting saws, and drills.

80-100	140-170	230-270
100-120	170-200	270-325
120-140	200-230	325-400

See tables D and E.

C

DIAMOND POWDER SIZES: MICRON SIZES

Note: 1 micron = 0.0001 mm = 0.0000394 inch.

Particle size range (Microns)	Average particle size (Microns)	Sieve size*
1 and fines	1	12,500
	2.5	5,000
2-5	3	
	5	2,500
4-8	6	
6-12	9	
	10	1,250
8-22	15	
	20	625
20-40	30	
30-60	45	
35-85	60	

* Estimated or hypothetical sieve or mesh size; no mechanical sieves are available in these sizes.

SIEVE OR MESH SIZES

Sieve number	Average particle size (microns)
230-235	74
170-230	106
120-170	150
100-120	193
80-100	230
60-80	302
40-60	473

Source: U.S. Department of Commerce Standard CS 123-1949.

D

Micron-Size Diamond Particles Available in the Trade: Natural Diamond

0-1/2	2-3	8-15
1/2-1	2-4	8-25
0-1	1-5	15-30
0-2	2-6	20-40
1/2-1/4	4-8	30-60
1/2-3	6-12	

E

Micron-Size Diamond Particles Available in the Trade: Synthetic Diamond

0-1/2	1-5	10-20
1/2-1-1/2	2-4	15-25
0-1	2-6	15-30
0-2	4-8	20-30
1/2-3	6-10	20-40
1-3	6-12	30-50
0-4	8-15	30-60
	8-25	

APPROXIMATE NUMBER OF DIAMOND GRAINS PER CARAT, MICRON SIZES

Size (microns)	No. per carat	Size (microns)	No. per carat
3,000	5	300	4,500
2,500	6.5	250	6,500
2,000	16	200	16,000
1,500	36	150	36,000
1,000	100	100	100,000
750	250	75	250,000
500	1,000	50	1,000,000

Source: F. Goetz., *Diamanten und Diamantwerkzeuge* (Düsseldorf; VDI-Verlag, 1968).

APPROXIMATE NUMBER OF DIAMOND STONES OF GIVEN DIAMETER IN 1 CARAT*

Diameter (inches)	No. of stones	Diameter (inches)	No. of stones
0.177	±1	0.083	11
0.169	1.5	0.077	14
0.161	1.7	0.075	16
0.153	2.1	0.071	19
0.146	2.4	0.067	22
0.137	2.9	0.065	24
0.130	3.4	0.060	31
0.128	3.6	0.059	33
0.122	4	0.055	47
0.114	5	0.052	52
0.111	5.3	0.051	55
0.106	6	0.049	70
0.102	6.5	0.047	76
0.100	6.8	0.045	90
0.098	7	0.043	105
0.091	9	0.042	112
0.089	9.5	0.041	120
		0.039	130
		0.036	170

* De Beers processed spheroidal stones usually used for drills.

CALCULATED SIZES AND WEIGHTS OF ROUGH DIAMOND CRYSTALS

The following calculated values are only approximate because they are based upon true geometrical shapes which seldom occur in natural diamond crystals. Grodzinski estimates that the possible error in spheroidal shapes reaches 13% greater, and for octahedrons 22% less, in weight. See table F.

DIAMOND PASTE COMPOUNDS

These consist of micron or sometimes mesh-size diamond suspended in a variety of proprietary vehicles which may be oily, requiring oils or petroleum derivatives to dissolve, water-soluble, or "universal" wherein dissolution can be effected with either oils and petroleum derivatives or water. "Extenders" are merely slow-evaporating fluids such as glycols for

Octahedrons (mm –apex to apex)	Spheroid diameter (mm)	Weight (carats)
1.895	1.295	0.02
2.57	1.755	0.05
3.24	2.21	0.1
4.09	2.79	0.2
4.675	3.19	0.3
5.15	3.51	0.4
5.54	3.785	0.5
5.89	4.02	0.6
6.20	4.23	0.7
6.49	4.43	0.8
6.75	4.61	0.9
6.98	4.77	1.0
7.53	5.14	1.25
7.99	5.46	1.50
8.42	5.75	1.75
8.80	6.01	2.0
9.47	6.47	2.5
10.08	6.88	3.0
10.61	7.25	3.5
11.08	7.57	4.0
11.94	8.15	5.0
12.69	8.66	6.0
13.36	9.13	7.0
13.97	9.54	8.0
14.53	9.91	9.0
15.05	10.28	10.0

Source: P. Grodzinski, *Diamond Technology* (London: N. A. G. Press, 1953), p. 758.

water-soluble pastes, or light petroleum oils for oil-based compounds. While the amount of diamond per gram of compound is generally a trade secret among makers, it is calculated on the basis of a monolayer of diamond particles when a spot of paste is properly flattened upon the lap. Diamond Boart, S.A., of Brussels, estimates that 1 gram of their compound covers 1 square meter of lap surface when properly spread. The data below are taken from a number of manufacturers' brochures and vividly show the confusion that exists in introducing coloring agents in compounds for purposes of identification. Several makers of compounds have now eliminated coloration entirely and depend on labeling of containers alone. See table G.

ALOXITE. Trade name for fused alumina of the Carborundum Company.

ALUMINA, ALUMINUM OXIDE. Al_2O_3. When pure a white crystalline powder, hexagonal (also cubic). $G = 3.93$-4.01, $H = 9.2$-9.3, $MP = 3,704°$ F. $(2,040°$ C.); softens $3,182°$ F. $(1,750°$ C.). R.I. $= 1.76$. Insol. in acids but slowly attacked by boil. conc. H_2SO_4. Prepared chemically from various aluminum compounds or from synthetic corundum which is the macrocrystalline counterpart. Brittle, fracturing into sharp-edged particles. Used as coarse to fine grits for lapping and fabrication of grinding wheels, papers, etc.; carefully classified powders are used for fine lapping and polishing and are available in sizes 3, 5, 9, 12, 15, 20, 25, and 30 microns; coarser grains are available in standard mesh sizes. Ordinary polishing, or levigated alumina is not much used in lapidary work, having been superseded largely by special chemically prepared hexagonal (alpha) and cubic (gamma) aluminas under various proprietary names, e.g., LINDE A and LINDE B (which see). However, classified micron-size alumina is still much used in the preparations of metallographic specimens either in dry powders or in distilled water suspensions.

ALUNDUM. Trade name for Norton Company fused alumina.

ARKANSAS STONE. A white to very pale grayish-white quartzitic rock (novaculite) from Arkansas much used for oilstones; porous, hard, wears slowly. Used to sharpen steel edges prior to stropping with rouge on leather.

BARNESITE. Proprietary trade name for rare-earth oxides used for polishing; color brown due to presence of rare-earth oxides other than ceria; polishes with same efficiency as purer ceria.

BERYLLIUM OXIDE. BeO. White or colorless crystalline, hexagonal, $G = 3.02$, $H = 9+$; $MP = 4,586°$ F. $(2,530°$ C.); R.I. $= 1.72$. Slowly sol. hot conc. HCl or HNO_3, more so in hot conc. H_2SO_4. Has been used for polishing carbides. Mineral counterpart is bromellite.

BLACK ROUGE. $FeFe_2O_4$; synthetic magnetite; isometric, magnetic, $G = 5.18$, $H = 5.5$-6.5; dec. c. $2,800°$ F. $(1,538°$ C.).

Grade number (microns)	Size range (microns)	Mesh size equivalent	Colors	Uses
	0-1/4	100,000	Gray	Extremely fine polish, especially on soft or very brittle materials
1/4	0-1/2	60,000	Gray Ivory White	Very fine polish on very soft or brittle materials
1/2	0-1	50,000	Orange Gray	Fine polish on hard metals or soft to medium hard minerals
1	0-2	14,000	White Ivory Orange Pale gray	Polish on hard metals, most hard minerals; appreciable material removal
	1/2-3		Pale Yellow	
	2-3		Bright Yellow	
3	2-4	8,000	Yellow Violet Blue	Fine lapping; appreciable material removal; polish on some hard gemstones
	2-6		Lemon Yellow	
6	4-8	3,000	Gray Orange Purple Indigo	Fine lapping; fairly rapid material removable; sanding of gemstones
	6-12		Green	
9	8-12	1,800	Dark blue Red	Rapid material removal; elimination of coarse scratches on gem materials
	8-15		Light Blue	
	10-20		Ultra-marine	
15	12-22	1,200	Pale blue Pale green Blue	Fast material removal; elimination coarse scratches of grinding or sanding
	20-40		Red	
25			Red	
30	22-36	600	Green Dark green	Very rapid material removal; roughing, shaping

Grade number (microns)	Size range (microns)	Mesh size equivalent	Colors	Uses
45	36-54	325	Yellow	Extremely rapid roughing and shaping
	40-60		Brown	
60	54-80	230	Tan	
90	(Mesh)	170	Orange	
120	(Mesh)	120	Red	
150	(Mesh)	100	Black	

Note: Micron grades 45 to 150 are very seldom sold.

Slightly sol. conc. acids. A black powder is chemically prepared for polishing metals, especially aluminum.

BORON CARBIDE. B_4C. Black crystals, grains, rhombohedral, G = 2.52, H = 9.5, MP = 4,262° F. (2,350° C.). Extremely hard synthetic sometimes used for lapping and grinding hard substances as carbides and sapphire.

BORON NITRIDE. BN. Isometric synthetic crystals made by same process as synthetic diamonds and about as hard as diamond; colorless when pure, also yellowish, brown to black. Does not alter in air up to 2,000° C.

BORT, BOART = DIAMOND.

CALCOTHAR, COLCOTHAR, COLCOTHAR OF VITRIOL = ROUGE.

CARBONADO = DIAMOND.

CARBORUNDUM. Trade name for silicon carbide made by Carborundum Company.

CERIUM OXIDE, CERIC OXIDE, CERIA. CeO_2 When pure a white powder, but usually contaminated by praseodymium oxide which imparts a pinkish to brownish cast; cubic; G = 7.132, MP = c. 4,700° F. (2,600° C.). Slowly sol. conc. H_2SO_4 or HNO_3; insol. dil. acids. Chemically prepared in micron sizes and used extensively for polishing glass, quartz, and silicate minerals, in which applications it has largely displaced other agents. Colored powder is just as effective as the far more expensive purer grades.

CHALK. Essentially $CaCO_3$, calcium carbonate, but commonly contaminated with quartz. A natural snow-white porous and highly absorbent rock ("chalk cliffs of Dover"). Scrapings have been used to polish bone, ivory, and similar soft substances. Precipitated chalk is chemically prepared and entirely free of silica.

CHALK, SILICEOUS. A natural chalky earth or marl from Germany, which however consists not of calcium carbonate but of silica (opal) skeletons of infusoria; used like tripoli.

CHARCOAL. Due to the content of very finely divided silica (opal) in various natural woods, charcoal possesses a very mild abrasive and polishing action which is taken advantage of in polishing some softer metals.

CHROMIUM OXIDE, CHROMIC OXIDE, CHROME OXIDE. Cr_2O_3. "Green rouge." A somewhat grayish, green powder, hexagonal, G = 5.21. H = 5.5, MP = 4,415° F. (2,435° C.), R.I. = 2.55. Chemically prepared in various ways, commonly by calcining the hydroxide and available in dry powder of about 15 microns size or specially classified powders of 0.5 or 1.0 microns suspended in water. Much used for polishing gemstones, especially those that undercut or consist of mixtures of minerals of varying hardnesses; also used for lapping and polishing metallographic specimens, especially steels; much used for buffing platinum and stainless steels. The powder readily penetrates crevices in gemstones and is difficult to remove, and for this reason is not always in favor.

COPPER OXIDE, CUPROUS OXIDE. A rarely used polishing agent.

CORUNDUM, CORUNDA. Al_2O_3. See properties under **ALUMINA**. Natural aluminum oxide (sapphire, ruby, etc.) occurring in hexagonal crystals or in coarse to fine grained granular masses; principal constituent of emery, which see. A useful lapping and polishing agent but seldom used now because of the difficulty in obtaining inexpensive ores of good purity and acceptable physical characteristics.

CROCUS, CROCUS MARTIS. An iron oxide made at the same time as **ROUGE**, which see. Coarser grain, darker, harder, and used as mild abrasive for polishing iron and steel, also other metals. Commonly applied to papers and papers covering sticks for fine filing action on metals.

CRYSTOLON. Trade name of Norton Company for silicon carbide.

DIAMANTINE, DIAMANTIN, DIAMONTINE. Mild abrasive and polishing powder prepared from synthetic corundum; contains no diamond; equivalent to ruby powder. Very useful for polishing platinum and white golds.

DIAMOND. C. Isometric carbon; G = 3.51, H = 10, MP = greater than $3,550°$ C., R.1. = 2.42. At red heat and higher slowly burns in air; unaffected by any reagents. Fragments and nongem crystals are crushed into grits and powders, and classified into many grades of mesh and micron sizes (see section on diamond abrasives, p. 000); bort, an impure type of diamond with cryptocrystalline structure is similarly treated but much is reserved as single masses for use in high-impact load applications such as drills and silicon carbide wheel dressers. Diamond is now synthesized by a number of firms in various countries and large quantities are supplied to the trade in small crystals suitable for saws and drills as well as grits and powders. Du Pont diamond is shock-synthesized and the structure of the diamond crystallites, with individual crystals of several microns size or less, closely resembles natural carbonado-type diamond which is also cryptocrystalline. Natural and synthetic grits and powders are used loose for lapping and polishing or may be fixed into more or less permanent positions in tools by embedment in sintered metals or in plastic, or fixation upon metal plates and bases with Ni-Cr platings. Because of its superior hardness, much above that of any commonly available hard abrasive or polishing material, diamond is uniquely useful. However, grains do break down, especially when fixed in position, and rate of cutting drastically lowers. For lapidary purposes diamond is used as a loose grit to charge metal laps for faceting, such as copper, tin, and bronze, or smeared on wood and other types of laps or buffs, either suspended in a suitable oil or in paste compounds. Mesh-size grains used for sintered segments in saws, drills, hole saws, etc.

DIATOMITE. Equivalent to tripolite; an earth consisting of the opaline skeletons of minute organisms known as diatoms; very highly absorptive and hence used as powder without binders like waxes, greases, etc. White when pure; wgt. about 5-16 lbs./cu. ft. Particle size 20, 30, 40, 50 microns. Sol. in strong alkalies. Used in polishing jewelry metals. Kieselguhr, a diatomite from Germany, has been used as an absorber of nitroglycerine in dynamites.

DUTCH RUSH. The common horsetail plant, *Equisetum;* the cylindrical stems of which contain considerable finely divided silica (opal). This property makes the dried rushes suitable for scouring and polishing silverware, alabaster, and marble, although other agents are now used instead.

EMERY. A very fine grained metamorphic rock consisting largely of corundum rendered impure by magnetite, hematite, and quartz, all of which are hard minerals, thus making emery useful as an abrasive and polishing agent. From Turkey, and other places. Opaque; dark gray to blue-black; H = c. 9; magnetic. Crushed to grits and powders as follows:

    4/0 = 700 mesh = 15 microns
    3/0 = 600 mesh = 18 microns
    2/0 = 550 mesh = 20 microns
    1/0 = 500 mesh = 22 microns
      1 = 350 mesh = 38 microns
      2 = 230 mesh = 60 microns
      3 = 180 mesh = 83 microns

All the above are available as loose powders and grits, or glued to paper for sanding or lapping purposes; the latter are much used for specimen preparation in metallography and electron microprobe work. Other sizes are available in coarse grits 6-46 mesh, fine grits 54-220 mesh, sizes F, 2F, 3F, and flours. Used in grinding wheels, abrasive blocks, oilstones, lapping grits and smoothing grits, and sometimes the finest grades for polishing metals.

FLINT. Used in England to provide crushed grains for sanding papers. The "flint" paper of the United States is made from quartz.

GARNET. $Fe_3Al_2Si_3O_{12}$, iron aluminum silicate, or, specifically, almandine, this being the garnet used almost solely for abrasive purposes. G = 3.9, H = 7.5, MP = $2,399°$ F. $(1,315°$ C.), R.I. = 1.76; isometric, ball-like crystals occur in metamorphic rocks and provide most of the raw material for crushing into abrasive grains. Extensively used in sandpapers, also as lapping grits, and in rotary grinding points.

GLASS. Sometimes used as a substitute for quartz in sandpapers.

GREASES, for binding abrasive and polishing powders into blocks and cakes. Most commonly used are stearic acid, mutton tallow, vaseline or other odorless pasty petroleum greases, beeswax, paraffin, and various other animal and vegetable waxes. The best binders are made from stearic acid, tallow, or beeswax.

GREEN ROUGE = CHROMIUM OXIDE.

HEMATITE. Specularite, or specular iron ore, has sometimes been crushed into abrasive grits and powders and then used like crocus; massive fibrous hematite ("kidney stone") has been used for whetstones.

INFUSORIAL EARTH = TRIPOLI.

KAOLIN. Levigated kaolin is a very mild polishing agent sometimes used on very soft materials.

KIESELGUHR = DIATOMITE.

LEVIGATED ALUMINA. Crushed alumina classified into more or less uniform particle size powders. See ALUMINA.

LINDE A. A proprietary chemically prepared alumina, alpha phase, or hexagonal in crystallization, particle size c. 0.3 micron. Much used in polishing of gemstones, metals and metallographic specimens, and other materials. Its efficacy can be attributed in part to the nature of the minute waferlike crystals which readily break down into smaller particles. While LINDE B is smaller in particle size (see below) it has not been found as fast nor as good a polishing agent among lapidaries.

LINDE B. Same as above, but gamma phase, or isometric in crystallization. Particle size on the order of 0.05 micron. Used as a fine polishing agent in metallographic work.

MAGNESIUM OXIDE. MgO, the synthetic counterpart of the mineral periclase. Colorless or white powder, G = 3.58, MP = $5,072°$ F. $(2,800°$ C.), BP over $3,600°$ C.; R.I. = 1.736. Sol. acids; slowly alters in air to the hydroxide, much more rapidly when in the form of polishing powder, requiring careful resealing of containers or storage in desiccated atmospheres. Considered by many metallurgists to be the best and most reliable final polishing agent for metal and ore specimens. See also VIENNA CHALK.

MANGANESE DIOXIDE. Black oxide of manganese sometimes used as a polishing powder but extremely dirty in use and staining skin with difficult-to-remove discolorations.

NEUBERG CHALK. A very fine-grained siliceous earth found in Germany and used for polishing metals.

NORBIDE. Trade name for Norton Company boron carbide.

OXIDES OF IRON = BLACK ROUGE or ROUGE.

PUMICE, PUMICITE, VOLCANIC DUST. Essentially obsidian, pervasively frothed by escaping or expanding gases within the molten material as it issues from volcano vents. Breaks down readily into numerous minute sharp-edged shards. Solid blocks are so porous they float on water, and when shaped, have been used as scouring blocks for sanding or rubbing down soft substances as varnishes and plastics. Consists primarily of aluminous and siliceous glasses; fibrous to platy structure, very brittle, H = 5-6. The powder is used for scours and also for cutting metals prior to further finishing, and at one time, found some favor as a loose sanding material on buffs for smoothing gemstones of H = 6 or less, e.g., opal.

PUTTY POWDER. White to yellowish impalpable powder prepared by calcining tin and lead to oxides, with high-grade putty powder containing from 85% to 90% tin oxide. Low grades containing no more than about 50% tin oxide were once used for polishing glass but the high lead content commonly caused lead poisoning and higher grades had to be substituted. All grades of putty powder are now largely superseded by rare-earth oxide polishing powders which are cheaper, more reliable, faster for polishing glass and silicate minerals, including the quartzes and opal.

QUARTZ. SiO_2. Rhombohedral, colorless, white, also other colors; G = 2.65, H = 7, MP = $2,930°$ F. $(1,610°$ C.). Crushed quartz, also sometimes FLINT (which see), is used to make sandpaper and abrasive grains for lapping; ordinary sand is used for coarse lapping, cutting stone with steel band saws, and other abrasive operations calling for very inexpensive abrasives.

ROTTENSTONE. A porous rock resulting from the deep weathering of certain siliceous-argillaceous limestones during which the calcite has been leached out. Soft, friable, uniform texture, gray-brown or olive-gray; largely finely divided silica which is the active abrasive and polishing agent. Has been used for faceting gemstones, and for the polishing of soft organic materials, plastics, varnishes, etc.

ROUGE, ENGLISH ROUGE, FRENCH ROUGE, CALCOTHAR, CALCOTHOR, etc. Essentially Fe_2O_3, iron oxide, made by calcining iron chlorides, sulfates, or oxalates under controlled conditions in crucibles. The natural counterpart is hematite. Black to red (blackish = crocus, and reddish = rouge); rhombohedral; G = 5.24, MP = $2,849°$ F. $(1,565°$ C.). Slowly sol. in warm acids. A very old and still popular polishing agent principally used for metals, although some is still used for polishing gemstones, especially the softer species. The commonly used agent for polishing glass lenses on pitch laps.

RUBY POWDER, RUBY DIX. Abrasive and polishing powders made from crushed synthetic ruby.

SAPPHIRE POWDER. Made from crushed synthetic sapphire.

SHEFFIELD LIME = VIENNA CHALK.

SILICA. Microcrystalline quartz, SiO_2, similar to tripoli and used in the same manner.

SILICON CARBIDE. SiC. Trade names include "Crystolon" and "Carborundum." Black, gray, greenish, sometimes brownish hexagonal crystals, rarely transparent; brittle, fracturing into sharp-edged grains. G = 3.12-3.22, H = 9.25-9.5, dec. $3,992°$ F. $(2,200°$ C.). R.I. = 2.74. Insol. in any acid or common reagent. Enormous quantities are used as loose grits for lapping, making cloths and papers, and for grinding wheels, hones, whetstones, etc. The most generally satisfactory inexpensive abrasive agent available. Readily available in mesh sizes 6, 8, 10, 12, 14, 16, 20, 24, 30, 36, 40, 50, 60, 70, 80, 90, 100, 150, 180, 220; also in powders F, 2F, 3F, and 280 to 600 mesh; carefully classified powders are available in micron sizes 5, 12, 15, 20, and 30. Silicon carbide reacts slowly in gemstone tumblers to form explosive gases which must be vented from time to time

STANNIC OXIDE = TIN OXIDE.

STEEL GRIT, STEEL SHOT. Molten cast-iron droplets, chilled, and then annealed, are used as a cheap abrasive for shot peening, sawing of building stone, and lapping of stone; also for core drilling and burnishing. Available in 15 sizes from 4 to 90 mesh. Steel grit is made from special high-carbon steel, treated to brittleness, and then crushed into grains. Available in 25 sizes from 20 to 200 mesh.

TANTALUM CARBIDE. Has been experimentally used to polish diamond.

TIN OXIDE, STANNIC OXIDE, in part PUTTY POWDER. SnO_2, the counterpart of the mineral cassiterite. Pure white impalpable powder, tetragonal, G = 6.95, H = 6.5, MP = $2,061°$ F. $(1,127°$ C.), R.I. = 2.00; insol. acids. Made by calcining tin in an oxidizing atmosphere; a very pure and extremely fine grained grade is made by dissolving tin in dil. HCl + HNO_3, precipitating with ammonia, and then calcining the precipitate. For many years an extremely important polishing agent for metals and gemstones, with the ability to polish almost all gemstones regardless of individual characteristics. Largely superseded by cerium oxide for quartz and silicate gems, and Linde A for others.

TITANIUM CARBIDE. Experimentally used to polish diamond.

TRIPOLI, TERRA TRIPOLITANA. Fine-grained natural abrasive and polishing agent containing the opaline skeletons of diatoms; diatomaceous earth. H = c. 5-6, G = c. 2.4. White to pink or yellowish. Usually supplied in powder or in cake form, the latter for applying to cloth buffs for first polishing metals. Has been used extensively for polishing gemstones, including faceted stones, but now used much less.

TRIPOLI (QUARTZ). The original tripoli was named after the country of origin, but another material, called by the same name but not consisting of opaline diatoms, has been mined for years in the United States and is the tripoli commonly offered as a fine abrasive agent. It is a white sedimentary rock, easily crushed, consisting of minute more or less uniform quartz particles which have formed from the weathering of siliceous limestones. It is much used in the polishing of aluminum.

VIENNA CHALK, VIENNA LIME. An excellent polishing agent made from calcining dolomite; during the process magnesium carbonate is converted to magnesium oxide, to which ingredient the agent owes its effectiveness; see MAGNESIUM OXIDE. Particles under 1 micron size. Especially effective for polishing Ni and Al. Readily reacts with acids and absorbs water from the atmosphere, requiring that containers be kept sealed or the powder preserved in a desiccated container.

WATER OF AYR STONE, SCOTCH STONE, SNAKE STONE. Pale gray, porous stone, with slightly darker spots, relatively soft but firm, readily breaking down with use and thus keeping up a continuously effective fine lapping action; used with water. Sold in sticks of various sizes. Used to file out coarse scratches in jewelry metals prior to tripoli.

WHITING. Chalk (calcium carbonate, calcite), ground and purified to remove silica particles, and used as a mild polishing agent on soft materials as plastics, varnishes, metals, etc. Rapidly absorbs greases and oils. Used as an adulterant in paints, putty powder, etc.

ZINC OXIDE. ZnO; the natural counterpart is zincite. Hexagonal, white powder, G = 5.61, H = 4.5, MP = $3,587°$ F. ($1,975°$ C.), R.I. = 2.01. Sol. rather rapidly in HCl and other acids. Used as a polishing agent from time to time but offers few if any advantages over other agents.

ZIRCONIUM CARBIDE. Experimentally used to polish diamond.

ZIRCONIUM DIOXIDE, ZIRCONIA. ZrO_2; the natural counterpart is baddeleyite. Monoclinic, white powder when pure but commonly red-brown in commercial grade. G = 5.6, H = 6.5, MP = $4,919°$ F. ($2,715°$ C.), R.I. = 2.19. Has been used as an effective polishing agent especially for metal and ore specimens.

References: W. Burkart, *Modernes Schleifen und Polieren* (Saulgau/Württemberg: Leuze Verlag, 1956).
H. P. Chandler, *Industrial Diamond,* Information Circular no. 8200 (Washington, D.C.: U.S. Bureau of Mines 1964).
L. Coes, Jr., *Abrasives* (New York: Springer-Verlag, 1971).
V. L. Eardley-Wilmot, *Abrasives* (Ottawa, Can.: Department of Mines, 1929), part 4, "Artificial Abrasives."
P. Grodzinski, *Diamond Technology* (London: N. A. G. Press, 1953).
C. Holtzapffel, *Turning and Mechanical Manipulation* (London, 1850), vol. 3, *Abrasive and Miscellaneous Processes.*
J. Sinkankas, *Gem Cutting,* 2d ed. (New York: Van Nostrand Reinhold, 1962).

MATERIALS USED IN BUFFS AND LAPS FOR LAPIDARY AND JEWELRY WORK

The properties of metals, alloys, waxes, resins, and other substances are furnished elsewhere; please consult index.

BABBITT METAL. Very seldom used for polishing laps; wide range of composition but primarily tin with antimony, lead and copper.

BAIZE = BILLIARD CLOTH.

BEESWAX. Used for wax laps; may be hardened by the addition of about 10% by wgt. carnauba wax.

BILLIARD CLOTH. Tightly woven green wool fabric, napped types used for polishing metallographic and petrographic specimens; usual grade 21 ounce, 100% wool, sheared. For curved buffs, cabochon work, offers no advantages over felt and is indeed far more expensive as well as troublesome to repeatedly replace.

BRASS. Available in many alloys; a harder lap material than tin alloys or zinc; used for lapping with loose grits or for polishing very hard gemstones as chrysoberyl and corundum with diamond. A good base lap material, or for covering with fabrics or pads for metallographic and petrographic sample preparation.

BRONZE. Used interchangeably with brass.

BUFFING STICKS, CORDS, STRINGS. Strips of leather, hard felt, etc., can be glued to small sticks to use as hand buffs for metals or for carvings; also useful are strings, cords, leather thongs, etc.

BURNISHERS. Polished hardened steel tools with curved surfaces for smoothing malleable jewelry metals; also made from agate.

CAMEL HIDE. A useful thick leather for buffs and polishers; the thickness makes it especially useful for cutting out small wheels for sanding and polishing carvings.

CANVAS (DUCK). Coarse, strong, tightly woven cotton fabric useful for sanding or polishing large works and flats of gem material. Usually tacked over convex wooden buffs, on wooden disks, or stretched over metal laps. Long-lasting, inexpensive, and performs well.

CARNAUBA WAX. A hard Brazilian palm wax used to make WAX LAPS (which see).

CAST IRON. Used to make the polishing scaifes of the diamond cutter; very useful for all types of loose grit lapping and somewhat better for this purpose than steels but not sufficiently so to warrant the added expense and trouble over obtaining steel laps. Small cast-iron faceting laps are very successfully used with micron-size diamond for polishing hard gems, also zircons (Thailand).

COPPER. Perhaps the most generally useful cutting laps of the lapidary. May be used with loose silicon carbide, emery, or alumina grits but most copper laps are charged with diamond in about 400 mesh to 1,200 mesh sizes, either by rolling in the powder or rubbing in with an agate block. Special knurling tools rolled over the surface before diamond is applied assist in impregnation of the latter. Cold rolled copper plate is the starting material for such laps but the circular disks cut from such plate must always be placed in a lathe and turned to flatness and parallelism. Copper laps have also been used for polishing with diamond paste compounds,

rottenstone, tripoli, or other agents. They are most suited for polishing of facets on the harder gemstones.

CORK. A fine granular pale-colored sheet cork has been used for polishing cabochons and flats but is weak and easily damaged. It must be firmly cemented flat if any durability is to be expected. Sheet in 1/4″ thickness is probably most useful and less likely to require frequent replacement. Cork is also useful for fine sanding with 1,200 mesh silicon carbide or appropriate diamond pastes.

COTTON TWILLS. Thin, hard-surfaced twilled fabrics useful for applying to flat laps for the polishing of metallographic and petrographic specimens; commonly used for very fine finishing or prepolishing.

EMERY PAPER. Used for smoothing surfaces of metallographic and petrographic specimens prior to fine finishing and polishing. Available in sizes shown, with corresponding mesh sizes in parens: 4/0 (700), 3/0 (600), 2/0 (550), 1/0 (500), 1 (350), 2 (230), 3 (180). Not waterproof and usually meant to be used dry; if clogging of surface is excessive may be used with petroleum distillates such as kerosene and heptane, or light oils, with paper placed on plate glass to retain flatness.

FELT. Short wool fibers interlocked ("felted") into more or less coherent masses which may take the form of sheets or blocks, or special molded shapes. Soft felts cannot stand up under either jewelry metal or gemstone polishing and should be avoided. The only useful felt is that known as "rock hard." It is white, very compact, yet porous and sufficiently yielding to accommodate the curved surfaces of cabochons or rounded metals in jewelry pieces. Felt sheet may be briefly soaked in lukewarm water to make it pliable and then molded over curved or domed buffs. Sheets may also be glued to backings for flat laps, buffing sticks, etc. Small felt wheels may be hardened by soaking in a very thin solution of plastic. Fine sanding or polishing can be done with felt wheels; also rouging and tripoli prepolishing.

FELT CLOTH. Similar to BILLIARD CLOTH (which see) and used the same way.

GLASS. Plate glass has been used for lapping and polishing flat metallographic and petrographic specimens wherein undercutting is very severe, but the hardness of the surface of glass plates is often more than offset by the tendency of particles dislodged from specimens to create extremely deep scores. Not recommended except for loose grit lapping.

KITTEN EAR CLOTH. A short pile fabric with a velvety surface and woven material as a base; used for polishing metallographic and petrographic specimens.

LEAD. Pure lead is very soft and peculiarly useful for laps for soft or sensitive faceted gemstones; conventional polishing agents, especially Linde A, are used, but also diamond pastes. A drawback is that surfaces readily corrode and form hard oxides, usually necessitating rescraping to brightness after a short period of use. May be alloyed with no more than 1% by wgt. of antimony or tin to harden. With fine lapping abrasives, e.g., 400 mesh and smaller, lead laps are very useful for grinding facets on easily cleavable gemstones as the rhombohedral carbonates. Very fine flat, nonundercut surfaces on metallographic and petrographic sections may be achieved by lapping on lead with ultrafine aluminas or magnesium oxide.

LEAD-TIN. A 50-50 alloy is very useful in faceting laps.

LEATHER. Among useful natural materials all types of leather take a very high place for their ability to accept either light abrasives or polishing agents, retain them well, wear for long periods, resist repeated wettings, and still apply sufficient force to work surfaces to accomplish smoothing and polishing as few other materials can. Leather is generally applied in strips or sheets over solid wood and tacked in place, or over sponge rubber to provide additional yield to the surface for cabochon work. Soaking for several hours in water helps soften leather so that it may be stretched without wrinkles over curved forms; soaking also helps to tauten leather when stretched over flat laps or the peripheries of wheels. Both sides of leathers work about equally well but some differences may be noted; in general, the rough side is better for retention of coarser abrasives and powders, while the smooth side is better with the finest abrasives and polishing agents.

Types of Leather and Uses

Buffalo (water buffalo, not American bison): Used for small thick buffing wheels.

Calfskin: Soft, thin leather marginally useful for polishing buffs.

Camelskin: Used for small, thick buffing wheels.

Chamois: Made from sheepskin and used mainly as a hand buffing leather with rouge for silver and gold wares, jewelry, etc. Marginally useful for polishing buffs.

Cowhide, steerhide, bullhide: The abundant leather used for shoes and shoe soles, the latter being specially compressed into a dense, hard leather by machine rolling. All grades are useful for buffs, polishing wheels, etc., and small thick wheels for carving can be made up of sole leather cemented together in several layers with waterproof glue. Sole leather is also useful with rouge for stropping steel tools, and with diamond for cutting and polishing cabochons set in rings or jewelry where it is either inconvenient to demount the stones or dangerous to attempt to polish against high speed revolving buffs.

Deerskin: A soft, thin leather, of marginal usefulness in lapidary work although thongs of this leather are excellent for polishing pierced openings in jewelry with tripoli and/or rouge.

Goatskin: A good leather, but expensive and not so much more useful than others that it pays to buy it.

Horsehide: A very useful tough, thin leather, much used for fine sanding and polishing buffs.

Kangaroo: A leather that is relatively rare and marginally useful.

Kidskin: A thin flexible leather of little value except for hand buffing of metals with rouge.

Lambskin: Marginal in value; tears easily.

Pigskin: A very tough, durable, and useful leather for polishing; may be used with any type of polishing agent, including diamond, but sometimes the smooth side is more effective, and at other times the rough is, depending on agent used. Very tear resistant; tends to shrink if wetted repeatedly and probably it is best to use oily polishes on same.

Sea lion: Some thick neck hide is used

for tough, hard leather used in making small polishing wheels.

Sheepskin: A generally poor, soft leather of not much value in lapidary work.

Suede: Any leather that has been surface-abraded on the rough side to provide a velvety finish; its usefulness depends on the type of leather from which it was made.

Walrus: The thick neck fold skin provides hard, dense leather very useful for small polishing wheels.

NYLON FABRIC. Several types of thin, hard-surfaced nylon fabrics find much use in metallographic and petrographic specimen preparation; they are stretched over a metal lap and charged with prepolish abrasives or micron size diamond pastes. A useful polishing type is 70 denier, 190 × 120 count, unnapped fabric.

PELLON. A proprietary fabriclike sheet composed of multitudes of plastic fibers cemented together into a porous mass with a structure quite similar to that observed in leather and with similar characteristics insofar as lapidary work is concerned; it is, however, much less tough than leather and may tear when wet. It is available in various degrees of porosity and softness (or hardness), from a very soft material sold in fabric shops and quite unsuited for any lapidary application, to sheets that are firm and strong and very useful for polishing. Mounting is by contact-cement upon metal plates, or snap-ring, the first method being preferred. Uniquely useful with cerium oxide for polishing quartz and chalcedony flats.

PEWTER. Used for faceting laps. The finest alloy is essentially pure tin to which less than 1% by wgt. copper has been added; modern "pewters" are largely mixtures of tin and lead in about equal proportions and are still very useful although they are not regarded so favorably by professional lapidaries as the alloy first mentioned. Classically, the pewter lap was and is used for grinding of faceted gems with loose abrasives as emery or silicon carbide, and polishing with rotten-stone, alumina, tin oxide, or diamond. For sensitive, soft, or otherwise delicate gemstones, pewter is highly recommended.

PITCH. The pitch polishing lap is made from about equal portions by wgt. of tree pitch and rosin (colophony), melted together until thoroughly mixed and then poured out into a suitable form upon a base lap plate. Traditionally used for polishing glass plates, lenses, and other objects, but still useful for placing extremely flat and beautifully polished surfaces upon large flats of chalcedony, obsidian, and other minerals; useful for undercutting gemstones. In warm rooms, the proportion of rosin is increased to prevent deformation of the lap. The powder used with the pitch lap is generally rouge but other agents may also be employed such as tin oxide, aluminas, cerium oxide. While difficult to prepare with parallel sides, very large laps can be made economically, which may not be the case with metal laps. Scoring is accomplished by cutting grooves in the chilled lap in checkerboard fashion, or impressing mosquito netting into the polishing surface while the mixture is still slightly yielding.

PLASTICS. Various plastics have been tried with varying degrees of success for polishing gemstones, particularly faceted stones. Of these, the most generally successful has been methacrylate resin (Plexiglas, Lucite, Perspex). Most commonly the agent used is cerium oxide but after an initial period of efficient working the laps become worn smooth, or if accidentally overheated, smeared upon the surface with entrapment of powder and stone fines. Since this happens rather quickly it is necessary to keep reworking the surface of the lap by abrasives or machining in a lathe. Many lapidaries have entirely discarded these laps in favor of metal laps.

PLYWOOD. Plywoods made from diffuse-porous hardwoods (see WOOD below) are excellent for lapping and polishing. Available are 1/8"-thick types in large sheets faced with birch, maple, and other suitable woods. Disks cut from these may be charged with oil-based diamond pastes and prove very fast and scratch-free in their operation. Water-based pastes or polishing agents can be expected to warp the wood.

PRESSED WOOD. Made from chips or dust and cemented together with waterproof or water-resistant resins; fairly hard, tough, and stable. Some types have been used with polishing agents, especially on the reverse rough sides, but offer few advantages over other kinds of laps.

RAYON-COTTON COMPOSITE FABRICS. Certain types are made with a nap of rayon upon a woven base of cotton and are useful in polishing of metallographic and petrographic specimens.

SANDING PAPERS AND CLOTHS. Ordinary types are cemented with water-soluble glue (see EMERY above), but those mostly used in lapidary work are waterproof. Papers are unsuited for high-speed applications because of tearing problems, nor are they stretchable over curved forms without wrinkling. However, when fastened or merely rested upon flat plates they are much used for the initial lapping stages of metallographic and petrographic specimen preparation. Waterproof cloths are tough and last a long time but glaze rather quickly because the grains are fixed in position and not free to roll about. If used dry, the pores clog readily and impart a glaze to the gemstones, but if used wet they cut at about the same rate from start to finish and no semipolish is obtained as is often the case with dry operation. Available in many mesh sizes, with 400 to 120 mesh being used most often in lapidary work. Waterproof cloths are stiff and cannot be stretched over curved forms except cylinders, and are therefore used as disks or as belts.

SELVYT. A napped cotton cloth with a soft, velvety surface used in polishing metallographic and petrographic specimens. Used with tin oxide, aluminas, cerium oxides, etc.

SILICON CARBIDE PAPERS. Much used in metallographic and petrographic work for flatting and smoothing sections; available in ordinary or waterproof papers in sizes 180, 240, 320, 400, and 600 mesh.

SILK FABRICS. Very thin silks, nearly translucent, are used over metal laps for abrading flat sections to prevent undercutting; they may be used in conjunction with conventional abrasives of fine size or similar size diamond pastes.

TIN. Pure tin is very satisfactory for polishing laps and is both reliable and versatile; however, it is sometimes considered too soft and a very slight amount of antimony may be added to harden. Polishing agents used on tin are Linde A, tin oxide, aluminas, cerium oxide, diamond, and others. As the surface wears, the irregularities and contaminants forced into the metal are generally removed by scraping and the lap is rescored.

TIN-LEAD. A very good lap for faceting gemstones is made from 50% tin and 50% lead by weight.

TIN-TYPEMETAL. Also useful is a faceting lap made from various proportions of tin alloyed with TYPEMETAL (see below). Such laps offer a firmer surface than tin, making them more useful for harder gemstones, but are more inclined to scratch than pure tin.

TYPEMETAL. An alloy consisting of lead with additions of tin, antimony, and copper; much used for faceting laps.

VINYL. This plastic has been used in thick sheets to make polishing laps for faceting but is marginal in value compared to some plastics of proven value.

WAX LAPS. Provide soft, shock-free surfaces for faceting soft, easily cleaved gems or those that scratch badly on other laps. Deform readily but may be easily resmoothed. May be laid on metal in a layer or over cloth, with the latter imparting more rigidity and preventing excessive creep of the surface. Beeswax is used, or beeswax hardened by additions of carnauba wax, or carnauba wax alone. May be smoothed after application by moistening surface with lighter fluid, benzene, heptane, or the like, and smearing with a flat agate or glass block. Used with Linde A or other agents as desired.

WOOD. A uniquely useful material for abrasive and polishing operations because of the nature of the surface which tends to accept particles of abrasive or powder and retain them just enough to cause drag on the surface of the gemstone or metal, hence effecting the removal of imperfections. Some abrasives, notably diamond, are impregnated in the wood and last for a long time but require wetting with a suitable liquid to make them effective. While it is almost always best to make laps from end-grain, that is, with the pores emerging on the lap surface, the difficulty of obtaining large enough sections of log to do so is considerable and composites must be used, glued up from smaller pieces. In many of the woods shown in the table below, however, little difference appears between end-grain and side-grain operation except that warping with side-grain tends to create a badly uneven surface.

Woods Suitable for Use in Sanding or Polishing Gemstones and Metals

See table below.

First column: most desirable by reason of diffuse pore structure, freedom from warping, checking, etc., and retention of smooth surface under repeated pressures of work. Second column: marginally desirable, generally softer and more yielding under pressure, or significant warping when wetted. Third column: woods which should be avoided.

ZINC. Sometimes used for faceting laps in which a fairly hard surface is required, but this metal has never been extensively used.

References: AB Metal Digest 10, no. 1 (Evanston, Ill.: Buehler Ltd., 1964).

C. Holtzapffel, *Turning and Mechanical Manipulation* (London, 1850), vol. 3, *Abrasive and Miscellaneous Processes.*

A. G. Ingalls, *Amateur Telescope Making* (Munn & Co., 1947), n.p.

J. Sinkankas, *Gem Cutting,* 2d ed. (New York: Van Nostrand Reinhold, 1962).

F. J. Sperisen, *The Art of the Lapidary,* rev. ed. (Milwaukee: Bruce Publishing Co., 1961).

G. Vargas and M. Vargas, *Faceting for Amateurs* (Thermal, Calif.: privately pub., 1969).

J. D. Willems, *Gem Cutting* (Peoria, Ill.: Charles A. Bennett, 1948).

POLISHING AGENT—LAP OR BUFF COMBINATIONS FOR MINERAL AND ORGANIC GEMSTONE MATERIALS

The recommendations below are gathered from numerous authorities as listed in the references following this section. In general, polishing agents are followed by several types of laps or buffs, any one of which will work with the agent. The sign "+" signifies "on" or "with"; the hyphen "-" signifies successive steps.

ABALONE. Dip in dil. HCl or HNO_3 to remove incrustations; scrub; grind off protuberances as required; smooth with wet tripoli + muslin buff; polish rouge, tin oxide + muslin.

ACTINOLITE. Facet: Linde Á + tin, tin-lead.

ALABASTER (Gypsum). Carvings, cabochons, etc.: sand with wet pumice + cloth; polish tin oxide + muslin buff; sand flats with pumice + wood, then prepolish pumice + cloth, final polish tin oxide + leather; avoid chromium or cerium oxide due to discoloration.

ALGODONITE. Cabochons: sand with wet 1,200 silicon carbide + leather; polish Linde A + leather or diamond paste (1-1/2 m).

Desirable	Marginal	Avoid
Apple	Alder	Ash
Beech	Aspen	Butternut
Birch	Basswood	Cedars
Boxwood	Cottonwood	Chestnut
Cherrys	Gum, U.S. red	Cypress
Cocobolo	Horse chestnut	Elms
Ebony	Lime (bass tree)	Firs
Holly	Poplars	Hemlocks
Hornbeam	Sour gum, U.S. tupelo	Hickories
Lignum vitae	Walnuts	Junipers
Mahogany, Honduran	Whitewood, U.S.	Larches
Maples		Mahogany, Philippine
Olive		Oaks
Pear		Pines
Plum, edible		Redwood
Rosewood		Spruces
Sandalwood		Sycamore
Teak		Tamarack
Willow		

Source: F. H. Titmuss, *Commercial Timbers of the World,* 3d ed. (Cleveland: Chemical Rubber Co., 1965).

AMBER. Carvings, cabochons: smooth by hand with emery paper 4/0 with oil; polish tripoli, rottenstone, with oil, on cloth, leather. Facet: Linde A, tin oxide + wax, wood.

AMBLYGONITE. Facet: Linde A + lead, tin-lead, tin, wax; cerium oxide + tin.

ANALCIME. Facet: cerium oxide, tin oxide + plastic; Linde A + tin-lead.

ANATASE. Facet: Linde A + tin-lead.

ANDALUSITE. Facet: tin oxide, Linde A + tin, tin-lead.

ANGLESITE. Facet: Linde A + wax.

ANHYDRITE. Facet: Linde A + wax.

ANTHOPHYLLITE. Cabochon: cerium oxide + felt; Linde A + leather.

ANTHRACITE. Carvings, cabochons, etc.: sand, preferably wet, to 4/0 or 600 mesh; rub with pumice on cloth; polish with felt pads or woolen cloths with rottenstone + oil, or tin oxide + oil; shoe polish or india ink to disguise crevices.

APATITE. Cabochon: Linde A + leather, felt. Facet: Linde A + wax, tin-lead, tin, lead, pitch, vinyl; tin oxide + tin, pitch, wax; cerium oxide + wax. Large facets, perfect, diamond (1/2-1/4 m) on plywood, wood.

APOPHYLLITE. Facet: Linde A + tin, tin-lead, lead.

ARAGONITE. Cabochon: treat like PETOSKEY STONE. Facet: Linde A + wax, tin-lead, phenolic, wood; diamond (1/2-1/4 m) + wood (large facets).

ARGILLITE. Carvings: emery paper to 4/0 + oil; rub with wood shavings and black stove polish.

AUGELITE. Facet: Linde A + wax, tin-lead; cerium oxide + vinyl.

AXINITE. Facet: Linde A, tin oxide + tin, tin-lead, typemetal; cerium oxide + plastic, phenolic.

AZURITE. Cabochon: treat like MALACHITE. Facet: Linde A + wax, tin-lead.

BANDED RHYOLITE. Cabochon: Linde A + wood; diamond (3-1-1/2 m) + wood.

BARITE. Cabochon: Linde A + leather; diamond + wood. Facet: Linde A, tin oxide + wax, vinyl.

BAUXITE. Flats: lap to 1,200 silicon carbide; polish Linde A, tin oxide + pitch; also diamond + wood.

BAYLDONITE. Cabochon: Linde A + leather.

BENITOITE. Facet: Linde A, tin oxide + tin, tin-lead; cerium oxide + plastic, vinyl, phenolic; tripoli + lead.

BERYL. Cabochon: Linde A + leather, wood; diamond (1/2 m) wood, leather; cerium oxide, chromium oxide + felt (slow). Facet: Linde A, tin oxide, cerium oxide + tin, typemetal, tin-typemetal; cerium oxide + metal laps named + plastic.

BERYLLONITE. Facet: tin oxide, Linde A + tin, tin-lead; cerium oxide + vinyl, phenolic, plastic.

BONE. Treat like AMBER; fill pores with whiting or tin oxide + paraffin wax.

BORACITE. Facet: Linde A + tin, tin-lead.

BORNITE. Cabochon: sanded 1,200 silicon carbide slurry on leather; polish Linde A + leather, pellon; rouge + muslin; diamond + leather.

BRAZILIANITE. Facet: Linde A + tin, tin-lead, typemetal; cerium oxide + plastic.

BREITHAUPTITE. Treat like BORNITE.

CALCITE. Massive: smooth to fine finish using any convenient abrasive, e.g., pumice; polish tin oxide, with or without oxalic acid added to muslin or canvas buff surface beforehand. Facet: lap only loose 400 silicon carbide + lead; polish Linde A, tin oxide + tin, tin-lead, wax; large facets polish perfectly on plywood with diamond (3-1-1/2-1/4 m). Large flats polish 1/2-1/4 m diamond on napped cloth, velvet; rouge alternate.

CALIFORNITE (Idocrase). Cabochon: diamond (3-1-1/2 m) + wood; Linde A, tin oxide, chrome oxide + leather. Facet: Linde A tin oxide + tin.

CANCRINITE. Cabochon: cerium oxide + felt, leather.

CANNEL COAL. Treat like ANTHRACITE.

CASSITERITE. Cabochon ("wood tin"): Linde A, diamond (1/2 m) + wood, leather. Facet: Linde A, levigated alumina, damascus ruby powder, diamond + tin.

CELESTITE. Facet: Linde A + wax; tin oxide + vinyl.

CERUSSITE. Cabochon: Linde A + leather. Facet: Linde A + wax; tin oxide + phenolic, wood.

CHALCEDONY. Cabochon: cerium oxide, tin oxide + felt, leather, wood. Flats: cerium oxide + pellon. Facet: cerium oxide, tin oxide + tin.

CHIASTOLITE. Cabochon: Linde A + leather.

CHLORASTROLITE. Cerium oxide, Linde A + felt, leather.

CHONDRODITE. Facet: Linde A + tin, tin-lead, phenolic, wood.

CHRYSOBERYL. Cabochon: diamond (15-9-6-3-1 m) sandings on wood; polish 1/2 or 1/4 m on wood, phenolic; also can prepare cabochons similarly on metal laps by which greater cutting pressure can be exerted; can also sand with silicon carbide-rubber wheels but slower. Facet: diamond + tin, tin-lead, tin-typemetal, zinc, copper, bronze, phenolic; older method tripoli on zinc or bronze and still useful for removing diamond striations.

CHRYSOPRASE. Cabochon: Linde A, chrome oxide, tin oxide + leather; diamond (3-1-1/2 m) + wood, leather.

CINNABAR. Facet: Linde A + wax.

CLINOZOISITE. Facet: Linde A + tin; cerium oxide + plastic.

COBALTITE. Treat like BORNITE.

COLEMANITE. Facet: Linde A + wax, tin-lead; cerium oxide + plastic; tin oxide + plastic.

COPPER RHYOLITE ("Cuprite" in eastern U.S.). Cabochon: Linde A + leather; diamond (9-6-3-1-1/2 m) + wood (better).

CORAL. Treat like massive CALCITE. Black coral polish rouge + cloth buff.

CORUNDUM. Cabochon: diamond (15-9-6-3-1 m) + wood, also same on metal laps; polish diamond (1/2-1/4 m) on wood, phenolic, lead, zinc, tin, copper. Indian opaque red corundum ("ruby"), also similar corundums from North Carolina and Australia require careful sanding with diamond on wood to remove many small pits (rhombohedral partings). Cabochons may be sanded with silicon carbide-rubber wheels but progress is slow. Facet: diamond (3-1-1/2-1/4) on tin, tin-type-metal, typemetal, zinc, bronze, copper, brass, etc.; also on phenolic and plastic. Tripoli on metal used by some to remove fine striations left by diamond.

COVELLITE. Cabochon: Linde A + leather.

CROCOITE. Facet: Linde A + wax.

CUPRITE. Facet: Linde A + wax, marginally on tin-lead.

DANBURITE. Linde A, tin oxide + tin, tin-lead, typemetal.

DATOLITE. Cabochon (massive material from Michigan): cerium oxide + felt; Linde A + leather; diamond + wood. Facet: Linde A, tin oxide + plastic, vinyl, phenolic, tin, tin-lead.

DIAMOND. Facet: diamond on cast iron.

DIOPSIDE. Cabochon: Linde A, tin oxide + wood, leather, tin. Facet: Linde A, tin oxide + tin, lead, tin-lead, phenolic, wax (for large facets).

DIOPTASE. Cabochon: Linde A + leather. Facet: Linde A + tin, tin-lead; cerium oxide + plastic.

DOLOMITE. Treat like massive CALCITE. Facet: Linde A + wax, tin, tin-lead.

DOMEYKITE. Treat like BORNITE.

DUMORTIERITE QUARTZ. Cabochon: Sand diamond (3-1) on wood, polish Linde A + leather; diamond (1/2 m) + wood, leather.

ENAMELS. Lap surfaces with water-of-ayr stones + water; smooth emery sticks, or silicon carbide waterproof papers or cloths; further smooth with tripoli on wood slips; polish cerium oxide, tin oxide + slips of wood, leather, felt on sticks.

ENSTATITE. Cabochon: Linde A + leather; diamond (1/2 m) + wood, leather. Facet: Linde A, tin oxide + tin, tin-lead.

EPIDOTE. Cabochon: Linde A, chrome oxide, diamond + wood, leather. Facet: Linde A, tin oxide + tin, tin-lead, typemetal; cerium oxide + vinyl, phenolic.

EUCLASE. Facet: Linde A, tin oxide + tin, tin-lead.

EUXENITE. Cabochon: Linde A + leather. Facet: Linde A + tin.

FELDSPAR. Cabochon: cerium oxide, Linde A + felt, leather, pellon. Facet: cerium oxide + plastic, tin, lead, tin-lead; Linde A + tin, tin-lead; tripoli + tin-lead.

FERGUSONITE. Facet: lap only 400 silicon carbide + lead; polish Linde A + tin, tin-lead.

FIBROLITE. Cabochon: Linde A + leather. Facet: loose 400 silicon carbide on lead lapping followed by Linde A + tin, tin-lead.

FLUORITE. Cabochon: sand 1,200 silicon carbide slurry on leather, polish Linde A, tin oxide + leather; or use diamond (9-6-3-1 m) on wood, polish diamond (1/2-1/4 m) + leather or wood. Facet: Linde A, tin oxide + wax, vinyl, tin-lead, wood, pewter, pitch; cerium oxide

+ phenolic. Large facets 1/4 m diamond on plywood.

FRIEDELITE. Cabochon: Linde A + leather; cerium oxide + felt. Facet: Linde A + tin, tin-lead.

GARNET. Cabochon: sand 1,200 silicon carbide slurry + leather, wood, or diamond (15-9-6 m) on wood; polish Linde A + leather, wood, final polish diamond (1/2-1/4 m) on leather; also chrome oxide + leather. Sanding with silicon carbide-rubber wheels useful. Facet: tin oxide, Linde A + tin, tin-lead, tin-typemetal; also cerium oxide + plastic.

GLASS. Cabochon: sand 1,200 silicon carbide slurry + leather, or use diamond (9-6-3 m) + wood or leather; polish cerium oxide + felt, leather. Polish flats cerium oxide + pellon. Facet: Linde A, cerium oxide, tin oxide + tin, tin-lead, typemetal.

GOETHITE. Cabochon: Linde A + leather; diamond (9-6-3-1 m) + wood, final polish diamond (1/2-1/4 m) + leather, wood. Facet: tin oxide, Linde A + heavily scored tin, lead, tin-lead; Linde A + wax.

GOLDSTONE. Treat like GLASS.

GRANITE. Cabochon: Linde A + leather, wood, Flats lapped to 1,200 silicon carbide on steel plate, polish cerium oxide + pellon, pitch; also tin oxide + heavily scored tin.

GYPSUM. Cabochon: cerium oxide + felt; Linde A + leather; rouge + muslin.

HAMBERGITE. Facet: Linde A + tin, tin-lead; tin oxide + tin, vinyl; cerium oxide, tin oxide + plastic.

HEMATITE. Cabochon: sand with silicon carbide 1,200 slurry on leather; or diamond (15-9-6-3 m) + wood, polish diamond (1-1/2 m) + wood, leather; cerium oxide, alumina, Linde A, magnesia + muslin buff, leather, wood. Facet: Linde A, damascus ruby powder, levigated alumina + tin; cerium oxide + wood; tin oxide, Linde A + wax.

HODGKINSONITE. Facet: Linde A + vinyl, tin, tin-lead; tin oxide + plastic, vinyl.

HORN. Scrape smooth, sand with fine emery papers to 4/0 using light oil; polish rottenstone + oil + flannel, felt; final polish dry + tin oxide, rottenstone, etc. + felt, flannel by hand.

HOWLITE. Cabochon: tin oxide + felt; Linde A + leather.

HYPERSTHENE. Facet: Linde A, tin oxide + tin, tin-lead.

IDOCRASE. Cabochon: diamond (9-6-3-1-1/2) + wood, leather; chrome oxide + leather; Linde A + leather. Facet: Linde A, tin oxide + tin, tin-lead; cerium oxide + plastic.

INDERITE. Facet: Linde A + wax; water soluble, use glycerine, kerosene.

IOLITE. Cabochon: Linde A + leather, lead lap; diamond (3-1-1/2 m) + wood, leather. Facet: Linde A, tin oxide + tin, tin-lead, cerium oxide + plastic.

IVORY. Shaved, scraped smooth, sanded to 4/0 emery with light oil; smoothed pumice powder, tripoli with flannel; polish by hand tin oxide + flannel.

JADEITE. Cabochon: diamond (9-6-3-1) + wood, polish diamond (1/2-1/4 m) wood, leather; Linde A, chrome oxide, tin oxide + leather, wood. Facet: Linde A, tin oxide + tin, tin-lead. Flats: grooved wood + diamond.

JET. Cabochon: smooth emery papers to 4/0 + oil; further smooth pumice + flannel, felt sticks; polish rottenstone + oil, rouge + oil, or any convenient polishing agent. Facet: tin oxide, Linde A + tin.

KORNERUPINE. Facet: Linde A + tin, tin-lead.

KURNAKOVITE. Treat like INDERITE.

KYANITE. Facet Linde A, tin oxide + tin, tin-lead.

LAPIS LAZULI. Cabochon: diamond (3-1-1/2-1/4 m) + wood; polish diamond (1/4 m) + leather; Linde A, tin oxide + wood, leather; chrome oxide + leather, wood. No felt. Facet: diamond (3-1-1/2 m) + wood, plastic, vinyl, tin; tin oxide + tin, pewter, pitch.

LAZULITE. Cabochon: chrome oxide, Linde A + leather. Facet: Linde A + tin-lead; tin oxide + pewter, wood, pitch.

LEGRANDITE. Facet: Linde A + tin-lead.

LEPIDOLITE. Cabochon: sand silicon carbide 1,200 slurry + leather; polish Linde A + leather, wood, better to use diamond (6-3-1-1/2 m) + wood, polish diamond (1/4 m) wood, leather.

LEUCITE. Facet: Linde A + lead, tin, tin-lead; cerium oxide + plastic.

LIMESTONE. Tin oxide, with or without oxalic acid + canvas, wood, leather, felt. Large areas: lap silicon carbide

1,200 slurry using wood or metal block; rub with wood block using tin oxide + oxalic acid, or buff with muslin.

LINTONITE. Linde A + leather; cerium oxide + felt.

LUDLAMITE. Facet: Linde A + wax.

MAGNESITE. Facet: Linde A + wax, tin-lead; cerium oxide + vinyl. Facets must be lapped first with 400 silicon carbide + lead.

MALACHITE. Cabochon: tin oxide, Linde A + leather; chrome oxide + leather, wood; tin oxide + wood. May need prior sanding silicon carbide 1,200 slurry on leather, or diamond (3-1 m) + leather, wood. Hand finish, Linde A, tin oxide + slip of damp fleible leather. Flats: lap to 1,200 silicon carbide; polish scored wood + tin oxide, or pitch using tin oxide, Linde A, rouge.

MARBLE. Tin oxide, with or without oxalic acid, on felt, cloth, leather. See also PETOSKEY STONE.

MARCASITE. Cabochons sand first 1,200 silicon carbide slurry on leather; polish Linde A + leather; also use diamond (1/2 m) on leather; also magnesium oxide on flannel, felt.

MEERSCHAUM. Scraped smooth; sanded finest papers; rubbed down fine tripoli, pumice, etc. by hand with cloth; apply melted paraffin wax to surface to fill pores, rebuff with plain cloth.

MESOLITE. Cabochons massive material cerium oxide + felt.

METALS. Generally processed through filing, smoothing with water of ayr stone or fine grit lappings, prepolished with tripoli, final polished rouge on felt, flannel, etc. Treatment jewelry metals dealt with in detail any standard jewelry-making textbook. Metallographic specimen preparation uses initial flatting-smoothing step on emery papers to 4/0 on plate glass, working by hand, followed by diamond smoothing using 6-3-1 micron paste on pellon, plywood, nylon, silk, etc., final polishing on napped cloth 1/4 m diamond, Linde A, magnesium oxide, etc.

MICROLITE. Faceted Linde A + tin, tin-lead.

MIMETITE. Cabochons tin oxide, Linde A + leather; faceted Linde A + wax.

MORDENITE. Massive fibrous polished cerium oxide + felt.

MOTHER OF PEARL. See SHELL.

MUSCOVITE. Treat like LEPIDOLITE.

NACRE. See SHELL.

NATROLITE. Faceted Linde A + tin, tin-lead; cerium oxide + phenolic, plastic.

NEPHRITE. Troublesome undercutter; cabochons best treated by diamond (6-3-1 m) on wood, polished 1/2-1/4 m diamond leather; also Linde A, chrome oxide + leather, but not certain to obtain uniform polish. Faceted, or flats chromium oxide on deeply scored wood; also tin oxide + same.

OBSIDIAN. Treat like GLASS.

ONYX (Calcite). Treat like LIMESTONE.

ONYX (Chalcedony). Treat like CHALCEDONY.

OPAL. Treat like GLASS; diamond (3-1-1/2 m) now preferred for final sanding, scratch removal prior to polish cerium oxide + felt. Facet: Linde A + tin, tin-lead; tin oxide + pewter, wood, pitch, vinyl.

PECTOLITE. Cabochon: Linde A + leather.

PERIDOT. Cabochon: Linde A + leather; diamond (1/4 m) + leather, wood. Facet: diamond (1-1/2 m) + tin, same on wood for large facets; tin oxide + tin; Linde A + tin, tin-lead, phenolic, typemetal; Linde B + tin-lead; Linde A + wax; tin oxide + metal laps, etc. Surest method: diamond.

PETALITE. Facet: Linde A + tin, tin-lead; cerium oxide + plastic, vinyl.

PETOSKEY STONE (Calcite). Cabochon: tin oxide + oxalic acid + muslin, velvet; acid added in sol. to buff prior to use.

PHENAKITE. Facet: tin oxide, Linde A + tin, tin-lead; diamond + metal laps.

PHOSGENITE. Facet: Linde A + wax.

PHOSPHOPHYLLITE. Facet: Linde A + wax.

PIEDMONTITE. Cabochon: diamond (3-1 m) + wood, polish diamond (1/2 m) wood, leather, or Linde A + leather, wood.

PLASTICS. Scrape, file, sand through some successively finer papers (wet-or-dry preferred with water) to 4/0 or about 600 mesh; prepolish pumice or tripoli; polish tin oxide, rouge, cerium oxide, etc., on any buff, but muslin probably about as good as any.

POLLUCITE. Facet: Linde A + tin, tin-lead; cerium oxide + plastic, phenolic.

PORPHYRIES. Treat like GRANITE.

PREHNITE. Cabochon: Linde A, tin oxide, zirconium oxide + leather; diamond (1-1/2 m) + leather, wood. Facet: Linde A + tin, tin-lead, vinyl.

PROUSTITE. Facet: Linde A + wax.

PSILOMELANE CHALCEDONY. Treat like CHALCEDONY.

PYRITE. Treat like BORNITE. Facet: Linde A + wax, wood, scored tin.

PYROXMANGITE. Facet: Linde A + tin.

QUARTZ (Crystalline). Cabochon: wet sanding required to 400 mesh; follow by slurry of 1,200 silicon carbide on leather to remove scratches; polish cerium oxide + felt. Flats: cerium oxide + pellon. Facet: cerium oxide + tin, plastic; tin oxide + tin, typemetal; Linde A + tin, tin-lead. Amethyst ripples eliminated by using metal laps rather than plastic.

REALGAR. Facet: Linde A + wax.

RHODIZITE. Facet: Linde A + tin-lead.

RHODOCHROSITE. Cabochon: sand smooth 1,200 silicon carbide slurry + leather; also can sand diamond (3-1 m) on wood to remove cleavage pits rapidly; polish Linde A + leather, diamond (1/2 m) leather, wood. Flats: lap 1,200 silicon carbide + steel lap; polish tin oxide + pellon, wood. Facet: Linde A + tin-lead, tin; tin oxide + tin.

RHODONITE. Cabochon: treat like RHODOCHROSITE; diamond on wood greatly improves surface. Facet: Linde A + tin-lead, tin; tin oxide + tin.

RUTILE. Facet: Linde A, diamond + tin; Linde B + tin-lead. Pitting problems on facets call for use of diamond.

SAMARSKITE. Cabochon: Linde A + leather; diamond (1/2 m) + leather, wood. Facet: Linde A + tin.

SCAPOLITE. Cabochon: tin oxide, cerium oxide + felt. Facet: Linde A + tin, tin-lead; tin oxide + tin, vinyl; cerium oxide + lead, plastic.

SCHEELITE. Facet: Linde A + tin-lead, lead, vinyl, wax, pitch; tin oxide + vinyl.

SCORZALITE. Treat like LAZULITE.

SERPENTINE. Cabochon: treat like NEPHRITE. Facet: Linde A + wax.

SHATTUCKITE. Cabochon: Linde A, tin oxide, diamond + leather, wood.

SHELL. Chip off adhering growths; grind off remainder as desired; clean dil.

HCl, or HNO_3 (2:1, 3:1 dil.). Porcelain type shells, clams, conches, etc., treat like CALCITE. Pearly types, treat like ABALONE. Abrasives may be applied any convenient method, e.g., cloths, leathers, wood blocks and slips, etc., turned by machine or worked by hand. Muslin buffs various sizes useful for reaching inner surfaces. Inlaid or mosaic flats rubbed flat with abrasives applied to wood blocks, pumice, fine silicon carbide grits, etc., then polished by rubbing with tin oxide slurry with wood blocks or leather-faced blocks, or even felt blocks.

SIDERITE. Facet: Linde A + tin-lead, wax.

SILICON CARBIDE. Facet: diamond + tin, copper, bronze, etc.

SIMPSONITE. Facet: Linde A + tin.

SINHALITE. Facet: Linde A + tin, tin-lead, plastic.

SMITHSONITE. Cabochon: Linde A, tin oxide + felt, leather; diamond (1/2-1/4 m) + leather, wood. Facet: Linde A + tin-lead, lead.

SODALITE. Cabochon: cerium oxide + felt. Facet: Linde A + tin; cerium oxide + plastic, vinyl.

SPHALERITE. Cabochon: Linde A + leather. Facet: Linde A + wax, tin-lead, vinyl. Large facets diamond 1/4 m on wood.

SPHENE. Facet: Linde A + tin, tin-lead, lead; tin oxide + tin, tin-lead, lead.

SPINEL. Cabochon: diamond (9-6-3-1 m) + wood, polish diamond (1/2-1/4 m) wood, leather, phenolic. Sanding can be done with silicon carbide-rubber wheels or 1,200 silicon carbide slurry on hard leather or wood. Facet: Linde A, damascus ruby powder, levigated alumina + tin, tin-typemetal, typemetal; diamond (1/2-1/4 m) + metal lap; chrome oxide, Linde A, tripoli + lead; Linde A + tin to clean up after diamond.

SPODUMENE. Cabochon: Linde A + leather, wood. Facet: Linde A + tin, tin-typemetal, typemetal, lead; tripoli + lead; tin oxide + lead.

STAUROLITE. Facet: Linde A + tin.

STIBIOTANTALITE. Facet: Linde A + tin, tin-lead.

STICHTITE. Cabochon: treat like NEPHRITE.

STRONTIUM TITANATE. Facet:

Linde A + tin, wax; diamond (1/2-1/4 m) + plastic, vinyl, wood, tin.

SULFUR. Facet: Linde A + wax.

TEKTITE. Treat like GLASS.

THAUMASITE. Cabochon: Linde A + leather; tin oxide + felt.

THOMSONITE. Cabochon: Linde A + leather; cerium oxide, tin oxide + felt.

THULITE. Diamond (6-3-1 m) + wood; polish diamond (1/2 m) wood, leather; chrome oxide (stains) + leather; Linde A + leather.

TIGEREYE. Cabochon: diamond (3-1 m) sanding to eliminate undercutting; polish cerium oxide, tin oxide + felt; Linde A + leather. Facet: cerium oxide, tin oxide + tin, plastic.

TOPAZ. Cabochon: sand 1,200 silicon carbide slurry + leather, wood; polish Linde A + leather; diamond (1/2 m) + leather, wood. Facet: Linde A + tin, tin-lead, tin-typemetal, pewter. Large facets polish diamond (1/2-1/4 m) on plywood, end-grain wood, heavily scored tin, phenolic; also on tin, heavily scored, with Linde A.

TORTOISE SHELL. Treat like HORN.

TOURMALINE. Cabochon: sand 1,200 silicon carbide slurry + leather, wood; sand diamond (6-3-1 m) + leather, wood; polish Linde A, tin oxide, diamond (1/2 m) + leather, wood; chrome oxide + leather, wood. Facet: Linde A, tin oxide + tin, tin-type metal, typemetal; tripoli + tin-lead. Catseye types: avoid colored polishing powder unless matches color of stone.

TREMOLITE. Cabochon: diamond (3-1 m) + leather, wood; polish diamond (1/2 m) + leather, wood; Linde A + leather. Facet: Linde A + tin, tin-lead, wax; tin oxide + plastic, phenolic; cerium oxide + vinyl, plastic.

TURQUOISE. Cabochon: Linde A, tin oxide + leather; cerium oxide + felt. Facet: Linde A + tin, wax.

ULEXITE. Cabochon: tin oxide, Linde A + felt, leather, muslin. Flats: Linde A, tin oxide + wood, wax.

UNAKITE. Treat like GRANITE.

VARISCITE. Treat like TURQUOISE.

VIVIANITE. Facet: Linde A + wax.

WILLEMITE. Cabochon: Linde A + leather, wood; diamond (3-1 m) + leather, wood, polish diamond (1/2 m) leather. Facet: Linde A + tin, tin-lead; cerium oxide + plastic, vinyl, tin-lead.

WITHERITE. Facet: Linde A + tin, tin-lead, wax.

WOLLASTONITE. Cabochon: Linde A + leather; cerium oxide + felt.

WONDERSTONE. Treat like BANDED RHYOLITE.

WULFENITE. Facet: Linde A + wax, tin; tin oxide + wax, vinyl.

ZINCITE. Facet: Linde A + wax, tin-lead.

ZIRCON. Facet: Linde A, tin oxide + tin, tin-lead, tin-typemetal, typemetal, pewter; diamond (3-1-1/2-1/4 m) + cast iron.

ZOISITE. Facet: Linde A, tin oxide, cerium oxide + tin; cerium oxide + plastic.

Petrographic Thin Sections

Lap down to 1,200 silicon carbide loose grit on steel lap, plate glass, agate, or other hard flat surface. Smooth 15-micron diamond paste on hardwood plywood disk; repeat with 6- or 3-micron on same; follow with 1-micron diamond paste on pellon. Polish 1/2- or 1/4-micron diamond on napped cloth, or use Linde A, tin oxide, magnesium oxide, or other final polishing agent. Alternatives: Linde A or magnesium oxide on wax; magnesium oxide or Linde A on lead.

Sulfide Ore Thin Sections

Treat as above but remember that all ordinary sulfides are extremely brittle and that preliminary smoothings on plywood with diamond should be prolonged in order to get below damaged zone which may crumble later and introduce scratching particles during fine finishing operations. Undercutting is severe, and it may be desirable to avoid use of pellon or napped cloth to lessen.

References: D. L. Hoffman, *Comprehensive Faceting Instructions* (Spokane, Wash.: Aurora Lapidary Books, 1968).

C. Holtzapffel, *Turning and Mechanical Manipulation* (London, 1850), vol. 3, *Abrasive and Miscellaneous Processes.*

L. Quick and H. Leiper, *Gemcraft* (Philadelphia: Chilton Company, 1959).

C. I. A. Ritchie, *Carving Shells and Cameos* (London: Arthur Barker, 1970).

J. Sinkankas, *Gem Cutting,* 2d ed. (New York: Van Nostrand Reinhold, 1962).

F. J. Sperisen, *The Art of the Lapidary*, rev. ed. (Milwaukee: Bruce, 1961).

G. Vargas and M. Vargas, *Faceting for Amateurs* (Thermal, Calif.: privately pub., 1969).

J. D. Willems, *Gem Cutting* (Peoria, Ill.: Charles A. Bennett, 1948).

FACET GEM ANGLES FOR CROWN AND PAVILION MAIN FACETS

The reference plane is that passing through the girdle; all angles are internal, measured from the girdle to the facet plane. Very wide variations in angles are to be noted in the table below, and aside from original studies by Eppler, Johnsen, Maier, Rösch, and Tolkowsky (see references below), appear to be based mainly upon subjective impressions of brilliancy rather than any scientific analysis or light measurement. On the whole, it is noted that the proportions of most faceted gemstones approach those of diamond, with necessary adjustments to take into consideration lower refractive powers. Perhaps the most radical changes in proportions were advocated by Eppler (1938), who proposed cutting low refractive index stones, e.g., opal and fluorite, with very low crown angles and increased pavilion angles, reversing the proportion changes in gemstones of higher refractive index so that crown angles were greatly increased while pavilion angles were decreased. The results were faceted gems that looked as if their tops had been sheared off in the one case, or bulged upward in the other. His recommendations were largely ignored. While the consensus fixes permissible angles for diamond within relatively narrow limits, this is not so for the other gemstones, and it is for this reason, and also for the lack of evidence of a scientific nature to the contrary, that the author (Sinkankas, 1962) recommended simplified angles based upon ranges of refractive index (compare Schlegel and Sperisen). Even among diamonds in which much is made of "perfect" proportions, it is illuminating to examine the discussions by Eulitz (1968) and Bruton (1970).

Ideal Brilliant Cut

Standard brilliant cut, with very small culet facet. Crown angle = 34.5°, pavilion angle = 40.75°, angle at apex of pavilion = 98.5°. Taking diameter at 100%, then the table facet diameter is 53%, the height of the crown is 16.2%, the depth of the pavilion is 43.1%, and the thickness of the girdle is 0.7%-1.7%. The total depth of the stone is 59.3% plus girdle percentage.

Reference: R. T. Liddicoat, Jr., and L. L. Copeland, *The Jewelers' Manual* (Los Angeles: Gemological Institute of America, 1967).

Table of Crown and Pavilion Main Facet Angles

Gemstone	Crown	Pavilion	Reference	Gemstone	Crown	Pavilion	Reference
Actinolite	40°	40°	10		35°	39°	11
	41	42	14		43	39	13
Almandite	49.2	39	4		41	42	14
	36	40	11	Andradite	46.6	39	4
	37	42	12		40	40	10
Amber	44.9	40.6	4		37	41	11
	40-50	43	10		37	42	13
	38	42	11		37	42	14
	42	43	14	Anglesite	40	40	10
Amblygonite	40	40	10		38	40	14
	42	43	14	Anhydrite	40-50	43	10
Analcime	40-50	43	10		42	43	14
	43	44	14	Apatite	43	39	8
Anatase	30	40	14		40	40	10
Andalusite	45	41	8		35	39	11
	40	40	10		43	39	13

Gemstone	Crown	Pavilion	Reference	Gemstone	Crown	Pavilion	Reference
	41°	42°	14	Clinozoisite	40°	40°	10
Apophyllite	40-50	43	10	Colemanite	40	40	10
	42	43	14		42	43	14
Aragonite	40	40	10	Corundum	50	39	3
	41	42	14		49.4	39	4
Augelite	40-50	43	10		37	42	6
	42	43	14		39	49.5	7
Axinite	40	40	10		37	42	8
	35	39	11		40	40	10
	40	42	14		36	40	11
Azurite	40	40	10		37	42	13
	40	41-35	14		40	42	14
Barite	40	40	10	Crocoite	30-40	37-40	10
	41	42	14		32	40	14
Benitoite	37	42	8	Cuprite	30-40	37-40	10
	40	40	10		28	39	14
	36	40	11	Danburite	40	40	10
	39	41	14		35	39	11
Beryl	50.8-54.3	39.7-39.1	4		41	42	14
	45	42	6	Datolite	40	40	10
	39.1	54.2	7		41	42	14
	42	43	8	Diamond	34.5	40.8	1
	40-50	43	10		41.7	38.4	2
	37	41	11		41.1	38.5	3
	42	43	13		41.1	38.7	5
	42	43	14		33.1	40.1	5
Beryllonite	40-50	43	10		36	41	6
	38	42	11		38.6	41.2	7
	42	43	14		38	42	11
Boracite	40	42	14		35	41	13
Brazilianite	40	40	10		32	40	14
	42	43	13		34.5	40.8	15
	41	42	14	Diopside	40	40	10
Bytownite	38	42	11		35	39	11
Calcite	40-50	43	10		41	42	14
	43	44	14	Dioptase	40	40	10
Cassiterite	30-40	37-40	10		35	39	11
	37	41	11		41	42	14
	36	40	14	Dolomite	42	43	14
Celestite	40	40	10	Enstatite	40	40	10
	41	42	14		35	39	11
Cerussite	40	40	10		41	42	14
	38	41	14	Epidote	37	42	8
Chondrodite	40	40	10		40	40	10
	41	42	14		35	39	11
Chrysoberyl	49.9	39	4		37	42	13
	37	42	6		40	42	14
	40	40	10	Euclase	40	40	10
	36	40	11		35	39	11
	37	42	13		41	42	14
	39	42	14	Feldspar	40-50	43	10
Cinnabar	30-40	37-40	10		42	43	13
	26	39	14		42	44	14
				Fibrolite	40	40	10

Gemstone	Crown	Pavilion	Reference	Gemstone	Crown	Pavilion	Reference
	35°	39°	11	Opal	13°	44°	4
	41	42	14		40-50	43	10
Fluorite	8	44.4	4		41	45	11
	40-50	43	10		41	45	13
	41	45	11		43	44	14
	41	45	13	Orthoclase	42.7	40.9	4
	43	45	14		39	43	11
Garnet	37-43	39-40	8	Periclase	40	40	10
	40	40	10	Peridot	51.6	39.1	4
	37	42	13		43	39	8
	37	42	14		40	40	10
Glass	40-50	43	10		35	39	11
Grossular	40	40	10		43	39	13
	35	39	11		41	42	14
	37	42	14	Petalite	40-50	43	10
Hambergite	40	40	10		42	43	14
	42	43	14	Phenakite	43	39	8
Hodgkin- sonite	40	40	10		40	40	10
	40	41	14		35	39	11
Hypersthene	35	39	11		41	42	14
Idocrase	40	40	10	Phosgenite	36	40	14
	35	39	11	Phospho- phyllite	40	40	10
	40	42	14		41	42	14
Inderite	43	44	14	Pollucite	40-50	43	10
Iolite	40-50	43	10		39	43	11
	38	42	11		42	43	14
	42	43	14	Prehnite	40	40	10
Kornerupine	40	40	10		41	42	14
	35	39	11	Proustite	30-40	37-40	10
	40	41	14		39	43	11
Kurnakovite	43	44	14		30	40	14
Kyanite	40	40	10	Pyrope	49.9	39	4
	35	39	11		40	40	10
	40	42	14		35	39	11
Labradorite	37	41	11		37	42	13
Lazulite	41	42	14		37	42	14
Legrandite	40	42	14	Pyroxmangite	40	41	14
Leucite	40-50	43	10	Quartz	44.9	40.6	4
	43	44	14		45	42	6
Ludlamite	40	42	14		39	54.85	7
Magnesite	40	40	10		42	43	8
	42	43	14		40-50	43	10
Microlite	30-40	37-40	10		38	42	11
	42	43	14		42	43	13
Moldavite	40-50	43	10		42	43	14
	41	45	11	Realgar	31	40	14
	43	44	14	Rhodizite	40	40	10
Natrolite	40-50	43	10		41	42	14
	43	44	14	Rhodo- chrosite	40	40	10
Obsidian	40-50	43	10		41	42	14
	43	44	14	Rhodonite	40	40	10
Oligoclase	38	42	11		40	42	14
				Rutile	34	41	8

Table of Crown and Pavilion Main Facet Angles (*Continued*)

Gemstone	Crown	Pavilion	Reference
	30-40°	37-40°	10
	38	42	11
	34	41	13
	30	40	14
Scapolite	48.9	40	4
	40-50	43	10
	38	42	11
	42	43	14
Scheelite	40	40	10
	38	41	14
Serpentine	40-50	43	10
	42	43	14
Silicon carbide	30-40	37-40	10
	38	40	14
Simpsonite	30-40	37-40	10
Sinhalite	40	40	10
	41	42	14
Smithsonite	40	40	10
	40	41	14
Sodalite	40-50	43	10
	43	44	14
Spessartine	40	40	10
	36	40	11
	37	42	13
	37	42	14
Sphalerite	30-40	37-40	10
	38	42	11
	33	40	14
Sphene	30-40	37-40	10
	37	41	11
	38	41	14
Spinel	50.5	39	4
	37	42	6
	39	50.3	7
	37	42	8
	40	40	10
	35	39	11
	37	42	13
	40	41	14
Spodumene	51.6	39.1	4
	43	39	6
	43	39	8
	40	40	10
	35	39	11
	43	39	13
	40	42	14
Staurolite	36	40	11
Stibio-tantalite	30-40	37-40	10
	32	40	14
Strontium titanate	30-40°	37-40°	10
Sulfur	38	41	14
Taaffeite	40	40	10
Tektite	40-50	43	10
	43	44	14
Topaz	53	39	3
	52.9	39.1	4
	43	39	6
	39.1	52.9	7
	42	40.5	8
	40	40	10
	36	40	11
	43	39	13
	41	42	14
Tourmaline	53.2	39.1	4
	43	39	6
	39.1	52.5	7
	43	39	8
	40	40	10
	36	40	11
	43	39	13
	41	42	14
Tremolite	40	40	10
	40	42	14
Uvarovite	40	40	10
	37	41	11
	37	42	13
	37	42	14
Vivianite	42	43	14
Willemite	40	40	10
	35	39	11
	40	42	14
Witherite	40	40	10
	41	42	14
Wulfenite	30-40	37-40	10
	33	40	14
Zincite	30-40	37-40	10
	36	41	14
Zircon	47	38.75	3
	45.8	38.9	4
	43	40	6
	38.9	46.6	7
	43	40	8
	40	40	10
	36	40	11
	35-37	41-42	13
	38	41	14

References:
1. M. Tolkowsky, *Diamond Design* (London: E. and F. N. Spon, 1919).
2. A. Johnsen, "Form und Brillanz der Brillanten," *Zs. Krist.* 64, no. 5/6 (1926): pp. 495-98.
3. S. Rösch, "Beitrag zum Brillanzproblem," *Zs. Krist.* 65, no. 1/2 (1927): pp. 46-68.

4. W. F. Eppler. "Die Brillanz durchsichtiger Edelsteine," *Fortschritte d. Min.* 23 (1938), 40 pp.

5. W. F. Eppler, "Beitrag zum Brillanzproblem," *Zentralbl. Min.,* part A (1940), pp. 93-96.

6. D. J. Willems, *Gem Cutting* (Peoria, Ill.: Charles A. Bennett, 1948).

7. W. Maier, *Brillanten und Perlen* (Stuttgart: Schweizerbart'sche Verlagsbuchhandlung, 1949).

8. L. Quick and H. Leiper, *Gemcraft* (Philadelphia: Chilton Co., 1959).

9. F. J. Sperisen, *The Art of the Lapidary* (Milwaukee: Bruce Publishing Co., 1961).

10. J. Sinkankas, *Gem Cutting,* 2d ed. (New York: Van Nostrand Reinhold, 1962).

11. C. J. Parsons, "Charles Schlegel's Facet Angles," *Gems and Minerals,* no. 342 (1966), pp. 27-29.

12. W. R. Eulitz, "The Optics of Brilliant-Cut Diamonds," *Gems and Gemology* 12, no. 9 (1968): 263-71.

13. D. L. Hoffman, *Comprehensive Faceting Instructions* (Spokane, Wash.: Aurora Lapidary Books, 1968).

14. G. Vargas and M. Vargas, *Faceting for Amateurs* (Thermal, Calif.: privately pub., 1969).

15. E. Bruton, *Diamonds* (London: N. A. G. Press, 1970).

Table Comparing Crown and Pavilion Main Facet Angle Recommendations

	Crown angles				Pavilion angles			
R.I.	Ref. 9	10	11	14	Ref. 9	10	11	14
1.40		40-50	41			43	45	
1.43		40-50	41	44-43		43	45	45
1.48		40-50	41	43		43	45	44
1.50	42	40-50	39	42-43	43	43	43	43-44
1.53	42	40-50	38	42	43	43	42	43
1.55	42	40-50	38	42-43	43	43	42	42-43
1.56	42	40-50	37-38	42	43	43	41-42	43
1.58	42	40-50	37	42	43	43	41	42-43
1.60	42	40-50	37	40-41	43	43-40	41	42
1.61	40	40	36	41	43	40	40	42
1.62	40	40	36	41	43	40	40	42
1.63	40	40	35	41	43	40	39	42
1.70	40	40	35	40	43	40	39	42
1.71	37	40	35	40	42	40	39	42
1.73	37	40	35	40	42	40	39	41-42
1.74	37	40	36		42	40	40	
1.76	37	40	36	39-40	42	40	40	41-42
1.80	37	40	36		42	40	40	
1.81	43	40			40	40		
1.82	43	40	37		40	40	41	
1.92	43	40	37	38	40	40	41	41
1.95		40	37	38		40	41	41
2.00		30-40	37	38		37-40	41	41
2.35		30-40		33		37-40		40
2.37		30-40	38			37-40	42	
2.42		30-40	38	32	41	37-40	42	40
2.50		30-40	38	30	41	37-40	42	40
2.62	32		38		41		42	
2.67	32			30	41			40
2.79	32		39		41		43	
2.90	32		39		41		43	
3.09			39				43	

Note: References no. 9, 10, and 11 are ranges, with no. 14 entries added for comparison.

Part 5 / Metals and Jewelry Data

METALS USED IN LAPIDARY AND JEWELRY WORK

ALUMINUM. Al. At. no. 13, at. wgt. 26.97, G = 2.699, MP = 1,220° F. (659.7° C.), BP = 3,272° F. (1,800° C.). Silvery-white malleable and ductile metal (second most malleable and sixth most ductile), very soft. Resistant to conc. HNO_3 and acetic acids; reacts readily with HCl and conc. H_2SO_4, also with alkalies; corroded readily by numerous soaps, detergents, etc. Anodizing improves corrosion resistance by providing tough adherent film Al_2O_3. "Thermit" is a mixture of Al and ferric oxide (Fe_2O_3) powders, ignited by powdered ·Mg to yield molten iron. Aluminum has been much used in lapidary machinery but tends to corrode badly unless kept dry or protected by paint. Some of the metal was used in jewelry when it was so rare as to be a novelty.

ALUMINUM ALLOYS. Pure Al is designated 2S; stronger is alloy 3S (contains 1.25% Mn) and much used in cooking utensils, appliances, tubing, extruded shapes, etc.; 4S (1.2% Mn, 1.0% Mg) also used extensively; high-strength alloys that must be heat-treated include 17S (4.0% Cu, 0.5% Mn, 0.5% Mg) and 24S (4.4% Cu, 0.5% Mn, 1.5% Mg).

ANTIMONY. Sb. At. no. 51, at. wgt. 121.76, G = 6.691, MP = 1,167° F. (630.5° C.), BP = 2,516° F. (1,380° C.). Very brittle, bright silvery metal. Small amounts extensively used in alloys (e.g., typemetal).

ARSENIC. As. At. no. 33, at. wgt. 74.91, G = 5.73, MP = sublimes when heated. Steel-gray brittle metal. Alloying constituent. At red heat very readily alloys with many metals, usually with embrittlement; care must be taken to avoid treating any mineral containing arsenic with platinum wire or in Pt crucibles.

BABBITT METALS. Used as low-friction liners in bearings. Typical composition 3.0% Cu, 75.0% Sn, 12.0% Sb, 10.0% Pb; MP = 363° F. (184°C.), FP = 583° F. (306° C.), poured at 710° F. (376° C.).

BISMUTH. Bi. At. no. 83, at. wgt. 209, G = 9.75, MP = 520° F. (271° C.), BP = 2,642° F. (1,450° C.). White brittle metal with pinkish hue. Much used in low-melt alloys.

BRASSES. Alloys of copper primarily, with zinc in various ratios and with or without other metals in small quantities. Semired brass (ASTM 5B): 76% Cu, 3% Sn, 6% Pb, 15% Zn; yellow brass (ASTM 6A): 71% Cu, 1% Sn, 3% Pb, 25% Zn; commercial no. 1 yellow brass (ASTM 6B): 66% Cu, 1% Sn, 3% Pb, 30% Zn; 6-40 yellow brass (ASTM 6C): 60% Cu, 1% Sn, 1% Pb, 37.85% Zn. MPs = 930 (499° C.) to 2,075° F. (1,135° C.); those mentioned above are in the lower range.

BRITANNIA METAL. Used as a substitute for pewter in utensils and the like. Less likely to tarnish than pewter. Comp.: 91% Sn, 7% Sb, 2% Cu; can be rolled.

BRONZES. Alloys of copper and tin, with additions in small amounts of other metals. A typical bronze is 88% Cu, 11% Sn, 1% Zn; a hard bronze is 78% Cu, 10% Sn, 1.5% Zn, 0.5% Pb. Commercial bronze is 86.5% Cu, 10% Sn, 2% Zn, 0.5% Ni. Aluminum bronze: 87.5% Cu, 3.50% Fe, 9.25% Al. The bronze MP range extends over approx. 570° F. (300° C.) to 1,925° F. (1,050° C.). Aluminum bronzes MPs 1,130° F. (610° C.) to 1,925° F. (1,050° C.).

CADMIUM. Cd. At. no. 48, at. wgt. 112.41, G = 8.65, MP = 610° F. (321° C.), BP = 1,413° F. (767° C.). Bluish-white metal, readily tarnishing to blue gray. Soft, malleable. Used mostly in alloys and protective platings; lowers flow point of silver solders.

CHROMIUM. Cr. At. no. 24, at. wgt. 52, G = 7.1, MP = 2,939° F. (1,615° C.), BP = 3,993° F. (2,200° C.). Very hard silvery metal with slight bluish tinge. Used in platings.

COPPER. Cu. At. no. 29, at. wgt. 63.5, G = 8.94, MP = 1,981° F. (1,083° C.), BP = 4,172° F. (2,300° C.). Bright reddish when fresh but rapidly tarnishing to reddish-brown; commonly forms greenish film or patina. Sol. HNO_3, also in hot H_2SO_4. Soft malleable, ductile; second only to silver in heat conduction; excellent electrical conductor. Used essentially pure or with slight additions of other elements to improve physical characteristics. Much used in brasses and bronzes. Used alone in jewelry, or as base for enameling. Readily stains when in contact with skin, producing greenish discolorations unless coated with transparent lacquer after fabrication. Principal alloying metal in sterling and coin silvers, also much used in alloying golds.

GOLD. Au. At. no. 79, at. wgt. 197, G = 19.32, MP = $1,945°$ F. ($1,063°$ C.), BP = $4,914°$ F. ($2,600°$ C.). Most malleable and ductile of metals, e.g., 1 cu. in. can be beaten into a foil of less than 5-millionths in. thickness, covering an area of over 14,000 square ft. Extremely soft when pure. Not affected by most acids and other reagents but sol. A. R. (1 pt. HNO_3 + 3 pts. HCl); also sol. in sol. of 4 pts. HCl + 1 pt. MnO_2. Amalgamates very readily with mercury. May be cleaned with HNO_3 when quite pure, also HF, the latter removing silicate minerals which may enclose the gold; rust stains removed by warm oxalic acid sol.

GOLD ALLOYS. In jewelry, pure gold is assigned the value 24 karats, meaning of 24 standard parts by weight, 24 are gold; lesser values, e.g., 12 kt express lesser amounts of gold, in this case, 50% by wgt.

Carat Versus the Precious Metal Karat

The official metric carat of 200 mg is a weight but the precious metal karat expresses the weight proportions of gold in alloys of this metal and certain other metals. The "fineness" of the alloy is expressed in 24 parts or "karats" such that pure gold is 24 karat, and lesser alloys given lesser karat values as follows.

Alloy (Karats)	Proportion of gold (24ths)	Proportion by weight
9	9/24	3/8
12	12/24	1/2
14	14/24	7/12
16	16/24	2/3
18	18/24	3/4
20	20/24	5/6
22	22/24	11/12
24	24/24	(all gold)

Note: To convert karats into parts of gold in milligrams per gram, multiply karats by 41.6667.

Karats Compared to Thousandths

Use the table just below to determine parts of gold that must be added to an alloy to give the corresponding karat value. Based on a total one thousand parts final weight.

Karat	Parts	Karat	Parts
1	41.66	13	541.46
2	83.33	14	585.00
3	125.00	15	625.00
4	166.66	16	666.66
5	208.33	17	708.33
6	250.00	18	750.00
7	291.66	19	791.66
8	333.00	20	883.33
9	375.00	21	875.00
10	416.66	22	916.66
11	458.33	23	958.33
12	500.00	24	1,000.00

Typical Gold Jewelry Alloys

(*Expressed in wgt. % of constituents and melting and flow points*)

Alloy	Color	Au	Cu	Ag	Zn	MP		FP		
10 kt	Yellow	41.7	43.8	5.5	9.0	1,574° F.	(857° C.)	1,675° F.	(913° C.)	(Wise)
10 kt	Yellow	41.7	48.0	6.6	3.7	1,609	876	1,710	932	(Wise)
10 kt	Yellow	41.7	40.8	11.7	5.8	1,447	786	1,634	890	(Wise)
10 kt	Yellow	–	–	–	–	1,510	821	1,530	832	(W. Bros.)
10 kt	Green	41.7	9.1	48.9	0.3	1,675	913	1,724	940	(Wise)
10 kt	Green	–	–	–	–	1,470	799	1,510	821	(W. Bros.)
10 kt	Pink	–	–	–	–	1,690	921	1,720	938	(W. Bros.)

Typical Gold Jewelry Alloys (*Continued*)
(*Expressed in wgt. % of constituents and melting and Flow points*)

Alloy	Color	Au	Cu	Ag	Zn	MP		FP		
10 kt	White	–	–	–	–	1,760	960	1,790	976	(W. Bros.)
14 kt	Yellow	58.3	31.3	4.0	6.4	1,526	830	1,625	885	(Wise)
14 kt	Yellow	58.3	29.2	8.3	4.2	1,499	815	1,625	885	(Wise)
14 kt	Yellow	58.3	39.7	10.0	2.0	1,499	815	1,609	876	(Wise)
14 kt	Yellow	58.3	25.0	16.5	0.2	1,476	802	1,567	858	(Wise)
14 kt	Yellow	58.3	16.8	24.8	0.1	1,476	802	1,549	843	(Wise)
14 kt	Yellow	–	–	–	–	1,555	846	1,580	860	(W. Bros.)
14 kt	Green	58.3	6.5	35.0	0.2	1,535	835	1,645	896	(Wise)
14 kt	Green	–	–	–	–	1,590	865	1,630	888	(W. Bros.)
14 kt	Pink	–	–	–	–	1,650	899	1,670	910	(W. Bros.)
14 kt	Red	–	–	–	–	1,660	904	1,680	915	(W. Bros.)
14 kt	White	–	–	–	–	1,690	921	1,810	988	(W. Bros.)
18 kt	Yellow	75.0	10.0	15.0	0.0	1,620	882	1,715	935	(Wise)
18 kt	Yellow	–	–	–	–	1,640	893	1,670	910	(W. Bros.)
18 kt	Green	–	–	–	–	1,750	954	1,800	982	(W. Bros.)
18 kt	White	–	–	–	–	1,650	899	1,680	915	(W. Bros.)
20 kt	Yellow	–	–	–	–	1,810	988	1,830	999	(W. Bros.)
22 kt	Yellow	–	–	–	–	1,850	1,010	1,870	1,021	(W. Bros.)

Sources: E. M. Wise, *Gold* (New York: Van Nostrand, 1964).
Wildberg Brothers Smelting and Refining Company Brochure (San Francisco).

Gold Solders

Quality no.	Color	Approximate MP		Recommended with
8	Yellow	1,210° F.	(654° C.)	8 kt yellow gold
10	Yellow	1,225	663	10 kt yellow gold
10	White	1,250	677	10 kt white gold
10	Green	1,300	704	10 kt green gold
10 (hard)	Yellow	1,235	678	10 kt yellow gold, new work
12	Yellow	1,250	677	12 kt yellow gold
14	Yellow	1,280	693	14 kt yellow gold
14	White	1,290	699	14 kt white gold
14	Green	1,320	716	14 kt green gold
14	Red	1,330	721	14 kt red or pink gold
14 (hard)	Yellow	1,350	732	14 kt yellow gold, new work
18	Yellow	1,500	816	18 kt yellow gold
18	White	1,550	843	18 kt white gold
18 (weld.)	White	1,600	871	18 kt white gold welding
20	White			18 kt white gold

Source: Wildberg Brothers Smelting and Refining Company, brochure (San Francisco).

Gold Solder Compositions

Au	Ag	Cu	Zn	Cd	MP		FP	
33.3	31.0	28.0	7.7		1,359° F.	(737° C.)	1,486° F.	(808° C.)
41.7	32.0	16.3	10.0		1,335	724	1,380	749
41.7	35.0	21.8	1.5		1,395	757	1,447	786
41.7	24.0	16.3	9.0	9.0	1,189	643	1,296	702

Gold Solder Compositions (*Continued*)

Au	Ag	Cu	Zn	Cd	MP		FP	
50.0	30.5	17.5	2.0		1,427	775	1,483	806
58.3	18.0	12.0	11.7		1,328	720	1,389	754
58.3	20.8	19.0	1.9		1,459	793	1,526	830
66.7	15.0	15.0	3.4		1,465	796	1,519	826

Source: E. M. Wise, *Gold* (New York: Van Nostrand, 1964).

Lost Wax Casting Gold Alloys: Contraction After Casting

Platinum contracts	1.59%
Gold contracts	1.49%
Zinc contracts	1.51%

Easy-Flowing Gold Casting Alloys

14 kt pale gold	Gold	58.5%	Alloy MP = 1,634° F. (890° C.)
	Silver	30.0	Casting Temp. = 1,994° F. (1,090° C.)
	Copper	11.5	G = 13.7
		100.0%	

18 kt reddish yellow	Gold	75.0%	Alloy MP = 1,607° F. (875° C.)
	Silver	10.0	Casting temp. = 1,967° F. (1,075° C.)
	Copper	15.0	G = 15.3
		100.0%	

Reference: W. Mahler, *Diebeners Goldschmiede-Jahrbuch,* no. 42 (Stuttgart: Ruehle-Diebener Verlag, 1960).

IRIDIUM. Ir. At. no. 77, at. wgt. 193, G = 22.42, MP = 4,262° F. (2,350° C.) [International Nickel gives MP = 4,449° F. (2,454° C.)], BP = over 4,800° C. White very hard metal, difficult to work. Heaviest of all elements except for osmium. Used in alloying Pt for jewelry (Pt 90%, Ir 10%).

IRON. Fe. At. no. 26, at. wgt. 55.85, G = 7.86, MP = 2,795° F. (1,535° C.), BP = 5,432° F. (3,000° C.). When pure silver-white, very ductile, magnetic. Very rarely used pure and mostly alloyed with carbon as in steels, and with a number of other elements to form a wide range of steels. Sol. by any mix H_2SO_4 + HCl; readily sol. with emission poisonous nitrogen oxide fumes in HNO_3; readily corrodes in moist atmospheres. Alnico is a very magnetic brittle alloy of Fe, Al, Ni, Co. Stainless steels are very tough, difficultly worked alloys in large variety which contain Cr as the principal alloying metal, with Ni, Mo,

Cu, W, Si. Iron has been used in some types of antique jewelry as a novelty metal.

LEAD. Pb. At. no. 82, at. wgt. 207, G = 11.35, MP = 621° F. (327° C.), BP = 2,948° F. (1,620° C.). Bluish-white, very soft, ductile, and malleable metal, rapidly tarnishing to dull light gray. Very resistant to corrosion; much used for acid containers and piping. Sol. HNO_3, but only slightly affected by H_2SO_4, HCl, or HF. Compounds slow cumulative poisons. Much used in alloys.

LEAD SOLDERS. Common soft: 50% Pb, 50% Sn (slight amount of Sb added), MP = 360° F. (182° C.), FP = 415° F. (213° C.); others vary proportions of Pb:Sn, with resulting increases in FPs. At red heat of silver, lead combines very readily and ruins any work in which common solder has been employed.

MERCURY. Hg. At. no. 80, at. wgt. 200.6, G = 13.55, MP = –38° F. (–39° C.),

BP = 675° F. (357° C.). Brilliant silvery metal, the only element fluid at room temperatures. Fair conductor of heat and electricity. Amalgamates very readily with gold, silver, etc., and must be kept away from these metals to avoid accidental harm to surface finishes. Sol. acids. Vapors poisonous and the metal must not be allowed to spill or to be exposed in large surface areas within closed rooms.

NICKEL. Ni. At. no. 28, at. wgt. 58.7, G = 8.90, MP = 2,651° F. (1,455° C.), BP = 5,252° F. (2,900° C.). White color, hard, ductile metal, malleable; somewhat magnetic. Much used in alloys and pure for high-temperature applications as crucibles; also much used in platings and in alloys of gold. Slowly sol. HCl, H_2SO_4, acetic acid, and other acids, rapidly sol. HNO_3. Monel metal is a useful alloy of 67% Ni, 28.4% Cu, with small amounts of Fe, Mn. Alnico magnet alloy contains Fe, Al, Ni, Co.

NICKEL SILVER. An alloy sometimes used in jewelry containing 60% Cu, 20% Ni, 20% Zn. MP = 1,959° F. (1,070° C.).

PALLADIUM. Pd. At. no. 46, at. wgt. 106.7, G = 12.16, MP = 2,827° F. (1,553° C.), BP = 3,992° F. (2,200° C.). White, ductile metal, fairly hard and used primarily in jewelry alloys or as platings of jewelry. Jewelry alloy: 95.5% Pd, 4.5% Ru.

PEWTER. Alloy of tin with not over 20% Pb. Dull tin-white when fresh but rapidly tarnishing to pale lead gray with dull surface. MP = about 500° F. (260° C.) or somewhat higher depending on composition. A typical modern pewter alloy contains 85% Sn, 7% Sb, 4% Cu, 4% Pb.

PLATINUM. Pt. At. no. 78, at. wgt. 195.23, G = 21.37, MP = 3,223° F. (1,773° C.), BP = c. 4,300°C. Tin-white metal, malleable, ductile, not hard unless alloyed. Does not oxidize in air at any temperature and thus makes it extremely useful for crucibles in which high temperature meltings or fusions are to take place. Insol. acids except in A.R. Typical jewelry alloy: 90% Pt, 10% Ir, or 95% Pt, 5% Ru; a softer alloy contains 95% Pt, 5% Ir. MP 5% Ir-platinum alloy = 3,225° F. (1,774° C.), FP = 3,265° F. (1,796° C.). MP 10% Ir-Pt = 3,250° F. (1,788° C.), FP = 3,280° F. (1,804° C.). MP 15% Ir-Pt = 3,310° F. (1,821° C.), FP = 3,340° F. (1,838° C.). (See table below)

Source: temperature data, Wildberg Brothers Smelting and Refining Company.

RHODIUM. Rh. At. no. 45, at. wgt. 102.91, G = 12.5, MP = 3,605° F. (1,985° C.), BP = over 2,500° C. Silver-white metal, much harder than pure Pt or Pd. Used to alloy Pt but primarily used as brilliant platings, especially over silver and silver alloys.

RUTHENIUM. Ru. At. no. 44, at. wgt. 101.7, G = 12.2, MP = 4,530° F. (2,499° C.), BP = over 2,700° C. Hard, white brittle metal, practically unworkable. Used in small amounts to harden Pd or Pt, being about twice as effective as Ir.

SILVER. Ag. At. no. 47, at. wgt. 107.9, G = 10.50, MP = 1,761° F. (960.5° C.), BP = 3,542° F. (1,950° C.). Brilliant white, somewhat less malleable and ductile

Platinum Solders

Grade	Type	Approximate MP	
1,100	Soft	1,633° F.	(890° C.)
1,200	Medium	1,782	972
1,300	Medium hard	1,831	999
1,400	Hard	2,080	1,138
1,500	Extra hard	2,227	1,220
1,600	Special welding	2,376	1,302
0	Welding extra hard	2,975	1,635
1	Welding hard	2,925	1,607
3	Welding medium hard	2,900	1,593
4	Welding medium	2,875	1,580

Source: Wildberg Brothers Smelting and Refining Company.

than gold. Best metal conductor of heat and electricity. Readily tarnishes when exposed to sulfur compounds. Sol. in HNO_3 but only v. slowly attacked by H_2SO_4 even when hot; HCl has no effect.

SILVER ALLOYS. In jewelry, the term "fine" refers to pure silver, while "sterling" refers to an alloy made with copper, in which silver comprises 925 parts out of 1,000, or 92.5% by weight. Coin silver is 90% silver and 10% copper.

SILVER SOLDERS. These are made in a wide range of compositions, some for jewelry purposes, and others for industrial uses where high-strength and heat-resistant joints are required. (See table below.)

TIN. Sn. At. no. 50, at. wgt. 118.7, G = 5.75 (gray tin), 6.55 (rhombic tin), 7.31 (white or tetragonal tin). MP = $450°$ F. $(232°$ C.), BP = $4,100°$ F. $(2,260°$ C.). Ordinary, or white tin, is very malleable at room temperatures but at higher temperatures it becomes increasingly brittle. When chilled to below freezing, down to about $-58°$ F. $(-50°$ C.) it changes to gray tin and crumbles. Slowly reacts with dil. sols. HCl or H_2SO_4; rapidly with hot H_2SO_4; sol. HNO_3 and very rapidly when hot. Also sol. hydroxide sols. Used in solders, tubing, plating, in polishing laps, and the white oxide is used as a polishing agent.

WHITE METALS. Low-melt casting alloys with tin-white appearance after casting and with good plating characteristics. A typical composition: 72% Sn, 22% Pb, 2% Cd, 2% Zn, 2% Cu.

WOODS METAL. Low-melt casting alloy, typical: 50% Bi, 25% Pb, 12.5% Sn, 12.5% Cd.

ZINC. Zn. At. no. 30, at. wgt. 65.4, G = 7.14, MP = $788°$ F. $(420°$ C.), BP = $1,665°$ F. $(907°$ C.). Bluish-white metal when fresh, tarnishing to dull pale gray. Very pure Zn reacts v. slowly with acids, but slightly impure metal rapidly with HCl or H_2SO_4, liberating H gas; also sol. HNO_3 and other acids. Much used in plating, in alloys, and in solders.

TESTING FINENESS OF PRECIOUS METALS

Standard acid test fluids for testing the fineness of precious metals alloys are as follows by weight:

8 kt Gold	1 part nitric acid to 1 part water
14 kt Gold	pure nitric acid, concentrated
18 kt Gold	40 parts nitric acid, 15 parts water, 1 part hydrochloric acid
20 kt Gold	12 parts nitric acid, 5 parts water, 1 part hydrochloric acid
Platinum	20 parts hydrochloric acid, 11 parts nitric acid, 6 grams potassium nitrate
Silver	10 grams potassium chromate dissolved in 100 cc of water; carefully add 7 grams of conc. sulfuric acid

Selected Silver Solders

Type	Ag	Cu	Zn	Cd	MP		FP		Source
ASTM 1	10	52	38	0.5	1,510° F.	(821° C.)	1,600° F.	(871° C.)	
2	20	45	35	0.5	1,430	777	1,500	825	
3	20	45	30	5	1,430	777	1,500	825	
4	45	30	25		1,250	677	1,370	743	
5	50	34	16		1,280	693	1,425	774	
6	65	20	15		1,280	693	1,325	718	
7	70	20	10		1,335	714	1,390	754	
8	80	16	4		1,360	738	1,460	793	
"Easy-Flo"	50	15.5	16.5	18	1,160	627	1,175	635	
Hard #1					1,425	774			(W. Bros.)
Silver Jewelry #3					1,375	746			(W. Bros.)
Ag, Cu, Ni, Monel #4					1,325	718			(W. Bros.)
Second Soldering #5					1,340	727			(W. Bros.)
Low Fusing, Second Soldering #14					1,150	621			(W. Bros.)

PRECIOUS METAL WEIGHT/VOLUME COMPARISONS

18 kt Yellow gold is	1.064	times as heavy as	18 kt white gold
	0.723	″ ″ ″ ″	platinum
	1.271	″ ″ ″ ″	palladium
	1.364	″ ″ ″ ″	lead
	1.885	″ ″ ″ ″	brass (65%-35%)
	1.480	″ ″ ″ ″	sterling silver
14 kt Yellow gold is	0.842	times as heavy as	18 kt. yellow gold
	1.035	″ ″ ″ ″	14 kt white gold
	0.609	″ ″ ″ ″	platinum
	1.071	″ ″ ″ ″	palladium
	1.149	″ ″ ″ ″	lead
	1.589	″ ″ ″ ″	brass
	1.248	″ ″ ″ ″	sterling silver
10 kt Yellow gold is	0.745	times as heavy as	18 kt yellow gold
	0.884	″ ″ ″ ″	14 kt white gold
	1.042	″ ″ ″ ″	10 kt white gold
	0.539	″ ″ ″ ″	platinum
	0.948	″ ″ ″ ″	palladium
	1.016	″ ″ ″ ″	lead
	1.406	″ ″ ″ ″	brass
	1.104	″ ″ ″ ″	sterling silver
Platinum is	1.758	times as heavy as	palladium
	0.953	″ ″ ″ ″	iridium
	0.995	″ ″ ″ ″	10% iridium-platinum
	0.993	″ ″ ″ ″	15% iridium-platinum
	1.717	″ ″ ″ ″	Rhodium
	1.771	″ ″ ″ ″	Ruthenium
	2.046	″ ″ ″ ″	sterling silver
Sterling silver is	0.984	times as heavy as	fine silver
	1.004	″ ″ ″ ″	coin silver
	0.675	″ ″ ″ ″	18 kt yellow gold
	0.801	″ ″ ″ ″	14 kt yellow gold
	0.905	″ ″ ″ ″	10 kt yellow gold
	0.488	″ ″ ″ ″	platinum
	1.273	″ ″ ″ ″	brass
Coin silver is	0.980	times as heavy as	fine silver
	0.995	″ ″ ″ ″	sterling silver

Source: Wildberg Brothers Smelting and Refining Company, brochure (San Francisco).

DECIMAL EQUIVALENTS OF DRILL SIZES

Size	Decimal equivalent	Size	Decimal equivalent	Size	Decimal equivalent
1/2	0.500	3	0.213	3/32	0.0937
31/64	0.4843	4	0.209	42	0.0935
15/32	0.4687	5	0.2055	43	0.089
29/64	0.4531	6	0.204	44	0.086
7/16	0.4375	13/64	0.2031	45	0.082
27/64	0.4218	7	0.201	46	0.081
Z	0.413	8	0.199	47	0.0785
13/32	0.4062	9	0.196	5/64	0.0781
Y	0.404	10	0.1935	48	0.076
X	0.397	11	0.191	49	0.073
25/64	0.3906	12	0.189	50	0.070
W	0.386	3/16	0.1875	51	0.067
V	0.377	13	0.185	52	0.0635
3/8	0.375	14	0.182	1/16	0.0625
U	0.368	15	0.180	53	0.0595
23/64	0.3593	16	0.177	54	0.055
T	0.358	17	0.173	55	0.052
S	0.348	11/64	0.1718	3/64	0.0468
11/32	0.3437	18	0.1695	56	0.0465
R	0.339	19	0.166	57	0.043
Q	0.332	20	0.161	58	0.042
21/64	0.3281	21	0.159	59	0.041
P	0.323	22	0.157	60	0.040
O	0.316	5/32	0.1562	61	0.039
5/16	0.3125	23	0.154	62	0.038
N	0.302	24	0.152	63	0.037
19/64	0.2968	25	0.1495	64	0.036
M	0.295	26	0.147	65	0.035
L	0.290	27	0.144	66	0.043
9/32	0.2812	9/64	0.1406	1/32	0.0312
K	0.281	28	0.1405	67	0.032
J	0.277	29	0.136	68	0.031
I	0.272	30	0.1285	69	0.029
H	0.266	1/8	0.125	70	0.028
17/64	0.2656	31	0.120	71	0.026
G	0.261	32	0.116	72	0.025
F	0.257	33	0.113	73	0.024
E−1/4	0.250	34	0.111	74	0.0225
D	0.246	35	0.110	75	0.021
C	0.242	7/64	0.1093	76	0.020
B	0.238	36	0.1065	77	0.018
15/64	0.2343	37	0.104	1/64	0.0156
A	0.234	38	0.1015	78	0.016
1	0.228	39	0.0995	79	0.0145
2	0.221	40	0.098	80	0.0135
7/32	0.2187	41	0.096		

TAPS, TAP DRILLS, AND WIRE SIZES

Size of tap NC	Outside diameter (inches)	Root diameter (inches)	Size of tap drill		Nearest wire size for matching screw Brown & Sharpe	
			No.	Decimal equivalent (inches)	Gauge	Decimal equivalent (inches)
#1-64	0.0730	0.0527	53	0.0595	12	0.0808
#2-56	0.0860	0.0628	50	0.0700	11	0.0907
#3-48	0.0990	0.0719	47	0.0785	10	0.1019
#4-40	0.1120	0.0795	43	0.0890	9	0.1144
#5-40	0.1250	0.0925	38	0.1015	8	0.1285
#6-32	0.1380	0.0974	36	0.1065	7	0.1443
#8-32	0.1640	0.1234	29	0.1360	5	0.1819
#10-24	0.1900	0.1359	25	0.1495	4	0.2043
#12-24	0.2160	0.1619	16	0.1770	3	0.2294

CIRCUMFERENCE AND AREAS OF CIRCLES AND SQUARES

Size (inches) Circle: diameter Square: length of side	Circle		Square
	Circumference (inches)	Area (square inches)	Area (square inches)
1/4	0.7854	0.0491	0.0625
1/2	1.571	0.1964	0.2500
3/4	2.356	0.4418	0.5625
1	3.142	0.7854	1.000
1-1/4	3.927	1.227	1.563
1-1/2	4.712	1.767	2.250
1-3/4	5.498	2.405	3.063
2	6.283	3.142	4.000
2-1/4	7.069	3.976	5.063
2-1/2	7.854	4.909	6.250
2-3/4	8.639	5.940	7.563
3	9.425	7.069	9.000
3-1/4	10.21	8.296	10.56
3-1/2	11.00	9.621	12.25
3-3/4	11.78	11.04	14.06
4	12.57	12.57	16.00
4-1/4	13.35	14.19	18.06
4-1/2	14.14	15.90	20.25
4-3/4	14.92	17.72	22.56
5	15.71	19.64	25.00
5-1/4	16.49	21.65	27.56
5-1/2	17.28	23.76	30.25
5-3/4	18.06	25.97	33.06
6	18.85	28.27	36.00

SHEET—PRECIOUS METALS

Weight per Square Inch by Brown & Sharpe Gauge

B & S gauge	Thickness (inches)	Fine gold (dwts.)	18 K Yellow gold (dwts.)	14 K Yellow gold (dwts.)	10 K Yellow gold (dwts.)	Platinum (oz.)	Palladium (oz.)	Sterling silver (oz.)
1	0.28930	59.0	47.5	39.8	35.3	3.27	1.83	1.58
2	0.25763	52.6	42.3	35.5	31.4	2.91	1.63	1.41
3	0.22942	46.8	37.7	31.6	28.0	2.59	1.45	1.26
4	0.20431	41.7	33.6	28.1	24.9	2.31	1.29	1.12
5	0.18194	37.1	29.9	25.1	22.2	2.06	1.15	0.996
6	0.16202	33.1	26.6	22.3	19.8	1.83	1.02	0.887
7	0.14428	29.4	23.7	19.9	17.6	1.63	0.912	0.790
8	0.12849	26.2	21.1	17.7	15.7	1.45	0.812	0.704
9	0.11443	23.3	18.8	15.8	14.0	1.29	0.723	0.627
10	0.10189	20.8	16.7	14.0	12.4	1.15	0.644	0.558
11	0.09074	18.5	14.9	12.5	11.1	1.03	0.574	0.497
12	0.08080	16.5	13.3	11.1	9.85	0.913	0.511	0.443
13	0.07196	14.7	11.8	9.91	8.77	0.813	0.455	0.394
14	0.06408	13.1	10.5	8.82	7.81	0.724	0.405	0.351
15	0.05706	11.6	9.37	7.86	6.96	0.645	0.361	0.313
16	0.05082	10.4	8.35	7.00	6.21	0.574	0.321	0.278
17	0.04525	9.23	7.43	6.23	5.52	0.511	0.286	0.248
18	0.04030	8.22	6.62	5.55	4.91	0.455	0.255	0.221
19	0.03589	7.32	5.89	4.94	4.38	0.406	0.227	0.197
20	0.03196	6.52	5.25	4.40	3.90	0.361	0.202	0.175
21	0.02846	5.81	4.67	3.92	3.47	0.322	0.180	0.156
22	0.02534	5.17	4.16	3.49	3.09	0.286	0.160	0.139
23	0.02257	4.60	3.71	3.11	2.75	0.255	0.143	0.124
24	0.02010	4.10	3.30	2.77	2.45	0.227	0.127	0.110
25	0.01790	3.65	2.94	2.46	2.18	0.202	0.113	0.0980
26	0.01594	3.25	2.62	2.19	1.94	0.180	0.101	0.0873
27	0.01419	2.89	2.33	1.95	1.73	0.160	0.0897	0.0777
28	0.01264	2.58	2.08	1.74	1.54	0.143	0.0799	0.0692
29	0.01125	2.29	1.85	1.55	1.37	0.127	0.0711	0.0616
30	0.01002	2.04	1.65	1.38	1.22	0.113	0.0633	0.0549
31	0.00892	1.82	1.46	1.23	1.09	0.101	0.0564	0.0489
32	0.00795	1.62	1.31	1.09	0.969	0.0898	0.0503	0.0435
33	0.00708	1.44	1.16	0.975	0.863	0.0800	0.0448	0.0388
34	0.00630	1.29	1.03	0.868	0.768	0.0712	0.0398	0.0345
35	0.00561	1.14	0.921	0.772	0.684	0.0634	0.0355	0.0307
36	0.00500	1.02	0.821	0.689	0.610	0.0565	0.0316	0.0274
37	0.00445	0.908	0.731	0.613	0.543	0.0503	0.0281	0.0244
38	0.00396	0.808	0.650	0.545	0.483	0.0448	0.0250	0.0217
39	0.00353	0.720	0.580	0.486	0.430	0.0399	0.0223	0.0193
40	0.00314	0.641	0.516	0.432	0.383	0.0355	0.0199	0.0172

ROUND WIRE – PRECIOUS METALS

Weight in Pennyweights or Ounces per Foot in Brown & Sharpe Gauge

B & S gauge	Thickness in inches	Fine silver (oz.)	Sterling silver (oz.)	Coin silver (ozs.)	Fine gold (dwts.)	10K Yellow gold (dwts.)	14K Yellow gold (dwts.)	18K Yellow gold (dwts.)	Platinum (oz.)	Palladium (oz.)
1	0.28930	4.38	4.32	4.30	161.0	96.2	109.	130.	8.91	4.99
2	0.25763	3.47	3.43	3.41	128.	76.3	86.1	104.	7.07	3.94
3	0.22942	2.75	2.72	2.70	101.	60.5	68.3	81.5	5.61	3.19
4	0.20431	2.18	2.15	2.14	80.3	48.0	54.2	64.6	4.45	2.42
5	0.18194	1.73	1.71	1.70	63.6	38.0	43.0	51.2	3.53	1.97
6	0.16202	1.37	1.36	1.35	50.5	30.2	34.1	40.6	2.80	1.56
7	0.14428	1.09	1.07	1.07	40.0	23.9	27.0	32.2	2.22	1.24
8	0.12849	0.863	0.852	0.848	31.7	19.0	21.4	25.6	1.76	0.984
9	0.11443	0.685	0.676	0.673	25.2	15.1	17.0	20.3	1.39	0.780
10	0.10189	0.543	0.536	0.533	20.0	11.9	13.5	16.1	1.11	0.619
11	0.09074	0.431	0.425	0.423	15.8	9.46	10.7	12.7	0.877	0.491
12	0.08080	0.341	0.337	0.335	12.6	7.50	8.47	10.1	0.695	0.389
13	0.07196	0.271	0.267	0.266	9.96	5.95	6.72	8.01	0.552	0.309
14	0.06408	0.215	0.212	0.211	7.89	4.72	5.33	6.36	0.437	0.495
15	0.05706	0.170	0.168	0.167	6.26	3.74	4.23	5.04	0.347	0.154

Gauge										
16	0.05082	0.135	0.133	0.133	4.97	2.97	3.35	4.00	0.275	0.154
17	0.04525	0.107	0.106	0.105	3.94	2.35	2.66	3.17	0.218	0.122
18	0.04030	0.0849	0.0838	0.0834	3.12	1.87	2.11	2.51	0.173	0.0968
19	0.03589	0.0674	0.0665	0.0662	2.48	1.48	1.67	1.99	0.137	0.0767
20	0.03196	0.0534	0.0527	0.0525	1.96	1.17	1.33	1.58	0.109	0.0609
21	0.02846	0.0424	0.0418	0.0416	1.56	0.931	1.05	1.25	0.0863	0.0483
22	0.02534	0.0336	0.0331	0.0330	1.23	0.738	0.833	0.994	0.0684	0.0383
23	0.02257	0.0266	0.0263	0.0262	0.979	0.585	0.661	0.789	0.0543	0.0304
24	0.02010	0.0211	0.0209	0.0208	0.777	0.464	0.524	0.625	0.0430	0.0241
25	0.01790	0.0168	0.0165	0.0165	0.616	0.368	0.416	0.496	0.0341	0.0191
26	0.01594	0.0133	0.0131	0.0131	0.489	0.292	0.330	0.393	0.0271	0.0151
27	0.01419	0.0105	0.0104	0.0103	0.387	0.231	0.261	0.312	0.0214	0.0120
28	0.01264	0.00835	0.00825	0.00821	0.307	0.184	0.207	0.247	0.0170	0.00952
29	0.01125	0.00662	0.00653	0.00650	0.243	0.145	0.164	0.196	0.0135	0.00754
30	0.01002	0.00525	0.00518	0.00516	0.193	0.115	0.130	0.155	0.0107	0.00598
31	0.00892	0.00416	0.00411	0.00409	0.153	0.0914	0.103	0.123	0.00847	0.00474
32	0.00795	0.00330	0.00326	0.00325	0.122	0.0726	0.0820	0.0978	0.00673	0.00377
33	0.00708	0.00262	0.00259	0.00258	0.0964	0.0576	0.0651	0.0776	0.00534	0.00299
34	0.00630	0.00208	0.00205	0.00204	0.0763	0.0456	0.0515	0.0614	0.00423	0.00286
35	0.00561	0.00165	0.00162	0.00162	0.0605	0.0362	0.0408	0.0487	0.00335	0.00188
36	0.00500	0.00131	0.00129	0.00128	0.0481	0.0287	0.0324	0.0387	0.00266	0.00149
37	0.00415	0.00104	0.00102	0.00102	0.0381	0.0228	0.0257	0.0306	0.00211	0.00118
38	0.00396	0.000820	0.000809	0.000806	0.0302	0.0180	0.0204	0.0243	0.00167	0.000934
39	0.00353	0.000652	0.000643	0.000640	0.0240	0.0143	0.0162	0.0193	0.00133	0.000742
40	0.00314	0.000516	0.000509	0.000507	0.0190	0.0113	0.0128	0.0153	0.00105	0.000587

Square wire is 1.27324 times as heavy as round wire of the same gauge.

PRECIOUS METAL CONVERSION TABLES

Pennyweights to Ounces Troy

Dwts.		Oz.	Dwts.		Oz.
1/4	=	0.0125	11	=	0.550
1/2	=	0.025	12	=	0.600
3/4	=	0.0375	13	=	0.650
1	=	0.050	14	=	0.700
2	=	0.100	15	=	0.750
3	=	0.150	16	=	0.800
4	=	0.200	17	=	0.850
5	=	0.250	18	=	0.900
6	=	0.300	19	=	0.950
7	=	0.350	20	=	1.000
8	=	0.400			
9	=	0.450			
10	=	0.500			

Grains to Pennyweights Troy

Grains		Dwts.	Grains		Dwts.
1/2	=	0.0208	13	=	0.5417
1	=	0.0417	14	=	0.5833
2	=	0.0833	15	=	0.6250
3	=	0.1250	16	=	0.6667
4	=	0.1667	17	=	0.7083
5	=	0.2083	18	=	0.7500
6	=	0.2500	19	=	0.7917
7	=	0.2917	20	=	0.8333
8	=	0.3333	21	=	0.8750
9	=	0.3750	22	=	0.9167
10	=	0.4167	23	=	0.9583
11	=	0.4583	24	=	1.0000
12	=	0.5000			

Ounces Troy and Ounces Avoirdupois

Ounces troy to ounces avoirdupois				Ounces avoirdupois to ounces troy			
Troy oz.	Avoir. oz.	Troy oz.	Avoir. oz.	Avoir. oz.	Troy oz.	Avoir. oz.	Troy oz.
1	1.1	7	7.7	1	.9115	9	8.203
2	2.2	8	8.8	2	1.823	10	9.115
3	3.3	9	9.9	3	2.734	11	10.026
4	4.4	10	11.0	4	3.646	12	10.937
5	5.5	11	12.1	5	4.557	13	11.849
6	6.6	12	13.2	6	5.469	14	12.760
			(1 lb.)	7	6.380	15	13.672
				8	7.292	16	14.583
							(1 lb.)

Metric Grams to Troy Weights

1 gram	=	15.4324 grains
1 gram	=	0.6430 dwts.
1 gram	=	0.03215 troy oz.
1.55517 grams	=	1 dwt.
31.10348 grams	=	1 troy oz.
1 kilogram	=	32.15076 troy oz.

APPROXIMATE TEMPERATURES OF VISIBLY GLOWING METALS

	°F.	°C.
Barely visible glow in darkness	900° F.	(480° C.)
Slight glow in darkness	980	525
Dull red	1,175	635
Medium dark red	1,275	700
Red	1,550	840
Bright red	1,670	900
Light red	2,100	1,150
White	2,200	1,200
Brilliant white	2,730	1,500

Brown & Sharpe	Thickness (inches)	Points on the spring gauge	Equivalent (mm)	Brown & Sharpe	Thickness (inches)	Points on the spring gauge	Equivalent (mm)
1	0.28930	38.57	7.348	21	0.02846	3.79	0.723
2	0.25763	34.34	6.544	22	0.02534	3.37	0.644
3	0.22942	30.58	5.827	23	0.02257	3.00	0.573
4	0.20431	27.24	5.189	24	0.02010	2.67	0.511
5	0.18194	24.25	4.621	25	0.01790	2.38	0.455
6	0.16202	21.60	4.115	26	0.01594	2.12	0.405
7	0.14428	19.23	3.665	27	0.01419	1.89	0.360
8	0.12849	17.13	3.264	28	0.01264	1.68	0.321
9	0.11443	15.25	2.907	29	0.01125	1.49	0.286
10	0.10189	13.58	2.588	30	0.01002	1.33	0.255
11	0.09074	12.09	2.305	31	0.00892	1.18	0.227
12	0.08080	10.77	2.052	32	0.00795	1.05	0.202
13	0.07196	9.59	1.828	33	0.00708	0.94	0.180
14	0.06408	8.54	1.628	34	0.00630	0.83	0.160
15	0.05706	7.60	1.449	35	0.00561	0.74	0.142
16	0.05082	6.77	1.291	36	0.00500	0.66	0.127
17	0.04525	6.03	1.149	37	0.00445	0.59	0.113
18	0.04030	5.37	1.024	38	0.00396	0.52	0.101
19	0.03589	4.78	0.912	39	0.00353	0.47	0.009
20	0.03196	4.26	0.812	40	0.00314	0.41	0.008

TEMPERING STEEL BY OXIDE COLORS

Steel heated to bright cherry red and then allowed to cool exhibits on bright, freshly filed spots a succession of colors caused by a film of oxides and reflecting the temperature of the steel. The correct temper is obtained by waiting for the corresponding color to appear upon the freshly filed spot (near the work or cutting edge) and then quenching in water, oil, or other suitable coolant.

References: Handbook of Chemistry and Physics, 51st ed. (Cleveland: Chemical Rubber Co., 1970).

L. L. Linick, *Jewelers' Workshop Practises* (Chicago: H. Paulson & Co., 1948).

L. S. Marks, *Mechanical Engineer's Handbook*, 4th ed. (New York: McGraw-Hill, 1941).

Color	Temperature		Tool use
No color	200° F.	(94° C.)	Scrapers
Pale straw	390	199	Taps
Pale straw	400	204	
Straw yellow	430	221	
Straw yellow	440	227	Punches, chasing tools
Straw yellow	450	232	
Dark yellow	475	246	
Brownish yellow	480	249	Engravers, wood chisels
Bronze	520	271	Hammers, drills
Purple	540	282	Shears, scissors
Dark blue	550	288	Cold chisels
Medium blue	570	299	Knives, saws, screwdrivers
Bright blue	590	310	Springs

STANDARD COLORED STONE SIZES IN MILLIMETERS

Rounds

Size no.	Mm	Size no.	Mm
1	1	24	5-1/4
2	1-1/8	25	5-3/8
3	1-1/4	26	5-1/2
4	1-1/2	27	5-3/4
5	1-3/4	28-29	6
6	2	30	6-1/4
7	2-1/8	31	6-1/2
8	2-1/4	32	6-3/4
9	2-1/2	33-34	7
10	2-3/4	35-36	7-1/2
11	3	38	8
12	3-1/8	39	8-1/4
13	3-1/4	40	8-1/2
14	3-3/8	41	8-3/4
15	3-1/2	42	9
16	3-3/4	43	9-1/2
17	4	44	10
18	4-1/8	45	10-1/4
19	4-1/4	46	10-1/2
20	4-3/8	47	11
21	4-1/2	48	11-1/2
22	4-3/4	49	11-3/4
23	5	50	12

Ovals (i.e., Ellipses)

2 x 3 mm	9 x 14	12 x 26	19 x 25
3 x 4	9 x 16	13 x 18	20 x 30
4 x 5	9 x 18	13 x 24	22 x 34
5 x 7	10 x 12	13 x 35	24 x 30
5 x 20	10 x 14	14 x 16	25 x 38
6 x 8	10 x 15	14 x 20	25 x 50
6 x 10	10 x 18	14 x 24	27 x 38
6-1/2 x 8	10 x 20	15 x 20	30 x 40
7 x 9	10 x 22	15 x 25	30 x 45
8 x 10	10 x 24	15 x 30	32 x 60
8 x 14	10 x 28	15 x 32	35 x 50
8 x 16	12 x 14	16 x 22	50 x 80
8 x 22	12 x 16	18 x 25	
8 x 28	12 x 18	18 x 35	
9 x 11	12 x 20	18 x 40	

Rectangles (Includes Octagons, Cushion, and Antique Cuts)

6 x 8	8 x 16	11 x 15	14 x 16
8 x 10	9 x 16	12 x 14	
8 x 12	10 x 12	12 x 16	
8 x 13	10 x 14	13 x 18	

APPROXIMATE WEIGHT OF ROUND NATURAL AND CULTURED PEARLS

Diameter (mm)	Weight (pearl grams)	Diameter (mm)	Weight (pearl grams)	Diameter (mm)	Weight (pearl grams)
1.0	0.02	5.7	5.25	10.4	32.00
1.1	0.03	5.8	5.50	10.5	33.00
1.2	0.04	5.9	5.75	10.6	34.00
1.3	0.05	6.0	6.00	10.7	35.00
1.4	0.06	6.1	6.50	10.8	36.00
1.5	0.08	6.2	6.75	10.9	37.00
1.6	0.11	6.3	7.00	11.0	38.00
1.7	0.14	6.4	7.50	11.1	39.00
1.8	0.18	6.5	7.75	11.2	40.00
1.9	0.21	6.6	8.00	11.3	41.00
2.0	0.25	6.7	8.50	11.4	42.00
2.1	0.28	6.8	9.00	11.5	43.00
2.2	0.32	6.9	9.25	11.6	44.00
2.3	0.36	7.0	9.75	11.7	45.00
2.4	0.42	7.1	10.00	11.8	46.00
2.5	0.50	7.2	10.50	11.9	47.00
2.6	0.53	7.3	11.00	12.0	48.00
2.7	0.59	7.4	11.50	12.1	49.00
2.8	0.65	7.5	12.00	12.2	50.00
2.9	0.70	7.6	12.50	12.3	51.00
3.0	0.75	7.7	13.00	12.4	52.00
3.1	0.82	7.8	13.50	12.5	53.00
3.2	0.90	7.9	14.00	12.6	54.00
3.3	1.00	8.0	14.50	12.7	55.00
3.4	1.10	8.1	15.00	12.8	56.00
3.5	1.25	8.2	15.50	12.9	59.00
3.6	1.30	8.3	16.00	13.0	61.00
3.7	1.40	8.4	16.50	13.1	63.00
3.8	1.50	8.5	17.00	13.2	65.00
3.9	1.60	8.6	17.50	13.3	67.00
4.0	1.75	8.7	18.00	13.4	69.00
4.1	1.90	8.8	18.50	13.5	71.00
4.2	2.00	8.9	19.00	13.6	73.00
4.3	2.25	9.0	19.50	13.7	75.00
4.4	2.40	9.1	20.00	13.8	77.00
4.5	2.50	9.2	20.50	13.9	79.00
4.6	2.75	9.3	21.00	14.0	81.00
4.7	2.90	9.4	22.00	14.1	83.00
4.8	3.00	9.5	23.00	14.2	85.00
4.9	3.25	9.6	24.00	14.3	87.00
5.0	3.50	9.7	25.00	14.4	89.00
5.1	3.75	9.8	26.00	14.5	91.00
5.2	4.00	9.9	27.00	14.6	93.00
5.3	4.25	10.0	28.00	14.7	95.00
5.4	4.50	10.1	29.00	14.8	97.00
5.5	4.75	10.2	30.00	14.9	99.00
5.6	5.00	10.3	31.00	15.0	101.00

Note: 1 metric carat = 4 pearl grains.
Source: R. T. Liddicoat, Jr., and L. L. Copeland *The Jewelers' Manual* (Los Angeles: Gemological Institute of America, 1967).

Grain		1/8	1/4	3/8	1/2	5/8	3/4	7/8
1	1.00	1.27	1.56	1.89	2.25	2.64	3.06	3.52
2	4.00	4.52	5.06	5.64	6.25	6.89	7.56	8.27
3	9.00	9.77	10.56	11.39	12.25	13.14	14.06	15.02
4	16.00	17.02	18.06	19.14	20.25	21.39	22.56	23.77
5	25.00	26.27	27.56	28.89	30.25	31.64	33.06	34.52
6	36.00	37.52	39.06	40.64	42.25	43.89	45.56	47.27
7	49.00	50.77	52.56	54.39	56.25	58.14	60.06	62.02
8	64.00	66.02	68.06	70.14	72.25	74.39	76.56	78.77
9	81.00	83.27	85.56	87.89	90.25	92.64	95.06	97.52
10	100.00	102.52	105.06	107.64	110.25	112.89	115.56	118.27
11	121.00	123.77	126.56	129.39	132.25	135.14	138.06	141.02
12	144.00	147.02	150.06	153.14	156.25	159.39	162.56	165.77
13	169.00	172.27	175.56	178.89	182.25	185.64	189.06	192.52
14	196.00	199.52	203.06	206.64	210.25	213.89	217.56	221.27
15	225.00	228.77	232.56	236.39	240.25	244.14	248.06	252.02
16	256.00	260.02	264.06	268.14	272.25	276.39	280.56	284.77
17	289.00	293.27	297.56	301.89	306.25	310.64	315.06	319.52
18	324.00	328.52	333.06	337.64	342.25	346.89	351.56	356.27
19	361.00	365.77	370.56	375.39	380.25	385.14	390.06	395.02
20	400.00	405.02	410.06	415.14	420.25	425.39	430.56	435.77
21	441.00	446.27	451.56	456.89	462.25	467.64	473.06	478.52
22	484.00	489.52	495.06	500.64	506.25	511.89	517.56	523.27
23	529.00	534.77	540.56	546.39	552.25	558.14	564.06	570.02
24	576.00	582.02	588.06	594.14	600.25	606.39	612.56	618.77
25	625.00	631.27	637.56	643.89	650.25	656.64	663.06	669.52

Base price above = $1.00.

Examples of Calculations

2-1/2 grain pearl @ $2.60 base would cost 6.25 X $2.60 = $16.25.

5-3/4 grain pearl @ $4.50 base would cost 33.06 X $4.50 = $148.77.

10-1/4 grain pearl @ $6.00 base would cost 105.06 X $6.00 = $630.36.

RESISTANCE OF GEMSTONES TO HEAT OR ACID DURING JEWELRY REPAIR WORK

GENERAL RULES. Demount any gem of 3/4 carat or larger before commencing work using heat or acid. Do not coat or allow to come in contact with any gem borax, boric acid, or other boron compound fluxes. Under high heat these fluxes may seriously attack and partly decompose certain gemstones.

Good Resistance: Diamond, sapphire, chrysoberyl.

Resistant with reservations: Diamond, sapphire, ruby, aquamarine, spinel, garnet, peridot.

Likely to be damaged: Emerald, topaz, garnet, tourmaline, zircon, amethyst, chrysoprase, smoky quartz, citrine.

Sure to be damaged: Glasses, opal, turquoise, lapis lazuli, malachite, moonstones and other feldspar gems, jades, coral, amber, jet.

All massive granular gemstones and those that are known to be porous are very likely to suffer damage from immersion in chemicals or acids.

STANDARD U.S. AND BRITISH
RING SIZES

U.S. size no.	British size	Average diameter (inches)
000	–	0.39
00	–	0.422
0	–	0.454
1/2	A	0.474
1	B	0.487
1-1/2	C	0.503
2	D	0.520
2-1/2	E	0.536
3	F	0.553
3-3/8	G	0.568
3-1/2	–	0.569
3-3/4	H	0.584
4	H-1/2	0.585
4-1/4	I	0.599
4-1/2	I-1/2	0.601
4-5/8	J	0.615
5	J-1/2	0.618
5-1/8	K	0.630
5-1/2	L	0.634
6	M	0.650
6-1/2	N	0.666
7	O	0.683
7-1/2	P	0.699
8	Q	0.716
8-1/2	–	0.732
8-5/8	R	0.739
9	–	0.748
9-1/8	S	0.754
9-1/2	–	0.764
9-5/8	T	0.77
10	T-1/2	0.781
10-1/4	U	0.785
10-1/2	U-1/2	0.797
10-5/8	V	0.801
11	V-1/2	0.814
11-1/8	W	0.816
11-1/2	–	0.830
11-5/8	X	0.832
12	Y	0.846
12-1/2	Z	0.862
13	–	0.879

Sources: R. T. Liddicoat, Jr., and L. L. Copeland, *The Jewelers' Manual* (Los Angeles: Gemological Institute of America, 1967).

A. Selwyn, ed., *Jewellers' and Watchmakers'
Pocket Book* (London: Heywood & Company,
1951).

Part 6 / Coloring Gemstones and Minerals

DYEING GEMSTONES

More or less permanent coloration in certain porous gemstones, notably chalcedony, is induced by chemical means but depends for success not only on the stability of the pigment but also on the porosity of the gemstone.

Source: Many of the following treatments for dyeing chalcedonies are taken from the authoritative booklet of instructions by Dr. O. Dreher, *Farben des Achates* (Idar: E. Kessler, 1913), 20 pp., based on personal observations of the methods used in the famous gem-cutting center of Idar-Oberstein in Germany.

TEST FOR DYE ACCEPTANCE BY CHALCEDONY. Place sliver in concentrated potassium chromate solution overnight; upon the next day, rinse and examine; if stone turned yellow it is porous enough to take dye.

CLEANING CHALCEDONY PRIOR TO DYEING. Before dyes will enter the stones the latter must be thoroughly cleaned to free pores of oils introduced during sawing and iron hydroxides naturally present in many kinds of chalcedony. The latter interfere with passage of coloring solutions and introduce a red color during the firing stage which may not be compatible with the desired final color. Two steps are required. First, remove oils by soaking stones in a strong solution of household washing soda (sodium carbonate, hydrous) brought to a boil. Cool, change to clean water, and bring nearly to a boil to remove traces of the soda. Second, immerse stones in cool concentrated nitric acid to remove iron compounds. Raise temperature to hot and keep so for 1 or 2 days. Near the end of the period raise temperature to the boiling point and then lower heat to maintain temperature just below the boil. Cool to room temperature, remove stones and thoroughly wash. Finally place stones in clean water and boil to remove traces of acid; do so three times.

RED AGATE. Dreher (1913) recipe. Prepare dye sol. as follows. Take 1/4 kg iron nails, dissolve in 1 kg conc. nitric acid (or 1/4 lb nails to 1 lb acid). Perform sol. outdoors or under lab. hood to avoid poisonous and corrosive brownish fumes. Let sol. stand for 1 day after bubbling ceases; decant clear liquid into another container avoiding slime at bottom of original vessel; repeat decantation three times with final liquid being clear red containing dissolved iron nitrate.

Soak cleaned agate slabs according to thickness: to 3 mm (1/8″) thick, 6-10 days; to 6 mm (1/4″), 2-3 wks.; to 10 mm (3/8″), 3-4 wks. Remove, rinse, wipe dry. Place in oven and raise temp. Gradually to 180° C. (356° F.); hold for several hours to extract all water and to reopen pores. Resoak in sol. using same time schedule.

Place stones in suitable crucible with lid and rewarm in oven for 2-3 days for thin slabs, or 8-10 days for thicker slabs, which step is vital to prevent rupturing (or even explosion!) of slabs from water flashing into steam when the strong firing takes place next. Without removing stones, raise temp. of oven until the "hearth," that is, the clay lining, reaches a red heat. Gradually reduce temp. to room conditions and then, and only then, remove crucible and open.

According to Dreher (p. 8), ordinary iron nitrate (ferrous nitrate) purchased from chemical supply houses does not produce the same "fine" red even though the sol. appears to be as red as that obtained by the more complicated and troublesome iron nail solution in acid.

The following step-by-step procedure was described by Hoffmann, who required red pigmentation for scientific investigations of agate: (1) Dissolve iron nails in conc. nitric acid. (2) Place specimens in resulting sol. for 12 days, maintaining sol. temp. c. 50° C. (122° F.). (3) Remove and dry at 110° C. (230° F.). (4) Return to dye bath and resoak for another 10 days. (5) Remove, dry at 110° C. (230° F.) for several hrs. for thin plates, longer for thicker. (6) Finally, place dried plates in oven and fire c. 500° C. (932° F.) for a short time to convert the iron nitrate in the agate to red oxides of iron.

Source: S. Hoffmann, *N. Jb. Min., B.* 77, part A (1942): 238-76.

Another red recipe: Soak stones in conc. iron chloride sol., follow with soak in conc. sol. potassium sulfocyanide (potassium thiocyanate (?), KNCS).

RED AGATES WITHOUT DYEING. Many agates, especially the smaller pebbles and nodules found in stream gravels or in moist ground, have absorbed enough iron compounds to turn red or brown when fired. Larger nodules over several inches (8 cm) diameter may only show outer zones of color because iron compounds have not infiltrated into interiors. Before firing, such material must be carefully dried as recommended above, preferably after sawing or fracturing into pieces not greater than about 2 cm (3/4″) diameter or thickness. Thicker specimens must be brought up to firing heat very slowly to prevent fracture. In India, according to Ball, pebbles of agate are exposed to the sun and dry atmosphere for about 2 months and then fired in clay pots surrounded by a dung fire for about 12 hours to change colors. On a small scale, agate pebbles can be embedded in sand within suitable metal containers and fired in an ordinary kitchen oven at its maximum setting, with the heat brought up slowly in increments of 50° F. (10° C.) with intervals of about 15-30 minutes between increments. Cooling simply involves shutting off the oven and waiting overnight to cool to room temperature. The small agate pebbles of streams in the region of Brazil and Uruguay are excellent for converting into attractive banded carnelians.

Source: V. Ball, *A Manual of the Geology of India* (1881), part 3, pp. 507-8.

BLACK AGATE. Dreher (1913) recipe. Make sugar sol. of 375 gm sugar per liter (approx. 13 oz. per qt.); the viscosity is like that of easily flowing honey. Honey was used earlier but has no real advantage over ordinary sugar. Soak slabs in lukewarm sugar sol. 2-3 wks., adding water to replace evaporative losses. Rinse slabs, dry carefully, and place immediately in conc. sulfuric acid. Warm acid slowly for 1 hr. until it is hot; let slabs steep 1-2 hrs. with acid brought up close to its boiling point (340° C., or 644° F.). Allow to cool to room temp. Remove slabs and wash thoroughly; residual acid removed by drying for 1-2 days or soaking in water for 5-6 hrs. and then drying at low heat. It is not necessary to bring the conc. acid to its BP in order to carbonize the sugar; some advocate soaking slabs afterward in warm conc. baking soda (sodium bicarbonate) sol. to neutralize trapped acid. Shortening time of acid treatment results in brown hues, increasing time results in black. Firing is neither required nor desired.

BLUE AGATE. Dreher (1913) recipe. In 1 liter lukewarm water dissolve 250 gm yellow prussiate of potassium (potassium ferricyanide), or 8.5 oz. in 1 qt. water. Immerse stones in lukewarm sol. 8-14 days. Very porous stones soaked only 6-10 days, and ordinary agates soaked 10-14 days as a rule. Sol. must not be allowed to get too warm or boil because stones will lose porosity or at least their ability to accept the second soaking which must follow. Also, if sol. too conc., the salts crystallize upon cooling. After soaking wash stones well. Now place in lukewarm sat. sol. ferrous sulfate for 8-10 days. During this second soaking the compounds react within the stones to form the blue known as Turnbull's blue, ferrous ferricyanide, $Fe_2[Fe(CN_6)]_2$. Remove, wash thoroughly, dry at gentle heat.

The reaction can be accelerated by making the second sol. hot but the resulting blue color is not as good. Also, the intensity of the blue can be increased if to the second sol. are added several drops each of conc. sulfuric and nitric acids.

Caution: Addition of acid causes generation extremely poisonous hydrocyanic (prussic) acid gas fumes which must not be inhaled! For blue dyeing, it is best to perform all operations in the open or under a hood.

A recipe from another source states that red prussiate of potash (potassium ferrocyanide) may be used instead of the yellow prussiate; also ferric sulfate instead of ferrous sulfate. The resulting blue is now Prussian blue, ferric ferrocyanide, $Fe_4[Fe(CN)_6]_3$.

Another recipe: Place slabs in iron chloride sol. followed by soak in yellow prussiate of potassium (potassium ferricyanide). Still another: Soak slabs in conc. copper sulfate sol., then soak in ammonia sol.

GREEN AGATE. Dreher (1913) recipe. Make sat. sol. chromium trioxide ("chromic acid") in 1 liter water, or approx. 620 gm/liter or about 23 oz./quart. Immerse thin slabs 8-14 days, slabs of 3-10 mm 2-8 wks. Remove, rinse, place in sealed vessel containing lumps of ammonium carbamate acid carbonate ("sal volatile," given by Dreher as "salt of hartshorn"); let stand at least 2 wks. Strongly heat slabs in separate crucible as for red agate. According to Dreher the results are often spotty, some slabs being excellent, others unevenly colored or dull and unattractive green. A better method is known, but Dreher states it is a trade secret.

Sol. potassium dichromate can be used instead of the chromium trioxide but Dreher says that the trade in Idar-Oberstein uses only the latter. Another source gives ammonium dichromate as a substitute and that the treated slabs should be fired at 235° C. (455° F.).

APPLE GREEN AGATE. Dreher (1913) gives no recipe for this hue. The process, using nickel nitrate, is supposed to be entirely analogous to that used with iron nitrate to produce red except that chemically pure nickel nitrate is used directly. One vague reference states that the soaking in nickel nitrate sol. should be followed by another in "soda" sol. (sodium carbonate?).

YELLOW AGATE. Dreher (1913) gives no recipe for this hue. Other sources give instructions as follow. Soak stones in crude commercial hydrochloric ("muriatic") acid which is colored yellow by small quantities of iron compounds; these compounds penetrate the stones and impart the yellow. One sources states that this soaking should be followed by firing, but probably this would result in formation of red oxides of iron.

A second recipe calls for soaking slabs 6-8 days in conc. sol. potassium chromate, then washing and drying. A third recipe states that two sols. must be used to produce yellow. Soak slabs in aqueous sol.

mercuric chloride, and then follow by soaking in potassium iodide dissolved in sulfuric acid sol. Soaking periods 2-3 wks. The yellow color is due to formation of yellow mercuric iodide. Probably the pigment breaks down under strong light as is common in iodine compounds.

CHRYSOPRASE. Natural chrysoprase from Silesia is said to be improved in color by soaking in water solutions of nickel salts but the value of such treatments is doubtful.

BLACK PETRIFIED WOOD. Black petrified (i.e., silicified) wood as from Eden Valley, Wyoming, can be bleached by soaking in oxalic acid solution or in ordinary household bleach solution.

TIGEREYE. Yellowish material can be bleached to straw yellow or to very pale yellow by soaking in oxalic acid solution or laundry bleach solution; the oxalic sol. is used warm. It is best to cut and polish stones first.

RED TIGEREYE. After heat treatment of ordinary yellow material to turn it red, the latter color is paled to various shades of pink by short to long soaking in one of the bleaching agents used for yellow tigereye. Similar results are obtainable using hydrochloric acid.

FALSE MOSS AGATE. Dye-receptive translucent gray chalcedony is cut into suitable flat cabochons and then carefully cleansed and dried as described in the first part of this section. Now soak in sodium chloride (table salt) solution for several hours; wipe dry and paint moss or tree designs on the cabochons using a concentrated solution of silver nitrate in water. The silver nitrate reacts with the sodium chloride to form silver chloride, which eventually darkens to gray or black.

BLACK DYED OPAL. Certain types of opal, notably from Andamooka, Australia, have been considerably improved in appearance by dyeing them by the sugar-sulfuric acid treatment previously described under BLACK AGATE. Only those specimens with considerable pore space, particularly the kinds which consist of granular aggregates of potch and small clear opal areas, accept dye in a satisfactory manner. Hyalite, glassy opals, and the common opals will not be affected by this treatment. According to Noel, it is best to clean the stones by first soaking for at least several days in distilled water, changing the water daily. This removes soluble salts which may be trapped in the pores. The stones are then dehydrated in an oven held at 60°-90° C. (150°-200° F.) for at least 4 hours, after which they are carefully cooled and then transferred to a concentrated sugar solution (1 part sugar by vol. to 3 parts water by vol.). Here they are allowed to soak for at least 2 days. From the sugar solution the stones are transferred to a concentrated solution of sulfuric acid which is then slowly raised to 60°-90° C. (150°-200° F.) and held at that temperature for 2 days. After cooling, the stones are removed from the acid bath and carefully washed in several changes of distilled water until all traces of acid are dissolved.

Source: A. C. Noel, *Lapidary Journal* 24, no. 7 (1970); 914, 919.

OPAL IMPREGNATION TREATMENTS. Various sources state that Hungarian opals and hydrophanes have been improved by soaking in warm melts of paraffin wax, Canada balsam, lanolin, ceresin, etc., presumably to fill cracks and pores with a translucent material of about the same refractive index. In hydrophanes it is said that the play of color is restored by this treatment. However, such treatments are probably ineffective inasmuch as they are not vouched for by any important authority in the gemological literature.

RESTORATION OF WATER TO OPALS. Great success is claimed in restoring water and the play of color to opals of the National Museum of Hungary in Budapest which were burnt in the fires set during the revolt of 1956. The damaged opals (from the Veresvagas deposits) were placed in distilled water under a vacuum of 700 mm for 8-12 days; some required repeated treatments to restore play of color. Treated stones remained unchanged after 6 months' exposure to normal atmosphere. Reheating experiments showed that treated opals lost only about 0.04% weight after heating at 125°-130° C. (257°-266° F.) for several hours, but when heated at 700°-800° C. (1,292°-1,472° F.) for 3 hours, the same stones lost 5.7% weight and also lost play of color.

Source: E. Hunek, "Regenerierte Edelopale," *N. Jb. Min.*, M.H., pp. 115-16.

ORGANIC DYED OPAL. Porous opals, some of the Hungarian type, have been dyed various hues using aniline dyes dissolved in a suitable solvent such as methyl (wood) alcohol. Dyes of this kind are very penetrating but unfortunately are apt to fade in time, and more rapidly when exposed to sunlight.

ALABASTER DYEING. Massive, fine-grained Italian alabasters are commonly dyed after preliminary heat treatment at about 90° C. (194° F.) for 15-30 minutes to distend the pores between grains and to deliberately introduce minute cleavages in the crystals. Warmed stones are placed in cold-water bath containing potassium dichromate (10% sol.) or in an alum sol. until cool. Probably such treated stones readily accept aniline and other organic dyes.

MICROCLINE PERTHITE. Much contains minute fissures between the lamellae of albite within the microcline groundmass which allow organic dyes dissolved in acetone or alcohol to penetrate very readily. Partially kaolinized material is even better but when alteration has progressed too far difficulties are encountered in polishing the material. Depth of penetration about 1 cm (3/8").

DYED TURQUOISES. Porous types of turquoise have been dyed with organic dyes as well as impregnated superficially by wax and oils applied either at atmospheric pressure or under moderate vacuum.

DYED JADEITE. Jadeite, especially the outer, partly altered rind sections of alluvial boulders, is fairly porous and can accept a variety of dyes. Heat treatment is desirable at about 230° C. (446° F.) to remove water and slightly expand pore spaces. Unaltered jadeite is usually too compact to allow dyeing by any method.

GLASS MARBLES. Heat colorless glass marbles in a frying pan for about 30-45 minutes, adjusting heat to produce a few small cracks around the periphery of each marble. Have ready a sol. of water sol. dye and when the marbles are "cracked" dump into the water. Experimentation is needed to determine the required amount of heat which should be enough to encourage formation of cracks when plunged into water but not enough to cause marbles to disintegrate.

Notes on Dyestuffs: Organic dyestuffs

useful for coloring porous gemstones are available in large variety. Most are readily soluble in acetone or alcohol, especially wood alcohol (methyl alcohol or methanol). A typical sol. for dyeing calls for dye to be dissolved in acetone, and then water added in the proportion acetone 60% and water 40% by vol. The same may be used for alcohol. Organic dyes generally fade in sunlight but some are more permanent than others. Ordinary water color pigments as used by artists are seldom satisfactory because most are ground from solids and the particles are simply too large to enter pores in stones satisfactorily.

COLOR CHANGES IN
MINERALS AND GEMSTONES

Changes may be produced by heat, sunlight, ultraviolet light, X-rays, electron beams, protons, neutrons, deuterons, alpha, beta and gamma particles. Considerations of cost of materials and equipment make application of heat the only commonly practised method.

Very few minerals or synthetics are able to resist cracking through abrupt changes in temperature. These include diamond, zircon, corundum, spinel, chrysoberyl, sphene, rutile, strontium titanate, rare-earth–alumina compounds with garnet structure (e.g., "yag"), spodumene, and olivine. In general, compounds formed from melts are very resistant to cracking with the exception of ordinary glass which is discussed below. Most other minerals and gemstones readily fracture if heat is supplied or removed too rapidly, and still others, particularly the sulfates, carbonates, phosphates, and halides, crack even when great care is taken.

The ideal heat-treatable material is glass or any mineral which resembles glass in its internal structure, e.g., opal and obsidian. Heat passes uniformly through such materials and expansion is absolutely uniform in all directions, if heat is supplied uniformly. However, all glassy substances are poor heat conductors compared to crystalline materials and therefore heat must be supplied in small increments over a considerable period of time to prevent building up heat in exterior zones while interiors are still cool. Among crystalline minerals, natural garnets (isometric) behave somewhat like glass and are very easily cracked by careless application of heat. Also, generally speaking, minerals belonging to the other crystal systems, that is, tetragonal, hexagonal, orthorhombic, monoclinic, and triclinic, display unequal expansions according to crystallographic direction and develop uneven stresses within them when heated which may cause them to crack rather readily at modest temperatures. Since hardness is a measure of how strongly atoms are bonded together in crystals, hard minerals also tend to be heat resistant and soft minerals tend to crack. Cleavage is not always important in predicting the ease with which any given crystal will crack with temperature rise, as for example in diamond which is extremely resistant to heat cracking despite its perfect cleavage. More important is the *ease* with which cleavage is developed, those crystals with easily developed cleavages being less heat resistant and vice versa.

Size of material being treated is extremely important inasmuch as internal stresses developed by temperature changes are in direct proportion to dimensions. Experience has shown that it is seldom possible really to heat-treat quartz crystals in excess of about 1″ (2.5 cm) diameter without cracking, beryl in excess of 2″ (5 cm), etc. In all cases, the presence of flaws of any kind, partly developed cleavages or surface cracks, narrow "necks" or other radical departures from approximately spherical shape, gas-fluid inclusions, sharp boundaries between color zones (tourmaline), and other defects in physical perfection promote cracking. Gemstones which must be heat-treated are therefore best chipped or sawed before heat treatment to eliminate defects, or better yet, processed into finished gems.

Aside from the above considerations, certain success in heat treatment depends on using apparatus which provides for gradual ingress and egress of heat. Such apparatus may be very simple, e.g., a metal can filled with fine sand, vermiculite, powdered asbestos, or other noncombustible material permitting only gradual flow of heat. Without temperature-reading devices, the point at which to stop applying heat and the time when to uncover the samples is a matter of judgment based on experience. One clever method used in Brazil to heat-treat amethysts to citrine employs a basin made from one half of a metal drum which is partly filled with sand. Upon the sand are placed the amethyst crystals, some fitted with thin wires which will enable them to be withdrawn later during heating. More sand is placed over the amethysts, and a fire built beneath the drum. After several hours, one of the wires is pulled and the amethyst examined to check progress of color change. This is repeated until it is seen that the change has occurred, at which time the fire is withdrawn and the basin allowed to cool before any attempt is made to disturb its contents.

Another Brazilian treatment directed toward changing green beryls to blue aquamarine uses bread dough, according to Frondel. (C. Frondel, Gemmologist 21 (1952): pp. 197-200.) The dough is worked up around the crystals and then placed in an oven to bake; after cooling, the bread is broken open to reveal the crystals which presumably have now altered to blue.

Where an oven with temperature indicator is available, the crystals are again placed in sand or other suitable material, and the oven turned to low heat. After intervals of say 15 to 30 minutes, the heat is raised in steps of $25°$ C. ($77°$ F.) until the final temperature is reached. Experience shows that at least 2 hours are required to bring up the temperature to prevent cracking of the stones, and even more time if the stones are delicate or large in size. Also at least 1/2 hour is needed at final temperature to allow the heat to "soak" through the insulating material into the stones.

Since most ovens are well insulated, decrease of temperature merely requires shutting off the source of heat and allowing the oven to cool to room temperature. Under no circumstances must the oven door be opened until the temperature is close to that of the room.

Professional heat treatment ovens are available which can be programmed for heat rise in specified increments, and still others, considerably more expensive, which can program temperature rise, plateau, and fall. All ovens should be calibrated and temperatures versus time recorded on a convenient graph. This is especially useful for the less expensive electric ovens which can be set to provide a "percent" input of current. By recording temperatures versus times at various percents, it is possible to easily plan a program for safe heat treatment.

ALBITE. Radium rays, no change.

ALMANDINE. Heat, no change; radiations, no change.

AMBLYGONITE. Under electron beam pale yellow-colorless Brazilian material changes to greenish yellow.

ANALCIME. Radium rays for 7 weeks, no change.

ANDALUSITE. Olive green Brazilian gem xls changed to pinkish when heat treated.

ANGLESITE. Radium rays, 30 days, from colorless to pale blue (Monteponi); this color is lost when specimen is heated.

ANHYDRITE. Blue or violet become colorless when heated, but if such specimens are irradiated the color is restored. Radium rays, 3 weeks, colorless to yellow (Aussee, Germany).

APATITE. Heated light violet, green, or gray specimens to colorless. Pink Mesa Grande, California, xls to pale grayish, grayish blue, or greenish. Green (Canada) to yellow. Yellow (Durango) to colorless. Purple (Mt. Apatite) at $500°$ C. ($932°$ F.) to colorless. Radium rays: pale yellow (Sulzbachtal, Austria), no change; purple (Mt. Apatite) to somewhat paler violet or greenish; colorless (Pinzgau), 42 days irradiation to violet, returning to colorless after 10 hr. UV. Heat-bleached violet (Schlaggenwald) returns to part violet, part greenish under Ra. Under UV: purple (Mt. Apatite) somewhat darker. Electron beam: yellow (Durango), no change; green (Canada), no change. X-rays: green to yellow-green.

APOPHYLLITE. Electron beam: colorless to somewhat greenish.

ARAGONITE. Grayish to brownish massive fibrous to fine-granular banded: heat treatment to $300°$ C. ($572°$ F.) bleaches groundmass and emphasizes banding; develops cracks which accept dyes. Colorless xls under 7 wks radium. no change.

ATACAMITE. Under radium 32 days, no change.

BARITE. Pale yellow under 44 days radium to pale blue; also other colors tend to blue. UV removes the blue color of Ra and results in blue-gray after 18 hrs.

irradiation. Color zoned xls behave non-uniformly. Some colorless xls turn blue when placed in sunlight.

BENITOITE. Electron beam, X-rays, etc., no changes observed.

BERYL. All authorities agree that emerald is unchanged in color by heat treatment. Frondel tested to 1,025° C. (1,877° F.). Red beryl of Utah to 1,025° C. (1,877° F.), no change (Frondel). Morganite is stable to 400° C. (752° F.) according to Frondel, but begins to bleach slightly at 440° C. (824° F.) after a 10-hour period, and rapidly decolorizes at 495° C. (923° F.); others report peach or apricot morganite turning to pink at 400° C. (752° F.); the author noted that Brazilian apricot beryl exposed for 1 week to the sunlight of San Diego turned completely pink. A pure golden brown beryl with no trace of green turned completely colorless when heated for many hours at 250° C. (482° F.), but faster when heated at 275°-300° C. (527°-572° F.), and a perceptible paling was noted when heated for 48 hours at 240° C. (464° F.) (Frondel). A reddish-yellow beryl from Madagascar turned to a fine pale blue when heated at 425°-450° C. (797°-842° F.); over 500° C. (932° F.) the same stone turned colorless. Another report states that a brownish stone turned pink at 400° C. (752° F.). According to Wild, yellow beryl changed to very pale blue at 400° C. (752° F.), and a brownish specimen changed to pink at the same temperature. Greenish-yellow, olive brown, and yellowish-green beryls lose their yellowish tinge in the range 250°-280° C. (482°-536° F.) and turn clear green, but when such beryl is heated again over about 280°-300° C. (536°-572° F.) it turns blue (Frondel). Heated green beryls first turn bluish about 280°-300° C. (536°-572° F.) with the rate of change increasing with rise in temperature, and over 400° C. (752° F.) occurring in a matter of minutes (Frondel); this investigator is also of the opinion that all green beryl changes to blue when heated. Wild gives the transition temperature from green to blue as 420° C. (788° F.). The depth of blue is directly proportional to the depth of the original green. The blue so obtained is stable to 1,025° C. (1,877° F.) (according to Frondel) but advice from others indicates that some blues become colorless or greenish at high temperatures. The finest blues are obtained from dark oil-green or dark olive-green specimens. The optimum heat appears to be 400°-450° C. (752°-842° F.), which reduces danger of cracking and prevents development of cloudiness. This range gives a complete change in an hour or less. Natural blue beryls are unchanged in hue to 1,025° C. (1,877° F.).

Exposed to radium rays, most beryls exhibit no change; however, a bluish-gray specimen is reported turning to a lighter and purer blue upon exposure to radium, and an emerald is said to have turned a purer green. Emerald is unchanged under X-rays, but a colorless beryl turned pale brown, and returned to colorless when heated. Frondel noted no changes in either the heated or unheated beryls after exposure to X-rays for 24 hours. A green beryl exposed to deuterons became turbid and developed basal cracks. Other reports state that X-rays turned pale blue beryl to pale green, reverting to the original color when heated, while pink morganite changed to a "muddy" pink after irradiation, and again reverted to its original color when heated. No changes under UV have been noted in emerald or pale blue specimens.

References: C. Frondel, *Gemmologist* 21 (1952): 197-200.

G. O. Wild, *Rocks and Minerals* 7 (1932): 9-13.

BORACITE. Slightly bluish xls (Stassfurt) to pale yellow under Ra rays.

BORAX. Radium rays, no change.

BRAZILIANITE. Olive-green Brazilian xls pale to yellowish-green and may bleach entirely under heat treatment. Electron beam, no change. Yellow under X-rays to slightly darker yellow.

BROMYRITE. Radium rays, 7 days, yellowish-brown color unchanged.

CALCITE. Colorless unchanged under radium rays, 7 days; violet under Ra rays, 10 days, to darker violet (Joplin), and when heated to 330° C. (626° F.) in CO_2 atmosphere no change, but strongly heated in O_2 changed to colorless. Cathode rays or UV, no change in colorless material. Some yellow xls (Joplin) lose color when heated, but regain same when irradiated under Ra.

Colorless material turns yellow under Ra and sometimes lilac or blue-gray under cathode rays. Mexican white banded onyx heat-treated to 500° C. (932° F.) develops sharp brown banding (iron oxides), as does the material from San Luis Province, Argentina; such bands can be dyed afterward to blue by immersion in dil. sol. calcium ferricyanide mixed with dil. HCl. Larger stones fracture under heat treatment.

CANCRINITE. Colorless, under X-rays develops bluish veinlets.

CARNALLITE. Unchanged by UV or radium rays.

CELESTITE. Natural blue color lost when heated but the bleached xls, and some naturally colorless xls become blue when irradiated. Colorless to blue under radium rays after 30 days; similar change under electron beam with zoning commonly observed.

CERARGYRITE. In daylight turns brownish violet with atmospheric moisture accelerating change; under radium rays or UV turns more brownish.

CERUSSITE. Some colorless material becomes bluish under radium rays.

CHRYSOBERYL. No changes under any heating or irradiation, alexandrite included.

CINNABAR. In daylight alters on surface, developing increasingly dark purplish black metallic coating; more rapid under UV; unchanged by radium rays.

CORUNDUM. Heating results are variable and apparently variable within specimens of the same color from the same locality. Purple (Ceylon) heated to 450° C. (842° F.) to pink. Blue (Ceylon) at 400° C. (752° F.) to faint yellow; other blues do not change. Very dark blue (Anakie) with o-ray pure dark blue and e-ray greenish-blue changed as follows when heated to about 1,275° C. (2,327° F.): o-ray to blue, gray-blue, green, pale yellow; e-ray to blue, blue-violet, violet, red-violet, red, and finally pale yellow. Ruby: following sequences of change reported by various observers when specimens heated to 1,300° C. (2,372° F.) and higher: (1) red → greenish, (2) red → no change even when heated to white glow, (3) red → green → colorless, (4) red → gray → greenish or colorless. Green color appears at about 1,300° C. (2,372° F.). All rubies returned to original red color after cooling. Synthetic ruby: o-ray (violet-red) to red, pale yellow, yellow, yellowish-green, pale green, pale yellow; e-ray (orange-red) to yellow, paler yellow.

Under UV the following changes were observed: ruby, more violet; blue to paler blue; dark blue unchanged; brownish violet unchanged; blue-green to slightly bluer.

X-rays seem to have no permanent effect, with all specimens returning to normal color under sunlight. Colorless synthetic, slightly brown; colorless natural, same. Pink synth., reddish-amber; rose-pink synth., same; and rose-red synth., no change. Pale salmon natural to amber. Yellow natural to somewhat darker yellow or amber. Blue (Ceylon) variable, some to bluish-gray or bluish-green, others unchanged. Blue also reported changing to dark green or darker blue. Blue-gray to amber. Lavender or blue-violet to amber.

Radium rays appear to create more enduring color changes although some changes are reversed by exposure to light. Colorless (Ceylon) to deep golden-yellow, or under Ra (12-24 hrs) to straw-yellow or golden, losing color when exposed to light. Blue (Ceylon) to deep golden-yellow or yellowish-brown. Pale blue (Ceylon), under Ra (12-24 hrs) to pale yellow or yellowish-green. Medium blue to green, thence to yellow. Dark blue (Siam, Australia, Kashmir, Germany), no change. Dark blue (Australia) with blue and yellow-green dichroism to greenish, but the latter destroyed by heating to 200° C. (392° F.). Some blues (Ceylon, Siam), unchanged even after weeks of exposure to Ra. Blue-green to greener. Ruby to violet, blue, green, and finally yellow; violet-red ruby to redder; red ruby to pure red; also rubies that are unchanged. Brown-violet to brown. Pale yellow (Ceylon) under Ra (12-24 hrs) to deep yellow, some of which darken further under UV or cathode rays. Other yellows do not change.

CRYOLITE. No change under radium.

CUPRITE. Light causes alteration of surface to darker hue, almost metallic in luster and hiding the deep red beneath.

DEMANTOID. No changes under irradiations or heating.

DIADOCHITE. From brown to orange under radium (4 days).

DIAMOND. Almost entirely unaffected

by heat; one example of a yellow diamond subjected to 1,500° C. (2,732° F.) became colorless but also cloudy.

Radium chloride rays are effective in changing color. Colorless to blue; colorless (Borneo) to yellowish; colorless (20 days) to slightly brownish; colorless to greenish but on surface only; colorless (16 days) to yellow, with failure to revert to original color even after 250° C. (482° F.); colorless, Brazil, no change. Yellow, South Africa, 100 days, to v. slightly yellower; brown, S. Africa, 32 hrs., to orange-grayish; brown to violet-brown; gray unchanged. Greenish, Brazil, to bluish-green (surface); green to slightly bluish.

X-rays sometimes affect color. Colorless unchanged; yellow to somewhat yellower; pale yellow to paler yellow(!); brown, South Africa, 32 hrs., slightly violet-grayish; pale brown to grayish-brown.

UV irradiation sometimes changes color. Brownish-gray, South Africa, to colorless; brown to brownish-violet; gray to somewhat paler.

Protons, deuterons, and neutrons change color permanently. Colorless diamonds change to green, but if allowed to become too hot, turn brown or yellow. Neutrons impart a blue color to some stones.

DIOPTASE. Electron beam or X-ray, no effect.

EUCLASE. Electron beam, no effect.

FLUORITE. An extensive literature exists on color in fluorites; see Doelter references below. Heated specimens are generally decolorized by 220° C. (428° F.); other changes include dark purple to green, green (Derbyshire) to pale violet, thence to colorless, and pink (Switzerland) to colorless. X-rays seem to have little effect with no change being observed on yellow or blue material. Cathode-ray treatment changed pale green to pale violet, and pink to darker pink. Heat-decolorized specimens, when treated with radium rays, tend to assume a final hue of blue-green or blue-violet, but decolorized pink has been noted changing to purplish-red; such induced colors vanish after about 8-14 days, more slowly in darkness. Blue-green (Appenzell), 4 days, changed to darker blue-green; further treatment to 3 months produced a much darker blue-green. Yellow (Freiberg), greenish-blue under

radium, and rose (Gotthard) to slightly darker rose. In some instances treatment of Ra-colored fluorites by UV results in restoration of original hues.

GARNIERITE. Green, radium rays (14 days) changed to bluish-green.

GREENOCKITE. Unchanged by radium, cathode rays, or UV.

GYPSUM. Colorless unchanged by radium rays (7 weeks). Alabaster heat treated 2 hrs. at 120° C. (248° F.) develops porosity which enables dyeing with organic dyes.

HALITE. See Doelter (1910) for extensive discussion of causes of color. Colorless, radium 7 days, slightly yellowish; some turns blue under cathode rays. Pale blue under 24 hrs. radium rays becomes brownish-yellow; deep indigo under Ra 2 weeks becomes deep claret. Dark blue heated to 340° C. (644° F.) begins to turn violet, and at 360° C. (680° F.) changes to purple, and finally, at 385° C. (725° F.) suddenly becomes colorless. Pale blue at 250° C. (482° F.) to rose, at 300° C. (572° F.) to colorless. Dark blue specimens tend to return to a lighter shade of blue via the same color route upon cooling.

HAUYNE. Pale blue (Germany) to deeper hue, somewhat violetish, under radium; to pale bluish-gray under UV; some Hauyne turns paler under sunlight. Bleached with difficulty by heat.

HEMATITE. No change under any radiation.

HEMIMORPHITE. Colorless to brownish-yellow after 30 days radium irradiation.

HYDROZINCITE. No change under cathode or radium rays.

IODYRITE. Gray Andreasberg material to dark gray after 7 days radium.

JADEITE. Some rind sections of waterworn pebbles from Burma can be heat treated at about 250°-300° C. (482°-572° F.) to convert the iron compounds infiltrated into the pores between xl grains to colored iron oxides, e.g., to red, orange, yellow.

KAINITE. Unchanged by UV or radium; other authorities state that colorless and lilac materials turn greenish-yellow under Ra; when heated to 200° C. (392° F.) kainite colors become cloudy; also some naturally lilac material heated to the same temperature turns colorless, but changes afterward to pale turquoise blue when irradiated.

KYANITE. Scarcely any change in color even up to 600° C. (1,112° F.) and then only a slight paling in hue is noted; no change under 7 days radium.

LANGBEINITE. Unchanged under UV or radium rays. Some violet material is bleached by heating at 200° C. (392° F.).

LAPIS LAZULI. No change in blue or white components under X-rays.

LEPIDOLITE. Pales rapidly after several months' exposure to direct sunlight, and less rapidly under artificial light; some specimens turn pale gray without trace of original purplish or pink hues.

MICA. Species not stated, colored brown under radium rays.

MICROCLINE. Electron beam turns ordinary pale colored material to gray; in pegmatitites, dark gray material is often found surrounding radioactive minerals, and when exposed to surface weathering, becomes heavily iron stained. Reddish color of some types of microcline is supposed by some to be due to irradiation from associated radioactive minerals. Amazonite loses color when strongly heated, or irradiated with radium or cathode rays; the color, according to some authorities, returns after irradiation with X-rays or radium rays.

NATROLITE. No change under radium rays after 7 weeks.

OBSIDIAN. Unaffected by radiation from cobalt-60 isotope; unchanged in color under pale red heat but exfoliates and turns silvery-white upon exterior when heated more strongly.

OLIGOCLASE. Colorless turns orange or green under X-rays.

OLIVINE (Peridot). No changes under heat treatment or irradiation.

ORTHOCLASE. Some turns brown under radium.

OPAL. Translucent material commonly turns white when dried; most opals, including Mexican cherry opal, hyalite, and transparent orange are unaffected by irradiation, UV, etc.

ORPIMENT. Becomes yellower under X-rays, and somewhat more orange under UV.

PHENAKITE. Colorless material to yellowish-brown under X-rays.

PREHNITE. No change under heat treatment or electron beam.

PROUSTITE. Rapidly darkens and develops silvery coating when exposed to strong light, especially sunlight.

PYROMORPHITE. Under radium or cathode rays some brown material turns to slightly darker brown. Originally brown material may turn paler brown when heated.

PYROPE. Under radium, red to paler red; otherwise no changes from heating or irradiation.

QUARTZ. The dyeing of porous cryptocrystalline varieties is dealt with elsewhere. Many white or pale gray chalcedonies contain iron compounds which are converted into reddish or brownish oxides by heat treatment, generally over 150° C. (302° F.). One investigator recommends use of an ordinary household oven with initial temperature set at 200° F. (93° C.), raising the temperature in increments of 50° F. (10° C.) each 15 minutes until a final temperature of 550° F. (288° C.) is reached. This treatment may be extended to petrified woods, silicified whalebone, and other quartz materials which contain iron compounds.

Heat treatment of tigereye turns the yellow pigment to red.

Translucent chalcedony becomes smoky when irradiated by gammas from a Co-60 source.

Smoky quartz is abundant in pegmatites, and when exposed in outcrops is commonly observed to be pale to colorless, apparently having bleached under sunlight. However, in a yearlong experiment with smoky quartz from Brazil, a piece placed on the author's house roof failed to change hue in the slightest degree, leading to the conclusion that much longer periods are required for significant changes. Decolorization is rapid and consistent under heat; Swiss smoky begins to decolorize at 277° C. (530° F.), and is colorless at 300° C. (572° F.). Other observers indicate loss of most color in the range 300°-450° C. (572°-842° F.) and absolute loss in the range 500°-600° C. (932°-1,112° F.). Another observer gives complete decolorization in 5 minutes at 600° C. (1,112° F.). In recent experiments, Dietrich (1971) observed that smoky quartz became slightly paler after 72 hours at 250° C. (482° F.), and colorless after 30 hours at 320° C. (608° F.) and after 14 hours at 450° C. (842° F.), and at higher temperatures; after 72 hours at 650° C. (1,202° F.) smoky quartz changed from colorless to milky.

Smoky citrine loses its smoky hue at 250°-350° C. (482°-662° F.), leaving a residual citrine hue, or yellowish-brownish, orange-yellow, etc.

Under radium or other "hard" radiations, smoky quartz (also rock crystal) becomes a peculiar brownish-black, the same hue so commonly observed in quartz cores of pegmatites bearing radioactive species. Smoky quartz is scarcely affected by X-rays, with induced smoky hues being quickly dispelled by heat.

Rock crystal turns smoky under radium rays, gammas, and Co-60 radiations, the hues ranging from pale brown to blackish-brown, depending on the material and the length of exposure. Synthetic hydro-thermal rock crystal turned smoky in 6 hours under Co-60 radiations.

Citrine from Brazil turned from yellow to brownish-red at 450°-550° C. (842°-1,022° F.); Madagascar material turned to the same hues at 530° C. (986° F.). Under radium rays citrine may turn blackish-brown, but there is no change under UV.

Amethyst begins to decolorize in the range 280°-300° C. (536°-572° F.) and is colorless in 400°-500° C. (752°-932° F.). Sometimes a weak purplish hue returns spontaneously after several months. Decolorized material is restored to some extent by irradiation with gammas from Co-60 or other source. Some observers claim no changes occur in amethyst under radium rays or UV but others observed loss of color in weakly pigmented specimens under Ra. One observer irradiated Jacobina, Brazil, amethyst with UV (Hg-quartz lamp) at a distance of 30 mm from the lamp lens and found loss of color in 8 hours; the greenish residual color observed in some specimens is not affected by further UV treatment. Decolorized amethyst may be restored by gamma radiation, but some heat-bleached Brazilian specimens turned variously grayish-brown, smoky violet, or dark violet. Prolonged exposure to X-rays causes amethyst to intensify in hue.

Recent heat-treatment work on amethyst by Dietrich (1971) showed that after 72 hours at 250° C. (482° F.) no change in color occurred but after 30 hours at 320° C. (608° F.) the specimens became slightly lighter in hue; after 14 hours at 450° C. (842° F.) colorless to white was achieved, and after 72 hours at 650° C. (1,202° F.), the amethyst turned from colorless to yellowish.

Burnt amethyst is the name applied to certain stones which are heat-treated to citrine hues, which appear about 430° C. (806° F.) and begin to disappear at 580° C. (1,076° F.), becoming very pale at 685° C. (1,265° F.) and finally changing to milky at 775° C. (1,427° F.). Other observers give the range for appearance of milkiness as 600°-750° C. (1,112°-1,382° F.). Traces of green in certain amethysts appear after cooling and such are known from many deposits, among them, the Four Peaks deposit in Arizona. The darkest greens are obtained from amethysts of the Monte-zuma mine, Minas Gerais, Brazil, after heat treatment to 510° C. (950° F.); the color is a peculiar grayish or oily green, with the cut gems apparently less brilliant than one would expect from rough that appears quite transparent and flawless. Miscellaneous observations of results of heat treatment of amethyst to citrine or colorless follow: Serra, Brazil, to yellow at 750°-775° C. (1,382°-1,427° F.); Uruguay to colorless at 575° C. (1,067° F.), or sometimes yellow at 750° C. (1,382° F.); Bahia, Brazil, colorless at 590° C. (1,094° F.), or yellow at 700° C. (1,292° F.); Madagascar, colorless over 500° C. (932° F.).

Dietrich (1971) heat-treated rose quartz and succeeded in driving off the color after 14 hours at 450° C. (842° F.) and at higher temperatures. Rose quartz is rapidly blackened by Co-60; under radium rays, a specimen turned dark brown after exposure for 35 days; under 32 hours of X-rays another sample turned pale brown as also occurred under the electron beam, but under UV one sample turned colorless.

REALGAR. Light, especially sunlight, rapidly alters realgar to orpiment (yellow powdery coating). UV, 20 hrs., produces similar rapid change; under radium rays, becomes darker red.

RHODOCHROSITE. Unchanged by irradiation; rapid blackening of surface promoted by light and moisture (rainfall).

RHODONITE. Unchanged by irradiation; similar blackening as with RHODOCHROSITE.

RUTILE. Natural material unaffected by any irradiation; synthetic material heat treated in O_2 atmosphere changes from starting black boule to very pale straw-yellow via a sequence of color changes: black, very dark blue, paler blue, green, red, etc. Heat treatment does not affect natural rutile in the slightest.

SANIDINE' Some turns brown under radium.

SCAPOLITE. Colorless to purple under X-rays and yellow to grayish-purple. Similar results under electron beam but color is fugitive.

SIDERITE. Pale yellow to brownish-yellow under radium rays.

SIMPSONITE. Unchanged under irradiation.

SMITHSONITE. Greenish material becomes paler and turns to white under 7 days radium rays. Not affected by light.

SODALITE. Colorless material (hackmannite) to red under X-rays; when pink, as when first removed from the ground, rapidly fades in daylight, sometimes in seconds, but restored by UV. Some bleached hackmannite turns purple under radium rays or UV. Heat treatment destroys blue color in some sodalites but this returns under radium irradiation. Colorless material turns blue or violet under radium.

SPHALERITE. Pale yellow or reddish yellow (Picos de Europa) becomes darker after 5 days under radium; also darker under UV. Normally unaffected by light or heat treatment.

SPHENE. Dark brown (Canada) heated to red heat changes to dark brownish-orange and becomes more transparent or translucent (personal communication from G. G. Waite). Brown of Baja California similarly treated becomes pale orange-brown; green and yellow unaffected. Yellow (Sulzbachtal) under 7 days radium to slightly yellower.

SPINEL. Red-purple (Ceylon) heated to 542° C. (975° F.) became red, at 936°-1,319° C. (1,717°-2,406° F.) pale yellow. Pale purplish-red (Ceylon) heated to 125° C. (257° F.) became pale red, at 520° C. (968° F.) pale yellow, at 913° C. (1,675° F.) yellowish-green, at 1,000° C. (1,832° F.) green, and at 1,313° C. (2,395° F.) pale yellow. Blue-green (Ceylon) passed through these colors during heating: paler blue-green, green, pale yellow-green, pale yellow at 1,242° C. (2,268° F.). Red passed through: brown or opaque black, then cooled via greenish, colorless, red, or also through violet when cooling. No permanent change as a result of heat treatment. Under X-ray, gray-blue slightly darkened, same for red.

SPODUMENE. Yellow, yellow-green (commonly called "hiddenite," but lacking Cr, from Brazil) are permanent and are unaffected by heat treatment as is the true hiddenite of North Carolina. A peculiar pale olive-greenish or bluish-green noted in some specimens rapidly disappears under exposure to light or under moderate heat in the vicinity of 150° C. (302° F.). The red or red purple tints of kunzite are somewhat more permanent, but generally kunzite is decolorized at 400° C. (752° F.). Some kunzites from Brazil, in which the peculiar greenish tints mentioned above are admixed, have been heat-treated in ordinary kitchen ovens at about 150° C. (302° F.) to remove the greenish hues and leave pure red or purplish tints. Hiddenite is unaffected by irradiation; yellow or yellow-green unchanged under Ra, or perhaps made slightly lighter; also made slightly lighter under UV. One observer notes that X-rays make hiddenite slightly darker, and radium rays, slightly lighter; he also notes that hiddenite heated in oxygen becomes pale gray but greener when heated in reducing atmospheres. Kunzite under X-ray to green, which fades quickly under light, and even more rapidly when heated to 200°-250° C. (392°-482° F.); under UV also green but not invariably so. Colorless to green under X-rays. Under radium, California kunzite changes pink to colorless to green, the last hue, when specimens heated or exposed to sunlight, returning to pink somewhat more intense than before. Pink bleached at 500° C. (932° F.) and exposed to radium turned green; when the green material was heated to 200° C. (392° F.) or exposed to sunlight, the pink returned; the final pink did not bleach after heating for 24 hrs. at 250° C. (482°

F.). The behavior of Madagascar kunzite was found to differ in turning brown after radium irradiation. When exposed to light, or when heated to 80° C. (176° F.), irradiated material turned to green, and when heated to 250° C. (482° F.), it turned pink. The pleochroism of kunzite is markedly changed after irradiation. In general, kunzites fade when exposed to tungsten light, and probably also under fluorescent light, and rapidly in sunlight but the process may take quite a number of years as shown by kunzites exhibited in museums that became colorless at least 30-50 years after mining.

STRONTIANITE. Colorless, no change under radium but some authorities claim that some becomes brownish-yellow.

STRONTIUM TITANATE. Colorless, no change under electron beam.

SULFUR. Yellow (Sicily) turned slightly greenish under radium rays after 32 days.

SYLVITE. No change under UV or radium.

THENARDITE. Some bluish-gray material is bleached by heat.

TOPAZ. Yellow, orange-yellow, orange-brown xls (Brazil) when heat-treated in the range 300°-450° C. (572°-842° F.) turn pink after cooling, the intensity of color directly proportional to the intensity of the starting hue. One observer states that xls heated in excess of 450° C. (842° F.) may be entirely decolorized upon cooling. The so-called "pinked" specimens are returned to orange-brown under X-rays. In general, X-rays intensify the hues of Brazilian yellows, oranges, and similar colors; UV sometimes causes yellow to turn lilac, while radium rays cause effects similar to X-rays. Pale brown xls (Utah) change to smoky brown under X-rays, such color being easily removed by heat; probably the Mexican rhyolite topaz xls react the same way although some of the latter are decidedly colored by very small acicular inclusions of rutile which of course does not change under any form of irradiation. Pale brown pegmatite xls lose color in light, rapidly in sunlight, turning either to colorless or blue, or to blue zoned xls; the blue is present at all times and is merely masked by the brown. Pale blue is permanent but under X-rays seems to become amber, a fugitive hue easily removed by heat. X-rays are reported to turn pale blue to brownish-purples, also removable by heat. Colorless xls to pale yellow under X-rays for 45 min.; removed by heat. Under radium colorless xls turn orange, also heat removable. Some pale blue Brazilian xls are unaffected by radium.

TOURMALINE. In general heat treatment of tourmaline produces few if any results in the majority of specimens, with some exceptions which may be confined to crystals from specific deposits only. Dark green (Brazil) reported to change to "emerald" at 300°-400° C. (572°-752° F.); similar results in this range also reported for dark green stones from Ceylon and Usakos, South West Africa. Another observer reports dark green becoming paler after treatment in the range 600°-650° C. (1,112°-1,202° F.), and blue-green to paler at 650° C. (1,202° F.). Red (rubellite) showed following color sequence during heating: brownish-red at 280° C. (536° F.), decolorization began at 370° C. (698° F.), milky green at 500° C. (932° F.); cooled to very slightly greenish, nearly colorless. Another observer gives dark red turning to pink after treatment in the range 550°-600° C. (1,022°-1,112° F.).

Under radium rays, colorless to reddish-orange, and to violet under UV; to permanent red hue under electron beam. Dark green under radium to dark reddish-purple; others report no change under radium, electron beam, or UV. Pale green under X-rays to pale yellow; pink to dark reddish-purple. Red to yellowish under radium, or to violet under UV.

UVAROVITE. No change under radium.

VIVIANITE. Colorless, transparent crystals in the ground very rapidly turn to pale blue, greenish-blue, dark blue, dark greenish-blue, indigo-blue, and to bluish-black upon exposure to light. In large crystals, exposure to light promotes disintegration due to creation of internal stresses.

WOLLASTONITE. White to very slightly yellowish under radium (100 days).

WULFENITE. No change under radium; colors extremely stable.

ZIRCON. Heat treatment of "high" or internally undamaged zircons produces spectacular results but "low" or metamict

Color Produced in Glasses by Certain Additives

Additive	Color(s)
Gold	Red, purple, blue
Cuprous oxide	Red, green, blue
Selenium	Ruby, orange
Silver salts	Yellow
Uranium salts	Yellow, green (fluorescent!)
Iron salts	Green, yellow
Sodium dichromate	Green
Cobalt oxide	Blue, black
Manganese dioxide (pyrolusite)	Purple, black
Calcium fluoride (fluorite)	Milky
Feldspar	Milky
Antimony sulfide	Yellow
Tin dioxide	Opaque
Titanium dioxide	Yellow, blue

zircons do not change color as in the typical milky greenish or olive-green crystals of Ceylon. The latter, and other metamict zircons, are heat-treated in the range 1,000°-1,200° C. (1,832°-2,192° F.) to restore crystallinity for purposes of X-ray work. Over about 150° C. (302° F.) natural red-brown or brownish-red crystals (Ceylon, Indochina, etc.) begin to change color via paling of the original hue, thence to some shade of straw or golden-yellow, orange-yellow, or colorless. Much higher temperatures, e.g., red or dull white heat, are required for rapid change. A brown-red crystal (Tasmania) began to pale at 200°-250° C. (392°-482° F.), bleaching at 300°-320° C. (572°-608° F.), with some trace of color left even after maintaining at 600° C. (1,112° F.) for 1 hr. Red-brown (Indochina) in oxidizing atmosphere, turned to colorless or yellowish over 700° C. (1,292° F.); red-brown (Ceylon) in reducing atmosphere, to blue or colorless at 700°-800° C. (1,292°-1,472° F.). Green-blue stones at 380°-500° C. (716°-932° F.) turn pure blue. Crystals or gems seldom crack under heat treatment, even when extremely sudden temperature changes are used.

Under X-rays, brown, no change; heat treated blue to grayer. Under UV, brown to brownish-gray and yellowish-gray-green to slightly paler. Under radium, natural red-brown not affected but decolorized specimens rapidly return to original colors. Heat-treated blues also return to red-brown after radium treatment, while yellowish-gray-green stones turn somewhat grayer.

ZOISITE. The recently discovered stones of Tanzania ("tanzanite") are regularly heat-treated at c. 370° C. (698° F.) to remove undesirable pleochroic components, namely, the brownish-purplish, reddish, or greenish tinges, and to leave behind the more heat-stable blues or purplish-blues. Heat treatment is done in an ordinary kitchen oven at about 180°-260° C. (356°-500° F.). Apparently the stones are resistant to cracking although they are customarily embedded in sand to cover.

References: R. V. Dietrich, "Quartz—Two New Blues," *Mineralogical Record* 2, no. 2 (1971): 79-82.

C. Doelter, *Das Radium und die Farben* (Dresden: T. Steinkopff, 1910).

C. Doelter, *Die Farben der Mineralien insbesondere der Edelsteine* (Braunschweig: Vieweg & Sohn, 1915).

C. Frondel, "Effect of Heat on the Colour of Beryl," *Gemmologist* 21 (1952): 197-200.

H. W. Kohn and B. M. Benjamin, "Radiation Coloration of Silica Minerals," *Amer. Mineral.* 46 (1961): 218-25.

O. I. Lee, "Reversible Photosensitivity in Hackmanite," *Amer. Mineral.* 21 (1936): 764.

J. Lietz and W. Munchberg, "Über die Färbung des Amethyst," *N. Jb. Min., Mh.* 2 (1957), pp. 25-33.

M. T. Mackowsky, "Farbveredlung von Schmucksteinen durch Brennen," *Deutsche Goldschmiede-Zeitung,* no. 23 (1939).

F. H. Pough, "Experiments in X-Ray

Irradiation of Gem Stones," *Amer. Mineral.* 32 (1947): 31-43.

F. H. Pough, "Coloration of Gemstones by Electron Bombardment, *Zs. Deutschen Ges. f. Edelsteinkunde,* Schlossmacher Festschrift (1957). 71-78.

K. Przibram, *Irradiation Colours and Luminescence* (London: Pergamon Press, 1956).

K. Simon, "Beiträge zur Kenntnis der Mineralfarben," *N. Jb. Min. B.* 26 (1908): 249-95.

O. Weigel, "Über die Farbenänderung von Korund und Spinell mit der Temperatur," *N. Jb. Min. B.* 48 (1923): 274-309.

G. O. Wild, "The Treatment of Gem Stones by Heat," *Rocks and Minerals* 7 (1932): 9-13.

Part 7 / Physical Properties of Minerals and Gemstones Aiding in Identification

SPECIFIC GRAVITY DETERMINATION

Archimedes' principle: A body wholly or partly immersed in a fluid loses weight equal to the weight of the fluid displaced. A floating body displaces fluid equal to its own weight.

Density: The concentration of mass per unit volume.

Specific gravity: The ratio of the mass of a body to the mass of water which has the same volume. Water has an SG of exactly 1, when measured at 4° C. (39.2° F.). At higher or lower temperatures its density is less and corrections must be made to SG determinations as explained below.

Properties of water: Maximum density is found at 3.98° C. (39° F.) but standard density of 1.0 is assumed at 4° C. (39.2° F.). Densities of water at ordinary working temperatures are as follows:

Temp. (°C.)	Temp. (°F.)	Density (gm/cc)
10	50.0	0.9997
15	59.0	0.9991
20	68.0	0.9982
25	77.0	0.9971
30	86.0	0.9957

Temperature corrections: For determinations at other than 4° C. (39.2° F.) *multiply* SG figure by water density for such temperature. For approximate values this correction may be neglected but for liquids other than water it cannot be safely ignored without serious error.

SPECIFIC GRAVITY FORMULAS. Express the ratio of the weight of the body to the weight of an equal volume of water:

$$SG = \frac{weight\ of\ body}{weight\ of\ displaced\ water} \quad (1)$$

Or, because the loss of weight by the body is equal to the weight of the displaced water, the formula is also written:

$$SG = \frac{weight\ of\ body}{weight\ loss\ in\ water} \quad (2)$$

And also, when the specimen is suspended in water, as from a string or wire attached to a balance, a loss of weight is noted, and the formula can be modified further as follows:

$$SG = \frac{weight\ of\ body\ in\ air}{weight\ in\ air - weight\ in\ water} \quad (3)$$

where the weight in air minus the weight in water expresses the weight loss in water.

A CRUDE DISPLACEMENT METHOD. Weigh specimen in gm. Partly fill glass cylinder graduated in cc with water to convenient level, noting volume. Drop in specimen and note new volume. Difference between volumes = volume of water displaced = weight of water displaced in gm.

For very large specimens, weigh as before in kg or lb. Fill bucket to brim with water hanging over another bucket or pan which has been previously weighed. Place specimen into upper bucket and catch overflow in bottom container which is now weighed and the weight of displaced water determined (after subtracting for the weight of the container).

A BETTER METHOD. Weigh specimen. Place a beaker partly filled with water on a balance and weigh. Leaving beaker and water in position, submerge the specimen by means of a very thin thread or wire into the water. The beaker + water gains weight; rebalance and note new reading. The difference between this new weight and the earlier weight is equal to the weight of water displaced by the specimen. The above method eliminates the need for pans, as explained in the method following.

USUAL METHOD (SUSPENSION). Weigh specimen in air by either placing in a wire basket or metal pan attached to one arm of a balance specifically for the purpose of SG determinations. Lacking these, attach the specimen by very thin thread or wire. Note weight. Now bring underneath a beaker of water such that the specimen is completely submerged. Read new weight on balance. This is "weight in water" and is entered in formula (3).

PYCNOMETER METHOD. The pyc- nometer is a small (about 5 cm or $2''$ tall) specially made glass bottle with close- fitting stopper pierced by a small vertical opening which enables the bottle to be filled to exactly the same amount each time without entrapment of air bubbles. It is designed for use with small grains of material. The method is troublesome, requires great care and is time consuming, but nevertheless is capable of great accuracy. The formula is given as follows:

$$SG = \frac{L(W_2 - W_1)}{(W_4 - W_1) - (W_3 - W_2)} \quad (4)$$

where:

L = density of liquid used
W_1 = pycnometer weight alone
W_2 = pycnometer wgt. + specimen wgt.
W_3 = pycnometer wgt. + specimen wgt. + liquid fill wgt.
W_4 = pycnometer wgt. + liquid wgt.

As can be seen, $W_2 - W_1$ gives weight of specimen in air, $W_4 - W_1$ gives weight of liquid, and $W_3 - W_2$ gives weight of the liquid *less* the volume displaced by the specimen. Hence when the last two quantities are subtracted as required by the formula the difference is equal to the weight of the displaced liquid (formula (1) above).

FINDING THE WEIGHT OF EACH MINERAL IN A TWO-MINERAL MIX- TURE. In a mass of gold-quartz, how much of it is gold? Solve as follows.

Determine SG of the entire mass as usual, and then the volume by using this formula:

$$\text{volume} = \frac{\text{weight of mass}}{SG} \quad (5)$$

Use the following formula to determine *weight percent* of one of the components, in this case, quartz, designated by the letter x.

vol. of entire mass =

$$\frac{\text{mass wgt\% } - \text{ quartz wgt\%}}{SG \text{ of gold}} +$$

$$\frac{\text{quartz wgt\%}}{SG \text{ of quartz}} \quad (6)$$

Example: The specimen of gold-quartz weighs 156 gm and its SG is 12. Assume SG of gold at 18 and that of quartz at 2.65. Using formula (5) the volume is found to be $\frac{156}{12} = 13$. Then

$$13 = \frac{100 - x}{18} + \frac{x}{2.65}.$$

Solve for x.

Answer: quartz is 23%, or the weight of the quartz is 36 grams while the weight of the gold (77%) is 120 grams.

Cause of Specific Gravity Determination Errors

1. Poor specimen. Select only specimens which are monomineralic. Avoid those with cracks, fissures, pockets, or other irregularities likely to entrap air. If cracked or fissured specimens must be used, place in fluid under bell jar and draw vacuum prior to weight-in-fluid step. Always use largest specimen compatible with size limitations of equipment.
2. Surface tension of water. Unless wetting agent is added to water, it fails to properly wet specimen and facilitate removal of bubbles and entrapped air from specimen and also from the suspension threads, wires, spirals, pans, etc., which are immersed in the water at the same time. A droplet of wetting agent (or household detergent) about the size of a head of a pin is usually enough to destroy surface tension in 1 quart or liter of water.
3. Failure to degas water. Use boiled distilled water and allow to cool to room temperature.

4. Failure to record and compensate for temperature corrections.
5. Failure to multiply SG by density of liquid other than water.
6. In pycnometer method, failure to ensure absolute dryness of bottle before work, and failure to carefully dry off exterior when overflow through stopper takes place.

DETERMINATION OF SG OF FLUIDS. Since rock crystal quartz is extremely constant at SG = 2.6508, use a clear, flawless piece (or gem) for the determination below.

SG of fluid =

$$\frac{\text{SG of quartz} \times \text{loss of wgt. in fluid}}{\text{wgt. of quartz}} \quad (7)$$

DENSITY FLUID INDICATORS. Indicators are small solids which float, sink, or remain poised in a given fluid when their SG matches that of the fluid. Very carefully calibrated indicators are sold by laboratory supply houses in a wide range of densities, 0.700-7.50. Good indicators for testing gems and minerals of medium densities can be cut from clear specimens of quartz, calcite, and green tourmaline, while a small crystal of diamond is useful for slightly higher values. Gem testing density fluid indicators made from glasses are sold by gemological instrument suppliers.

FLUID SG BY HYDROMETER. Small glass hydrometers can quickly determine SG of fluids when of the proper SG range for the fluids involved. If a hydrometer calibrated in the Beaume scale should be used the following conversion gives the SG of the fluid.

$$\text{SG of fluid} = \frac{145}{145 - \text{Beaume reading}} \quad (8)$$

FLUID SG BY REFRACTOMETER READING. Mixtures of liquids display varying refractive indices according to relative proportions of fluids present in the mixture. Several mixtures are made and SG determined by means of indicators; droplets are placed on the prism of the refractometer and an index determined for each SG. Plot on graph paper using SG versus refractive index, and connect points to form a line graph of the function (usually a straight line). A fluid of any specified SG can be prepared simply by mixing components until the refractive index shows that it is at value corresponding to the desired SG.

MAIN TABLE OF DENSITY LIQUIDS

For details on properties see "Chemicals List" (p. 23) also see abbreviated list following for principal heavy liquids in common use.

Chemical name	G at 20° C. (68° F.)
Hexane	0.66
Heptane	0.68
Isopropyl alcohol [propanol]	0.79
Methyl alcohol [wood alcohol, methanol]	0.79
Ethyl alcohol [grain alcohol, ethanol]	0.79
Acetone	0.79
Kerosene, variable	0.80-0.84
Amyl alcohol	0.814
Mineral oil, variable	0.84
Toluene	0.867
Amyl acetate ["banana oil"]	0.88
Ethyl valerate	0.88
o-Xylene	0.88
Ethyl butyrate	0.88
Benzene	0.88
Decalin	0.896
Methyl butyrate	0.898

Chemical name	G at 20° C. (68° F.)
Cineole [eucalyptol]	0.927
NN-Dimethylformamide	0.934 (25°)
Xylidine [NN-dimethylaniline]	0.956
Cyclohexanol [hexalin]	0.96
o-Toluidine	0.998
Water	1.00
Aniline	1.02
Benzaldehyde [oil of bitter almonds]	1.04
Cinnamaldehyde	1.05
Quinaldine	1.06
Triethyl ester phosphoric acid	1.069
Quinoline	1.09
Chlorobenzene	1.106
Benzyl benzoate	1.11
Glycol [ethylene glycol]	1.11
Diethylene glycol ["antifreeze"]	1.12
Table salt in water, for amber, 40 gm/250 ml	1.12-1.14
2-Nitrotoluene [o-nitrotoluene]	1.16
Methyl salicylate [oil of wintergreen]	1.17
1,1-Dichloroethane	1.176
1,3-Dichloropropane [trimethylene chloride]	1.188
1-Chloronaphthalene [monochloronaphthalene]	1.194
Nitrobenzene	1.20
1,2-Dichloroethane [ethylene chloride]	1.235
Glycerine	1.26
Carbon disulfide	1.26
Dichloromethane [methylene chloride]	1.327
2-Bromotoluene	1.42
Bromoethane [ethyl bromide]	1.46
Chloroform	1.483
1-Bromonaphthalene [monobromonaphthalene]	1.483
Bromobenzene	1.495
unsymm.-Tetrachlorethane	1.541
Carbon tetrachloride	1.594
symm.-Tetrachlorethane [acetylene tetrachloride]	1.595
Hexachloro-1,3-butadiene	1.682
	1.671 (25°)
Pentachlorethane [pentalin]	1.690
1-Iodonaphthalene [monoiodonaphthalene]	1.74
Iodobenzene [monoiodobenzene]	1.83
Ethyl iodide [iodoethane]	1.936
1,3-Dibromopropane [trimethylene bromide]	1.98
1,1-Dibromoethane	2.06
1,2-Dibromoethane [ethylene bromide]	2.18
1,2-Dibromoethanol [symm.-dibromoethylene]	2.246
1,2-Dibromoethanol (trans.) [dibromoethylene]	2.31
Dibromomethane [methylene bromide]	2.497
unsymm.-Tetrabromoethane	2.87
Bromoform	2.89
symm.-Tetrabromoethane [acetylene tetrabromide]	2.966
Sonstadt's or Thoulet's solution (saturated sol. pot. mercuric iodide in water)*	3.18

Table (Continued)

Chemical name	G at $20°$ C. $(68°$ F.)
Klein's solution (cadmium borotungstate in water)	3.28
Methylene iodide [diiodomethane]	3.325
Arsenic tribromide, MP = $33°$ C. $(91°$ F.)	3.54
Methylene iodide + iodine + iodoform	3.6
Clerici's solution (equal mol. proportions thallium formate and thallium malonate in water)†	range = 4.05-4.2
	4.28 $(20°)$
	4.85 $(80°)$
Retger's salt (thallium silver nitrate), MP = $75°$ C. $(167°$ F.)	4.6
Mercury, to test Pt nuggets, which sink	13.55

* Sonstadt's (Thoulet's) sol. prepared by diss. 87 gm mercuric iodide + 75 gm potassium iodide in 27 cc water; evaporate gently until thin x1 film forms on surface or until a small piece of fluorite (G = 3.18) just begins to rise from bottom. Allow to cool. Clear greenish-yellow; max. density 3.19; corrosive and destructive to organic materials, producing bad skin burns; deteriorates.

† All thallium compounds and formulations are extremely poisonous!

CLERICI SOLUTION SPECIFIC GRAVITIES VERSUS REFRACTIVE INDICES. A direct relationship exists between the specific gravity of this solution, according to how much water is present, and the refractive index. A convenient straight-line graph can therefore be prepared by connecting these two sets of values: n = 1.550 and G = 3.008, n = 1.670 and G = 4.023.

Source: R. Webster, *The Gemmologists' Compendium,* 3d ed. rev. (1964), p. 225.

METHYLENE IODIDE SPECIFIC GRAVITIES VERSUS REFRACTIVE INDICES. In a similar manner, when methylene iodide is diluted with toluene, a graph is prepared using these values: n = 1.610 and G = 2.007, and n = 1.740 and G = 3.304.

Source: Ibid.

In addition to the indicators above, Anderson also recommends (p. 85) use of pink tourmaline (3.05), fluorite (3.18), peridot (3.34), colorless topaz (3.56), yellow chrysoberyl (3.72), demantoid garnet (3.85), and sphalerite (4.09), with variations in value in these minerals up to ±0.02.

STORAGE OF FLUIDS. Use brown glass, wide-mouth jars. Indicators may be kept in the jars to show that the correct density is being maintained.

CLEANING OF FLUIDS. Some immersion fluids can be cleaned by passing through fuller's earth over filter paper, or by shaking several gm of the earth with 100-150 ml of the fluid and then drawing off the liquid by means of a separation funnel. Commonly, liquids darkened by liberation of iodine, e.g., methylene iodide, are clarified by adding strips or wires of bright copper to the liquid and shaking periodically. The copper absorbs the iodine

Anderson Gem Testing Set

Liquid	G	Indicator
Bromoform, dil. by 1-bromonaphthalene to	2.65	Quartz
Bromoform, dil. by 1-bromonaphthalene to	2.71	Calcite
Methylene iodide, dil. by 1-bromonaphthalene to	3.06	Green tourmaline
Methylene iodide, pure	3.325	
Clerici sol., dil. by dist. water to	3.52	Diamond
Clerici sol., dil. by dist. water to	4.00	Synthetic ruby

Source: B. W. Anderson, *Gem Testing* (1964), p. 81.

and keeping fresh copper in the liquid container serves to keep the liquid clear and bright.

References: The preparation and recovery of heavy liquids are explained in U.S. Bureau of Mines Report of investigations, no. 2897 (1928). See also E. S. Larsen, and H. Berman, "The Microscopic Determination of the Nonopaque Minerals," *U. S. Geological Survey Bulletin,* no. 848 (2d ed., 1934), and R. E. K. Benjamin, "Recovery of Heavy Liquids from Dilute Solutions," *Amer. Mineral.* 56 (1971): 613-19. See Table A below.

TABLES OF SPECIFIC GRAVITY: MINERALS

The following tables furnish specific gravities of most minerals as published up to July 1971. The arrangement is by increasing values rounded off to the second decimal place. Values are *measured* with the exception of a small number of *calculated* values mostly for newer species. Some older determinations are superseded by more recent data which are believed to be more accurate. In general, most species are repeated as many times in the tables as necessary to cover the known ranges, but some appear only once, usually because the mineral varies very little in density or absence of specimens from a variety of sources permitted only one determination. In a very few cases, two widely separated values may appear in the tables representing apparently valid determinations but without sufficient information to connect the two into a range of values. Discredited species are excluded.

Principal species are in caps.

Abbreviations: G = gem; M = massive; MG = massive gem material; xls = crystals.

Table A.

Principal Density Liquids in Common Use

Liquid	G (20° C.)
Table salt in water, for amber (40 gm/250 ml)	1.12 - 1.14
Nitrobenzene	1.20
2-Bromotoluene	1.42
Bromoethane	1.46
1-Bromonaphthalene	1.483
Bromobenzene	1.495
Carbon tetrachloride	1.594
symm.-Tetrachlorethane	1.595
1-Iodonaphthalene	1.74
1,3-Dibromopropane	1.98
1,1-Dibromoethane	2.06
1,2-Dibromoethane	2.18
1,2-Dibromoethanol	2.246
Dibromomethane	2.497
Bromoform	2.89
symm.-Tetrabromoethane	2.966
Sonstadt's or Thoulet's solution (saturated sol. potassium mercuric iodide in water)	3.18
Klein's solution (cadmium borotungstate in water)	3.28
Methylene iodide	3.325
Rohrbach's solution (barium mercuric iodide in water)	3.58
Methylene iodide + iodine + iodoform	3.6
Clerici solution (equal mol. proportions thallium formate and thallium malonate in water)*	4.05 - 4.2
Retger's salt (thallium silver nitrate, liquid at 75° C. (167° F.))	4.6
Mercury, to test Pt nuggets which sink	13.55

Main Table of Specific Gravities

1.03 Copalite, retinite, AMBER
1.04-1.05 Retinite, AMBER, bitumen
1.07 AMBER, bitumen, succinite, elaterite, uintahlite
1.09 AMBER, flagstaffite
1.10 AMBER, albertite, jet, libollite, meerschaum
1.12 JET, meerschaum, shungite
1.20 JET, meerschaum
1.21 JET, idrialite
1.35 JET, carpathite
1.40 JET, mineral coal, oxammite
1.43 Oxammite, hoelite
1.46 Oxammite, sassolite, nitromagnesite
1.48 Oxammite, sassolite, natron
1.49 Oxammite, sassolite, mirabilite
1.50 Oxammite, sassolite, calclacite
1.51 Oxammite, hydroglauberite
1.53 Oxammite, sal ammoniac
1.55 Oxammite, anthracite
1.57 Oxammite, teschemacherite
1.60 Oxammite, bischofite, carnallite
1.61-1.62 Stercorite
1.62 Zhemchuzhnikovite
1.64 Mellite
1.65 Mellite, ammonia alum, julienite
1.66 Aluminite, cadwaladerite
1.67 Aluminite, soda alum, tachyhydrite
1.68 Aluminite, epsomite
1.69 Aluminite, lansfordite, zhemchuzhnikovite, stepanovite
1.70 Aluminite, satimolite
1.71 Aluminite, BORAX, struvite, sborgite
1.72 Aluminite, BORAX, boussingaultite, phosphoroesslerite
1.73 Aluminite, phosphoroesslerite, mendozite, pickeringite
1.75 Aluminite, mendozite, pickeringite, kalinite, cyprusite, quisqueite
1.76 Aluminite, mendozite, pickeringite, potash alum, kirovite, hexahydrite, ammonioborite
1.77 Aluminite, mendozite, pickeringite, kirovite, alunogen, ettringite, mascagnite, ammonioborite
1.78 Aluminite, pickeringite, kirovite, apjohnite, ettringite
1.79 Aluminite, pickeringite, kirovite
1.80 Aluminite, kirovite, dietrichite
1.81 Aluminite, kirovite, ihleite, letovicite, moraesite
1.82 Aluminite, kirovite
1.83 Schertelite, kirovite, hydrochlorborite, meta-aluminite

1.84 Kirovite, MELANTERITE, meta-aluminite
1.85 Kirovite, MELANTERITE, KURNAKOVITE, mallardite, nesquehonite, anthraxolite, scarbroite, meta-aluminite
1.86 Kirovite, MELANTERITE, INDERITE, mohrite, meta-aluminite
1.87 Kirovite, MELANTERITE, pascoite, macallisterite, meta-aluminite
1.88 MELANTERITE, inyoite, TINCALCONITE, bilinite, wardsmithite, schoderite
1.89 MELANTERITE, HALOTRICHITE, hannayite
1.90 MELANTERITE, nitrocalcite, larderellite
1.91 KERNITE, THAUMASITE, faujasite, slavikite, larderellite, rivadavite
1.92 Faujasite, behoite, kribergite
1.93 Faujasite, trudellite, weddellite
1.94 Weddellite, roesslerite, racewinite, jouravskite, sanjuanite
1.95 Weddellite, earlandite, morenosite, pisanite, jouravskite
1.96 Bieberite, vashegyite, beta sulfur, ULEXITE, jouravskite
1.97 Beta sulfur, mullerite, OPAL (G), hellyerite, moorhouseite
1.98 Beta sulfur, OPAL (G), goslarite, koenenite, SYLVITE
1.99 OPAL (G), SYLVITE, gaylussite, erionite, gowerite
2.00 OPAL (G), SYLVITE, erionite, INDERBORITE, richellite, cryptohalite, manasseite, GMELINITE, LEVYNITE, gowerite (to 2.01), pentahydroborite
2.03 OPAL (G), manasseite, GMELINITE, LEVYNITE, picromerite, hydrotalcite, boothite, ameghinite (±0.006), bolivarite, scarbroite, hannayite (± 0.02)
2.04 OPAL (G), manasseite, GMELINITE, LEVYNITE, hydrotalcite, boothite, retgersite, bolivarite
2.05 OPAL (G), manasseite, GMELINITE, LEVYNITE, hydrotalcite, ezcurrite, boothite, CHABAZITE, luenebergite, barbertonite, gamma sulfur, bolivarite, bayleyite, ivigtite, melanophlogite, uralolite
2.07 OPAL (G), manasseite, GMELINITE, LEVYNITE, hydrotalcite, boothite, CHABAZITE, luenebergite, barber-

tonite, SULFUR, tamarugite, bianchite, makatite, uralolite

2.08 Manasseite, GMELINITE, LEVY-
NITE, hydrotalcite, boothite,
CHABAZITE, barbertonite, sjogrenite, COPIAPITE, magnesium
copiapite, cuprocopiapite, minguzzite,
nobleite, uralolite

2.09 Manasseite, GMELINITE, LEVY-
NITE, hydrotalcite, boothite, CHA-
BAZITE, barbertonite, sjogrenite,
COPIAPITE, Mg-copiapite, Cu-copia-
pite, GRAPHITE, ginorite, nobleite,
uralolite, koktaite

2.10 Manasseite, GMELINITE, LEVY-
NITE, boothite, CHABAZITE, bar-
bertonite, sjogrenite, COPIAPITE,
Mg-copiapite, Cu-copiapite, GRAPH-
ITE, STILBITE, HEULANDITE, gis-
mondine, epistilbite, THOMSONITE
(MG), niter, newberryite, COQUIM-
BITE, paracoquimbite, pyraurite,
uralolite

2.11 GMELINITE, LEVYNITE, boothite,
barbertonite, sjogrenite, uralolite,
COPIAPITE, Mg-copiapite, Cu-copia-
pite, GRAPHITE, STILBITE, HEU-
LANDITE, gismondine, epistilbite,
THOMSONITE (MG), COQUIM-
BITE, paracoquimbite, pyraurite,
iowaite

2.12 GMELINITE, LEVYNITE, barber-
tonite, boothite, sjogrenite, uralolite,
COPIAPITE, Mg-copiapite, Cu-co-
piapite, GRAPHITE, STILBITE,
HEULANDITE, gismondine, epistil-
bite, THOMSONITE, COQUIM-
BITE, paracoquimbite, pyraurite,
MORDENITE, carboborite,
MEYERHOFFERITE, stellerite

2.13 GMELINITE, LEVYNITE, boothite,
barbertonite, sjogrenite, uralolite,
COPIAPITE, Mg-copiapite, Cu-copiapite, GRAPHITE, STILBITE,
HEULANDITE, gismondine, epistilbite, THOMSONITE, pyraurite,
MORDENITE (MG), kaliborite, garronite

2.14 GMELINITE, LEVYNITE, boothite,
barbertonite, sjogrenite, COPIAPITE,
Mg-copiapite, Cu-copiapite, GRAPH-
ITE, STILBITE, HEULANDITE, gismondine, epistilbite, THOMSONITE,
pyraurite, MORDENITE (MG), botryogen, brugnatellite, probertite,

TRONA, fluellite, kreuzbergite, frolovite, garronite, uralolite

2.15 GMELINITE, LEVYNITE, boothite,
barbertonite, COPIAPITE, ezcurrite,
Mg-copiapite, Cu-copiapite, GRAPH-
ITE, STILBITE, HEULANDITE, gismondine, epistilbite, THOMSONITE,
MORDENITE (MG), fluellite, kainite, hydrocalumite, baratite, quenstedtite, sideronatrite, ferrierite,
taranakite, teruggite, stichtite (G),
dypingite, garronite

2.16 GMELINITE, LEVYNITE, boothite,
COPIAPITE, Mg-copiapite, Cu-copiapite, GRAPHITE, STILBITE, HEU-
LANDITE, gismondine, epistilbite,
THOMSONITE, fluellite, sideronatrite, stichtite (G), douglasite, garronite

2.17 GMELINITE, LEVYNITE, boothite,
COPIAPITE, Mg-copiapite, Cu-copiapite, GRAPHITE, STILBITE, HEU-
LANDITE, gismondine, epistilbite,
THOMSONITE, fluellite, sideronatrite, HALITE, hydroboracite,
roemerite, stichtite (G), loughlinite,
garronite

2.18 GMELINITE, LEVYNITE, boothite,
GRAPHITE, STILBITE, HEU-
LANDITE, gismondine, epistilbite,
THOMSONITE, sideronatrite, melite,
chalcedony (ignited), stichtite (G),
zincocopiapite

2.19 GMELINITE, LEVYNITE, boothite,
GRAPHITE, STILBITE, HEULAN-
DITE, gismondine, epistilbite, THOM-
SONITE, sideronatrite, amarantite,
silica glass, amarillite, tyretskite,
halurgite, bearsite, zebadassite, stichtite (G)

2.20 GMELINITE, LEVYNITE, GRAPH-
ITE, STILBITE, HEULANDITE, gismondine, epistilbite, THOMSONITE,
sideronatrite, amarantite, silica glass,
NATROLITE (G), PHILLIPSITE,
LAUMONTITE, cacoxenite, berborite, darapskite, hohmannite,
CHRYSOTILE, leonite, bobierrite,
viseite, hydrophilite, berillyte, roz-
enite, zincbotryogen, vugawaralite,
penwithite, SODALITE (MG), stichtite (G), amarillite

2.21 GRAPHITE, gismondine, epistilbite,
THOMSONITE, sideronatrite, ama-
rantite, NATROLITE (G), LAU-
MONTITE, gonnardite, cacoxenite,

silica glass, nahcolite, SODALITE (MG), whewellite

2.22 GRAPHITE, gismondine, epistilbite, THOMSONITE, sideronatrite, amarantite, NATROLITE (G), LAUMONTITE, gonnardite, cacoxenite, BLOEDITE, glaucochroite, SODALITE (MG), ANALCIME (G)

2.23 GRAPHITE, gismondine, epistilbite, THOMSONITE, sideronatrite, amarantite, NATROLITE (G), LAUMONTITE, gonnardite, cacoxenite, BLOEDITE, gordonite, alumohydrocalcite, portlandite, rhomboclase, whewellite, olshanskyite, SODALITE (MG), ANALCIME (G), glucine

2.24 Gismondine, epistilbite, THOMSONITE, sideronatrite, amarantite, NATROLITE (G), LAUMONTITE, gonnardite, cacoxenite, BLOEDITE, hydromagnesite, soda niter, ANALCIME (G), SODALITE (MG), chalconatronite

2.25 Gismondine, epistilbite, THOMSONITE, sideronatrite, amarantite, NATROLITE (G), LAUMONTITE, gonnardite, cacoxenite, BLOEDITE, soda niter, ANALCIME (G), SCOLECITE, MESOLITE, cavansite, glucine, TRIDYMITE, humberstonite, lucianite, SODALITE (MG), chalconatronite

2.26 Gismondine, epistilbite, THOMSONITE, sideronatrite, amarantite, NATROLITE, LAUMONTITE, gonnardite, cacoxenite, BLOEDITE, glucine, soda niter, ANALCIME (G), SCOLECITE, MESOLITE, cavansite, thermonatrite, zinc aluminite, wairikite, nitratine, SODALITE (MG), chalconatronite

2.27 Gismondine, epistilbite, THOMSONITE, sideronatrite, amarantite, LAUMONTITE, gonnardite, cacoxenite, BLOEDITE, soda niter, ANALCIME (G), SCOLECITE, MESOLITE, cavansite, SODALITE (G), pinnoite, chalconatronite, chukhrovite, glucine, macdonaldite

2.28 Gismondine, epistilbite, THOMSONITE, sideronatrite, amarantite, LAUMONTITE, gonnardite, cacoxenite, BLOEDITE, soda niter, ANALCIME (G), SCOLECITE, cavansite, SODALITE (G), humboldtine, okenite,

wellsite, oxalite, tugtupite (MG), chalconatronite, chukhrovite, glucine

2.29 Gismondine, epistilbite, THOMSONITE, sideronatrite, amarantite, LAUMONTITE, gonnardite, cacoxenite, soda niter, ANALCIME (G), SCOLECITE, MESOLITE (MG), cavansite, SODALITE (G), okenite, glucine, wellsite, volkovskite, CHALCANTHITE, chalcoalumite, chukhrovite, clinoungemachite, ungemachite, APOPHYLLITE (G), chalconatronite

2.30 Gismondine, epistilbite, THOMSONITE (MG), sideronatrite, LAUMONTITE, gonnardite, cacoxenite, nosean, cavansite, SODALITE (G), okenite, wellsite, volkovskite, gibbsite, jefferisite, swartzite, ardealite, ameghinite, APOPHYLLITE, VARISCITE (MG), glucine, kingite, vanalite, ALABASTER (MG), chalconatronite, chukhrovite

2.31 THOMSONITE (MG), sideronatrite, gonnardite, APOPHYLLITE (G), glucine, cacoxenite, nosean, cavansite, SODALITE (G), okenite, wellsite, volkovskite, buddingtonite, GIBBSITE, GYPSUM, chlormanganokalite, kornelite, griffithite, VARISCITE (MG), ALABASTER (MG), chukhrovite, vanalite

2.32 THOMSONITE (MG), sideronatrite, gonnardite, APOPHYLLITE (G), vanalite, cacoxenite, nosean, cavansite, SODALITE (G), okenite, wellsite, volkovskite, GIBBSITE, GYPSUM, vishnevite, CRISTOBALITE, belyankinite, glucine, coalingite, buddingtonite, jennite, VARISCITE (MG) chukhrovite, ALABASTER (MG), erythrosiderite

2.33 THOMSONITE (MG), sideronatrite, gonnardite, APOPHYLLITE (G), vanalite cacoxenite, nosean, cavansite, SODALITE (G), okenite, wellsite, volkovskite, buddingtonite, aplowite, GIBBSITE, vishnevite, CRISTOBALITE, brushite, glucine, felsobanyite, bukovskyite, VARISCITE (MG), ALABASTER (MG), chukhrovite, belyankinite

2.34 THOMSONITE (MG), sideronatrite, gonnardite, cacoxenite, nosean, APOPHYLLITE (G), cavansite, wellsite, volkovskite, GIBBSITE, vishnevite, wegscheiderite, tatarskite, glucine, CRISTOBALITE, truscottite, GYROLITE, kehoite, chukhrovite, magnalite, VARISCITE (MG), SODALITE (G), belyankinite, vanalite, bikitaite

2.35 THOMSONITE (MG), sideronatrite, gonnardite, cacoxenite, nosean, cavansite, wellsite, GIBBSITE, vishnevite, APOPHYLLITE (G), glucine, truscottite, GYROLITE, METAVAUXITE, rinneite, pirssonite, sigloite, VARISCITE (MG), SODALITE (MG), HAMBERGITE (G), vanalite, felsobanyite, belyankinite, chukhrovite

2.36 THOMSONITE (G), gonnardite, cacoxenite, nosean, cavansite, chukhrovite, wellsite, GIBBSITE, vishnevite, APOPHYLLITE (G), truscottite, glucine, GYROLITE, PARAVAUXITE, HAMBERGITE (G), birunite, tacharanite, WAVELLITE, foshagite, VARISCITE (MG), nifontovite, vanalite, rauenthalite, tarasovite, SODALITE (MG), belyankinite, rhodesite, mountainite

2.37 THOMSONITE (MG), gonnardite, cacoxenite, nosean, wellsite, chukhrovite, GIBBSITE, vishnevite, APOPHYLLITE (G), truscottite, GYROLITE, glucine, loewite, HAMBERGITE, VARISCITE (MG), SODALITE (MG), belyankinite, vanalite, aksaite

2.38 THOMSONITE (MG), gonnardite, cacoxenite, nosean, GIBBSITE, chukhrovite, vishnevite, truscottite, GYROLITE, loewite, LAZURITE, BRUCITE, northupite, monohydrocalcite, glucine, VARISCITE (MG), SODALITE (MG), belyankinite, vanalite

2.39 THOMSONITE (MG), gonnardite, cacoxenite, nosean, GIBBSITE, glucine, vishnevite, truscottite, GYROLITE, loewite, LAZURITE, chukhrovite, sulfoborite, vauxite, kolbeckite, VARISCITE (MG), SODALITE (MG), PETALITE (G), belyankinite, vanalite, huemulite

2.40 Gonnardite, cacoxenite, nosean, GIBBSITE, vishnevite, truscottite, GYROLITE, loewite, LAZURITE (G), sulfoborite, GLAUCONITE, katangite, PETALITE (G), VARISCITE (MG), SODALITE (MG), chukhrovite, glucine, belyankinite, satpaevite

2.41 GIBBSITE, vishnevite, truscottite, GYROLITE, loewite, LAZURITE, sulfoborite, HARMOTOME, PETALITE (G), liebigite, genthite, pholidolite, VARISCITE (MG), alvanite, vanalite

2.42 GIBBSITE, vishnevite, truscottite, GYROLITE, loewite, LAZURITE, sulfoborite, HARMOTOME, PETALITE (G), COLEMANITE (G), CANCRINITE (MG), davyne, mitscherlichite, indianite, PRICEITE, hautfeuillite, VARISCITE (MG) goldichite, redondite, uklonskovite

2.44 Truscottite, GYROLITE, LAZURITE, sulfoborite, HARMOTOME, CANCRINITE (MG), davyne, HAUYNE, dawsonite, sterrettite, microsommite, PETALITE (G), VARISCITE (MG), nordstrandite

2.45 Truscottite, GYROLITE, LAZURITE, sulfoborite, HARMOTOME, CANCRINITE (MG), davyne, HAUYNE, BREWSTERITE, SEARLESITE, rossite, minyulite, VARISCITE (MG), PETALITE (G), LEUCITE (G), carletonite

2.46 HARMOTOME, CANCRINITE (MG), davyne, HAUYNE, metasideronatrite, ektropite, TUNELLITE, despujolsite, fischerite, PETALITE (G), VARISCITE (MG), tychite, connarite, LEUCITE (G), pseudolaueite, lithiophosphate

2.47 HARMOTOME, CANCRINITE (MG), davyne, HAUYNE, LEUCITE (G), mooreite, eriochalcite, bardolite, metaborite, VARISCITE (MG), tychite, connarite, STRUNZITE

2.48 CANCRINITE (MG), davyne, HAUYNE, LEUCITE (G), montgomeryite, wapplerite, VARISCITE (MG), tychite, connarite, STRUNZITE

2.50 CANCRINITE (MG), davyne, HAUYNE, LEUCITE (G), ferruccite, uklonskovite, metavoltine, sulfohalite, LIZARDITE, chlormanganokalite, MARIALITE, foshallasite, keatite, ussingite, neotocite, spadaite, VARISCITE (MG), tychite, azovskite, connarite, SERPENTINE (MG), rabbitite, STRUNZITE

2.51 CANCRINITE, LIZARDITE, MARIALITE, avogadrite, schroeckingerite, carnegieite, tunisite, VARISCITE (xls), tychite, connarite,

SERPENTINE (MG), STRUNZITE, SULFOHALITE

2.52 LIZARDITE, MARIALITE, avogadrite, anauxite, tychite, epichlorite, variscite (xls), connarite, SERPENTINE (MG), STRUNZITE

2.53 LIZARDITE, MARIALITE, avogadrite, HOWLITE, calcioferrite, overite, radiophyllite, VARISCITE (xls), tychite, connarite, SERPENTINE (MG), STRUNZITE, gerasimovskite

2.54 LIZARDITE, MARIALITE, avogadrite, HOWLITE, metavariscite, sphaerite, iddingsite, vimsite, VARISCITE (xls), tychite, connarite, SERPENTINE (MG), AMAZONITE (MG), STRUNZITE, gerasimovskite

2.55 LIZARDITE, MARIALITE, avogadrite, HOWLITE, ORTHOCLASE, MICROCLINE, AMAZONITE (MG), ferrinatrite, butlerite, parabutlerite, hewettite, epidydymite, afghanite, CHALCEDONY, eudidymite, VARISCITE (xls), tychite, connarite, karpinskyite, STRUNZITE, gerasimovskite, SERPENTINE (MG), Ceylon MOONSTONE, ELAEOLITE (G)

2.56 LIZARDITE, MARIALITE, avogadrite, HOWLITE, ORTHOCLASE (G), MICROCLINE, AMAZONITE (MG), ANORTHOCLASE, ADULARIA, PERTHITES, SANIDINE, ferrinatrite, CHALCEDONY, NEPHELINE, ralstonite, HANKSITE, rivaite, gerasimovskite, lithidionite, ELAEOLITE (G), VARISCITE (xls), tychite, connarite, SERPENTINE (MG), Ceylon MOONSTONE, navajoite, STRUNZITE

2.57 LIZARDITE, MARIALITE, avogadrite, HOWLITE, ORTHOCLASE (G), MICROCLINE, AMAZONITE (MG), ANORTHOCLASE, PERTHITES, SANIDINE, NEPHELINE, ralstonite, ferrinatrite, CHALCEDONY, ALBITE, coeruleolactite, ZARATITE, VARISCITE (xls), MILARITE, leifite, burkeite, kieserite, dipyre, CORDIERITE (G), ELAEOLITE (G), tychite, connarite, delhayelite, SERPENTINE (MG), gerasimovskite, hoernesite, VARISCITE, Ceylon MOONSTONE

2.58 LIZARDITE, MARIALITE, avogadrite, HOWLITE (MG), ORTHOCLASE, MICROCLINE, ANORTHOCLASE, PERTHITES, SANI-

DINE, ALBITE, HYALOPHANE, ferrinatrite, CHALCEDONY, NEPHELINE, ralstonite, coeruleolactite, ZARATITE, dipyre, CORDIERITE (G), delhayelite, syngenite, elpidite, oldhamite, sarmientite, dimorphite, fedorite, barrandite, tychite, connarite, SERPENTINE (MG), hoernesite, VARISCITE, Ceylon MOONSTONE, ELAEOLITE (G), MARBLE (MG), gerasimovskite

2.59 LIZARDITE, MARIALITE, avogadrite, HOWLITE, ORTHOCLASE, delhayelite, MICROCLINE, ANORTHOCLASE, PERTHITES, SANIDINE, ALBITE, HYALOPHANE, ferrinatrite, CHALCEDONY, NEPHELINE, ralstonite, coeruleolactite, ZARATITE, dipyre, CORDIERITE (G), syngenite, wightmanite, tungusite, kalsilite, tychite, connarite, ELAEOLITE (G), SERPENTINE (MG), hoernesite, VARISCITE (MG), MARBLE (MG)

2.60 LIZARDITE, MARIALITE, avogadrite, ORTHOCLASE, MICROCLINE, ANORTHOCLASE, PERTHITES, SANIDINE, ALBITE, HYALOPHANE, ferrinatrite, CHALCEDONY (MG), NEPHELINE, ralstonite, coeruleolactite, ZARATITE, dipyre, CORDIERITE (G), delhayelite, syngenite, kalsilite, galeite, zirklerite, BERTRANDITE, shortite, roedderite, egueite, riversideite, uralborite, TURQUOISE (MG), ELAEOLITE (G), connarite, SERPENTINE (MG), picropharmacolite, hoernesite, volatite, VARISCITE (MG), MARBLE (MG), BASTITE (MG)

2.61 MARIALITE, SCAPOLITE (G), avogadrite, ORTHOCLASE, MICROCLINE, ANORTHOCLASE, PERTHITES, SANIDINE, ALBITE, HYALOPHANE, ferrinatrite, CHALCEDONY (MG), NEPHELINE, ralstonite, coeruleolactite, ZARATITE, dipyre, CORDIERITE (G), delhayelite, kalsilite, lanthanite, galeite, kaliophilite, schairerite, connarite, SERPENTINE (MG), ELAEOLITE (G), PHARMACOLITE, picropharmacolite, hoernesite, voltaite, TURQUOISE (MG), MARBLE (MG)

2.62 MARIALITE, avogadrite, SCAPOLITE (G), CHALCEDONY (MG), ORTHOCLASE, MICROCLINE,

ANORTHOCLASE, PERTHITES, SANIDINE, ALBITE, OLIGOCLASE, HYALOPHANE, NEPHELINE, ralstonite, coeruleolactite, ZARATITE, dipyre, CORDIERITE (G), delhayelite, kalsilite, lanthanite, Norway SUNSTONE (MG), szaibelyite, naujakasite, AFWILLITE, ELAEOLITE (G), connarite, SERPENTINE (MG), PHARMACOLITE, hoernesite, voltaite, TURQUOISE (MG), MARBLE (MG) picropharmacolite, schairerite

2.63 ORTHOCLASE, MICROCLINE, PERTHITES, ALBITE, OLIGOCLASE, Norway SUNSTONE (MG), HYALOPHANE, CHALCEDONY, SCAPOLITE (G), NEPHELINE, coeruleolactite, ZARATITE, dipyre, CORDIERITE (G), delhayelite, kalsilite, lanthanite, AFWILLITE, ransomite, donbassite, couzeranite, spodiophyllite, ELAEOLITE (G), SERPENTINE (MG), PHARMACOLITE, hoernesite, voltaite, TURQUOISE (MG), MARBLE (MG), picropharmacolite

2.64 CHALCEDONY (MG), SCAPOLITE (G), PERTHITES, OLIGOCLASE, Norway SUNSTONE (MG), ANDESINE, HYALOPHANE, NEPHELINE, coeruleolactite, ZARATITE, dipyre, CORDIERITE (G), picropharmacolite, lanthanite, englishite, berlinite, SERPENTINE (MG), PHARMACOLITE, hoernesite, voltaite, TURQUOISE (MG), ELAEOLITE (G), MARBLE (MG), simplotite

2.65 CHALCEDONY (MG), PERTHITES, OLIGOCLASE, Norway SUNSTONE (MG), ANDESINE, HYALOPHANE, ELAEOLITE (G), NEPHELINE, coeruleolactite, ZARATITE, dipyre, CORDIERITE (G), SCAPOLITE (G), lanthanite, englishite, aphthitalite, antigorite, lublinite, patronite, leuchtenbergite, schaurteite, QUARTZ, SERPENTINE (MG), PHARMACOLITE, hoernesite, carbonatecyanotrichite, voltaite, TURQUOISE (MG), BERYL (emerald), MARBLE (MG)

2.66 NEPHELINE, OLIGOCLASE, ANDESINE, HYALOPHANE, coeruleolactite, ZARATITE, dipyre, CORDIERITE (G), guerinite, lanthanite, chkalovite, englishite, carbonatecyanotrichite, aphthitalite, BERYL

(emerald), THENARDITE, arcanite, PHARMACOLITE, d'ansite, hoernesite, voltaite, TURQUOISE (MG), MARBLE (MG), faheyite

2.67 OLIGOCLASE, ANDESINE, HYALOPHANE, NEPHELINE, coeruleolactite, ZARATITE, dipyre, zincsilite, lanthanite, aphthitalite, BERYL (emerald), chalcophyllite, VIVIANITE, chlorothionite, torreyite, hieratite, MIZZONITE, carbonatecyanotrichite, ekmanite, eucryptite, PHARMACOLITE, hoernesite, voltaite, TURQUOISE (MG), MARBLE (MG), guerinite

2.68 ANDESINE, LABRADORITE, HYALOPHANE, coeruleolactite, ZARATITE, dipyre, zincsilite, lanthanite, aphthitalite, VIVIANITE, MIZZONITE, rumpfite, suolunite, PHARMACOLITE, hoernesite, voltaite, TURQUOISE (MG), BERYL (emerald, green), MARBLE (MG), guerinite

2.69 ANDESINE, LABRADORITE, HYALOPHANE, coeruleolactite, ZARATITE, dipyre, zincsilite, lanthanite, aphthitalite, VIVIANITE, MIZZONITE, vanthoffite, manandonite, borickite, lopezite, hillebrandite, liberite, PHARMACOLITE, hoernesite, voltaite, TURQUOISE (MG), BERYL (emerald, green, colorless, blue), guerinite, MARBLE (MG), liberite, reedmergnerite

2.70 LABRADORITE (G), ANORTHITE, HYALOPHANE, lanthanite, aphthitalite, MIZZONITE, SCAPOLITE (G), borickite, augelite (G), TALC (MG), coconinoite, EDINGTONITE, yagiite, PHARMACOLITE, hoernesite, voltaite, TURQUOISE (MG), BERYL (emerald, green, colorless, blue, yellow), MARBLE (MG), huntite, zincsilite, guerinite, guildite

2.71 LABRADORITE (G), ANORTHITE, BYTOWNITE, HYALOPHANE, lanthanite, aphthitalite, MIZZONITE, borickite, TALC (MG), EDINGTONITE, CREEDITE, CALCITE, XONOTLITE, didymolite, hilgardite, canasite, parahilgardite, malladrite, PHARMACOLITE, hoernesite, voltaite, TURQUOISE (MG), BERYL (emerald, green, blue), MARBLE (MG), callaghanite

2.72 LABRADORITE (G), ANORTHITE,

BYTOWNITE, HYALOPHANE, lanthanite, MIZZONITE, TALC (MG), EDINGTONITE, CREEDITE, CALCITE, XONOTLITE, guildite, hoernesite, voltaite, TURQUOISE (MG), BERYL (emerald, green, blue), MARBLE (MG), zincsilite

2.73 ANORTHITE, BYTOWNITE, HYALOPHANE, lanthanite, MIZZONITE, TALC (MG), EDINGTONITE, CREEDITE, CALCITE, MEIONITE, nissonite, bultfonteinite, bradleyite, hoernesite, voltaite, TURQUOISE (MG), BERYL (emerald, green, blue), MARBLE (MG), rusakovite

2.74 ANORTHITE, BYTOWNITE, HYLOPHANE, lanthanite, MIZZONITE, MEIONITE, TALC (MG), EDINGTONITE, CALCITE, bavenite, CYANOTRICHITE, alumian, manganophyllite, voltaite, TURQUOISE (MG), BERYL (emerald), PECTOLITE (MG), MARBLE (MG), fenaksite, rusakovite

2.75 ANORTHITE, BYTOWNITE, HYALOPHANE, TALC (MG), CALCITE, MEIONITE, CYANOTRICHITE, narsarsukite, GLAUBERITE, catapleiite, amesite, glaucocerinite, VEATCHITE, jurupaite, voltaite, TURQUOISE (MG), BERYL (emerald, morganite), MARBLE (MG), rusakovite, PECTOLITE (MG), gorgeyite, heidornite

2.76 ANORTHITE, HYALOPHANE, TALC (MG), CALCITE, MEIONITE, CYANOTRICHITE, GLAUBERITE, amesite, PHLOGOPITE, Mn-hoernesite, zeophyllite, bazzite, voltaite, TURQUOISE (MG), BERYL (emerald, morganite), PECTOLITE (MG), narsarsukite, VEATCHITE, rusakovite, borcarite

2.77 HYALOPHANE, TALC (MG), MEIONITE, GLAUBERITE, amesite, PHLOGOPITE, MUSCOVITE, scawtite, cryolithionite, calcium catapleite, bazzite, gearksuktite, borcarite, voltaite, narsarsukite, rusakovite, hendersonite, VEATCHITE, TURQUOISE (MG), BERYL (emerald, morganite), PECTOLITE (MG)

2.78 HYALOPHANE, TALC (MG), MEIONITE, GLAUBERITE, amesite, PHLOGOPITE, MUSCOVITE, POLYHALITE, CRANDALLITE, sakhaite, voltaite, TURQUOISE (MG), PECTOLITE (MG), rusakovite, hendersonite, borcarite, bazzite, BERYL (emerald, morganite), cryolithionite, VEATCHITE

2.79 HYALOPHANE, TALC (MG), GLAUBERITE, amesite, PHLOGOPITE, MUSCOVITE, CRANDALLITE, sakhaite, villiaumite, voltaite, TURQUOISE (MG), PECTOLITE (MG), BERYL (morganite), sherwoodite, hendersonite, narsarsukite, VEATCHITE, rusakovite

2.80 HYALOPHANE, TALC (MG), GLAUBERITE, amesite, PHLOGOPITE, MUSCOVITE, LEPIDOLITE, CRANDALLITE, sakhaite, EUDIALYTE, TURQUOISE (MG), (Persian), xanthoxenite, BERAUNITE, PHARMACOSIDERITE, harbortite, reevesite, andersonite, ceruleite, tabergite, fabianite, voltaite, BERYL (morganite), PECTOLITE (MG), PYROPHYLLITE (MG), BERYLLONITE (G), WOLLASTONITE (MG), PREHNITE (MG), rusakovite, farringtonite, sherwoodite, narsarsukite, VEATCHITE

2.81 HYALOPHANE, GLAUBERITE, amesite, PHLOGOPITE, MUSCOVITE, LEPIDOLITE, CRANDALLITE, sakhaite, EUDIALYTE, xanthoxenite, BERAUNITE, WARDITE (MG), anapaite, bandylite, BERYLLONITE (G), tinaksite, TURQUOISE (MG), BERYL (morganite), PECTOLITE (MG), PREHNITE (MG), WOLLASTONITE (MG), sherwoodite, VEATCHITE, strontioborite

2.82 HYALOPHANE, GLAUBERITE, amesite, PHLOGOPITE, MUSCOVITE, tinaksite, LEPIDOLITE, CRANDALLITE, sakhaite, EUDIALYTE, xanthoxenite, BERAUNITE, WARDITE, corvusite, TURQUOISE (MG), BERYL (morganite), PECTOLITE (MG), BERYLLONITE (G), WOLLASTONITE (MG), PREHNITE (MG), dalyite

2.83 GLAUBERITE, amesite, PHLOGOPITE, MUSCOVITE, LEPIDOLITE, sakhaite, CRANDALLITE, EUDIALYTE, xanthoxenite, BERAUNITE, WARDITE, LANGBEINITE, MILLISITE, TURQUOISE (MG), BERYL (morganite), PECTOLITE (MG),

BERYLLONITE (G), WOLLASTON-ITE (MG), PREHNITE (MG), dalyite

2.84 GLAUBERITE, amesite, PHLOG-OPITE, MUSCOVITE, LEPIDOLITE, EUDIALYTE, CRANDALLITE, xan-thoxenite, BERAUNITE, WARDITE, DOLOMITE, bermanite, ganophyllite, murmanite, krausite, sincosite, ban-nisterite, combeite, TURQUOISE (MG), BERYL (morganite), PECTO-LITE (MG), BERYLLONITE (G), sinoite, WOLLASTONITE (MG), PREHNITE (MG), dalyite, nenadke-vichite, mayenite

2.85 GLAUBERITE, amesite, PHLOGO-PITE, MUSCOVITE, LEPIDOLITE, PARAGONITE, CRANDALLITE, EUDIALYTE, xanthoxenite, BERAU-NITE, WARDITE, DOLOMITE, davisonite, haidingerite, zircosulfate, FLUOBORITE, BERYL (morganite), PECTOLITE (MG), BERYLLONITE (G), WOLLASTONITE (MG), PREH-NITE (MG), POLLUCITE (G), dalyite, nenadkevichite, zircosulfate, bermanite

2.86 PHLOGOPITE, MUSCOVITE, LEPI-DOLITE, CRANDALLITE, EUDIA-LYTE, xanthoxenite, BERAUNITE, WARDITE, DOLOMITE, FLUO-BORITE, PECTOLITE (MG), taenio-lite, minguetite, BERYL, WOL-LASTONITE (MG), PREHNITE (MG), POLLUCITE (G), dalyite, nenadkevichite, rustumite, bermanite

2.87 PHLOGOPITE, MUSCOVITE, LEPI-DOLITE, CRANDALLITE, EUDIA-LYTE, dillnite, xanthoxenite, BERA-UNITE, WARDITE, FLUOBORITE, PECTOLITE (MG), WOLLASTON-ITE (MG), STRENGITE (xls), merrihueite, caryopilite, BERYL, PREHNITE (MG), POLLUCITE (G), cuprorivaite, nenadkevichite

2.88 PHLOGOPITE, MUSCOVITE, LEPI-DOLITE, CRANDALLITE, EUDIA-LYTE, xanthoxenite, BERAUNITE, FLUOBORITE, PECTOLITE (MG), WOLLASTONITE (MG), BAKERITE, prosopite, ZUNYITE, salmonsite, valleite, BERYL, PREHNITE (MG), yavapaiite, POLLUCITE (G), nenad-kevichite, calciborite, vinogradovite,

2.89 PHLOGOPITE, LEPIDOLITE, CRAN-DALLITE, EUDIALYTE, xanthoxen-ite, BERAUNITE, FLUOBORITE,

PECTOLITE, WOLLASTONITE (MG), prosopite, lehiite, epistolite, ferrisym-plesite, martinite, rosenhahnite, BERYL, PREHNITE (MG), POLLU-CITE (G), nenadkevichite, tuhualite

2.90 PHLOGOPITE, LEPIDOLITE, ZINN-WALDITE, CRANDALLITE, EUDIA-LYTE, xanthoxenite, BERAUNITE, FLUOBORITE, PECTOLITE, labunt-sovite, WOLLASONITE (MG), proso-pite, DATOLITE (MG), hsianghualite, KROEHNKITE, molysite, tilleyite, PREHNITE (MG), carbonate APATITE, hydroxyl APATITE, POLLUCITE (G), LIROCONITE, sogdianovite, sorensenite, panethite, braitschite, roweite, BERYL, NEPH-RITE

2.91 CRANDALLITE, EUDIALYTE, xan-thoxenite, BERAUNITE, FLUO-BORITE, WOLLASTONITE, ZINN-WALDITE, DATOLITE (MG), sua-nite, PREHNITE (MG), carb. APATITE, hydrox. APATITE, LIRO-CONITE, panethite, BORACITE, COESITE, hsianghualite, labuntsovite, PSEUDOWOLLASTONITE, roweite, BERYL, POLLUCITE (G), NEPH-RITE

2.92 CRANDALLITE, EUDIALYTE, xan-thoxenite, BERAUNITE, FLUO-BORITE, WOLLASTONITE, ZINN-WALDITE, faustite, PREHNITE (MG), carb.APATITE, hydrox. APATITE, hsianghualite, labuntso-vite, LIROCONITE, panethite, BORACITE, COESITE, sarcolite, PARAWOLLASTONITE, isoclasite, roscherite, roweite, POLLUCITE (G), DATOLITE (MG), NEPHRITE

2.93 EUDIALYTE, xanthoxenite, BERA-UNITE, FLUOBORITE, WOLLA-STONITE, ZINNWALDITE, latium-ite, PREHNITE (MG), carb. APATITE, hydrox.APATITE, LIRO-CONITE, panethite, BORACITE, COESITE, roweite, monetite, mo-sandrite, eakerite, kochite, carpholite, POLLUCITE (G), DATOLITE (MG), NEPHRITE, hsianghualite, labuntso-vite

2.94 EUDIALYTE, xanthoxenite, BE-RAUNITE, FLUOBORITE, WOLLA-STONITE, ZINNWALDITE, morinite, grantsite, chudobaite, labuntsovite, PREHNITE (MG), carb.APATITE, hydrox.APATITE, LIROCONITE, panethite, BORACITE, COESITE, roweite, ARAGONITE (G), akermanite, kempite, carpholite, harkerite, STEWARTITE, spodiosite, POLLUCITE (G), DATOLITE (MG), NEPHRITE, aminoffite, hsianghualite

2.95 EUDIALYTE, xanthoxenite, BERAUNITE, FLUOBORITE, WOLLASTONITE, ZINNWALDITE, PREHNITE (MG), carb.APATITE, hydrox. APATITE, LIROCONITE, panethite, BORACITE, COESITE, mosandrite, ARAGONITE, melitlite, HERDERITE morinite, cuspidine, leightonite, osteolite, switzerite, DATOLITE (MG), NEPHRITE, hsianghualite, labuntsovite.

2.96 EUDIALYTE, xanthoxenite, BERAUNITE, FLUOBORITE, WOLLASTONITE, morinite, ZINNWALDITE, harkerite, carb. APATITE, hydrox. APATITE, LIROCONITE, panethite, BORACITE (G), HERDERITE, melilite, mosandrite, DATOLITE (G), weberite, CRYOLITE, leucophane, nocerite, dresserite, cebollite, cabrerite, NEPHRITE, PHENAKITE (G), labuntsovite, likasite, ajoite, hsianghualite

2.97 EUDIALYTE, xanthoxenite, BERAUNITE, FLUOBORITE, WOLLASTONITE, ZINNWALDITE, amakinite, carb. APATITE, hydrox. APATITE, LIROCONITE, panethite, BORACITE, HERDERITE, melilite, DATOLITE (G), mosandrite, weberite, CRYOLITE, schizolite, AMPHIBOLE ASBESTOS, melkovite, NEPHRITE, shcherbakovite, ktenasite, likasite, hsianghualite, bokite

2.98 EUDIALYTE, BERAUNITE, FLUOBORITE, WOLLASTONITE, ZINNWALDITE, likasite, carb. APATITE, hydrox. APATITE, LIROCONITE, panethite, HERDERITE, melilite, DATOLITE (G), mosandrite, CRYOLITE, schizolite, MAGNESITE, DANBURITE, BRAZILIANITE, PACHNOLITE, PHENAKITE, amakinite, ANHYDRITE, thomsenolite, scacchite, MONTEBRASITE, bementite, bokite, justite, NEPHRITE, TREMOLITE (xls, G), hsianghualite, betpakdalite

2.99 EUDIALYTE, BERAUNITE, WOL-

LASTONITE, ZINNWALDITE, amakinite, MAGNESITE, carb. APATITE, hydrox. APATITE, LIROCONITE, panethite, BRAZILIANITE (G), justite, HERDERITE, melilite, bementite, DATOLITE (G), DANBURITE, mosandrite, schizolite, collinsite, MARGARITE, asbolane, magnodravite, FERRIMOLYBDITE, MONTEBRASITE, bokite, NEPHRITE, hsianghualite

3.00 LEPIDOMELANE, TOURMALINE (pink), EUDIALYTE, BERAUNITE, WOLLASTONITE, ZINNWALDITE, bokite, MAGNESITE (MG), carb. APATITE, hydrox. APATITE, MONTEBRASITE, NEPHRITE, LIROCONITE, panethite, justite, HERDERITE (G), melilite, bementite, DATOLINE (G), DANBURITE (G), mosandrite, schizolite, MARGARITE, CHIOLITE, clinoholmquistite, elpasolite, meliphane (G), seybertite, bityite, ephesite, grandidierite, minnesotaite, HOPEITE, spurrite, hisingerite, phosphoferrite, EUCLASE, ekermannite, thorosteenstrupine, KUTNAHORITE, CROCIDOLITE, hsianghualite, REDDINGITE, tyrolite, monsmedite, wallisite, birnessite, delrioite

3.01 Seybertite, EUDIALYTE, minnesotaite, carb. APATITE, hydrox. APATITE, BERAUNITE, WOLLASTONITE, ZINNWALDITE, MAGNESITE (MG), HOPEITE, phosphoferrite, EUCLASE, REDDINGITE, tyrolite, TOURMALINE (pink), LEPIDOMELANE, LIROCONITE, justite, HERDERITE, melilite, bementite, DANBURITE, mosandrite, schizolite, MARGARITE, ANKERITE, symplesite, woodhouseite, hydroxyl HERDERITE, thorosteenstrupine, bokite, NEPHRITE, MONTEBRASITE, delrioite

3.02 Seybertite, EUDIALYTE, minnesotaite, carb. APATITE, hydrox. APATITE, BERAUNITE, WOLLASTONITE, ZINNWALDITE, MAGNESITE (MG), HOPEITE, phosphoferrite, EUCLASE, REDDINGITE, thorosteenstrupine, tyrolite, TOURMALINE (pink, red), LEPIDOMELANE, ANKERITE, justite, melilite, bementite, DANBURITE, mosandrite, schizolite, MARGARITE, bromellite, kurchatovite, bokite, imerinite, manganolangbeinite, NEPHRITE, MONTEBRASITE (G, "amblygonite"), delrioite, sainfeldite

3.03 Seybertite, EUDIALYTE, minnesotaite, carb. APATITE, hydrox. APATITE, BERAUNITE, WOLLASTONITE, HOPEITE, phosphoferrite, EUCLASE, tyrolite, REDDINGITE, TOURMALINE (pink, red), LEPIDOMELANE, ANKERITE, justite, melilite, bementite, DANBURITE, mosandrite, schizolite, MARGARITE, landesite, mullite, SPODUMENE, inesite, mansfieldite, szomolnokite, MAGNESITE (MG), thorosteenstrupine, sainfeldite, MONTEBRASITE (G, "amblygonite"), neighborite, bokite

3.04 Seybertite, EUDIALYTE, minnesotaite, carb. APATITE, hydrox. APATITE, BERAUNITE, WOLLASTONITE, HOPEITE, phosphoferrite, EUCLASE, tyrolite, REDDINGITE, TOURMALINE (pink, red, green), LEPIDOMELANE, justite, melilite, bementite, thorosteenstrupine, sainfeldite, schizolite, MARGARITE, mullite, SPODUMENE, mansfieldite, szomolnokite, NATROMONTEBRASITE, gehlenite, dehrnite, EOSPHORITE, gorceixite, MAGNESITE (MG), bokite

3.05 Seybertite, EUDIALYTE, minnesotaite, carb. APATITE, hydrox. APATITE, BERAUNITE, WOLLASTONITE, HOPEITE, phosphoferrite, EUCLASE, tyrolite, REDDINGITE, sainfeldite, TOURMALINE (pink, red, green, brown), justite, bokite, melilite, LEPIDOMELANE, bementite, orientite, leucosphenite, LAWSONITE, uvite, harstigite, hibschite, MAGNESITE (MG), NATROMONTEBRASITE

3.06 Seybertite, EUDIALYTE, minnesotaite, carb. APATITE, hydrox. APATITE, BERAUNITE, WOLLASTONITE, HOPEITE, phosphoferrite, EUCLASE, tyrolite, REDDINGITE, TOURMALINE (red, green, brown), LEPIDOMELANE, justite, bementite, schizolite, MARGARITE, mullite, SPODUMENE, mansfieldite, szomolnokite, NATROMONTE-

BRASITE, EOSPHORITE, dehrnite, gorceixite, LAWSONITE, pennantite, holmquistite, banalsite, pyrosmalite, FRIEDELITE, voelckerite, MAGNESITE (MG), bokite, sainfeldite

3.07 Seybertite, EUDIALYTE, minnesotaite, carb. APATITE, hydrox. APATITE, BERAUNITE, WOLLASTONITE, HOPEITE, phosphoferrite, EUCLASE, tyrolite, REDDINGITE, TOURMALINE (green, brown), LEPIDOMELANE, justite, bementite, schizolite, MARGARITE, mullite, SPODUMENE, mansfieldite, szomolnokite, NATROMONTEBRASITE, EOSPHORITE, dehrnite, gorceixite, LAWSONITE, holmquistite, saryarkite, SERPIERITE, pyrosmalite, FRIEDELITE (G), voelckerite, ellestadite, MAGNESITE (MG), parasymplesite, nasledovite, tirodite, bokite, ernstite

3.08 Seybertite, EUDIALYTE, minnesotaite, carb. APATITE, hydrox. APATITE, BERAUNITE, WOLLASTONITE, HOPEITE, phosphoferrite, EUCLASE, tyrolite, REDDINGITE, TOURMALINE (green, brown, achroite), LEPIDOMELANE, justite, bementite, schizolite, MARGARITE, mullite, SPODUMENE, mansfieldite, NATROMONTEBRASITE, EOSPHORITE, dehrnite, gorceixite, LAWSONITE, holmquistite, pyrosmalite, FRIEDELITE, voelckerite, seamanite, LAZULITE, trolleite, FAIRFIELDITE, MONTICELLITE, PHOSPHOPHYLLITE, LEWISTONITE, pecoraite, cirrolite, saryarkite, xanthophyllite, grothine, MAGNESITE (MG), bokite

3.09 Seybertite, EUDIALYTE, minnesotaite, carb. APATITE, hydrox. APATITE, WOLLASTONITE, HOPEITE, phosphoferrite, EUCLASE, REDDINGITE, tyrolite, TOURMALINE (green, brown, achroite, blue), LEPIDOMELANE, justite, bementite, schizolite, trolleite, mullite, SPODUMENE, saryarkite, yaroslavite, mansfieldite, LAZULITE, NATROMONTEBRASITE, dehrnite, gorceixite, LAWSONITE, holmquistite, pyrosmalite, FRIEDELITE, voelckerite, MONTICELLITE, PHOSPHOPHYLLITE, grothine, suzalite, arakawaite, MAGNESITE (MG), bokite

3.10 Seybertite, EUDIALYTE, minnesotaite, carb. APATITE, hydrox. APATITE, HOPEITE, phosphoferrite, EUCLASE (G), REDDINGITE, tyrolite, TOURMALINE (green, achroite, blue), LEPIDOMELANE, justite, bementite, schizolite, mullite, SPODUMENE, mansfieldite, NATROMONTEBRASITE, gorceixite, LAWSONITE, holmquistite, pyrosmalite, FRIEDELITE, voelckerite, MONTICELLITE, PHOSPHOPHYLLITE, merrillite, bassettite, bertossite, kotoite, moissanite, muskoxite, AUTUNITE, wilkeite, cassidyite, CELSIAN, blakeite, brianite, GEDRITE, MAGNESITE (MG), LAZULITE (G), wadeite, bokite, saryarkite, trolleite, rasvumite

3.11 Phosphoferrite, REDDINGITE, tyrolite, TOURMALINE (achroite, blue), LEPIDOMELANE, justite, bementite, schizolite, mullite, SPODUMENE, mansfieldite, gorceixite, holmquistite, pyrosmalite, FRIEDELITE, MONTICELLITE, PHOSPHOPHYLLITE, moissanite, muskoxite, AUTUNITE, cassidyite, CELSIAN, GEDRITE, ANTHOPHYLLITE, AMBLYGONITE, ammoniojarosite, MAGNESITE (MG), saryarkite

3.12 Phosphoferrite, REDDINGITE, tyrolite, TOURMALINE (achroite), LEPIDOMELANE, justite, bementite, schizolite, mullite, SPODUMENE, mansfieldite, gorceixite, holmquistite, pyrosmalite, FRIEDELITE, MONTICELLITE, PHOSPHOPHYLLITE, moissanite, muskoxite, AUTUNITE, cassidyite, CELSIAN, GEDRITE, ANTHOPHYLLITE, LUDLAMITE, nimite, WHITLOCKITE, MAGNESITE (MG), saryarkite, vladimirite

3.13 Phosphoferrite, REDDINGITE, tyrolite, LEPIDOMELANE, justite, bementite, schizolite, mullite, SPODUMENE, mansfieldite, gorceixite, holmquistite, pyrosmalite, FRIEDELITE, MONTICELLITE, moissanite, PHOSPHOPHYLLITE, muskoxite, AUTUNITE, cassidyite, CELSIAN, GEDRITE, ANTHOPHYLLITE, LUDLAMITE, devilline, ANDALUSITE, forbesite, wenkite, lacroix-

ite, vladimirite, fluosiderite, HETEROGENITE, saryarkite, manganpyrosmalite, grovesite

3.14 Phosphoferrite, REDDINGITE, tyrolite, LEPIDOMELANE, justite, bementite, mullite, SPODUMENE, gorceixite, pyrosmalite, FRIEDELITE, MONTICELLITE, moissanite, muskoxite, AUTUNITE, cassidyite, CELSIAN, GEDRITE, ANTHOPHYLLITE, LUDLAMITE, ANDALUSITE, spencerite, SPANGOLITE, churchite, krauskopfite, mckelveyite, vladimirite, strigovite, valleriite, grovesite, goetzenite, saryarkite

3.15 Phosphoferrite, REDDINGITE, tyrolite, LEPIDOMELANE, justite, bementite, mullite, SPODUMENE, gorceixite, pyrosmalite, FRIEDELITE, MONTICELLITE, moissanite, muskoxite, AUTUNITE, cassidyite, CELSIAN, GEDRITE, ANTHOPHYLLITE, LUDLAMITE, ANDALUSITE (G), HUREAULITE, MERWINITE, NORBERGITE, sellaite, WAGNERITE, szmikite, stanfieldite, ZOISITE, grovesite, barnesite, saryarkite, zussmanite, vladimirite

3.16 Phosphoferrite, REDDINGITE, tyrolite, LEPIDOMELANE, justite, bementite, mullite, SPODUMENE, gorceixite, pyrosmalite, FRIEDELITE, MONTICELLITE, moissanite, muskoxite, AUTUNITE, cassidyite, CELSIAN, GEDRITE, ANTHOPHYLLITE, LUDLAMITE, ANDALUSITE, HUREAULITE, cahnite, NORBERGITE, kinoite, CHLORASTROLITE (MG), lawrenceite, CHONDRODITE, ZOISITE, grovesite, vladimirite

3.17 Phosphoferrite, REDDINGITE, tyrolite, LEPIDOMELANE, justite, bementite, SPODUMENE (G), gorceixite, pyrosmalite, FRIEDELITE, MONTICELLITE, moissanite, muskoxite, AUTUNITE, cassidyite, CELSIAN, GEDRITE, ANTHOPHYLLITE, LUDLAMITE, HUREAULITE, NORBERGITE, ZOISITE, CHONDRODITE, CHLORAPATITE, FLUORITE (G), grovesite, ericaite

3.18 Phosphoferrite, REDDINGITE, tyrolite, LEPIDOMELANE, justite, bementite, SPODUMENE (G), ZOISITE, gorceixite, pyrosmalite, FRIEDELITE, MONTICELLITE, moissanite, muskoxite, AUTUNITE, cassidyite, CELSIAN, GEDRITE, ANTHOPHYLLITE, LUDLAMITE, HUREAULITE, NORBERGITE, CHONDRODITE, NATROJARO-SITE, ERYTHRITE, PUMPELLYITE, FLUORITE (G), fueggerite, FLUOR-APATITE, CHLORASTROLITE (MG), bababudanite, hainite, vayryenite, grovesite, ericaite

3.19 Phosphoferrite, REDDINGITE, tyrolite, LEPIDOMELANE, justite, bementite, SPODUMENE (G), gorceixite, pyrosmalite, FRIEDELITE, MONTICELLITE, moissanite, muskoxite, AUTUNITE, cassidyite, CELSIAN, GEDRITE, ANTHOPHYLLITE, LUDLAMITE, HUREAULITE, CHONDRODITE, PUMPELLYITE, FLUORAPATITE, yttrian apatite, NEPTUNITE, stokesite, akrochordite, CLINOENSTATITE, nimite, weibyeite, ZOISITE, FLUORITE (G), ericaite

3.20 Phosphoferrite, REDDINGITE, tyrolite, LEPIDOMELANE, justite, bementite, SPODUMENE (G), MONTI-CELLITE, moissanite, muskoxite, AUTUNITE, cassidyite, CELSIAN, GEDRITE, ANTHOPHYLLITE, HUREAULITE, CHONDRODITE, PUMPELLYITE, FLUORAPATITE, HUMITE, FERRISICKLERITE, HELVITE, PURPURITE, guarinite, HET-EROSITE, ZEUNERITE, sampleite, weloganite, bavalite, keldyshite, johannite, nitrobarite, gunningite, raimondite, ZOISITE, CHLORAS-TROLITE (MG), arthurite, kalistrontite, sabugalite, ericaite

3.21 Tyrolite, justite, SPODUMENE (G), MONTICELLITE, moissanite, CEL-SIAN, torendrikite, DIOPSIDE (G), CHONDRODITE, PUMPELLYITE, FLUORAPATITE, HUMITE, FERRI-SICKLERITE, HELVITE, PUR-PURITE, HETEROSITE, ZOISITE, CLINOHUMITE, ENSTATITE, weloganite, hibbenite, pseudoaenigmatite, zoisite, CLINOZOISITE, ericaite

3.22 Tyrolite, justite, SPODUMENE (G), MONTICELLITE, CELSIAN, CHON-DRODITE, PUMPELLYITE, HUMITE, FERRISICKLERITE, HEL-VITE, PURPURITE, FORSTERITE, HETEROSITE, TORBERNITE, svan-

bergite, CHILDRENITE, DIOPSIDE (G), CHALCOSIDERITE, ZOISITE, CLINOZOISITE, palermoite, ericaite

3.23 Tyrolite, justite, SPODUMENE (G), MONTICELLITE, CELSIAN, CHON-DRODITE, PUMPELLYITE, HUMITE, FERRISICKLERITE, HEL-VITE, PURPURITE, ericaite, HET-EROSITE, FORSTERITE, CHIL-DRENITE, pyrochroite, SILLI-MANITE, ANNABERGITE, DIOP-SIDE (G), fluotaramite, ZOISITE, CLINOZOISITE

3.24 Tyrolite, justite, MONTICELLITE, CELSIAN, CHONDRODITE, HU-MITE, FERRISICKLERITE, HEL-VITE, PURPURITE, HETEROSITE, FORSTERITE, CHILDRENITE, pyrochroite, SILLIMANITE, fluotaramite, ericaite, ZOISITE, CLINO-ZOISITE, DIOPSIDE (G), duttonite

3.25 Tyrolite, MONTICELLITE, CEL-SIAN, CHONDRODITE, HUMITE, HELVITE, FERRISICKLERITE, PURPURITE, HETEROSITE, FOR-STERITE, CHILDRENITE, pyro-chroite, SILLIMANITE (G), fluotaramite, dundasite, rancieite, sursassite, ericaite, tikhonenkovite, ZOISITE (G), CLINOZOISITE, papagoite, zellerite, DIOPSIDE (G), EN-STATITE (G)

3.26 MONTICELLITE, CELSIAN, CHON-DRODITE, HUMITE, FERRISICK-LERITE, HELVITE, PURPURITE, HETEROSITE, FORSTERITE, CHILDRENITE, ericaite, pyrochroite, SILLIMANITE, fluotaramite, ran-cieite, AXINITE, goyazite, ZOISITE (G), CLINOZOISITE, CHLORITOID, DIOPSIDE (G), ENSTATITE (G), DUMORTIERITE (MG), tikhonen-kovite

3.27 MONTICELLITE, CELSIAN, HU-MITE, FERRISICKLERITE, HEL-VITE, PURPURITE, HETEROSITE, FORSTERITE, CHILDRENITE, doloresite, tikhonenkovite, pyro-chroite, SILLIMANITE, ericaite, fluotaramite, rancieite, AXINITE (G), weinschenkite, KORNERUPINE, lo-seyite, saleeite, hiortdahlite, OLI-VINE, ZOISITE (G), CLINO-ZOISITE, CHLORITOID, DIOPSIDE (G), ENSTATITE (G), DUMORTIER-ITE (MG), isokite

3.28 CELSIAN, HUMITE, FERRISICK-LERITE, HELVITE, PURPURITE, HETEROSITE, CHILDRENITE, fluotaramite, rancieite, AXINITE (G), KORNERUPINE, OLIVINE, DANALITE, DIOPTASE, SCORODITE, jeremejevite, EKANITE (G), pseudoautunite, ZOISITE (G), CLINOZOISITE, CHLORITOID, DIOPSIDE (G), ENSTATITE (G), DUMORTIERITE (MG), calkinsite, willemseite, doloresite, cafetite

3.29 CELSIAN, HUMITE, FERRISICKLERITE, HELVITE, PURPURITE, HETEROSITE, fluotaramite, rancieite, AXINITE (G), KORNERUPINE, OLIVINE, tavorite, DANALITE, DIOPTASE, SCORODITE, doloresite, TINZENITE, tienshanite, ZOISITE (G), CLINOZOISITE, CHLORITOID, DIOPSIDE (G), ENSTATITE (G), DUMORTIERITE (MG)

3.30 CELSIAN, HUMITE, FERRISICKLERITE, HELVITE, PURPURITE, HETEROSITE, fluotaramite, rancieite, AXINITE, KORNERUPINE, OLIVINE, keldyshite, DANALITE, DIOPTASE (G), SCORODITE, BUERGERITE, TINZENITE, ROCKBRIDGEITE, willemseite, johnstrupite, kozulite, lime, rosenbuschite, DUMORTIERITE, frondelite, doloresite, GOETHITE, vezelyite, sharpite, SUSSEXITE, paraschoepite, ASTROPHYLLITE, JADEITE (MG), DIASPORE, troegerite, ZN-SCHEFFERITE, ottrelite, ZOISITE (G), CLINOZOISITE, CHLORITOID, DIOPSIDE (G), ENSTATITE (G), HYPERSTHENE (G), novacekite, coffinite

3.31 CELSIAN, HUMITE, FERRISICKLERITE, HELVITE, PURPURITE, HETEROSITE, fluotaramite, AXINITE, KORNERUPINE, OLIVINE, DANALITE, DIOPTASE, SCORODITE, TINZENITE, ROCKBRIDGEITE, DUMORTIERITE (MG), frondelite, vezelyite, ASTROPHYLLITE, DIASPORE, ZN-SCHEFFERITE, PARAHOPEITE, PARACELSIAN, RHODIZITE, ferghanite, BUERGERITE, willemseite, ZOISITE (G), CLINOZOISITE, CHLORITOID, DIOPSIDE (G), JADEITE (MG),

HYPERSTHENE (G), doloresite, ekanite (G), khryzhanovskite

3.32 CELSIAN, HUMITE, FERRISICKLERITE, HELVITE, PURPURITE, HETEROSITE, fluotaramite, AXINITE, KORNERUPINE (G), OLIVINE, DANALITE, niocalite, DIOPTASE, SCORODITE, TINZENITE, ROCKBRIDGEITE, DUMORTIERITE (MG), frondelite, vezelyite, ASTROPHYLLITE, doloresite, DIASPORE, ZN-SCHEFFERITE, PARACELSIAN, RHODIZITE, posnjakite, johannite, lovchorrite, pinnoite, BUSTAMITE, YTTROFLUORITE, ZOISITE (G), CLINOZOISITE, CHLORITOID, freirinite, DIOPSIDE (G), BUERGERITE, JADEITE (MG), HYPERSTHENE (G)

3.33 CELSIAN, FERRISICKLERITE, HELVITE, PURPURITE, HETEROSITE, AXINITE, KORNERUPINE, OLIVINE, DANALITE, DIOPTASE, SCORODITE, TINZENITE, ROCKBRIDGEITE, DUMORTIERITE (MG), frondelite, veszelyite, DIASPORE, ASTROPHYLLITE, ZN-SCHEFFERITE, RHODIZITE, BUSTAMITE, YTTROFLUORITE, IDOCRASE, CLINOHEDRITE, koettigite, laubmannite, buttgenbachite, ZOISITE (G), CLINOZOISITE, CHLORITOID, HYPERSTHENE (G), DIOPSIDE (G), JADEITE (MG), doloresite, meta-kirchheimerite

3.34 CELSIAN, FERRISICKLERITE, HELVITE, PURPURITE, HETEROSITE, AXINITE, KORNERUPINE, OLIVINE (peridot G), DANALITE, DIOPTASE, SCORODITE, TINZENITE, ROCKBRIDGEITE, DUMORTIERITE (MG), frondelite, veszelyite, ASTROPHYLLITE, DIASPORE, ZN-SCHEFFERITE, RHODIZITE, BUSTAMITE, YTTROFLUORITE, IDOCRASE, kainosite, warwickite, TRIPHYLITE, henritermierite, noonkambalite, ZOISITE (G), HYPERSTHENE (G), CLINOZOISITE, CHLORITOID, DIOPSIDE (G), JADEITE (MG)

3.35 CELSIAN, FERRISICKLERITE, HELVITE, PURPURITE, HETEROSITE, AXINITE, OLIVINE, DANALITE, DIOPTASE, SCORODITE, TINZENITE, ROCKBRIDGEITE,

DUMORTIERITE (MG), frondelite, veszelyite, ASTROPHYLLITE, DIASPORE, ZN-SCHEFFERITE, RHODIZITE, BUSTAMITE, YTTROFLUORITE, IDOCRASE (MG), kainosite, warwickite, TRIPHYLITE, chalcomenite, ZOISITE (G), CLINOZOISITE, gaudefroyite, CHLORITOID, JADEITE (MG), HYPERSTHENE (G), haiweeite

3.36 CELSIAN, FERRISICKLERITE, HELVITE, PURPURITE, HETEROSITE, AXINITE, OLIVINE, DANALITE, SCORODITE, TINZENITE, ROCKBRIDGEITE, frondelite, DUMORTIERITE (MG), JADEITE (Guatemala), veszelyite, ASTROPHYLLITE, DIASPORE, ZN-SCHEFFERITE, RHODIZITE, BUSTAMITE, YTTROFLUORITE, IDOCRASE (MG), kainosite, warwickite, TRIPHYLITE, homilite, BABINGTONITE, CONNELLITE, PLANCHEITE, gaudefroyite, ZOISITE ("tanzanite" G), ZOISITE (G), CLINOZOISITE, CHLORITOID, HYPERSTHENE (G)

3.37 CELSIAN, FERRISICKLERITE, HELVITE, PURPURITE, HETEROSITE, OLIVINE, DANALITE, SCORODITE, TINZENITE, ROCKBRIDGEITE, frondelite, veszelyite, ASTROPHYLLITE, DIASPORE, ZN-SCHEFFERITE, RHODIZITE, BUSTAMITE, YTTROFLUORITE, IDOCRASE (MG), kainosite, TRIPHYLITE, PLANCHEITE, schallerite, Mg-chlorophoenicite, ZOISITE (G), CLINOZOISITE, CHLORITOID, ahlfeldite, HYPERSTHENE (G), CLINOENSTATITE (G), gaudefroyite

3.38 CELSIAN, FERRISICKLERITE, HELVITE, PURPURITE, HETEROSITE, DANALITE, SCORODITE, TINZENITE, ROCKBRIDGEITE, frondelite, veszelyite, ASTROPHYLLITE, DIASPORE, ZN-SCHEFFERITE, RHODIZITE, BUSTAMITE, YTTROFLUORITE, IDOCRASE (MG, xls), kainosite, TRIPHYLITE, EPIDOTE, dickinsonite, SCORZALITE, krinovite, mesitite, CLINOZOISITE, CHLORITOID, HYPERSTHENE (G), howieite, gaudefroyite

3.39 CELSIAN, FERRISICKLERITE, HELVITE, PURPURITE, HETERO-

SITE, DANALITE, SCORODITE, TINZENITE, ROCKBRIDGEITE, frondelite, veszelyite, ASTROPHYLLITE, DIASPORE, ZN-SCHEFFERITE, BUSTAMITE, YTTROFLUORITE, IDOCRASE (MG), kainosite, TRIPHYLITE, EPIDOTE, dickinsonite, vogtite, CHLORITOID, HYPERSTHENE (G), yoderite, gaudefroyite

3.40 HELVITE, PURPURITE, HETEROSITE, DANALITE, SCORODITE, TINZENITE, ROCKBRIDGEITE, frondelite, veszelyite, ASTROPHYLLITE, DIASPORE, BUSTAMITE, YTTROFLUORITE, IDOCRASE (MG), kainosite, TRIPHYLITE, EPIDOTE, dickinsonite, SICKLERITE, tagilite, gerhardtite, GILLESPITE, rinkolite, GRIPHITE, hardystonite, steenstrupine, ALLUAUDITE, Mn-alluaudite, SAPPHIRINE, hendricksite, CHLORITOID, GROSSULAR, UVAROVITE, johachidolite, HYPERSTHENE (G), CHLOROMELANITE (MG), ahlfeldite, gaudefroyite

3.41 HELVITE, DANALITE, SCORODITE, TINZENITE, ROCKBRIDGEITE, frondelite, veszelyite, DIASPORE, BUSTAMITE, YTTROFLUORITE, IDOCRASE (MG), kainosite, TRIPHYLITE, EPIDOTE, dickinsonite, SICKLERITE, tagilite, gerhardtite, steenstrupine, ALLUAUDITE, Mn-alluaudite, SAPPHIRINE, natrophilite, cenosite, magbasite, CHLORITOID, GROSSULAR, UVAROVITE, cymrite

3.42 HELVITE, DANALITE, TINZENITE, ROCKBRIDGEITE, FRONDELITE, VESZELYITE, DIASPORE, BUSTAMITE, YTTROFLUORITE, IDOCRASE (MG), kainosite, wiserite, TRIPHYLITE, EPIDOTE, SICKLERITE, tagilite, gerhardtite, steenstrupine, ALLUAUDITE, Mn-alluaudite, SAPPHIRINE, serendibite, woehlerite, kassite, niobophyllite, lorenzenite, CHLORITOID, GROSSULAR, UVAROVITE, bredigite

3.43 HELVITE, DANALITE, ROCKBRIDGEITE, frondelite, veszelyite, DIASPORE, BUSTAMITE, YTTROFLUORITE, IDOCRASE (MG), kainosite, TRIPHYLITE, EPIDOTE, kirschsteinite, batisite, RHODIZITE, attakolite, SICKLERITE, tagilite, gerhardtite, steenstrupine, ALLUAU-DITE, Mn-alluaudite, SAPPHIRINE, roeblingite, fillowite, chaoite, ramsayite, CHLORITOID, GROSSULAR, UVAROVITE, nordite

3.44 HELVITE, DANALITE, ROCKBRIDGEITE, frondelite, veszelyite, DIASPORE, YTTROFLUORITE, kainosite, TRIPHYLITE, EPIDOTE, SICKLERITE, RHODIZITE, tagilite, steenstrupine, ALLUAUDITE, Mn-alluaudite, SAPPHIRINE, IDOCRASE (MG), johannsenite, euchroite, taramite, Fe-schallerite, CHLORITOID, GROSSULAR, UVAROVITE

3.45 ROCKBRIDGEITE, frondelite, veszelyite, DIASPORE, YTTROFLUORITE, kainosite, TRIPHYLITE, EPIDOTE (G), SICKLERITE, tagilite, ALLUAUDITE, Mn-alluaudite, steenstrupine, SAPPHIRINE, johannsenite, taramite, HEMIMORPHITE, uranospinite, PIEMONTITE, lamprophyllite, TITANITE, IDOCRASE (MG), cronstedtite, yttrocerite, Mn-babingtonite, CHLORITOID, GROSSULAR, UVAROVITE, hydrougrandite, RHODIZITE

3.46 ROCKBRIDGEITE, frondelite, veszelyite, DIASPORE, YTTROFLUORITE, kainosite, TRIPHYLITE, EPIDOTE, tagilite, steenstrupine, ALLUAUDITE, Mn-alluaudite, SAPPHIRINE, johannsenite, taramite, PIEMONTITE, lamprophyllite, TITANITE, CHLOROPHOENICITE, HAUERITE, rinkite, glinkite, CHLORITOID, GROSSULAR, UVAROVITE

3.47 ROCKBRIDGEITE, frondelite, veszelyite, DIASPORE, YTTROFLUORITE, kainosite, TRIPHYLITE, EPIDOTE, tagilite, steenstrupine, ALLUAUDITE, Mn-alluaudite, SAPPHIRINE, johannsenite, taramite, PIEMONTITE, lamprophyllite, TITANITE, trimerite, natrochalcite, weilite, CHLORITOID, GROSSULAR, UVAROVITE, SINHALITE (xls, G), seidozerite, CHAMBERSITE

3.48 ROCKBRIDGEITE, frondelite, veszelyite, DIASPORE, YTTROFLUORITE, kainosite, TRIPHYLITE, EPIDOTE, tagilite, ALLUAUDITE,

Mn-alluaudite, SAPPHIRINE, johannsenite, taramite, PIEMONTITE, lamprophyllite, TITANITE, REALGAR, langite, glaucochroite, melanovanadite, weilite, andrewsite, natrochalcite, CHLORITOID, GROSSULAR, UVAROVITE, SINHALITE (xls, G), CHAMBERSITE, voltzite, akatoreite

3.49 ROCKBRIDGEITE, frondelite, veszelyite, DIASPORE, YTTROFLUORITE, kainosite, CHAMBERSITE, TRIPHYLITE, EPIDOTE, tagilite, ALLUAUDITE, Mn-alluaudite, SAPPHIRINE, johannsenite, PIEMONTITE, lamprophyllite, TITANITE, REALGAR, langite, ORPIMENT, TOPAZ, hematolite, erikite, weilite, natrochalcite, CHLORITOID, GROSSULAR, UVAROVITE, SINHALITE (xls, G)

3.50 Veszelyite, DIASPORE, YTTROFLUORITE, kainosite, TRIPHYLITE, tagilite, ALLUAUDITE, Mn-alluaudite, SAPPHIRINE, johannsenite, PIEMONTITE, lamprophyllite, TITANITE, REALGAR, langite, TOPAZ (brown, G), natrochalcite, DIAMOND (G), BORT, GROSSULAR, UVAROVITE, PYROPE, METATORBERNITE, RHODOCHROSITE (MG), HEDENBERGITE, varulite, LITHIOPHILITE, burbankite, lavenite, arfvedsonite, manganbabingtonite, ferrohastingsite, CHLORITOID, tombarthite, CUPROSKLODOWSKITE, ROSELITE, CHAMBERSITE

3.52 YTTROFLUORITE, kainosite, RHODOCHROSITE (MG), tagilite, DIAMOND (G), SAPPHIRINE, johannsenite, PIEMONTITE, lamprophyllite, TITANITE, REALGAR, TOPAZ (G, brown), HEDENBERGITE, varulite, LITHIOPHILITE, tombarthite, fermorite, dannemorite, urbanite, METATORBERNITE, ROSELITE, CHLORITOID, GROSSULAR, UVAROVITE, PYROPE

3.53 YTTROFLUORITE, kainosite, tagilite, SAPPHIRINE, RHODOCHROSITE (MG), johannsenite, lamprophyllite, TITANITE (G), REALGAR, TOPAZ (G, yellow, brown), HEDENBERGITE, varulite, LITHIOPHILITE, DIAMOND, tombarthite, urbanite, KYANITE, uranocircite, METATORBERNITE, ROSELITE, CHLORITOID, GROSSULAR, UVAROVITE, PYROPE, carbocernaite

3.54 YTTROFLUORITE, kainosite, tagilite, SAPPHIRINE, RHODOCHROSITE (MG), johannsenite, lamprophyllite, TITANITE (G), REALGAR, TOPAZ (G, yellow, brown), HEDENBERGITE, varulite, LITHIOPHILITE, tombarthite, KYANITE, caswellite, meta-ankoleite, METATORBERNITE, ROSELITE, CHLORITOID, SKLODOWSKITE, GROSSULAR, UVAROVITE, PYROPE

3.55 YTTROFLUORITE, kainosite, tagilite, SAPPHIRINE, RHODOCHROSITE (MG), johannsenite, TITANITE (G), REALGAR, TOPAZ (G, yellow brown, blue), HEDENBERGITE, varulite, LITHIOPHILITE, tombarthite, KYANITE, AEGERINE, ARROJADITE, PERICLASE, SPINEL, ACMITE, JEFFERSONITE, epidydymite, METATORBERNITE, ROSELITE, CHLORITOID, SKLODOWSKITE, GROSSULAR, UVAROVITE, PYROPE

3.56 YTTROFLUORITE, kainosite, tagilite, SAPPHIRINE, RHODOCHROSITE (MG), REALGAR, TOPAZ (G, yellow, brown, blue, colorless), hedenbergite, varulite, LITHIOPHILITE, tombarthite, KYANITE, AEGERINE, ACMITE, JEFFERSONITE, PERICLASE, METATORBERNITE, ROSELITE, CHLORITOID, SKLODOWSKITE, GROSSULAR, UVAROVITE, PYROPE

3.57 Kainosite, tagilite, SAPPHIRINE, RHODOCHROSITE (MG), TOPAZ (G, yellow, brown, blue), varulite, LITHIOPHILITE, tombarthite, KYANITE, AEGERINE, ACMITE, JEFFERSONITE, RHODONITE, synadelphite, hemafibrite, mazapilite, PERICLASE, METATORBERNITE, ROSELITE, CHLORITOID, SKLODOWSKITE, GROSSULAR, UVAROVITE, PYROPE, magniotriplite

3.58 RHODOCHROSITE (MG), TOPAZ (G, yellow, brown, blue), RHODONITE, tagilite, kainosite, synadelphite, varulite, LITHIOPHILITE, tombarthite, KYANITE,

AEGERINE, ACMITE, JEFFERSONITE, thortveitite, gageite, chapmanite, METATORBERNITE, ROSELITE, SKLODOWSKITE, GROSSULAR, UVAROVITE, PYROPE, SPINEL (G, pink, purple, red), sodium autunite

3.59 RHODOCHROSITE (MG), TOPAZ (G, brown, blue), RHODONITE, tagilite, kainosite, synadelphite, varulite, tombarthite, KYANITE, AEGERINE, ACMITE, JEFFERSONITE, florenceite, METATORBERNITE, ROSELITE, SKLODOWSKITE, GROSSULAR, UVAROVITE, PYROPE, SPINEL (G, pink, purple, red)

3.60 RHODOCHROSITE (MG), TOPAZ (G, brown, blue), RHODONITE (MG), tagilite, kainosite, varulite, tombarthite, synadelphite, florenceite, ferrohypersthene, KYANITE, AEGERINE, ACMITE, JEFFERSONITE, ureyite, chalcocyanite, ardennite, Ce-vesuvianite, arseniosiderite, MALACHITE, LUDWIGITE, sobralite, ilimaussite, ellsworthite, samiresite, METATORBERNITE, benstonite, walstromite, ROSELITE, TRIPLITE, stottite, SKLODOWSKITE, GROSSULAR, barbosalite, UVAROVITE, PYROPE, SPINEL (G, pink, red, purples, blue), taaffeite (G)

3.61 JEFFERSONITE, KYANITE, tombarthite, benstonite, RHODOCHROSITE (MG), MALACHITE, chalcocyanite, ferrohypersthene, florenceite, synadelphite, RHODONITE (MG), kainosite, pyroxmangite, TRIPLITE, ashcroftine, yttrocerite, METATORBERNITE, ROSELITE, SKLODOWSKITE, UVAROVITE, PYROPE, taaffeite (G), SPINEL (G, pink, red, purple, blue)

3.62 Pyroxmangite, JEFFERSONITE, KYANITE, tombarthite, RHODOCHROSITE (MG), benstonite, MALACHITE, chalcocyanite, ferrohypersthene, florenceite, synadelphite, RHODONITE (MG), dietzeite, barytolamprophyllite, METATORBERNITE, ROSELITE, TRIPLITE, SKLODOWSKITE, UVAROVITE, PYROPE, SPINEL (G, red, purple, blue), vanuralite, verplanckite

3.63 Barytolamprophyllite, dietzeite, RHODOCHROSITE (MG), pyrox-

mangite, JEFFERSONITE, KYAN-
ITE, tombarthite, benstonite,
MALACHITE, chalcocyanite, ferro-
hypersthene, florenceite, synadel-
phite, RHODONITE (MG), kemmlitz-
ite, azoproite, METATORBERNITE,
ROSELITE, TRIPLITE, SKLODOWS-
KITE, UVAROVITE, PYROPE,
SPINEL (G, red, purple, blue),
ceylonite (G)

3.64 Barytolamprophyllite, dietzeite,
RHODOCHROSITE (MG), pyroxmangite, KYANITE, tombarthite,
benstonite, MALACHITE, chalcocyanite, ferrohypersthene, florenceite,
synadelphite, RHODONITE (MG),
rhoenite, AURICHALCITE, SAR-
COPSIDE, STRONTIANITE, META-
ZEUNERITE, ROSELITE, META-
TORBERNITE, TRIPLITE,
SKLODOWSKITE, UVAROVITE,
PYROPE, SPINEL (G, red, purple,
blue), ceylonite (G), vanuranylite

3.65 STRONTIANITE, SARCOPSIDE,
RHODOCHROSITE (MG), bary-
tolamprophyllite, dietzeite, pyroxmangite, KYANITE (G), tombarthite,
benstonite, MALACHITE, chalcocyanite, ferrohypersthene, florenceite,
synadelphite, RHODONITE (MG),
hinsdalite, hemafibrite, BENITOITE
(G), CHRYSOBERYL, META-
TORBERNITE, ROSELITE, TRIP-
LITE, SKLODOWSKITE, UVARO-
VITE, PYROPE (G), GROSSULAR
(G, hessonite), SPINEL (G, blue),
ceylonite (G)

3.66 STRONTIANITE, SARCOPSIDE,
RHODOCHROSITE (MG), barytolamprophyllite, dietzeite, pyrxo-
mangite, benstonite, MALACHITE,
chalcocyanite, ferrohyspersthene,
florenceite, synadelphite, RHO-
DONITE (MG), CHRYSOBERYL,
argentojarosite, barytocalcite, triploidite, METATORBERNITE, ROSE-
LITE, TRIPLITE, SKLODOWKSITE,
UVAROVITE, PYROPE (G), SPINEL
(G, blue), ceylonite (G), BENITOITE
(G), boggildite

3.67 STRONTIANITE, SARCOPSIDE,
RHODOCHROSITE (xls), dietzeite,
pyroxmangite, MALACHITE, chalcocyanite, ferrohypersthene, florenceite,
synadelphite, RHODONITE (MG),
CHRYSOBERYL, barytocalcite,

brandtite, todorokite, eveite, al-
stonite, GRAFTONITE, PLUMBO-
JAROSITE, METATORBERNITE,
ROSELITE, TRIPLITE, SKLODOWS-
KITE, UVAROVITE, PYROPE (G),
SPINEL (G, blue), ceylonite (G),
BENITOITE (G)

3.68 STRONTIANITE, SARCOPSIDE,
RHODOCHROSITE (xls), dietzeite,
MALACHITE, pyroxmangite, chalco-
cyanite, ferrohypersthene, florenceite,
synadelphite, RHODONITE (MG),
CHRYSOBERYL (G), barytocalcite,
alstonite, GRAFTONITE, akdalaite,
pyroxferrite, METATORBERNITE,
ROSELITE, TRIPLITE, SKLODOWS-
KITE, UVAROVITE, PYROPE (G),
SPINEL (G, blue), ceylonite (G),
garrelsite

3.69 STRONTIANITE, SARCOPSIDE,
RHODOCHROSITE (xls), dietzeite,
pyroxmangite, MALACHITE, chalcocyanite, ferrohypersthene, florenceite,
synadelphite, RHODONITE (MG),
CHRYSOBERYL (G), barytocalcite,
alstonite, GRAFTONITE, pyroxferrite, poechite, METATORBERN-
ITE, ROSELITE, TRIPLITE,
SKLODOWSKITE, UVAROVITE,
PYROPE (G), SPINEL (G, blue),
ceylonite (G)

3.70 STRONTIANITE, SARCOPSIDE,
RHODOCHROSITE (xls), dietzeite,
MALACHITE, pyroxmangite, chalco-
cyanite, ferrohypersthene, florenceite,
gaspeite, synadelphite, RHODONITE
(MG), CHRYSOBERYL, barytocal-
cite, alstonite, GRAFTONITE,
pyroxferrite, asbecasite, tundrite,
beusite, adelite, uranopilite, META-
TORBERNITE, ROSELITE, TRIP-
LITE, uramphite, SKLODOWSKITE,
UVAROVITE, PYROPE (G),
ANDRADITE, STAUROLITE (al-
tered), SPINEL (G, blue), ceylonite
(G), brockite

3.71 STRONTIANITE, SARCOPSIDE,
pyroxmangite, MALACHITE, ferro-
hypersthene, florenceite, synadel-
phite, RHODONITE, CHRYSO-
BERYL (G), barytocalcite, alstonite,
GRAFTONITE, pyroxferrite, adelite,
uranopilite, gaspeite, ROSELITE,
TRIPLITE, SKLODOWSKITE,
UVAROVITE, PYROPE (G),
ANDRADITE, goldmanite, traskite,

SPINEL (G, blue), ceylonite (G), beta-roselite, brockite, woodruffite, hagendorfite

3.72 STRONTIANITE, SARCOPSIDE, pyroxmangite, MALACHITE, ferro-hypersthene, synadelphite, RHODONITE, CHRYSOBERYL (G), GRAFTONITE, pyroxferrite, adelite, uranopilite, picrotephroite, agardite, ROSELITE, mcgovernite, TRIPLITE, SKLODOWSKITE, UVAROVITE, PYROPE (G), brockite, ANDRADITE, gaspeite, SPINEL (G, blue), ceylonite (G), redledgeite, goldmanite

3.73 STRONTIANITE, SARCOPSIDE, pyroxmangite, MALACHITE, ferro-hypersthene, synadelphite, RHODONITE, CHRYSOBERYL (G), GRAFTONITE, pyroxferrite, adelite, uranopilite, eulite, AZURITE, ROSELITE, TRIPLITE, SKLODOWSKITE, UVAROVITE, PYROPE (G), ANDRADITE, SPINEL (G, blue), ceylonite (G), brockite, goldmanite

3.74 STRONTIANITE, pyroxmangite, MALACHITE (MG), ferrohypersthene, synadelphite, RHODONITE, CHRYSOBERYL (G), GRAFTONITE, pyroxferrite, adelite, uranopilite, eulite, PARATACAMITE, STAUROLITE, enigmatite, AZURITE, ROSELITE, TRIPLITE, SKLODOWSKITE, UVAROVITE, PYROPE (G), goldmanite, ANDRADITE, SPINEL (G, blue), brockite, ceylonite (G), abernathyite

3.75 STRONTIANITE, pyroxmangite, MALACHITE (MG), ferrohypersthene, synadelphite, RHODONITE, CHRYSOBERYL (G), GRAFTONITE, pyroxferrite, adelite, uranopilite, eulite, STAUROLITE, enigmatite, tilasite, dussertite, ATACAMITE, AZURITE, TRIPLITE, goldmanite, UVAROVITE, PYROPE (G), ANDRADITE, SPINEL (G, blue), ceylonite (G), brockite

3.76 STRONTIANITE, pyroxmangite, MALACHITE (MG), synadelphite, RHODONITE, CHRYSOBERYL (G), GRAFTONITE, pyroxferrite, adelite, brockite, uranopilite, eulite, STAUROLITE, enigmatite, tilasite, ATACAMITE, knorringite, eveite, AZURITE, TRIPLITE, goldmanite, UVAROVITE, PYROPE (G),

ANDRADITE, ceylonite (G), brownmillerite

3.77 STRONTIANITE, pyroxmangite, MALACHITE (MG), synadelphite, CHRYSOBERYL (G), GRAFTONITE, uranopilite, eulite, STAUROLITE, enigmatite, tilasite, ATACAMITE, AZURITE (xls), brockite chalcolamprite, TRIPLITE, UVAROVITE, PYROPE (G), goldmanite, ANDRADITE, ceylonite (G)

3.78 STRONTIANITE, pyroxmangite, MALACHITE (MG), synadelphite, CHRYSOBERYL (G) GRAFTONITE, uranopilite, eulite, STAUROLITE, enigmatite, tilasite, ATACAMITE, TEPHROITE, jarlite, AZURITE (xls), TRIPLITE, UVAROVITE, PYROPE (G), ANDRADITE, ceylonite (G), brockite

3.79 Pyroxmangite, MALACHITE (MG), synadelphite, GRAFTONITE, urano-pilite, eulite, STAUROLITE, enigmatite, tilasite, TEPHROITE, jarlite, mixite, SHATTUCKITE, TRIPLITE, UVAROVITE, PYROPE (G), ANDRADITE, ceylonite (G), brockite

3.08 Pyroxmangite, MALACHITE (MG), uranopilite, STAUROLITE (xls), eulite, enigmatite, TEPHROITE, jarlite, URANOPHANE, teinite, brockite, hyalotekite, ILVAITE, daubreelite, TRIPLITE, UVAROVITE, PYROPE (G), ANDRADITE (G), SHATTUCKITE (MG), SPESSARTINE, ceylonite (G), baotite

3.81 Uranopilite, eulite, STAUROLITE (xls), enigmatite, TEPHROITE, jarlite, URANOPHANE, ILVAITE, daubreelite, MALACHITE (MG), hoegbomite, strashimirite, SCHORLOMITE, TRIPLITE, ANDRADITE (G), SPESSARTINE, ceylonite (G), brockite

3.82 Uranopilite, eulite, STAUROLITE (xls), enigmatite, TEPHROITE, jarlite, URANOPHANE, ILVAITE, daubreelite, MALACHITE (MG), brockite, SCHORLOMITE, corvusite, calcio-ancylite, TRIPLITE, ANDRADITE (G), SPESSARTINE, ceylonite (G), ANATASE, sonolite

3.83 Uranopilite, eulite, STAUROLITE (xls), enigmatite, TEPHROITE, jarlite, URANOPHANE, ILVAITE,

MALACHITE (MG), SCHORLO-
MITE, brockite, wolfeite, allactite,
joesmithite, uranotile, TRIPLITE,
ANDRADITE (G, demantoid),
SPESSARTINE, ceylonite (G),
ANATASE, norsethite

3.84 Uranopilite, eulite, enigmatite,
TEPHROITE, jarlite, URANO-
PHANE, ILVAITE, MALACHITE
(MG), SCHORLOMITE, sohngeite,
TRIPLITE, ANDRADITE (G,
demantoid), SPESSARTINE, RHO-
DOLITE (G), ceylonite (G),
ANATASE, HIBONITE, iriginite,
norsethite, brockite, deerite

3.85 Uranopilite, eulite, enigmatite,
TEPHROITE, jarlite, URANO-
PHANE, ILVAITE, MALACHITE
(MG), SCHORLOMITE, wicken-
burgite, LEUCOPHOENICITE, TRIP-
LITE, ANDRADITE (G, demantoid),
SPESSARTINE, ALMANDINE (G),
ceylonite (G), ANATASE, sodium
uranospinite, brockite

3.86 Uranopilite, eulite, TEPHROITE,
jarlite, URANOPHANE, ILVAITE,
MALACHITE (MG), SCHOR-
LOMITE, SULVANITE, ARSENO-
LITE, TRIPLITE, brockite, ANDRA-
DITE (G), stenonite, muirite,
SPESSARTINE, ALMANDINE (G),
waylandite, ceylonite (G), ANATASE

3.87 Uranopilite, TEPHROITE, jarlite,
URANOPHANE, ILVAITE, MALA-
CHITE (MG), SCHORLOMITE,
SULVANITE, ARSENOLITE, flink-
ite, TRIPLITE, brockite, ANDRA-
DITE (G), SPESSARTINE, ALMAN-
DINE (G), ceylonite (G), ANATASE

3.88 Uranopilite, TEPHROITE, jarlite,
URANOPHANE, ILVAITE, MALA-
CHITE (MG), SCHORLOMITE,
SULVANITE, ARSENOLITE, pina-
kiolite, ANTLERITE, brockite,
TRIPLITE, ANDRADITE (G),
SPESSARTINE, ALMANDINE (G),
ceylonite (G), ANATASE

3.89 Uranopilite, TEPHROITE, jarlite,
URANOPHANE, ILVAITE, MALAC-
HITE (MG), SULVANITE, JOA-
QUINITE, wickmanite, getchellite,
TRIPLITE, ANDRADITE (G),
brockite, SPESSARTINE, ALMAN-
DINE (G), ceylonite (G), ANATASE,
osarizawite, doverite

3.90 Uranopilite, TEPHROITE, jarlite,

URANOPHANE, ILVAITE, MALA-
CHITE (MG), SULVANITE, CHAL-
COPHANITE, cafarsite, djerfisherite,
SYNCHISITE, Mg-orthite, SPHALER-
ITE, ALABANDITE, WILLEMITE,
ANATASE, malacon, TRIPLITE,
ANDRADITE (G), SPESSARTINE
(G), ALMANDINE (G), ceylonite (G),
GAHNOSPINEL (G), osarizawite,
brockite, getchellite

3.91 Uranopilite, TEPHROITE, jarlite,
URANOPHANE, ILVAITE, MALA-
CHITE (MG), SULVANITE, CHAL-
COPHANITE, SPHALERITE, ALA-
BANDITE, WILLEMITE, malacon,
hodgkinsonite, nagatelite, ANDRA-
DITE, SPESSARTINE (G), ALMAN-
DINE (G), GAHNOSPINEL (G),
ANATASE, getchellite, osarizawite,
brockite

3.92 Uranopilite, TEPHROITE, jarlite,
URANOPHANE, ILVAITE, MAL-
ACHITE (MG), SULVANITE,
CHALCOPHANITE, SPHALERITE,
ALABANDITE, WILLEMITE, get-
chellite, taramellite, ANDRADITE,
SPESSARTINE (G), ALMANDINE
(G), GAHNOSPINEL (G), ANA-
TASE, osarizawite, brockite, getchel-
lite

3.93 Uranopilite, TEPHROITE, jarlite,
URANOPHANE, ILVAITE, MAL-
ACHITE (MG), SULVANITE,
CHALCOPHANITE, SPHALERITE,
ALABANDITE, WILLEMITE, chene-
vixite, ferropicotite, ANDRADITE,
SPESSARTINE (G), ANATASE,
ALMANDINE (G), GAHNOSPINEL
(G), osarizawite, brockite, getchellite

3.94 Uranopilite, TEPHROITE, URANO-
PHANE, ILVAITE, MALACHITE
(MG), SULVANITE, CHALCO-
PHANITE, SPHALERITE, ALABAN-
DITE, WILLEMITE, anandite,
RHABDOPHANE, DURANGITE,
meymacite, ANDRADITE, SPESSAR-
TINE (G), ALMANDINE (G),
GAHNOSPINEL (G), ANATASE,
getchellite, osarizawite, brockite

3.95 Uranopilite, TEPHROITE, URANO-
PHANE, ILVAITE, MALACHITE
(MG), SULVANITE, CHALCO-
PHANITE, SPHALERITE, ALABAN-
DITE, WILLEMITE, RHABDO-
PHANE, DURANGITE, sonoraite,
meymacite, ANCYLITE, osarizawite,

brockite, SIDERITE, roepperite, ANDRADITE, SPESSARTINE (G), ALMANDINE (G), getchellite, GAHNOSPINEL (G), ANATASE

3.96 Uranopilite, TEPHROITE, URANO-PHANE, ILVAITE, MALACHITE, SULVANITE, CHALCOPHANITE, SPHALERITE, ALABANDITE, WIL-LEMITE, RHABDOPHANE, DU-RANGITE, meymacite, SIDERITE, roepperite, CELESTITE, knebelite, orthoferrosilite, LEGRANDITE, AN-DRADITE, SPESSARTINE (G), ANATASE, ALMANDINE (G), GAHNOSPINEL (G), CORUNDUM (G, yellow), brockite, osarizawite

3.97 Uranopilite, TEPHROITE, URANO-PHANE, ILVAITE, MALACHITE, SULVANITE, CHALCOPHANITE, SPHALERITE, ALABANDITE, WIL-LEMITE, RHABDOPHANE, DU-RANGITE, meymacite, SIDERITE, roepperite, CELESTITE, knebelite, LEGRANDITE, PEROVSKITE, pare-drite, BROCHANTITE, LIBETHEN-ITE, brockite, ANDRADITE, SPESSARTINE (G), ALMANDINE (G), GAHNOSPINEL (G), ANA-TASE, CORUNDUM (G, yellow, Burma ruby), osarizawite

3.98 Uranopilite, TEPHROITE, URANO-PHANE, ILVAITE, MALACHITE, SULVANITE, CHALCOPHANITE, SPHALERITE, ALABANDITE, WIL-LEMITE, RHABDOPHANE, DU-RANGITE, meymacite, roepperite, CELESTITE, knebelite, LEGRAND-ITE, PEROVSKITE, kamarezite, kalkowskite, WURTZITE, ANDRA-DITE, jimboite, SPESSARTINE (G), ALMANDINE (G), GAHNOSPINEL (G), CORUNDUM (G, yellow, B. ruby), painite, osarizawite, brockite

3.99 Uranopilite, TEPHROITE, URANO-PHANE, ILVAITE, MALACHITE, SULVANITE, CHALCOPHANITE, SPHALERITE, ALABANDITE, WIL-LEMITE, RHABDOPHANE, DU-RANGITE, meymacite, roepperite, knebelite, LEGRANDITE, brockite, PEROVSKITE, kalkowskite, MAR-GAROSANITE, CYRTOLITE, AN-DRADITE, SPESSARTINE (G), ALMANDINE (G), GAHNOSPINEL (G), CORUNDUM (G, yellow, ruby, colorless, green), painite, osarizawite

4.00 Uranopilite, TEPHROITE, URANO-PHANE, ILVAITE, MALACHITE, SULVANITE, CHALCOPHANITE, SPHALERITE, kimzeyite, ALABAN-DITE, WILLEMITE, RHABDO-PHANE, DURANGITE, meymacite, roepperite, knebelite, LEGRANDITE, PEROVSKITE, kalkowskite, MAR-GAROSANITE, CYRTOLITE, CO-RUNDUM (G, yellow, ruby, green, etc.), barylite, OLIVENITE, GAHNO-SPINEL (G), ROSASITE, brockite, niggliite, SENGIERITE, renardite, partschinite, osarizawite, greigite, BEUDANTITE, pandaite, ZIRCON (low), ANDRADITE, moluranite, SPESSARTINE (G), ALMANDINE (G), painite

4.01 TEPHROITE, ILVAITE, MAL-ACHITE, CHALCOPHANITE, painite (G), brockite, SPHALERITE, ALABANDITE, WILLEMITE, RHAB-DOPHANE, DURANGITE, meyma-cite, roepperite, knebelite, LEGRAN-DITE, PEROVSKITE, brockite, kalkowskite, MARGAROSANITE, CYRTOLITE, CORUNDUM (G), ROSASITE, OLIVENITE, BEUDAN-TITE, PLUMBOGUMMITE, ZIRCON (low), ANDRADITE, SPESSARTINE (G), osarizawite, ALMANDINE (G), GAHNOSPINEL (G), arsenosulvanite

4.02 TEPHROITE, ILVAITE, MAL-ACHITE, CHALCOPHANITE, SPHAL-ERITE, brockite, ALABANDITE, WILLEMITE, DURANGITE, meyma-cite, roepperite, knebelite, LEGRAN-DITE, PEROVSKITE, kalkowskite, osarizawite, MARGAROSANITE, CYRTOLITE, CORUNDUM (G), ROSASITE, OLIVENITE, vesignieite, tundrite, BEUDANTITE, alleghany-ite, ZIRCON (low), ANDRADITE, SPESSARTINE (G), ALMANDINE (G), GAHNOSPINEL (G)

4.03 TEPHROITE, ILVAITE, MAL-ACHITE (xls), CHALCOPHANITE, SPHALERITE, ALABANDITE, WIL-LEMITE (G), DURANGITE, meyma-cite, roepperite, knebelite, LEGRAN-DITE, PEROVSKITE, kalkowskite, MARGAROSANITE, CYRTOLITE, CORUNDUM (G), ROSASITE, OLIVENITE, BEUDANTITE, GAL-AXITE, CUBANITE, pisekite, HANCOCKITE, ZIRCON (low),

ANDRADITE, smythite, SPESSAR-TINE (G), orthopinakiolite, brockite, pabstite, ALMANDINE (G), GAHNO-SPINEL (G), vesignieite

4.04 TEPHROITE, ILVAITE, MAL-ACHITE (xls), CHALCOPHANITE, SPHALERITE, ALABANDITE, WIL-LEMITE, DURANGITE, meymacite, roepperite, knebelite, LEGRANDITE, PEROVSKITE, kalkowskite, MAR-GAROSANITE, CYRTOLITE, CO-RUNDUM (G), ROSASITE, OLIVE-NITE, BEUDANTITE, CUBANITE, erinite, thorbastnaesite, ZIRCON (low), ANDRADITE, SPESSARTINE (G), smythite, ALMANDINE (G), GAHNOSPINEL (G), vesignieite, metaheinrichite, brockite

4.05 TEPHROITE, ILVAITE, MAL-ACHITE (xls), CHALCOPHANITE, SPHALERITE, WILLEMITE, DU-RANGITE, meymacite, roepperite, knebelite, ROSASITE, LEGRAN-DITE, PEROVSKITE, MARGARO-SANITE, CORUNDUM (G), OLIVE-NITE, BEUDANTITE, CUBANITE, uhligite, LEPIDOCROCITE, geikiel-ite, brockite, greigite, zemannite, ANDRADITE, SPESSARTINE (G), ALMANDINE (G), GAHNOSPINEL (G), vesignieite, smythite

4.06 TEPHROITE, ILVAITE, MAL-ACHITE (xls), CHALCOPHANITE, SPHALERITE, WILLEMITE, DU-RANGITE, meymacite, roepperite, knebelite, LEGRANDITE, MARG-AROSANITE, CORUNDUM, ROSA-SITE, OLIVENITE, BEUDANTITE, CUBANITE, uhligite, LEPIDOCRO-CITE, dosulite, ANDRADITE, SPESSARTINE (G), ALMANDINE (G), GAHNOSPINEL (G), vesignieite, smythite, brockite

4.07 TEPHROITE, ILVAITE, MAL-ACHITE (xls), CHALCOPHANITE, SPHALERITE, WILLEMITE, DU-RANGITE, meymacite, roepperite, knebelite, ROSASITE, MARGARO-SANITE, kennedyite, brockite, CORUNDUM, OLIVENITE, BEU-DANTITE, CUBANITE, uhligite, LEPIDOCROCITE, ANDRADITE, SPESSARTINE (G), smythite, ALMANDINE (G), vesignieite

4.08 TEPHROITE, ILVAITE, CHALCO-PHANITE, SPHALERITE (G),

WILLEMITE, lueshite, meymacite, roepperite, knebelite, MARGARO-SANITE, CORUNDUM, ROSASITE, OLIVENITE, meta-uranocircite, brockite, greigite, CUBANITE, uhligite, LEPIDOCROCITE, BEU-DANTITE, brookite, berzeliite, smythite, SARKINITE, ANDRA-DITE, SPESSARTINE (G), vesig-nieite, ALMANDINE (G)

4.09 TEPHROITE, ILVAITE, CHALCO-PHANITE, SPHALERITE (G), WILLEMITE (troosite), meymacite, knebelite, MARGAROSANITE, CO-RUNDUM, RASASITE, CUBANITE, OLIVENITE, uhligite, LEPIDOCRO-CITE, BEUDANTITE, SARKINITE, smythite, BROOKITE, naegite, ANDRADITE, SPESSARTINE (G), ALMANDINE (G), brockite

4.10 TEPHROITE, ILVAITE, CHALCO-PHANITE, SPHALERITE (G), WILLEMITE, meymacite, knebelite, MARGAROSANITE, CORUNDUM, ROSASITE, CUBANITE, OLIVE-NITE, uhligite, LEPIDOCROCITE, BEUDANTITE, SARKINITE, BROOKITE, CORNETITE, STERN-BERGITE, CARNOTITE, CONICH-ALCITE, magnesiochromite, CHAL-COPYRITE, bolivianite, cuprozincite, blomstrandine, ANDRADITE, SPES-SARTINE (G), ALMANDINE (G), weeksite, bergenite, malayite, brockite

4.11 Knebelite, MARGAROSANITE, ROSASITE, OLIVENITE, CUBAN-ITE, uhligite, LEPIDOCROCITE, BEUDANTITE, SARKINITE, BROOKITE, STERNBERGITE, CO-NICHALCITE, magnesiochromite, CHALCOPYRITE, blomstrandine, holdenite, SPESSARTINE (G), ALMANDINE (G), malayite, SHAT-TUCKITE

4.12 Knebelite, MARGAROSANITE, ROSASITE, OLIVENITE, CUBAN-ITE, uhligite, LEPIDOCROCITE, BEUDANTITE, SARKINITE, BROOKITE, STERNBERGITE, CO-NICHALCITE, magnesiochromite, CHALCOPYRITE, blomstrandine, brezinaite, TARBUTTITE, SPESSAR-TINE (G), ALMANDINE (G), malayite

4.13 Knebelite, MARGAROSANITE,

ROSASITE, OLIVENITE, CUBAN-
ITE, uhligite, LEPIDOCROCITE,
BEUDANTITE, SARKINITE,
BROOKITE, STERNBERGITE, CO-
NICHALCITE, magnesiochromite,
CHALCOPYRITE, blomstrandine,
spherocobaltite, AUSTINITE, urano-
thorite, COBALTOCALCITE, DY-
SANALYTE, yoshimuraite, melano-
cerite, SPESSARTINE (G), ALMAN-
DINE (G), malayite

4.14 Knebelite, MARGAROSANITE,
ROSASITE, OLIVENITE, CUBAN-
ITE, uhligite, BEUDANTITE,
SARKINITE, BROOKITE, STERN-
BERGITE, CONICHALCITE, mag-
nesiochromite, CHALCOPYRITE,
blomstrandine, nantokite, malayite,
para-aurichalcite, SHATTUCKITE,
SPESSARTINE (G), ALMANDINE
(G), GROUTITE

4.15 Knebelite, MARGAROSANITE,
ROSASITE, OLIVENITE, CUBAN-
ITE, uhligite, BEUDANTITE,
SARKINITE, BROOKITE (G),
STERNBERGITE, CONICHALCITE,
magnesiochromite, CHALCOPYRITE,
blomstrandine, claudetite, beckelite,
retzian, SPESSARTINE (G), ALMAN-
DINE (G), malayite

4.16 Knebelite, MARGAROSANITE,
ROSASITE, OLIVENITE, CUBAN-
ITE, uhligite, BEUDANTITE,
SARKINITE, BROOKITE, STERN-
BERGITE, CONICHALCITE, mag-
nesiochromite, CHALCOPYRITE,
blomstrandine, arsenoclasite, SPES-
SARTINE (G), ALMANDINE (G)

4.17 Knebelite, MARGAROSANITE,
ROSASITE, OLIVENITE, CUBAN-
ITE, uhligite, BEUDANTITE,
SARKINITE, BROOKITE, STERN-
BERGITE, CONICHALCITE, mag-
nesiochromite, CHALCOPYRITE,
blomstrandine, CORNWALLITE, do-
lerophanite, SPESSARTINE (G),
ALMANDINE (G)

4.18 Knebelite, MARGAROSANITE,
ROSASITE, OLIVENITE, CUBAN-
ITE, uhligite, BEUDANTITE,
SARKINITE, BROOKITE, STERN-
BERGITE, CONICHALCITE, mag-
nesiochromite, CHALCOPYRITE,
sonoraite, GOETHITE, SPESSAR-
TINE (G), ALMANDINE (G)

4.19 Knebelite, MARGAROSANITE,

ROSASITE, OLIVENITE, uhligite,
BEUDANTITE, BROOKITE, STERN-
BERGITE, CONICHALCITE, mag-
nesiochromite, CHALCOPYRITE,
GOETHITE, manganberzeliite, SAN-
BORNITE, SPESSARTINE (G),
ALMANDINE (G), roentgenite,
belovite

4.20 Knebelite, MARGAROSANITE,
ROSASITE, OLIVENITE, uhligite,
BEUDANTITE, BROOKITE, mangan-
berzeliite, sedovite, STERN-
BERGITE, CONICHALCITE, mag-
nesiochromite, GOETHITE, CHAL-
COPYRITE, dixenite, tritomite,
FAYALITE, nordenskioldine,
knopite, SPESSARTINE (G),
ALMANDINE (G), gallite, mourite

4.21 Knebelite, MARGAROSANITE,
OLIVENITE, uhligite, BEUDAN-
TITE, STERNBERGITE, gagarinite,
manganberzeiliite, CONICHALCITE,
magnesiochromite, CHALCOPYRITE,
GOETHITE, FAYALITE, RUTILE
(G), POWELLITE, SPESSARTINE,
ALMANDINE, idaite

4.22 Knebelite, MARGAROSANITE,
OLIVENITE, uhligite, BEUDAN-
TITE, STERNBERGITE, CONICH-
ALCITE, magnesiochromite, CHAL-
COPYRITE, GOETHITE, mangan-
berzeliite, FAYALITE, RUTILE (G),
POWELLITE, SPESSARTINE, AL-
MANDINE

4.23 Knebelite, MARGAROSANITE,
OLIVENITE, uhligite, BEUDAN-
TITE, CONICHALCITE, magnesio-
chromite, CHALCOPYRITE,
GOETHITE, FAYALITE, RUTILE
(G), POWELLITE, thalenite, arman-
gite, staszicite, SPESSARTINE,
ALMANDINE, manganberzeliite, fres-
noite

4.24 Knebelite, MARGAROSANITE,
OLIVENITE, uhligite, BEUDAN-
TITE, CONICHALCITE, magnesio-
chromite, CHALCOPYRITE,
GOETHITE, FAYALITE, RUTILE
(G), POWELLITE, thalenite, talnak-
hite, GADOLINITE, SPESSARTINE,
ALMANDINE

4.25 Knebelite, MARGAROSANITE,
OLIVENITE, uhligite, BEUDAN-
TITE, CONICHALCITE, magnesio-
chromite, CHALCOPYRITE,
GOETHITE, FAYALITE, RUTILE

(G), POWELLITE, thalenite, GADO-
LINITE, arizonite, SPESSARTINE,
ALMANDINE, wakefieldite
4.26 MARGAROSANITE, OLIVENITE,
BEUDANTITE, CONICHALCITE,
magnesiochromite, CHALCOPYRITE,
GOETHITE, FAYALITE, thalenite,
GADOLINITE, ALMANDINE, LIND-
GRENITE, wakefieldite
4.27 MARGAROSANITE, OLIVENITE,
BEUDANTITE, CONICHALCITE,
magnesiochromite, CHALCOPYRITE,
GOETHITE (xls), FAYALITE,
thalenite, GADOLINITE, ALMAN-
DITE, WITHERITE (G), reinerite
4.28 MARGAROSANITE, OLIVENITE,
BEUDANTITE, CONICHALCITE,
magnesiochromite, CHALCOPYRITE,
FAYALITE, thalenite, WITHERITE
(G), GADOLINITE, hulsite, ALMAN-
DINE, stishovite
4.29 MARGAROSANITE, OLIVENITE,
BEUDANTITE, CONICHALCITE,
magnesiochromite, CHALCOPYRITE,
FAYALITE, thalenite, GADOLI-
NITE, WITHERITE (G), swedenborgite, caryinite, manjiroite,
stannoidite, strontiobarite, caryo-
cerite, ALMANDINE
4.30 MARGAROSANITE, OLIVENITE,
BEUDANTITE, CONICHALCITE,
magnesiochromite, CHALCOPYRITE,
FAYALITE, thalenite, GADOLI-
NITE, corkite, CHEVKINITE,
schafarzikite, yttrialite, perrierite,
wittichenite, STANNITE, ALMAN-
DINE, magnussonite, freudenbergite,
PSEUDOMALACHITE (xls), SMITH-
SONITE (MG), sahamalite
4.31 MARGAROSANITE, OLIVENITE,
CONICHALCITE, FAYALITE, thal-
enite, GADOLINITE, CHEVKINITE,
yttrialite, perrierite, wittichenite,
STANNITE, cordylite, babefphite,
PSEUDOMALACHITE (xls), AL-
MANDINE, SMITHSONITE (MG)
4.32 MARGAROSANITE, OLIVENITE,
SMITHSONITE (MG), CONICHAL-
CITE, FAYALITE, thalenite,
GADOLINITE, CHEVKINITE, yttria-
lite, perrierite, STANNITE, wittichen-
ite, ADAMITE, MANGANITE,
Mn-fayalite, PSEUDOMALACHITE
(xls), ALMANDINE
4.33 MARGAROSANITE, OLIVENITE,
SMITHSONITE (MG), CONICHAL-

CITE, FAYALITE, thalenite,
GADOLINITE, CHEVKINITE, yttria-
lite, perrierite, STANNITE, wittichen-
ite, ADAMITE, MANGANITE,
PARISITE, PSEUDOBROOKITE,
higginsite, hydrohematite, PSEUDO-
MALACHITE (xls), smythite
4.34 MARGAROSANITE, OLIVENITE,
SMITHSONITE (MG), FAYALITE,
thalenite, GADOLINITE, CHEVKIN-
ITE, yttrialite, perrierite, wittichenite,
STANNITE, ADAMITE, MANGAN-
ITE, PARISITE, PSEUDOBROOK-
ITE, PSEUDOMALACHITE (xls)
4.35 MARGAROSANITE, OLIVENITE,
SMITHSONITE (MG), FAYALITE,
thalenite, GADOLINITE, CHEVKIN-
ITE, yttrialite, perrierite, wittichenite,
STANNITE, ADAMITE, PARISITE,
PSEUDOBROOKITE, plumalsite, ren-
ardite, PSEUDOMALACHITE (xls),
abukamalite
4.36 MARGAROSANITE, SMITHSONITE
(MG), OLIVENITE, FAYALITE,
thalenite, GADOLINITE, CHEVKIN-
ITE, yttrialite, perrierite, wittichenite,
STANNITE, ADAMITE, PARISITE,
PSEUDOBROOKITE, beaverite,
PSEUDOMALACHITE (xls)
4.38 MARGAROSANITE, OLIVENITE,
SMITHSONITE (MG), FAYALITE,
thalenite, GADOLINITE, CHEVKIN-
ITE, yttrialite, wittichenite, STAN-
NITE, ADAMITE, PARISITE,
PSEUDOBROOKITE, clinoclase, no-
wackiite, PSEUDOMALACHITE (xls)
4.39 MARGAROSANITE, OLIVENITE,
SMITHSONITE (MG), FAYALITE,
thalenite, GADOLINITE, CHEVKIN-
ITE, yttrialite, wittichenite, STAN-
NITE, ADAMITE, PARISITE,
PSEUDOBROOKITE, nowackiite,
HERCYNITE, PSEUDOMALACHITE
(xls)
4.40 Thalenite, GADOLINITE, CHEVKIN-
ITE, yttrialite, wittichenite, STAN-
NITE, ADAMITE, PSEUDOBROOK-
ITE, nowackiite, OLIVENITE,
SMITHSONITE (MG), cappelenite,
marthozite, latrappite, ENARGITE,
ZIRCON (intermed.), PSEUDOMAL-
ACHITE (xls), renierite, pravdite
4.41 Thalenite, GADOLINITE, CHEVKIN-
ITE, yttrialite, wittichenite, STAN-
NITE, ADAMITE, nowackiite,
OLIVENITE, SMITHSONITE (MG),

ENARGITE, HATCHETTOLITE, pravdite

4.42 Thalenite, GADOLINITE, CHEVKIN-ITE, yttrialite, wittichenite, STAN-NITE, ADAMITE, nowackiite, OLIVENITE, SMITHSONITE (MG), ENARGITE, HATCHETTOLITE, CALCIUM LARSENITE, landauite, chromohercynite, pravdite

4.43 Thalenite, GADOLINITE, CHEVKIN-ITE, yttrialite, wittichenite, STAN-NITE, ADAMITE, nowackiite, OLIVENITE, SMITHSONITE (xls), ENARGITE, HATCHETTOLITE, armangite, villamanite, pravdite

4.44 Thalenite, GADOLINITE, CHEVKIN-ITE, yttrialite, wittichenite, STAN-NITE, ADAMITE, nowackiite, OLIVENITE, SMITHSONITE (xls), ENARGITE, HATCHETTOLITE, mendeleyeevite, pravdite

4.45 Thalenite, GADOLINITE, CHEVKIN-ITE, yttrialite, wittichenite, STAN-NITE, ADAMITE, nowackiite, OLIVENITE, SMITHSONITE (xls), ENARGITE, HATCHETTOLITE, mendeleyeevite, PYROCHLORE, XENOTIME, sakuraite, vaesite, pravdite

4.46 GADOLINITE, CHEVKINITE, yttria-lite, wittichenite, STANNITE, ADAMITE, nowackiite, OLIVENITE, ENARGITE, crichtonite, HATCHET-TOLITE, mendeleyeevite, XENO-TIME, GERMANITE, Mn-berzeliite, pravdite

4.47 GADOLINITE, CHEVKINITE, yttrialite, wittichenite, STAN-NITE, ADAMITE, nowackiite, ENARGITE, HATCHETTOLITE, mendeleyeevite, XENOTIME, GER-MANITE, huanghoite, FAMATINITE, welinite, BARITE (MG), pravdite

4.48 GADOLINITE, CHEVKINITE, yttria-lite, wittichenite, STANNITE, ADAMITE, nowackiite, huanghoite, ENARGITE, HATCHETTOLITE, mendeleyeevite, XENOTIME, GER-MANITE, FAMATINITE, BARITE (MG), pravdite

4.49 GADOLINITE, CHEVKINITE, yttria-lite, wittichenite, STANNITE, nowackiite, ENARGITE, HATCHET-TOLITE, mendeleyeevite, XENO-TIME, GERMANITE, FAMATINITE, BARITE (MG), huanghoite

4.50 GADOLINITE, CHEVKINITE, yttria-lite, wittichenite, STANNITE, ENARGITE, HATCHETTOLITE, mendeleyeevite, XENOTIME, GER-MANITE, FAMATINITE, BARITE (MG), catoptrite, COLUSITE, epigenite, CHROMITE, LINNAEITE, anthoinite, SIEGENITE, CARROL-LITE, VIOLARITE, koppite, POLYDYMITE, THOROGUMMITE, molybdite, palmierite, huanghoite

4.51 GADOLINITE, CHEVKINITE, yttria-lite, HATCHETTOLITE, mendele-yeevite, XENOTIME, GERMANITE, FAMATINITE, anthoinite, LINNAE-ITE, CHROMITE, SIEGENITE, VIOLARITE, POLYDYMITE, CAR-ROLLITE, huanghoite

4.52 GADOLINITE, CHEVKINITE, yttria-lite, mendeleyeevite, XENOTIME, GERMANITE, FAMATINITE, antho-inite, LINNAEITE, CHROMITE, SIEGENITE, VIOLARITE, POLYDY-MITE, CARROLLITE, EMMONSITE

4.53 GADOLINITE, CHEVKINITE, yttria-lite, mendeleyeevite, XENOTIME, GERMANITE, FAMATINITE, antho-inite, LINNAEITE, CHROMITE, SIEGENITE, VIOLARITE, POLY-DYMITE, CARROLLITE, EMMONS-ITE, derbylite, stishovite

4.54 GADOLINITE, CHEVKINITE, yttria-lite, mendeleyeevite, XENOTIME, GERMANITE, FAMATINITE, antho-inite, LINNAEITE, CHROMITE, SIEGENITE, VIOLARITE, POLY-DYMITE, CARROLLITE, pyrophan-ite, kesterite

4.55 GADOLINITE, CHEVKINITE, yttria-lite, mendeleyeevite, XENOTIME, GERMANITE, FAMATINITE, antho-inite, LINNAEITE, CHROMITE, SIEGENITE, kesterite, VIOLARITE, POLYDYMITE, CARROLLITE, fran-cevillite

4.56 GADOLINITE, CHEVKINITE, yttria-lite, mendeleyeevite, XENOTIME, GERMANITE, FAMATINITE, antho-inite, LINNAEITE, CHROMITE, SIEGENITE, VIOLARITE, POLY-DYMITE, CARROLLITE, magnesio-ferrite, kesterite

4.57 GADOLINITE, CHEVKINITE, yttria-lite, mendeleyeevite, GERMANITE, FAMATINITE, anthoinite, LIN-NAEITE, CHROMITE, SIEGENITE,

VIOLARITE, POLYDYMITE, CAR-
ROLLITE, magnesioferrite, stillwell-
ite, kesterite
4.58 GADOLINITE, CHEVKINITE, yttria-
lite, mendeleyeevite, GERMANITE,
anthoinite, LINNAEITE, CHRO-
MITE, SIEGENITE, VIOLARITE,
POLYDYMITE, CARROLLITE, magnesioferrite, PYRRHOTITE, kesterite
4.59 GADOLINITE, CHEVKINITE, yttria-
lite, mendeleyeevite, GERMANITE,
anthoinite, LINNAEITE, CHRO-
MITE, SIEGENITE, VIOLARITE,
CARROLLITE, POLYDYMITE, magnesioferrite, PYRRHOTITE, lauterite,
kesterite
4.60 GADOLINITE, CHEVKINITE,
yttrialite, mendeleyeevite, anthoinite, LINNAEITE, CHROMITE,
SIEGENITE, VIOLARITE, POLY-
DYMITE, CARROLLITE, magnesioferrite, PYRRHOTITE, PENTLAND-
ITE, loranskite, pilbarite, hydrohetae-
rolite, ZIRCON, hutchinsonite,
COVELLITE, MONAZITE, TEN-
NANTITE
4.61 GADOLINITE, CHEVKINITE, men-
deleyeevite, anthoinite, LINNAEITE,
CHROMITE, SIEGENITE, VIO-
LARITE, POLYDYMITE, CARROL-
LITE, ZIRCON, magnesioferrite,
PYRRHOTITE, PENTLANDITE, CO-
VELLITE, MONAZITE, STIBNITE,
heazlewoodite, TENNANTITE
4.62 GADOLINITE, CHEVKINITE, men-
deleyeevite, anthoinite, LINNAEITE,
CHROMITE, SIEGENITE, VIOLAR-
ITE, POLYDYMITE, CARROLLITE,
ZIRCON, magnesioferrite, PYR-
RHOTITE, PENTLANDITE, COVEL-
LITE, MONAZITE, STIBNITE,
parwelite, MOLYBDENITE, BRAVO-
ITE, TENNANTITE, GAHNITE,
gamagarite, marokite
4.63 GADOLINITE, CHEVKINITE, men-
deleyeevite, anthoinite, LINNAEITE,
CHROMITE, SIEGENITE, VIO-
LARITE, POLYDYMITE, CARROL-
LITE, marokite, magnesioferrite,
PYRRHOTITE, PENTLANDITE,
ZIRCON, COVELLITE, MONAZITE,
STIBNITE, MOLYBDENITE, BRA-
VOITE, TENNANTITE, soddyite,
stenhuggarite
4.64 GADOLINITE, CHEVKINITE, men-
deleyeevite, anthoinite, LINNAEITE,

CHROMITE, SIEGENITE, VIO-
LARITE, POLYDYMITE, CARROL-
LITE, ZIRCON, magnesioferrite,
PYRRHOTITE, PENTLANDITE, CO-
VELLITE, MONAZITE, STIBNITE,
MOLYBDENITE, BRAVOITE, TEN-
NANTITE, plumbobetafite, BERTH-
IERITE, wyartite, cornubite,
marokite
4.65 GADOLINITE, CHEVKINITE, men-
deleyeevite, anthoinite, LINNAEITE,
CHROMITE, SIEGENITE, VIOLA-
RITE, POLYDYMITE, CARROL-
LITE, ZIRCON, magnesioferrite,
PYRRHOTITE, PENTLANDITE, CO-
VELLITE, MONAZITE, STIBNITE,
MOLYBDENITE, BRAVOITE, TEN-
NANTITE, wyartite, marokite
4.66 Mendeleyeevite, anthoinite, LIN-
NAEITE, CHROMITE, SIEGENITE,
ZIRCON, VIOLARITE, POLYDY-
MITE, CARROLLITE, PYRRHOT-
ITE, PENTLANDITE, COVELLITE,
MONAZITE, wyartite, MOLYBDEN-
ITE, BRAVOITE, TENNANTITE,
GADOLINITE
4.67 Mendeleyeevite, anthoinite, LINNAE-
ITE, CHROMITE, SIEGENITE,
ZIRCON, VIOLARITE, POLYDY-
MITE, CARROLLITE, PYRRHOT-
ITE, PENTLANDITE, COVELLITE,
MONAZITE, MOLYBDENITE, TEN-
NANTITE, GADOLINITE, TROIL-
ITE, CUMENGEITE, wyartite
4.68 Mendeleyeevite, anthoinite, LIN-
NAEITE, CHROMITE, SIEGENITE,
VIOLARITE, POLYDYMITE, CAR-
ROLLITE, PENTLANDITE, ZIRCON
(high), COVELLITE, MONAZITE,
MOLYBDENITE, TENNANTITE,
GADOLINITE, TROILITE, KER-
MESITE, ILMENITE, wyartite
4.69 Mendeleyeevite, anthoinite, LINNAE-
ITE, CHROMITE, SIEGENITE,
VIOLARITE, POLYDYMITE, CAR-
ROLLITE, PENTLANDITE, ZIRCON
(high), COVELLITE, MONAZITE,
MOLYBDENITE, TENNANTITE,
GADOLINITE, TROILITE, ILMEN-
ITE, lessingite, percylite, wyartite,
nolanite
4.70 Mendeleyeevite, anthoinite, LIN-
NAEITE, CHROMITE, SIEGENITE,
VIOLARITE, POLYDYMITE, CAR-
ROLLITE, PENTLANDITE, ZIRCON
(high), COVELLITE, MONAZITE,

MOLYBDENITE, TENNANTITE, GADOLINITE, TROILITE, ILMENITE, paigeite, trechmannite, PSILOMELANE, kishtymite, baotite, ramsdellite, wyartite, hydroxyl-bastnaesite

4.72 Mendeleyeevite, LINNAEITE, CHROMITE, SIEGENITE, VIOLARITE, POLYDYMITE, CARROLLITE, PENTLANDITE, ZIRCON (high), COVELLITE, MONAZITE, MOLYBDENITE, TENNANTITE, TROILITE, ILMENITE, BRAUNITE, PSILOMELANE, molybdophyllite, salesite, wyartite, baotite

4.73 Mendeleyeevite, LINNAEITE, CHROMITE, SIEGENITE, VIOLARITE, POLYDYMITE, CARROLLITE, PENTLANDITE, ZIRCON (high), COVELLITE, MONAZITE, MOLYBDENITE, TENNANTITE, TROILITE, ILMENITE, BRAUNITE, salesite, loparite, wyartite

4.74 Mendeleyeevite, LINNAEITE, CHROMITE, SIEGENITE, VIOLARITE, POLYDYMITE, CARROLLITE, PENTLANDITE, ZIRCON (high), COVELLITE, MONAZITE, TENNANTITE, TROILITE, ILMENITE, BRAUNITE, salesite, loparite, zirkelite, scheteligite, wyartite, hydroxyl-bastnaesite

4.75 Mendeleyeevite, LINNAEITE, CHROMITE, SIEGENITE, VIOLARITE, POLYDYMITE, CARROLLITE, PENTLANDITE, ZIRCON (high), COVELLITE, MONAZITE, TENNANTITE, TROILITE, ILMENITE, BRAUNITE, salesite, loparite

4.76 Mendeleyeevite, LINNAEITE, CHROMITE, SIEGENITE, VIOLARITE, POLYDYMITE, CARROLLITE, PENTLANDITE, ZIRCON (high), COVELLITE, MONAZITE, TENNANTITE, TROILITE, ILMENITE, BRAUNITE, salesite, loparite, sychnodymite, JACOBSITE

4.77 Mendeleyeevite, LINNAEITE, CHROMITE, SIEGENITE, VIOLARITE, POLYDYMITE, CARROLLITE, PENTLANDITE, ZIRCON (high), MONAZITE, TENNANTITE, TROILITE, BRAUNITE, salesite, loparite, POLYMIGNITE

4.79 LINNAEITE, CHROMITE, SIEGENITE, VIOLARITE, POLYDYMITE,

CARROLLITE, PENTLANDITE, ZIRCON (high), MONAZITE, TENNANTITE, TROILITE, BRAUNITE, salesite, POLYMIGNITE, styloptypite, rhodostannite

4.80 LINNAEITE, CHROMITE, SIEGENITE, VIOLARITE, POLYDYMITE, CARROLLITE, PENTLANDITE, ZIRCON (high), MONAZITE, TENNANTITE, BRAUNITE, salesite, POLYMIGNITE, stylotypite, SCHOEPITE, selenium, yttrocrasite, lubeckite, cattierite, fukuchilite, trippkeite, lautite

4.81 Salesite, BRAUNITE, POLYMIGNITE, ZIRCON (high), PENTLANDITE, lautite, stylotypite, MONAZITE, TETRAHEDRITE

4.82 Salesite, BRAUNITE, POLYMIGNITE, ZIRCON (high), PENTLANDITE, lautite, stylotypite, MONAZITE, TETRAHEDRITE, NI-PYRITE

4.83 BRAUNITE, POLYMIGNITE, ZIRCON (high), PENTLANDITE, lautite, stylotypite, MONAZITE, TETRAHEDRITE, HAUSMANNITE

4.84 POLYMIGNITE, ZIRCON (high), PENTLANDITE, lautite, stylotypite, MONAZITE, TETRAHEDRITE, HAUSMANNITE

4.85 POLYMIGNITE, ZIRCON (high), PENTLANDITE, lautite, stylotypite, PRIORITE, MONAZITE, TETRAHEDRITE, HAUSMANNITE, mounanaite, PSEUDOBOLEITE

4.86 ZIRCON (high), PENTLANDITE, lautite, stylotypite, MONAZITE, TETRAHEDRITE, PRIORITE, CERITE, mackayite, angelellite, guilleminite

4.87 PENTLANDITE, lautite, stylotypite, MONAZITE, TETRAHEDRITE, PRIORITE, CERITE, chernovite, hawleyite, angelellite, guilleminite

4.88 PENTLANDITE, lautite, stylotypite, MONAZITE, TETRAHEDRITE, smithite, PRIORITE, CERITE, bellingerite, guilleminite, curienite, BLOMSTRANDINE

4.89 PENTLANDITE, lautite, stylotypite, MONAZITE, TETRAHEDRITE, PRIORITE, CERITE, bellingerite, BLOMSTRANDINE, MARCASITE, guilleminite, angelellite, mackensite

4.90 PENTLANDITE, lautite, stylotypite, MONAZITE, TETRAHEDRITE, PRI-

ORITE, CERITE, bellingerite, BLOMSTRANDINE, GREENOCKITE, POLYCRASE, EUXENITE, BASTNAESITE, CHALCOSTIBITE, LYNDOCHITE, guilleminite, angelellite

4.91 PENTLANDITE, lautite, stylotypite, MONAZITE, TETRAHEDRITE, PRIORITE, CERITE, BLOMSTRANDINE, POLYCRASE, EUXENITE, BASTNAESITE, struverite, CHALCOSTIBITE, angelellite

4.92 PENTLANDITE, lautite, stylotypite, MONAZITE, TETRAHEDRITE, PRIORITE, BLOMSTRANDINE, POLYCRASE, EUXENITE, BASTNAESITE, CHALCOSTIBITE, struverite, langbanite, angelellite

4.94 PENTLANDITE, lautite, stylotypite, MONAZITE, TETRAHEDRITE, PRIORITE, BLOMSTRANDINE, POLYCRASE, EUXENITE, BASTNAESITE, CHALCOSTIBITE, struverite, tornebohmite, armalcolite, angelellite

4.95 PENTLANDITE, lautite, stylotypite, HEMATITE (MG), MONAZITE, PRIORITE, TETRAHEDRITE, BLOMSTRANDINE, POLYCRASE, EUXENITE, BASTNAESITE, CHALCOSTIBITE, struverite, angelellite, BIXBYITE, hollandite, lewisite

4.96 PENTLANDITE, lautite, stylotypite, HEMATITE (MG), MONAZITE, PRIORITE, TETRAHEDRITE, BLOMSTRANDINE, POLYCRASE, EUXENITE, BASTNAESITE, CHALCOSTIBITE, struverite, weslienite

4.97 PENTLANDITE, lautite, stylotypite, HEMATITE (MG), MONAZITE, PRIORITE, TETRAHEDRITE, BLOMSTRANDINE, POLYCRASE, EUXENITE, BASTNAESITE, CHALCOSTIBITE, struverite, weslienite, CO-PYRITE, ROMEITE

4.99 PENTLANDITE, lautite, stylotypite, HEMATITE (MG), MONAZITE, PRIORITE, TETRAHEDRITE, BLOMSTRANDINE, POLYCRASE, EUXENITE, BASTNAESITE, CHALCOSTIBITE, struverite, CREDNERITE, ROMEITE, PYRITE, spiroffite

5.00 PENTLANDITE, lautite, stylotypite, HEMATITE (MG), MONAZITE, PRIORITE, TETRAHEDRITE, BLOMSTRANDINE, POLYCRASE, EUXENITE, BASTNAESITE, CHAL-

COSTIBITE, struverite, CREDNERITE, caracolite, yeatmanite, KLOCKMANNITE, livingstonite, ROMEITE, PYRITE, spiroffite

5.01 Stylotypite, MONAZITE, HEMATITE (MG), PRIORITE, POLYCRASE, EUXENITE, BASTNAESITE, struverite, CREDNERITE, tazheranite, AG-TETRAHEDRITE, ROMEITE, PYRITE, calzirtite, spiroffite

5.03 Stylotypite, MONAZITE, HEMATITE (MG), PRIORITE, POLYCRASE, EUXENITE, BASTNAESITE, struverite, CREDNERITE, AG-TETRAHEDRITE, atopite, vandenbrandite, dewindtite, ROMEITE, PYRITE, spiroffite

5.04 Stylotypite, MONAZITE, PRIORITE, HEMATITE (MG), POLYCRASE, EUXENITE, BASTNAESITE, struverite, AG-TETRAHEDRITE, PYROLUSITE (xls), toddite, ROMEITE

5.05 Stylotypite, MONAZITE, PRIORITE, HEMATITE (MG), POLYCRASE, EUXENITE, BASTNAESITE, AG-TETRAHEDRITE, PYROLUSITE (xls), BOLEITE, ROMEITE, ferdisilicate, rodalquilarite, denningite

5.06 Stylotypite, MONAZITE, HEMATITE (MG), POLYCRASE, EUXENITE, BORNITE, BASTNAESITE, PYROLUSITE (xls), rodalquilarite, cerphosphorhuttonite, HG-TETRAHEDRITE, donathite, ROMEITE

5.07 Stylotypite, MONAZITE, HEMATITE (MG), POLYCRASE, EUXENITE, BORNITE, BASTNAESITE, PYROLUSITE (xls), rodalquilarite, HG-TETRAHEDRITE, donathite, FRANKLINITE, ROMEITE

5.08 Stylotypite, MONAZITE, HEMATITE (MG), POLYCRASE, EUXENITE, BORNITE, BASTNAESITE, PYROLUSITE (xls), HG-TETRAHEDRITE, donathite, FRANKLINITE, SARTORITE, ROMEITE

5.10 Stylotypite, MONAZITE, HEMATITE (MG), POLYCRASE, EUXENITE, donathite, BASTNAESITE, rodalquilarite, HG-TETRAHEDRITE, FRANKLINITE, SARTORITE, caracolite, ROMEITE, schuilingite, BECQUERELITE

5.11 Stylotypite, MONAZITE, HEMAT-

ITE (MG), BASTNAESITE, rodalquilarite, FRANKLINITE, ianthinite, BECQUERELITE, SARTORITE, manzeliite, ROMEITE, schuilingite

5.12 Stylotypite, MONAZITE, HEMATITE (MG), BASTNAESITE, rodalquilarite, FRANKLINITE, SARTORITE, BECQUERELITE, ROMEITE, schuilingite, ianthinite

5.14 Stylotypite, MONAZITE, HEMATITE (MG), BASTNAESITE, rodalquilarite, FRANKLINITE, ESCHYNITE, ROMEITE, ianthinite, BECQUERELITE

5.15 Stylotypite, MONAZITE, HEMATITE (MG), BASTNAESITE, rodalquilarite, FRANKLINITE, ESCHYNITE, COLUMBITE, ROMEITE, ianthinite

5.16 Stylotypite, MONAZITE, HEMATITE (MG), BASTNAESITE, FRANKLINITE, ESCHYNITE, COLUMBITE, TREVORITE, ianthinite, ROMEITE

5.17 Stylotypite, MONAZITE, HEMATITE (MG), BASTNAESITE, FRANKLINITE, ESCHYNITE, COLUMBITE, ianthinite, ROMEITE, coulsonite, magnocolumbite

5.18 Stylotypite, MONAZITE, HEMATITE (MG), BASTNAESITE, FRANKLINITE, ESCHYNITE, ianthinite, coulsonite, COLUMBITE, MAGNETITE, HETAEROLITE, ROMEITE, eskolaite

5.20 MONAZITE, BASTNAESITE, HEMATITE (MG), FRANKLINITE, ESCHYNITE, THORITE, COLUMBITE, coulsonite, ianthinite, MIARGYRITE, sinnerite, ROMEITE, robinsonite

5.22 MONAZITE, FRANKLINITE, HEMATITE (MG), ESCHYNITE, COLUMBITE, THORITE, MIARGYRITE, CARMINITE, ROMEITE

5.23 MONAZITE, ESCHYNITE, HEMATITE (MG), COLUMBITE, MIARGYRITE, THORITE, FULOPPITE, ROMEITE, stranskiite

5.24 MONAZITE, ESCHYNITE, HEMATITE (MG), COLUMBITE, MIARGYRITE, THORITE, SAMIRESITE, ROMEITE, demesmaekerite

5.25 MONAZITE, COLUMBITE, HEMATITE (xls), MIARGYRITE, THORITE, ZINKENITE, ambatoarinite, ROMEITE, demesmaekerite

5.26 MONAZITE, MIARGYRITE, HEMATITE (xls), THORITE, ZINKENITE, twinnite, ROMEITE

5.27 Vrbaite, MONAZITE, MIARGYRITE, THORITE, ZINKENITE, ROMEITE

5.28 Demesmaekerite, MONAZITE, MIARGYRITE, THORITE, ZINKENITE, vrbaite, ROMEITE, cheralite, billietite

5.29 Cesarolite, MONAZITE, MIARGYRITE, THORITE, ZINKENITE, vrbaite, ROMEITE

5.30 MONAZITE, MIARGYRITE, THORITE, ZINKENITE, vrbaite, senaite, paxite, liveingite, demesmaekerite, guettardite (approx.), MILLERITE, ARSENOLAMPRITE, onoratoite, ROMEITE, bystromite

5.32 MONAZITE, THORITE, ZINKENITE, vrbaite, MILLERITE, ARSENOLAMPRITE, twinnite, billietite, waltherite, ROMEITE, bystromite, demesmaekerite

5.33 MONAZITE, THORITE, ZINKENITE, vrbaite, MILLERITE, ARSENOLAMPRITE, billietite, BAUMHAUERITE, ANDORITE, RATHITE, ROMEITE, bystromite

5.35 MONAZITE, THORITE, ZINKENITE, MILLERITE, ARSENOLAMPRITE, billietite, ANDORITE, RATHITE, LINARITE, ROMEITE, bystromite

5.36 MONAZITE, THORITE, MILLERITE, ARSENOLAMPRITE, billietite, ANDORITE, RATHITE, MANGANOSITE, eichbergite, ROMEITE, bystromite

5.37 MONAZITE, THORITE, MILLERITE, ARSENOLAMPRITE, ANDORITE, RATHITE, ROMEITE, parsonsite, bystromite

5.38 MONAZITE, THORITE, MILLERITE, ARSENOLAMPRITE, RATHITE, bystromite, pyrobelonite, FERGUSONITE, SELIGMANNITE, ROMEITE, xanthiosite, osbornite

5.40 MONAZITE, THORITE, MILLERITE, ARSENOLAMPRITE, RATHITE, SELIGMANNITE, XANTHOCONITE, BADDELEYITE, robinsonite, ROMEITE, xanthiosite, bystromite

5.41 MILLERITE, ARSENOLAMPRITE, RATHITE, SELIGMANNITE, XANTHOCONITE, BADDELEYITE, DIABOLEITE, delafossite, SCHNEEBERGITE, bystromite

5.43 MILLERITE, ARSENOLAMPRITE, DIABOLEITE, SELIGMANNITE, XANTHOCONITE, BADDELEYITE, nasonite, ramdohrite, CYLINDRITE, bystromite, jagoite

5.44 MILLERITE, ARSENOLAMPRITE, SELIGMANNITE, XANTHOCO-NITE, BADDELEYITE, CYLINDRITE, CORONADITE, parabayldo-nite, bystromite

5.48 MILLERITE, ARSENOLAMPRITE, XANTHOCONITE, BADDELEYITE, CYLINDRITE, parabayldonite, para-jamesonite, bystromite

5.49 MILLERITE, ARSENOLAMPRITE, XANTHOCONITE, BADDELEYITE, CYLINDRITE, parabayldonite, guet-tardite, bystromite

5.50 MILLERITE, ARSENOLAMPRITE, XANTHOCONITE, BADDELEYITE, TUNGSTITE, parabayldonite, BAYL-DONITE, YTTROTANTALITE, CHALCOCITE, bystromite, DUFRE-NOYSITE, SENARMONTITE, tin-tinaite, rankamaite, cuproplumbite

5.51 MILLERITE, XANTHOCONITE, BADDELEYITE, parabayldonite, CHALCOCITE, YTTROTANTA-LITE, DUFRENOYSITE, SAMSON-ITE, tintinaite

5.52 MILLERITE, XANTHOCONITE, BADDELEYITE, YTTROTANTA-LITE, CHALCOCITE, DUFRENOY-SITE, magnetoplumbite, sorbyite

5.53 MILLERITE, XANTHOCONITE, BADDELEYITE, YTTROTANTA-LITE, CHALCOCITE, DUFRENOY-SITE, LORANDITE

5.54 MILLERITE, XANTHOCONITE, BADDELEYITE, YTTROTANTA-LITE, CHALCOCITE, DUFRENOY-SITE, PLAGIONITE, yttrotungstite

5.56 MILLERITE, XANTHOCONITE, BADDELEYITE, YTTROTANTA-LITE, CHALCOCITE, DUFRENOY-SITE, PLAGIONITE, DIGENITE, CHLORARGYRITE, PROUSTITE (G)

5.57 MILLERITE, XANTHOCONITE, BADDELEYITE, YTTROTANTA-LITE, CHALCOCITE, PLAGIONITE, DIGENITE, PROUSTITE (G), ferri-tungstite

5.58 MILLERITE, XANTHOCONITE, BADDELEYITE, YTTROTANTA-LITE, CHALCOCITE, PLAGIONITE,

DIGENITE, PROUSTITE (G), STIBI-CONITE (approx.), sorbyite (approx.)

5.60 MILLERITE, XANTHOCONITE, BADDELEYITE, YTTROTANTA-LITE, CHALCOCITE, DIGENITE, PROUSTITE (G), aramayoite, SAM-ARSKITE, CALEDONITE, MUTH-MANNITE, Sc-ixiolite, paratellurite

5.62 MILLERITE, XANTHOCONITE, BADDELEYITE, YTTROTANTA-LITE, CHALCOCITE, DIGENITE, PROUSTITE (G), SAMARSKITE, CALEDONITE, umangite

5.63 MILLERITE, XANTHOCONITE, BADDELEYITE, YTTROTANTA-LITE, CHALCOCITE, DIGENITE, PROUSTITE (G), SAMARSKITE, CALEDONITE, JAMESONITE, AR-SENIC

5.64 MILLERITE, XANTHOCONITE, BADDELEYITE, YTTROTANTA-LITE, CHALCOCITE, DIGENITE, PROUSTITE (G), SAMARSKITE, CALEDONITE, ARSENIC, miersite, ZINCITE (G)

5.65 MILLERITE, XANTHOCONITE, BADDELEYITE, YTTROTANTA-LITE, CHALCOCITE, DIGENITE, SAMARSKITE, CALEDONITE, AR-SENIC, ZINCITE (G), dumontite, MICROLITE (G)

5.68 MILLERITE, XANTHOCONITE, BADDELEYITE, YTTROTANTA-LITE, CHALCOCITE, SAMAR-SKITE, CALEDONITE, ARSENIC, ZINCITE (G), MARSHITE, anilite, STIBIOCOLUMBITE, TANTEUX-ENITE, rijkeboerite

5.69 MILLERITE, BADDELEYITE, YTTROTANTALITE, CHALCO-CITE, SAMARSKITE, CALEDON-ITE, ARSENIC, IODARGYRITE, STIBIOCOLUMBITE, rijkeboerite

5.70 MILLERITE, BADDELEYITE, YTTROTANTALITE, CHALCO-CITE, SAMARSKITE, CALEDON-ITE, ARSENIC, ANNERODITE, AR-SENOBISMITE, STIBIOCOLUM-BITE, melanotekite, rijkeboerite

5.72 BADDELEYITE, YTTROTANTA-LITE, CHALCOCITE, SAMARS-KITE, CALEDONITE, ARSENIC, STIBIOCOLUMBITE, playfairite, rijkeboerite

5.73 BADDELEYITE, YTTROTANTA-LITE, CHALCOCITE, SAMARS-

KITE, CALEDONITE, ARSENIC, STIBIOCOLUMBITE, HETEROMORPHITE, rijkeboerite

5.74 BADDELEYITE, YTTROTANTALITE, CHALCOCITE, SAMARSKITE, CALEDONITE, ARSENIC, STIBIOCOLUMBITE, ganomalite, rijkeboerite

5.75 BADDELEYITE, YTTROTANTALITE, CHALCOCITE, SAMARSKITE, CALEDONITE, ARSENIC rijkeboerite, STIBIOCOLUMBITE, launayite, djalmaite

5.76 BADDELEYITE, YTTROTANTALITE, CHALCOCITE, SAMARSKITE, CALEDONITE, ARSENIC, STIBIOCOLUMBITE, djalmaite, rijkeboerite, VALENTINITE, dadsonite

5.77 BADDELEYITE, YTTROTANTALITE, CHALCOCITE, SAMARSKITE, CALEDONITE, ARSENIC, STIBIOCOLUMBITE, djalmaite, moctezumite, rijkeboerite

5.78 BADDELEYITE, YTTROTANTALITE, CHALCOCITE, SAMARSKITE, ARSENIC, STIBIOCOLUMBITE, djalmaite, rijkeboerite

5.80 BADDELEYITE, YTTROTANTALITE, CHALCOCITE, SAMARSKITE, STIBIOCOLUMBITE, djalmaite, TENORITE, MOTTRAMITE, LENGENBACHITE, ALLEMONTITE, COTUNNITE, playfairite, BOURNONITE, kettnerite, rijkeboerite, aerugite

5.81 BADDELEYITE, YTTROTANTALITE, STIBIOCOLUMBITE, djalmaite, TENORITE, MOTTRAMITE, LENGENBACHITE, ALLEMONTITE, BOURNONITE, aerugite, Ti-samarskite

5.82 BADDELEYITE, YTTROTANTALITE, STIBIOCOLUMBITE, djalmaute, TENORITE, MOTTRAMITE, LENGENBACHITE, ALLEMONTITE, BOURNONITE, HEDYPHANE, TRIPUHYITE, thorutite, marrite, aerugite

5.85 BADDELEYITE, YTTROTANTALITE, STIBIOCOLUMBITE, djalmaite, TENORITE, MOTTRAMITE, LENGENBACHITE, ALLEMONTITE, BOURNONITE, PYRARGYRITE, sterryite, aerugite

5.86 BADDELEYITE, YTTROTANTALITE, STIBIOCOLUMBITE, djalma-

ite, TENORITE, MOTTRAMITE, ALLEMONTITE, BOURNONITE, aerugite

5.88 BADDELEYITE, YTTROTANTALITE, STIBIOCOLUMBITE, djalmaite, TENORITE, MOTTRAMITE, ALLEMONTITE, fiedlerite, TELLURITE, aerugite

5.90 BADDELEYITE, YTTROTANTALITE, SCHEELITE, STIBIOCOLUMBITE, TENORITE, MOTTRAMITE, ALLEMONTITE, TELLURITE, GERSDORFFITE, FRANCKEITE, LARSENITE, khuniite, SIMPSONITE, aerugite

5.92 STIBIOCOLUMBITE, TENORITE, MOTTRAMITE, SCHEELITE, ALLEMONTITE, TELLURITE, BADDELEYITE, billingsleyite, veenite

5.93 FLUOCERITE, STIBIOCOLUMBITE, SCHEELITE, TENORITE, MOTTRAMITE, ALLEMONTITE, BADDELEYITE

5.94 STIBIOCOLUMBITE, TENORITE, MOTTRAMITE, SCHEELITE, ALLEMONTITE, BADDELEYITE, FLUOCERITE, PYROSTILPNITE, schultenite, GUITERMANNITE

5.96 STIBIOCOLUMBITE, TENORITE, ALLEMONTITE, SCHEELITE, BADDELEYITE, FLUOCERITE, KASOLITE, CROCOITE

5.97 STIBIOCOLUMBITE, TENORITE, MOTTRAMITE, SCHEELITE, ALLEMONTITE, BADDELEYITE, FLUOCERITE, CROCOITE

5.98 TENORITE, MOTTRAMITE, ALLEMONTITE, SCHEELITE, BADDELEYITE, FLUOCERITE, CROCOITE, STIBIOTANTALITE, madocite

6.00 TENORITE, MOTTRAMITE, ALLEMONTITE, BADDELEYITE, FLUOCERITE, CROCOITE, STIBIOTANTALITE, POLYBASITE, weissite, sterryite, corynite, SCHEELITE (G)

6.01 TENORITE, ALLEMONTITE, BADDELEYITE, FLUOCERITE, CROCOITE, STIBIOTANTALITE, POLYBASITE, KLAPROTHITE, SCHEELITE (G), TSUMEBITE

6.02 TENORITE, ALLEMONTITE, BADDELEYITE, FLUOCERITE, CROCOITE, STIBIOTANTALITE, POLYBASITE, VAUQUELINITE, SCHEELITE (G)

6.03 TENORITE, ALLEMONTITE, FLU-

OCERITE, STIBIOTANTALITE, POLYBASITE, owyheeite, SEMSE-YITE, SCHEELITE (G)

6.04 TENORITE, ALLEMONTITE, FLU-OCERITE, STIBIOTANTALITE, POLYBASITE, SEMSEYITE, PARA-MELACONITE, DIAPHORITE, FREIESLEBENITE, SCHEELITE (G)

6.05 TENORITE, ALLEMONTITE, FO-URMARIERITE, brackebuschite, SCHEELITE (G), FLUOCERITE, STIBIOTANTALITE, POLYBASITE, SEMSEYITE, FREIESLEBENITE

6.08 TENORITE, ALLEMONTITE, FLU-OCERITE, STIBIOTANTALITE, POLYBASITE, SEMSEYITE, FREIESLEBENITE, SCHEELITE (G)

6.09 TENORITE, ALLEMONTITE, FLU-OCERITE, STIBIOTANTALITE, POLYBASITE, FREIESLEBENITE, SCHEELITE (G), rezbanyite

6.10 TENORITE, ALLEMONTITE, FLU-OCERITE, STIBIOTANTALITE, POLYBASITE, FREIESLEBENITE, SCHEELITE (G), rezbanyite, SMALTITE (G), TELLURIUM, NI-SKUTTERUDITE, CHLOAN-THITE, DESCLOIZITE

6.12 TENORITE, ALLEMONTITE, FLU-OCERITE, STIBIOTANTALITE, POLYBASITE, FREIESLEBENITE, SCHEELITE, rezbanyite, SMALTITE (G), CHLOANTHITE, SKUTTERUD-ITE, NI-SKUTTERUDITE, DESCLO-IZITE, TELLURIUM, CUPRITE

6.13 TENORITE, ALLEMONTITE, FLU-OCERITE, STIBIOTANTALITE, POLYBASITE, FREIESLEBENITE, rezbanyite, SMALTITE, CHLOAN-THITE, SKUTTERUDITE, NI-SKUT-TERUDITE, DESCLOIZITE, TELLU-RIUM, PHOSGENITE, TSUMEBITE, TYSONITE, PEARCEITE, CUPRITE

6.14 TENORITE, ALLEMONTITE, FLU-OCERITE, STIBIOTANTALITE, POLYBASITE, FREIESLEBENITE, rezbanyite, SMALTITE, CHLOAN-THITE, SKUTTERUDITE, NI-SKUT-TERUDITE, DESCLOIZITE, TELLU-RIUM, CUPRITE (G), PEARCEITE, betekhtinite

6.15 TENORITE, ALLEMONTITE, CUP-RITE, STIBIOTANTALITE, POLY-BASITE, FREIESLEBENITE, rezban-yite, SMALTITE, CHLOANTHITE, SKUTTERUDITE, NI-SKUTTERUD-

ITE, DESCLOIZITE, TELLURIUM, PEARCEITE, PARALAURIONITE

6.17 TENORITE, ALLEMONTITE, STIBI-OTANTALITE, POLYBASITE, FREIESLEBENITE, rezbanyite, SMALTITE, CHLOANTHITE, SKUTTERUDITE, NI-SKUTTE-RUDITE, DESCLOIZITE, TELLUR-IUM, PEARCEITE

6.18 TENORITE, ALLEMONTITE, STIBI-OTANTALITE, POLYBASITE, FREIESLEBENITE, rezbanyite, SMALTITE, CHLOANTHITE, SKUT-TERUDITE, NI-SKUTTERUDITE, DESCLOIZITE, TELLURIUM, hod-rushite, fersilicate, arsenpolybasite

6.19 TENORITE, ALLEMONTITE, STIBI-OTANTALITE, POLYBASITE, FRE-IESLEBENITE, rezbanyite, SMAL-TITE, CHLOANTHITE, SKUTTER-UDITE, NI-SKUTTERUDITE, DES-CLOIZITE, TELLURIUM, cuprodes-cloizite

6.20 TENORITE, ALLEMONTITE, STIBI-OTANTALITE, FREIESLEBENITE, rezbanyite, SMALTITE, CHLOAN-THITE, SKUTTERUDITE, NI-SKUT-TERUDITE, DESCLOIZITE, TELLU-RIUM, GRATONITE, STROMEYER-ITE, ishikawaite, reinite, kentrolite

6.22 TENORITE, ALLEMONTITE, STIBI-OTANTALITE, FREIESLEBENITE, rezbanyite, SMALTITE, CHLOAN-THITE, SKUTTERUDITE, NI-SKUT-TERUDITE, DESCLOIZITE, TELLU-RIUM, GRATONITE, STROMEYER-ITE, ishikawaite, STEPHANITE

6.23 TENORITE, ALLEMONTITE, STIBI-OTANTALITE, FREIESLEBENITE, rezbanyite, SMALTITE, CHLOAN-THITE, SKUTTERUDITE, NI-SKUT-TERUDITE, DESCLOIZITE, TELLU-RIUM, GRATONITE, STROMEYER-ITE, ishikawaite, STEPHANITE, BOULANGERITE

6.24 TENORITE, ALLEMONTITE, STIBI-OTANTALITE, rezbanyite, SMAL-TITE, CHLOANTHITE, SKUT-TERUDITE, NI-SKUTTERUDITE, DESCLOIZITE, GRATONITE, TEL-LURIUM, STROMEYERITE, ishika-waite, STEPHANITE, LAURIONITE

6.25 TENORITE, ALLEMONTITE, STIBI-OTANTALITE, rezbanyite, SMAL-TITE, CHLOANTHITE, SKUTTERU-DITE, NI-SKUTTERUDITE, DES-

CLOIZITE, GRATONITE, TELLU-RIUM, STROMEYERITE, ishika-waite, STEPHANITE, ARGYRO-DITE, GUANAJUATITE

6.27 TENORITE, ALLEMONTITE, STIBI-OTANTALITE, rezbanyite, SMAL-TITE, CHLOANTHITE, SKUTTERU-DITE, NI-SKUTTERUDITE, DES-CLOIZITE, GRATONITE, TELLU-RIUM, STROMEYERITE, ishika-waite, STEPHANITE, ARGYRO-DITE, bideauxite, FORNACITE, GUANAJUATITE

6.28 TENORITE, ALLEMONTITE, STIBI-OTANTALITE, rezbanyite, SMAL-TITE, CHLOANTHITE, SKUTTERU-DITE, NI-SKUTTERUDITE, DES-CLOIZITE, GRATONITE, TELLU-RIUM, STROMEYERITE, ishika-waite, STEPHANITE, ARGYRO-DITE, CANFIELDITE, GLAUCO-DOT, GUANAJUATITE

6.30 TENORITE, ALLEMONTITE, STIBI-OTANTALITE, rezbanyite, SMAL-TITE, CHLOANTHITE, SKUTTERU-DITE, NI-SKUTTERUDITE, DES-CLOIZITE, GRATONITE, STRO-MEYERITE, TELLURIUM, ishika-waite, ARGYRODITE, GLAUCO-DOT, GEOCRONITE, GUANAJUA-TITE, chervetite (to 6.32)

6.33 Rezbanyite, SMALTITE, CHLOAN-THITE, SKUTTERUDITE, NI-SKUT-TERUDITE, GRATONITE, ishika-waite, GLAUCODOT, TENORITE, STIBIOTANTALITE, GEOCRO-NITE, KOBELLITE, COBALTITE (MG), JORDANITE, antimonpear-ceite, GUANAJUATITE

6.34 Rezbanyite, SMALTITE, CHLOAN-THITE, SKUTTERUDITE, NI-SKUT-TERUDITE, GRATONITE, ishika-waite, GLAUCODOT, TENORITE, STIBIOTANTALITE, GEOCRO-NITE, JORDANITE, benjammite, GUANAJUATITE, antimonpearceite

6.35 Rezbanyite, SMALTITE, CHLOAN-THITE, SKUTTERUDITE, NI-SKUT-TERUDITE, GRATONITE, ishika-waite, GLAUCODOT, TENORITE, STIBIOTANTALITE, GEOCRO-NITE, JORDANITE, MENEG-HINITE, hodrushite, GUANAJUA-TITE, antimonpearceite

6.36 Rezbanyite, SMALTITE, CHLOAN-THITE, SKUTTERUDITE, NI-SKUT-

TERUDITE, GRATONITE, ishika-waite, GLAUCODOT, TENORITE, GEOCRONITE, JORDANITE, ME-NEGHINITE, STIBIOTANTALITE, uranosphaerite, TEALLITE, GUAN-AJUATITE

6.37 Rezbanyite, SMALTITE, CHLOAN-THITE, SKUTTERUDITE, NI-SKUT-TERUDITE, GRATONITE, ishika-waite, GLAUCODOT, TENORITE, GEOCRONITE, JORDANITE, ME-NEGHINITE, STIBIOTANTALITE, wolfachite, ANGLESITE, GUAN-AJUATITE

6.38 Rezbanyite, SMALTITE, CHLOAN-THITE, SKUTTERUDITE, NI-SKUT-TERUDITE, GRATONITE, ishika-waite, GLAUCODOT, TENORITE, GEOCRONITE, JORDANITE, STIBI-OTANTALITE, ANGLESITE, em-plectite, GUANAJUATITE

6.39 Rezbanyite, SMALTITE, CHLOAN-THITE, SKUTTERUDITE, NI-SKUT-TERUDITE, GRATONITE, ishika-waite, GLAUCODOT, TENORITE, GEOCRONITE, JORDANITE, STIBI-OTANTALITE, ANGLESITE (G), hallimondite, clarkeite, GUAN-AJUATITE

6.40 SMALTITE, CHLOANTHITE, SKUT-TERUDITE, NI-SKUTTERUDITE, GRATONITE, ishikawaite, GLAUCO-DOT, TENORITE, GEOCRONITE, JORDANITE, raguinite, STIBIOTAN-TALITE, hauchecornite, GUAN-AJUATITE, daubreeite

6.42 SMALTITE, CHLOANTHITE, SKUT-TERUDITE, NI-SKUTTERUDITE, GLAUCODOT, GEOCRONITE, JOR-DANITE, STIBIOTANTALITE, hemi-hedrite, GUANAJUATITE

6.43 SMALTITE, CHLOANTHITE, SKUT-TERUDITE, NI-SKUTTERUDITE, schapbachite, GLAUCODOT, GEO-CRONITE, JORDANITE, STIBIO-TANTALITE, GUANAJUATITE

6.45 SMALTITE, CHLOANTHITE, SKUT-TERUDITE, NI-SKUTTERUDITE, GLAUCODOT, GEOCRONITE, STIBIOTANTALITE, wherryite, GUANAJUATITE

6.49 SMALTITE, CHLOANTHITE, SKUTTERUDITE, NI-SKUT-TERUDITE, GLAUCODOT, GEO-CRONITE, STIBIOTANTALITE, ala-

mosaite, cuprobismite, GUANAJUA-
TITE
6.50 SMALTITE, CHLOANTHITE, SKUT-
TERUDITE, NI-SKUTTERUDITE,
GLAUCODOT, GEOCRONITE,
STIBIOTANTALITE, WULFENITE,
BEYERITE, BROMARGYRITE,
URANINITE (M), VANADINITE,
GUANAJUATITE, westgrenite
6.52 SMALTITE, CHLOANTHITE, SKUT-
TERUDITE, NI-SKUTTERUDITE,
GLAUCODOT, STIBIOTANTALITE,
WULFENITE, BEYERITE, URANI-
NITE (M), VANADINITE, GUAN-
AJUATITE
6.53 STIBIOTANTALITE, WULFENITE,
BEYERITE, SMALTITE, CHLOAN-
THITE, SKUTTERUDITE, NI-SKUT-
TERUDITE, CERUSSITE, URANI-
NITE (M), VANADINITE, GUAN-
AJUATITE
6.54 STIBIOTANTALITE, WULFENITE,
BEYERITE, SMALTITE, CHLOAN-
THITE, SKUTTERUDITE, NI-SKUT-
TERUDITE, CERUSSITE, cannizza-
rite, URANINITE (M), VANADI-
NITE, GUANAJUATITE, pavonite
6.55 STIBIOTANTALITE, WULFENITE,
BEYERITE, SMALTITE, CHLOAN-
THITE, SKUTTERUDITE, NI-SKUT-
TERUDITE, CERUSSITE (G),
ARSENOPYRITE, LEADHILLITE,
wolframixiolite, olsacherite, URANI-
NITE (M), VANADINITE, GUAN-
AJUATITE
6.56 STIBIOTANTALITE, WULFENITE,
BEYERITE, SMALTITE, CHLOAN-
THITE, SKUTTERUDITE, NI-SKUT-
TERUDITE, CERUSSITE, ARSENO-
PYRITE, URANINITE (M), VANA-
DINITE, GUANAJUATITE
6.57 STIBIOTANTALITE, WULFENITE,
SMALTITE, CHLOANTHITE, SKUT-
TERUDITE, NI-SKUTTERUDITE,
CERUSSITE, ARSENOPYRITE, clif-
fordite, PUCHERITE, URANINITE
(M), VANADINITE, GUANAJUA-
TITE, athabascaite (to 6.59?)
6.60 STIBIOTANTALITE, WULFENITE,
SMALTITE, CHLOANTHITE, SKUT-
TERUDITE, NI-SKUTTERUDITE,
ARSENOPYRITE, eulytine, alloclase,
chrominium, chalcothallite, VANADI-
NITE, URANINITE (M), GUAN-
AJUATITE
6.61 STIBIOTANTALITE, WULFENITE,

SMALTITE, CHLOANTHITE, SKUT-
TERUDITE, NI-SKUTTERUDITE,
ARSENOPYRITE, mckinstryite, AN-
TIMONY, ULLMANNITE, penfield-
ite, VANADINITE, URANINITE (M),
GUANAJUATITE, trustedtite (6.62)
6.64 STIBIOTANTALITE, WULFENITE,
SMALTITE, CHLOANTHITE, SKUT-
TERUDITE, NI-SKUTTERUDITE,
ARSENOPYRITE, ANTIMONY,
ULLMANNITE, CERVANTITE,
VANADINITE, URANINITE (M),
GUANAJUATITE, ordonezite
6.67 STIBIOTANTALITE, WULFENITE,
SMALTITE, CHLOANTHITE, SKUT-
TERUDITE, NI-SKUTTERUDITE,
ARSENOPYRITE, ANTIMONY,
ULLMANNITE, VANADINITE, ga-
brielsonite, URANINITE (M),
GUANAJUATITE, itoite
6.69 STIBIOTANTALITE, WULFENITE,
SMALTITE, CHLOANTHITE, SKUT-
TERUDITE, NI-SKUTTERUDITE,
ARSENOPYRITE, ANTIMONY,
ULLMANNITE, walpurgite, VANA-
DINITE, URANINITE (M), GUAN-
AJUATITE
6.70 STIBIOTANTALITE, WULFENITE,
SMALTITE, CHLOANTHITE, SKUT-
TERUDITE, NI-SKUTTERUDITE,
ARSENOPYRITE, ANTIMONY, pen-
roseite, sanmartinite, berryite,
VANADINITE, URANINITE (M),
GUANAJUATITE, novakite
6.71 STIBIOTANTALITE, WULFENITE,
SMALTITE, CHLOANTHITE, SKUT-
TERUDITE, NI-SKUTTERUDITE,
ARSENOPYRITE, ANTIMONY, pen-
roseite. BERZELIANITE, VANA-
DINITE, URANINITE (M), GUAN-
AJUATITE
6.72 STIBIOTANTALITE, WULFENITE,
SMALTITE, CHLOANTHITE, SKUT-
TERUDITE, ARSENOPYRITE, AN-
TIMONY, penroseite, gudmundite,
saukovite, barysilite, VANADINITE,
URANINITE (M), GUANAJUATITE,
kullerudite
6.73 STIBIOTANTALITE, WULFENITE,
SMALTITE, CHLOANTHITE, SKUT-
TERUDITE, NI-SKUTTERUDITE,
ARSENOPYRITE, penroseite, ham-
marite, VANADINITE, URANINITE
(M), GUANAJUATITE
6.74 STIBIOTANTALITE, WULFENITE,
SMALTITE, CHLOANTHITE, SKUT-

TERUDITE, NI-SKUTTERUDITE, ARSENOPYRITE, penroseite, VANADINITE, schirmerite, URANINITE (M), GUANAJUATITE

6.75 STIBIOTANTALITE, WULFENITE, SMALTITE, CHLOANTHITE, SKUTTERUDITE, NI-SKUTTERUDITE, ARSENOPYRITE, penroseite, BISMUTHINITE, VANADINITE, URANINITE (M), GUANAJUATITE

6.76 STIBIOTANTALITE, WULFENITE, SMALTITE, CHLOANTHITE, SKUTTERUDITE, NI-SKUTTERUDITE, ARSENOPYRITE, penroseite, BISMUTHINITE, COSALITE, VANADINITE, URANINITE (M), GUANAJUATITE, chloroxiphite

6.78 STIBIOTANTALITE, WULFENITE, SMALTITE, CHLOANTHITE, SKUTTERUDITE, NI-SKUTTERUDITE, ARSENOPYRITE, penroseite, BISMUTHINITE, ALASKAITE, chloroxiphite, VANADINITE, URANINITE (M), GUANAJUATITE

6.80 STIBIOTANTALITE, WULFENITE, CASSITERITE (MG), SMALTITE, CHLOANTHITE, SKUTTERUDITE, NI-SKUTTERUDITE, ARSENOPYRITE, penroseite, ALASKAITE, BISMUTHINITE, chloroxiphite, HYDROCERUSSITE, wolsendorfite, VANADINITE, URANINITE (M), GUANAJUATITE

6.81 STIBIOTANTALITE, WULFENITE, CASSITERITE (MG), SMALTITE, CHLOANTHITE, SKUTTERUDITE, NI-SKUTTERUDITE, ARSENOPYRITE, penroseite, ALASKAITE, BISMUTHINITE, chloroxiphite, VANADINITE, URANINITE (M), GUANAJUATITE

6.82 STIBIOTANTALITE, WULFENITE, SMALTITE, CHLOANTHITE, SKUTTERUDITE, NI-SKUTTERUDITE, ARSENOPYRITE, penroseite, chloroxiphite, ALASKAITE, atelestite, VANADINITE, URANINITE (M), jalpaite, GUANAJUATITE, CASSITERITE (MG)

6.84 STIBIOTANTALITE, WULFENITE, SMALTITE, CHLOANTHITE, SKUTTERUDITE, NI-SKUTTERUDITE, ARSENOPYRITE, PENROSEITE, chloroxiphite, ALASKAITE, quenselite, VANADINITE, URANINITE

(M), CASSITERITE (MG), GUANAJUATITE

6.85 WULFENITE, STIBIOTANTALITE, SMALTITE, CHLOANTHITE, SKUTTERUDITE, NI-SKUTTERUDITE, ARSENOPYRITE, penroseite, chloroxiphite, ALASKAITE, VANADINITE, URANINITE (M), GUANAJUATITE, CASSITERITE (MG)

6.86 STIBIOTANTALITE, WULFENITE, CASSITERITE (MG), SMALTITE, CHLOANTHITE, SKUTTERUDITE, NI-SKUTTERUDITE, penroseite, chloroxiphite, ALASKAITE, rooseveltite, VANADINITE, URANINITE (M), GUANAJUATITE

6.87 STIBIOTANTALITE, CASSITERITE (MG), WULFENITE, SMALTITE, CHLOANTHITE, SKUTTERUDITE, NI-SKUTTERUDITE, penroseite, chloroxiphite, ALASKAITE, VANADINITE, GUANAJUATITE, URANINITE (M), willyamite

6.88 STIBIOTANTALITE, WULFENITE, CASSITERITE (MG), SMALTITE, CHLOANTHITE, SKUTTERUDITE, NI-SKUTTERUDITE, penroseite, chloroxiphite, ALASKAITE, VANADINITE, URANINITE (M), GUANAJUATITE, schmitterite

6.89 STIBIOTANTALITE, CASSITERITE (MG), WULFENITE, SMALTITE, CHLOANTHITE, SKUTTERUDITE, NI-SKUTTERUDITE, penroseite, chloroxiphite, costibite, heliophyllite, VANADINITE, URANINITE (M), GUANAJUATITE

6.90 STIBIOTANTALITE, WULFENITE, CASSITERITE (MG), SMALTITE, CHLOANTHITE, SKUTTERUDITE, NI-SKUTTERUDITE, penroseite, chloroxiphite, zinc, crookesite, MATILDITE, BUNSENITE, paracostibite, VANADINITE, URANINITE (M), GUANAJUATITE

6.92 STIBIOTANTALITE, WULFENITE, CASSITERITE (MG), penroseite, zinc, chloroxiphite, paracostibite, LANARKITE, chiviatite, URANINITE (M), VANADINITE, GUANAJUATITE, oregonite

6.93 STIBIOTANTALITE, WULFENITE, CASSITERITE (MG), penroseite, zinc, chloroxiphite, paracostibite, chiviatite, VANADINITE, URANINITE (M), GUANAJUATITE

6.95 STIBIOTANTALITE, WULFENITE, penroseite, CASSITERITE (MG), zinc, paracostibite, chiviatite, SAFFLORITE, URANINITE (M), VANADINITE, GUANAJUATITE

6.96 STIBIOTANTALITE, WULFENITE, CASSITERITE (MG), penroseite, zinc, paracostibite, chiviatite, SAFFLORITE, gladite, URANINITE (M), VANADINITE, GUANAJUA-TITE, wilkmanite, weibullite

6.97 STIBIOTANTALITE, WULFENITE, CASSITERITE (xls), penroseite, zinc, paracostibite, chiviatite, SAF-FLORITE, POLYARGYRITE, wei-bullite, URANINITE (M), VANA-DINITE, GUANAJUATITE

6.98 STIBIOTANTALITE, WULFENITE, CASSITERITE (xls), penroseite, zinc, paracostibite, chiviatite, SAF-FLORITE, DUFTITE, URANINITE (M), VANADINITE, GUANAJUA-TITE

6.99 STIBIOTANTALITE, WULFENITE, penroseite, zinc, paracostibite, chiviatite, SAFFLORITE, laurite, CASSITERITE (xls), VANADINITE, URANINITE (M)

7.00 STIBIOTANTALITE, WULFENITE, penroseite, zinc, paracostibite, chiviatite, SAFFLORITE, LILLIAN-ITE, RAMMELSBERGITE, schreiber-site, PYROMORPHITE, URANINITE (M), VANADINITE

7.01 STIBIOTANTALITE, penroseite, zinc, paracostibite, chiviatite, SAFFLORITE, LILLIANITE, RAM-MELSBERGITE, PHOENICOCHRO-ITE, schreibersite, PYROMORPHITE, lindstromite, nuffieldite, URAN-INITE (M), VANADINITE

7.02 STIBIOTANTALITE, penroseite, zinc, paracostibite, chiviatite, SAFFLORITE, LILLIANITE, RAM-MELSBERGITE, schreibersite, neyite, PYROMORPHITE, NADORITE, URANINITE (M), VANADINITE

7.03 STIBIOTANTALITE, penroseite, zinc, paracostibite, chiviatite, SAFFLORITE, formanite, LILLIAN-ITE, RAMMELSBERGITE, schreiber-site, PYROMORPHITE, URANINITE (M), VANADINITE

7.04 STIBIOTANTALITE, penroseite, zinc, paracostibite, chiviatite, SAFFLORITE, LILLIANITE, RAM-MELSBERGITE, schreibersite, VA-NADINITE, PYROMORPHITE, ga-lenobismutite, URANINITE (M)

7.06 STIBIOTANTALITE, penroseite, zinc, paracostibite, chiviatite, SAFFLORITE, LILLIANITE, RAM-MELSBERGITE, schreibersite, PYROMORPHITE, galenobismutite, sederholmite, aikinite, chalcostibite, URANINITE (M), VANADINITE

7.08 STIBIOTANTALITE, penroseite, zinc, paracostibite, chiviatite, SAFFLORITE, LILLIANITE, RAM-MELSBERGITE, schreibersite, aiki-nite, PYROMORPHITE, galenobis-mutite, chalcostibite, URANINITE (M), VANADINITE

7.10 STIBIOTANTALITE, penroseite, zinc, paracostibite, chiviatite, SAFFLORITE, LILLIANITE, RAM-MELSBERGITE, schreibersite, VA-NADINITE, galenobismutite, TE-TRADYMITE, georgiadesite, URAN-INITE (M)

7.12 Zinc, chiviatite, SAFFLORITE, LILLIANITE, RAMMELSBERGITE, bismoclite, schreibersite, galenobis-mutite, TETRADYMITE, molybdo-menite, STIBIOTANTALITE, para-rammelsbergite, MATLOCKITE, HUEBNERITE, URANINITE (M)

7.14 Zinc, chiviatite, SAFFLORITE, LILLIANITE, RAMMELSBERGITE, ecdemite, schreibersite, TETRA-DYMITE, STIBIOTANTALITE, ixio-lite, HUEBNERITE, URANINITE (M)

7.15 Zinc, chiviatite, SAFFLORITE, LILLIANITE, RAMMELSBERGITE, CALOMEL, schreibersite, TETRADY-MITE, STIBIOTANTALITE, HUEB-NERITE, URANINITE (M)

7.17 Zinc, SAFFLORITE, LILLIANITE, RAMMELSBERGITE, schreibersite, TETRADYMITE, STIBIOTAN-TALITE, staringite, HUEBNERITE, URANINITE (M)

7.20 Zinc, SAFFLORITE, LILLIANITE, RAMMELSBERGITE, schreibersite, TETRADYMITE, STIBIOTANTA-LITE, ACANTHITE, ARGENTITE, cohenite, HUEBNERITE, WOLFRA-MITE, URANINITE (M), wodginite (7.19), kitkaite (7.22), makinenite (7.22)

7.24 SAFFLORITE, schreibersite, TETRA-

DYMITE, STIBIOTANTALITE, ACANTHITE, ARGENTITE, cohenite, DOMEYKITE, MENDIPITE, MIMETITE, HUEBNERITE, WOLFRAMITE, URANNITE (M)

7.26 SAFFLORITE, schreibersite, TETRADYMITE, STIBIOTANTALITE, ACANTHITE, ARGENTITE, cohenite, DOMEYKITE, CURITE, HUEBNERITE, WOLFRAMITE, URANINITE (M)

7.27 SAFFLORITE, schreibersite, TETRADYMITE, STIBIOTANTALITE, ACANTHITE, ARGENTITE, cohenite, DOMEYKITE, finnemanite, beegerite, HUEBNERITE, WOLFRAMITE, URANINITE (M)

7.28 SAFFLORITE, schreibersite, TETRADYMITE, STIBIOTANTALITE, ACANTHITE, ARGENTITE, cohenite, DOMEYKITE, tin, WOLFRAMITE, URANINITE (M)

7.29 SAFFLORITE, schreibersite, TETRADYMITE, STIBIOTANTALITE, ACANTHITE, ARGENTITE, cohenite, DOMEYKITE, IRON, WOLFRAMITE, URANINITE (M)

7.30 SAFFLORITE, schreibersite, TETRADYMITE, STIBIOTANTALITE, ACANTHITE, ARGENTITE, cohenite, DOMEYKITE, IRON, WOLFRAMITE, URANINITE (M)

7.31 SAFFLORITE, TETRADYMITE, STIBIOTANTALITE, ARGENTITE, cohenite, DOMEYKITE, IRON, WOLFRAMITE, URANINITE (M)

7.32 SAFFLORITE, TETRADYMITE, STIBIOTANTALITE, ARGENTITE, DOMEYKITE, wittite, cohenite, IRON, WOLFRAMITE, URANINITE (M)

7.33 SAFFLORITE, TETRADYMITE, STIBIOTANTALITE, ARGENTITE, cohenite, russellite, DOMEYKITE, IRON, WOLFRAMITE, URANINITE (M)

7.35 WOLFRAMITE, melonite, SAFFLORITE, TETRADYMITE, STIBIOTANTALITE, ARGENTITE, cohenite, DOMEYKITE, IRON, URANINITE (M), blixite

7.36 NAGYAGITE, SAFFLORITE, TETRADYMITE, ARGENTITE, cohenite, IRON, DOMEYKITE, WOLFRAMITE, URANINITE (M)

7.39 SAFFLORITE, TETRADYMITE,

ARGENTITE, cohenite, DOMEYKITE, IRON, FERBERITE, NAGYAGITE, LORETTOITE, LOELLINGITE, schwartzembergite, URANINITE (M)

7.40 SAFFLORITE, TETRADYMITE, ARGENTITE, cohenite, DOMEYKITE, IRON, FERBERITE, NAGYAGITE, LORETTOITE, LOELLINGITE, TUNGSTENITE, URANINITE (M)

7.41 SAFFLORITE, TETRADYMITE, cohenite, DOMEYKITE, IRON, FERBERITE, NAGYAGITE, LORETTOITE, LOELLINGITE, URANINITE (M)

7.45 SAFFLORITE, TETRADYMITE, cohenite, DOMEYKITE, IRON, FERBERITE, NAGYAGITE, LORETTOITE, URANINITE (M)

7.46 TETRADYMITE, cohenite, DOMEYKITE, IRON, FERBERITE, NAGYAGITE, LORETTOITE, URANINITE (M)

7.50 TETRADYMITE, cohenite, DOMEYKITE, IRON, FERBERITE, LORETTOITE, URANINITE (M)

7.51 Cohenite, DOMEYKITE, IRON, FERBERITE, LORETTOITE, URANINITE (M)

7.54,Cohenite, DOMEYKITE, IRON, FERBERITE, LORETTOITE, rickardite, URANINITE (M)

7.56 Cohenite, DOMEYKITE, IRON, FERBERITE, LORETTOITE, daubreeite, URANINITE (M)

7.57 GALENA, cohenite, DOMEYKITE, IRON, FERBERITE, LORETTOITE, URANINITE (M)

7.59 AGUILARITE, cohenite, DOMEYKITE, IRON, LORETTOITE, GALENA, URANINITE (M)

7.60 EUCAIRITE, oruetite, cohenite, DOMEYKITE, IRON, LORETTOITE, URANINITE (M)

7.61 Cohenite, DOMEYKITE, IRON, LORETTOITE, URANINITE (M), EMPRESSITE, EUCAIRITE

7.65 METACINNABAR, cohenite, DOMEYKITE, IRON, LORETTOITE, EUCAIRITE, URANINITE (M)

7.70 Hematophanite, DOMEYKITE, IRON, LORETTOITE, EUCAIRITE, URANINITE (M)

7.75 Awaruite, DOMEYKITE, IRON,

LORETTOITE, EUCAIRITE, URAN-INITE (M)
7.78 NICCOLITE, DOMEYKITE, IRON, LORETTOITE, EUCAIRITE, URAN-INITE (M)
7.80 DOMEYKITE, IRON, LORETTOITE, EUCAIRITE, CLAUSTHALITE, NI-IRON, tellurbismuth, URANINITE (M), ikunolite
7.81 Behierite, DOMEYKITE, IRON, NI-IRON, LORETTOITE, URAN-INITE (M)
7.82 Behierite, macedonite, DOMEYKITE, IRON, NI-IRON, URANINITE (M)
7.85 Behierite, DOMEYKITE, IRON, NI-IRON, LORETTOITE, TAPIO-LITE, MOSSITE, URANINITE (M)
7.87 Behierite, DOMEYKITE, IRON, NI-IRON, LORETTOITE, TAPIO-LITE, MOSSITE, NAUMANNITE, URANINITE (M)
7.88 Behierite, DOMEYKITE, IRON, NI-IRON, LORETTOITE, TAPIO-LITE, MOSSITE, ixiolite, URAN-INITE (M), zavaritskite
7.90 Behierite (to 7.91), DOMEYKITE, IRON, NI-IRON, LORETTOITE, TAPIOLITE, STOLZITE, MOSSITE, TANTALITE, URANINITE (M), zavaritskite
7.95 LORETTOITE, NI-IRON, TAPIO-LITE, MOSSITE, TANTALITE, STOLZITE, sahlinite, chubutite, URANINITE (M), zavaritskite
7.98 NI-IRON, TANTALITE, STOLZITE, URANINITE (M), platynite
8.00 NI-IRON, TANTALITE, STOLZITE, URANINITE (M, xls), kleinite, MAUCHERITE, nisbite, onofrite, zavaritskite, stuetzite
8.04 Coloradoite, NI-IRON, STOLZITE, URANINITE (M, xls), zavaritskite
8.08 Gruenlingite, NI-IRON, STOLZITE, URANINITE (M, xls), zavaritskite
8.09 CINNABAR, NI-IRON, STOLZITE, URANINITE (M, xls), zavaritskite
8.10 NI-IRON, STOLZITE, cadmium oxide, URANINITE (M, xls), zavaritskite
8.12 NI-IRON, STOLZITE, URANINITE (M, xls), zavaritskite, laitakarite
8.15 ALTAITE, NI-IRON, STOLZITE, URANINITE (M, xls), zavaritskite
8.16 SYLVANITE, NI-IRON, STOLZITE, URANINITE (M, xls), perite, zavaritskite

8.18 Joseite, NI-IRON, STOLZITE, URANINITE (M, xls), schuetteite, zavaritskite
8.19 NI-IRON, STOLZITE, TIEMAN-NITE, URANINITE (M, xls), zavaritskite
8.22 NI-IRON, STOLZITE, TIEMAN-NITE, URANINITE (M, xls), zavaritskite
8.23 BREITHAUPTITE, STOLZITE, TIE-MANNITE, URANINITE (M, xls), zavaritskite
8.24 HESSITE, STOLZITE, TIEMAN-NITE, URANINITE (M, xls), zavaritskite
8.26 HESSITE, STOLZITE, TIEMAN-NITE, URANINITE (M, xls), zavaritskite, BISMUTOTANTALITE
8.29 HESSITE, STOLZITE, TIEMAN-NITE, URANINITE (M, xls), zavaritskite, koechlinite
8.33 HESSITE, STOLZITE, TIEMAN-NITE, URANINITE (M, xls), zavaritskite, eglestonite
8.34 HESSITE, STOLZITE, TIEMAN-NITE, URANINITE (M, xls), zavaritskite, eglestonite, sukulaite
8.38 HESSITE, TIEMANNITE, URAN-INITE (M, xls), ALGODONITE, kutinaite, wehrlite, eglestonite
8.40 HESSITE, TIEMANNITE, URAN-INITE (M, xls), eglestonite, wehrlite, vysotskite
8.42 HESSITE, TIEMANNITE, URAN-INITE (M, xls), eglestonite, wehrlite, cuprostibite
8.44 HESSITE, TIEMANNITE, eglstonite, wehrlite, URANINITE (M, xls)
8.45 HESSITE, TIEMANNITE, eglestonite, URANINITE (M, xls)
8.46 TIEMANNITE, URANINITE (M, xls), RASPITE
8.47 TIEMANNITE, URANINITE (M, xls)
8.50 URANINITE (M, xls), whitneyite
8.62 URANINITE (xls), KRENNERITE
8.64 URANINITE (xls), BISMITE
8.70 URANINITE (xls), BISMITE, PETZITE
8.72 URANINITE (xls), BISMITE, PETZITE, shandite
8.73 URANINITE (xls), BISMITE, PETZITE, terlinguaite
8.80 URANINITE (xls), BISMITE, PETZITE, sillenite
8.81 URANINITE (xls), BISMITE, PETZITE, horsfordite

8.90 URANINITE (xls), BISMITE, PETZITE, MINIUM
8.91 URANINITE (xls), BISMITE, PETZITE, MINIUM, nickel
8.95 URANINITE (xls), BISMITE, PETZITE, MINIUM, COPPER
9.00 URANINITE (xls), BISMITE, PETZITE, MINIUM
9.02 URANINITE (xls), BISMITE, PETZITE, MINIUM
9.14 URANINITE (xls), BISMITE, MINIUM, LITHARGE
9.20 URANINITE (xls), BISMITE, MINIUM
9.22 URANINITE (xls), BISMITE, CALAVERITE
9.26 URANINITE (xls), CALAVERITE
9.40-9.50 URANINITE (xls), PLATT-NERITE
9.50 URANINITE (xls), cooperite, stibiopalladinite, michenerite
9.56 URANINITE (xls), MASSICOT
9.60 URANINITE (xls), DYSCRASITE
9.70 URANINITE (xls), DYSCRASITE, THORIANITE, BISMUTH
9.81 URANINITE (xls), DYSCRASITE, BISMUTH
9.83 URANINITE (xls), BISMUTH
9.91 URANINITE (xls), aurostibite
10.00 URANINITE (xls), braggite, allargentum
10.10 SILVER
10.58-10.73 SILVER, sperrylite
11.10 SILVER
11.20 Tantalum
11.23 Montroydite
11.37 LEAD
11.90 Palladium
12.50-12.60 Froodite
13.32 Zyvagintsevite
13.48 Moschellandsbergite, potarite
13.60 Moschellandsbergite, potarite, MERCURY
13.71 Moschellandsbergite, potarite
14.00 PLATINUM, potarite
14.68 PLATINUM, potarite, ELECTRUM
15.47 PLATINUM, potarite, ELECTRUM, gold amalgam
15.70 PLATINUM, potarite, ELECTRUM, maldonite
15.96 PLATINUM, ELECTRUM, potarite, GOLD
16.11 PLATINUM, potarite, GOLD
16.72 PLATINUM, GOLD
19.00 PLATINUM, GOLD, iridosmine-siserskite

19.30 GOLD, iridosmine-siserskite
20.00 Iridosmine-siserskite, aurosmiridium
21.00 Iridosmine-siserskite
22.65-22.84 Platiniridium

Supplementary List of Specific Gravities

1.80-2.20 Evansite
1.80-2.25 OPAL
1.84-2.52 Fibroferrite
1.85-3.00 CLAY MINERALS
1.99-2.83 Delvauxite
2.00-2.40 Diadochite, vermiculite
2.00-2.50 Lindackerite
2.20-2.50 Pitticite
2.20-2.57 VARISCITE
2.20-2.80 TALC SOAPSTONE
2.26-2.48 Hydronephelite
2.30-2.50 MOLDAVITE, CHRYSOCOLLA, OBSIDIAN
2.30-2.65 Leucophosphite
2.40-2.95 GLAUCONITE
2.47-3.24 Nepouite
2.50-2.78 WERNERITE (scapolite)
2.50-2.91 Carphosiderite
2.50-3.00 Stilpnochlorane, LAPIS LAZULI
2.50-3.50 Greenalite
2.51-2.94 Metahewettite
2.53-2.73 PHARMACOLITE
2.53-2.78 CORDIERITE
2.55-3.39 FELDSPARS
2.58-2.82 HYALOPHANE
2.58-2.83 TALC
2.59-2.85 Parsettensite
2.59-2.96 STILPNOMELANE
2.60-2.90 Alunite, natroalunite
2.60-3.20 CLINTONITES (brittle micas)
2.60-3.30 CHLORITES
2.69-2.90 PYROPHYLLITE
2.70-4.30 LIMONITE
2.77-3.13 Murmanite-lomonosovite
2.80-3.00 APHROSIDERITE
2.80-3.40 SIDEROPHYLLITE
2.80-4.40 WAD
2.80-4.20 ALLANITE
2.90-3.20 APATITES
2.90-3.50 CARBONADO DIAMOND
2.91-3.26 JAROSITE
3.00-3.30 Ferrazite
3.05-3.40 Spencite
3.10-3.34 DUFRENITE
3.13-3.59 HYDROGROSSULAR
3.21-3.68 Niningerite
3.30-4.29 GOETHITE
3.30-4.35 Tyuyaminite
3.35-3.70 Hellandite

3.36-4.64 Ampangabeite
3.40-3.52 SOUTH AFRICAN "JADE"
3.40-3.80 STAUROLITE
3.44-3.70 GENTHELVITE
3.50-3.80 VOLBORTHITE, svabite
3.50-3.86 Trichalcite
3.50-4.00 HYDROZINCITE
3.60-3.80 Obruchevite
3.61-4.50 Samiresite
3.70-5.00 BETAFITE
3.81-3.93 Metatyuyamunite
3.90-6.40 GUMMITE
4.00-4.40 PSEUDOMALACHITE
4.00-4.86 ZIRCONS
4.02-4.24 Zirconolite
4.20-4.40 Fleischerite
4.20-6.40 PYROCHLORE-MICROLITE
4.24-4.67 Nsutite
4.40-5.00 PYROLUSITE
4.40-5.11 XENOTIME
4.50-5.43 Brannerite
4.55-4.93 Umohoite
4.60-5.60 BINDHEIMITE
4.70-5.40 ROMEITE
5.40-5.90 Tanteuxenite
5.94-7.29 Monimolite
6.10-7.10 Trigonite
6.10-7.70 BISMUTITE
6.40-6.80 Tyrrellite

Olivines

3.22-4.39 range
3.22   Forsterite; 3.3-3.6   Chrysolite,
3.5-3.75 Hyalosiderite, 3.7-4.1 Hortonalite,
4.0-4.3 Ferrohortonalite, 4.2-4.39 Fayalite

Clinopyroxenes

2.96-3.34 Fassaite
3.19   Clinoenstatite
3.20-3.55 Clinohypersthene
3.20-3.60 Diallage
3.20-3.60 Salite
3.20-3.60 Ferrosalite
3.22-3.38 Diopside
3.23-3.52 Augite
3.24-3.43 Jadeite
3.26-3.42 Acmite-augite
3.27-3.32 Diopside-jadeite
3.29-3.37 Omphacite
3.30-3.46 Pigeonite
3.30-3.56 Aegerine
3.30-3.60 Titanaugite
3.40-3.55 Aegerine-augite
3.44-3.55 Johannsenite
3.50-3.56 Hedenbergite

3.50-3.70 Clinoferrosilite
3.55-3.60 Acmite

Orthopyroxenes

3.25-3.30 Enstatite
3.30-3.45 Bronzite
3.43-3.60 Hypersthene
3.59-3.75 Ferrohypersthene
3.73-3.86 Eulite
3.96   Orthoferrosilite

Amphiboles

2.85-3.57 Anthophyllite
2.85-3.57 Gedrite
2.90-3.02 Nephrite
2.97-3.45 Richterite
3.00   Ekermannite
3.00-3.40 Crocidolite
3.00-3.50 Hastingsite
3.02-3.42 Riebeckite
3.02-3.44 Actinolite
3.02-3.44 Ferroactinolite
3.02-3.44 Byssolite
3.02-3.45 Uralite
3.02-3.45 Ferroedenite
3.02-3.45 Edenite
3.02-3.45 Hornblende
3.02-3.45 Tschermakite
3.02-3.45 Ferrotschermakite
3.05   Pargasite
3.06-3.13 Holmquistite
3.08-3.30 Glaucophane
3.10-3.40 Crossite
3.10-3.60 Cummingtonite
3.10-3.60 Gruenerite
3.19-3.30 Basaltic hornblende
3.20-3.28 Kaersutite
3.20-3.50 Kataphorite
3.20-3.50 Mg-kataphorite
3.21   Torendrikite
3.50   Ferrohastingsite
3.24-3.83 Fe-anthophyllite
3.50-3.52 Barkevikite
3.50   Arfvedsonite

Micas

2.60-2.85 Hydroparagonite
2.60-2.90 Hydromuscovite
2.60-2.90 Hydrophlogopite
2.60-3.30 Hydrobiotite
2.70-3.30 Biotite
2.76-2.90 Phlogopite
2.77-2.88 Muscovite
2.79-2.81 Agalmatolite

Tables of Specific Gravity: Minerals / **167**

2.80-2.90 Lepidolite
2.80-3.40 Siderophyllite
2.83-2.86 Tainiolite
2.85   Paragonite
2.86-3.43 Hendricksite
2.90-3.02 Zinnwaldite
2.97   Roscoelite
3.10   Lepidomelane

Chlorites

1.85-1.89 Allophane
2.27-2.87 Garnierite
2.60-3.00 Clinochlore
2.60-3.10 Kaemmererite
2.60-3.10 Penninite
2.63   Donbassite
2.69   Cookeite
2.70-2.90 Corundophyllite
2.70-2.90 Delessite
2.70-2.90 Diabantite
2.75-3.10 Daphnite
2.80-3.10 Brunsvigite
2.80-3.30 Thuringite
2.88-3.08 Ripidolite
3.01   Gonyerite
3.06   Pennantite

Clays

2.00-2.20 Halloysite
2.00-3.00 Beidellite
2.00-3.00 Hectorite
2.00-3.00 Saponite
2.00-3.00 Sauconite
2.00-3.00 Stevensite
2.08   Sepiolite
2.20-2.70 Montmorillonite
2.20-2.70 Volchonskoite
2.50-3.00 Nontronite
2.60-2.68 Kaolinite
2.62   Dickite
2.64-2.69 Illite
2.65-2.80 Sheridanite
2.69   Cookeite
2.69   Manandonite
2.70-2.90 Tinticite
2.90-3.10 Chamosite

Sources: J. D. Dana and E. S. Dana, *The System of Mineralogy,* 6th ed. (New York, 1920), with appendices 1-3.

E. S. Dana and W. E. Ford, *A Textbook of Mineralogy,* 4th ed. (New York, 1932).

The System of Mineralogy, 7th ed. (New York, 1944-62), vols. 1-2 by C. Palache et al.; vol. 3 by C. Frondel.

A. N. Winchell and H. Winchell, *Elements of Optical Mineralogy,* 4th ed. (New York, 1951), part 2, "Descriptions."

B. W. Anderson, *Gem Testing,* 7th ed. (London, 1964).

R. Webster, *The Gemmologists' Compendium,* 3d ed. rev. (London, 1964).

R. V. Dietrich, "Mineral Tables," *Bull. Virginia Polytechnic Inst.* 59, no. 3 (1966).

American Mineralogist 1-55 (1916-70).

M. Fleischer, "Index of New Mineral Names," *Amer. Mineral.* 51, no. 8 (1966).

M. H. Hey, *An Index of Mineral Species and Varieties,* 2d ed. rev. (London, 1962).

SPECIFIC GRAVITY: GEM SUBSTANCES

The following table gives specific gravities of the organic and inorganic substances used in gems and ornamental objects arranged according to increasing values. Important substances in capitals.

Abbreviations: G = facet grade; MG = massive gem grade material; U = usual value.

1.03 AMBER, copal
1.05 AMBER, copal, POLYSTYRENE
1.06 AMBER, copal (U)
1.10 AMBER, copal, MEERSCHAUM, JET
1.18 ACRYLIC PLASTICS (plexiglas, lucite, perspex), JET, MEER-SCHAUM
1.19 ACRYLICS, JET, MEERSCHAUM
1.20 JET, MEERSCHAUM
1.25 BAKELITE (amber imitations), JET
1.26 TORTOISESHELL, JET, BAKELITE (U)
1.29 TORTOISESHELL, JET, BAKELITE, CELLULOSE ACETATE PLASTICS
1.30 TORTOISESHELL (U), JET, BAKELITE, CELLULOSE ACE-TATES
1.32 Casein plastics, TORTOISESHELL, JET, CELLULOSE ACETATES
1.34 Casein plastics, CELLULOSE ACETATES, TORTOISESHELL, JET
1.35 TORTOISESHELL, CELLULOSE ACETATES, JET
1.36 Cellulose nitrate plastics (celluloids), CELLULOSE ACETATES, JET
1.38 Cellulose nitrates (U), CELLULOSE ACETATES, vegetable ivory, JET
1.40 Cellulose nitrates, CELLULOSE ACETATES, vegetable ivory (U), mineral coal
1.42 Cellulose nitrates, vegetable ivory

1.70 Elephant-mammoth IVORY
1.85 Elephant-mammoth-hippo-walrus-narwhal IVORIES
1.90 Hippo-walrus-narwhal IVORIES
1.91 Hippo-walrus-narhwal IVORIES, thaumasite (MG)
1.94 Bone, hippo-walrus-narhwal IVORIES
1.95 OPAL, hippo-walrus-narwhal IVORIES, bone
1.97 FIRE OPAL, hippo-walrus-narwhal IVORIES, bone, ulexite (MG)
1.98 OPAL, hippo-walrus-narwhal IVORIES, bone, Ulexite (MG)
2.00 FIRE OPAL (G, U), bone (U)
2.06 FIRE OPAL, bone
2.10 White or black PRECIOUS OPAL (U), bone
2.12 Mordenite (MG), OPAL
2.15 Mordenite (MG), stichtite (MG), OPAL
2.20 Stichtite (MG), natrolite (G), chrysocolla (MG), gypsum, SODALITE (MG), OPAL
2.21 Natrolite (G), gypsum, SODALITE (MG), SILICA GLASS (U)
2.22 Natrolite (G), gypsum, analcime (G), SODALITE (MG)
2.23 Whewellite (G), natrolite (G), gypsum, analcime (G), SODALITE (MG)
2.25 Natrolite (G), gypsum, analcime (G), SODALITE (MG)
2.28 Gypsum, analcime (G), tugtupite (MG) (Kola, USSR), SODALITE (MG)
2.29 Gypsum, analcime (G), mesolite (MG), SODALITE (MG), apophyllite (G)
2.30 Gypsum, SODALITE (MG, U), ALABASTER (MG), porcelain, MOLDAVITE (G), OBSIDIAN, apophyllite (G), thomsonite (MG)
2.33 Gypsum, ALABASTER (MG), SODALITE (MG), MOLDAVITE (G), OBSIDIAN, apophyllite (G), thomsonite (MG)
2.35 Gypsum, SODALITE (G), MOLDAVITE (G, U), OBSIDIAN (U), apophyllite (G), thomsonite (MG), hambergite (G, U)
2.39 Gypsum, SODALITE (G), MOLDAVITE (G), OBSIDIAN, apophyllite (G), thomsonite (MG), petalite (G, U)
2.40 Gypsum, SODALITE (G), petalite (G), MOLDAVITE (G), OBSIDIAN, apophyllite (G), thomsonite (MG),

lazurite (G), blue (or gray) PEARL, VARISCITE (MG), hauyne (G)
2.42 Colemanite (G), blue (or gray) PEARL, petalite (G), MOLDAVITE (G), OBSIDIAN, apophyllite (G), cancrinite (MG), VARISCITE (MG)
2.45 Leucite (G), cancrinite (MG), blue (or gray) PEARL, petalite (G), MOLDAVITE (G), OBSIDIAN, apophyllite (G), VARISCITE (MG)
2.46 Leucite (G, U), cancrinite (MG), VARISCITE (MG), blue (or gray) PEARL, petalite (G), MOLDAVITE (G), OBSIDIAN, apophyllite (G)
2.50 Leucite (G), SERPENTINE, LAPIS LAZULI, cancrinite (MG), VARISCITE (MG), blue (or gray) PEARL, MOLDAVITE (G), OBSIDIAN, apophyllite (G), rhyolite ("wonderstone," approx.)
2.54 LAPIS LAZULI, SERPENTINE, VARISCITE (MG), blue (or gray) PEARL, AMAZONITE
2.55 MOONSTONE (Ceylon), AMAZONITE, LAPIS LAZULI, SERPENTINE, elaeolite, VARISCITE (MG, U), blue PEARL
2.56 ORTHOCLASE (Madagascar, yellow) (G), MOONSTONE (Ceylon), perthite, adularia (G), sanidine (G), AMAZONITE (U), LAPIS LAZULI, SERPENTINE, VARISCITE (MG), blue (or gray) PEARL, elaeolite
2.57 ORTHOCLASE (Madagascar, yellow) (G, U), MOONSTONE (Ceylon) (G, U), albite (MG), perthite, sanidine (G), AMAZONITE, LAPIS LAZULI, SERPENTINE, VARISCITE (MG), blue (or gray) PEARL, elaeolite, IOLITE
2.58 MOONSTONE (Ceylon), sanidine (G), perthite, albite (MG), LAPIS LAZULI, SERPENTINE, VARISCITE (MG), blue (or gray) PEARL, elaeolite, IOLITE (G, U), howlite, bowenite, MARBLE, JASPER
2.60 Sanidine (G), perthite, albite (MG), LAPIS LAZULI, SERPENTINE, VARISCITE (MG), blue (or gray) PEARL, elaeolite, IOLITE (G, U), bowenite (U), MARBLE, TURQUOISE, pseudophite ("Styrian jade"), bastite (MG), slate, CORAL, williamsite, JASPER, CHALCEDONY (U), SCAPOLITE, pinite, kaemmererite (MG)

2.61 Sanidine (G), perthite, albite (MG), LAPIS LAZULI, CHALCEDONY, slate, SERPENTINE, blue (or gray) PEARL, elaeolite, IOLITE, bowenite, MARBLE, TURQUOISE, pink SCAPOLITE (G, MG), williamsite, CORAL, JASPER, pinite, kaemmererite (MG), pseudophite

2.62 Sanidine (G), perthite, albite (G), SUNSTONE (oligoclase, Norway) (MG), LAPIS LAZULI, SERPENTINE, blue (or gray) PEARL, elaeolite, IOLITE, bowenite, MARBLE, TURQUOISE, pink SCAPOLITE (G, MG), JASPER, pinite, kaemmererite (MG), pseudophite, slate, CORAL, CHALCEDONY

2.63 Perthite, albite (G), SUNSTONE (oligoclase, Norway) (MG), LAPIS LAZULI, TURQUOISE, pseudophite, slate, CORAL, CHALCEDONY, SCAPOLITE (blue, violet, pink, and catseyes) (U), JASPER, pinite, kaemmererite (MG), SERPENTINE, elaeolite, IOLITE, MARBLE

2.64 Perthite, oligoclase (G), SUNSTONE (oligoclase, Norway) (MG, U), LAPIS LAZULI, TURQUOISE, pseudophite, slate, CORAL, CHALCEDONY, pink SCAPOLITE, JASPER, pinite, kaemmererite (MG), SERPENTINE, elaeolite, IOLITE, MARBLE

2.65 Perthite, SUNSTONE (oligoclase, Norway) (MG), LAPIS LAZULI, TURQUOISE, pseudophite, slate, CORAL, CHALCEDONY, JASPER, pinite, pink SCAPOLITE, kaemmererite, PEARL (blue, gray, black), clam pearl, ROCK CRYSTAL, synth. quartz, CRYSTALLINE QUARTZES, EMERALD, SYNTH. EMERALD, MARBLE

2.68 CORAL (U), slate, pseudophite, TURQUOISE, LAPIZ LAZULI, JASPER, pinite, kaemmererite (MG), golden BERYL, SYNTH. EMERALD, greenish BERYLS, MARBLE

2.69 Blue AQUAMARINE (G, U), GOSHENITE, yellow BERYL (G, U), EMERALD, SYNTH. EMERALD, greenish BERYLS, CORAL, slate, pseudophite, TURQUOISE, LAPIS LAZULI, fine PEARL, CULTURED PEARL, MARBLE, JASPER, pinite, kaemmererite (MG)

2.70 LABRADORITE (G, U), fine PEARL, Venezuela PEARL, CULTURE PEARL, augelite (G), LAPIS LAZULI, MARBLE, OPHICALCITE, TURQUOISE, slate, CORAL, talc, yellow SCAPOLITE (G, U), freshwater PEARL, SYNTH. EMERALD, EMERALD, GOSHENITE, yellow BERYL, pinite, JASPER, blue AQUAMARINE

2.71 LABRADORITE (G), fine PEARL, oriental natural PEARL (U), Australian PEARL, LAPIS LAZULI, talc, MARBLE, TURQUOISE, CULTURED PEARL, pseudophite, JASPER, pinite, kaemmererite, calcite (U), EMERALD (U), SYNTH. EMERALD, greenish BERYL, blue AQUAMARINE

2.72 LABRADORITE, fine PEARL, CULTURED PEARL, talc, MARBLE, TURQUOISE, pseudophite, greenish BERYL, EMERALD, SYNTH. EMERALD, blue AQUAMARINE, JASPER, pinite, kaemmererite, LAPIS LAZULI

2.73 Fine PEARL, Australian PEARL, CULTURED PEARL, LAPIS LAZULI, talc, TURQUOISE, MARBLE, pseudophite, greenish BERYL, blue AQUAMARINE, EMERALD, SYNTH. EMERALD, talc, JASPER, pinite, kaemmererite

2.74 Fine PEARL, Australian PEARL, CULTURED PEARL, LAPIS LAZULI, talc, TURQUOISE, MARBLE, pseudophite, pectolite (MG), JASPER, pinite, EMERALD, SYNTH. EMERALD, kaemmererite

2.75 Fine PEARL, Australian PEARL, CULTURED PEARL, LAPIS LAZULI, talc (MG, U), TURQUOISE, MARBLE, pseudophite, EMERALD, SYNTH. EMERALD, MORGANITE, pectolite (MG), JASPER, pinite, kaemmererite

2.76 CULTURED PEARL, LAPIS LAZULI, TURQUOISE, pseudophite, talc, JASPER, pinite, kaemmererite, muscovite (fine grained MG), EMERALD, SYNTH. EMERALD, pectolite (MG), pink or colorless BERYL

2.78 CULTURED PEARL, LAPIS LAZULI, TURQUOISE, pseudophite, talc, JASPER, pectolite (MG), pinite, kaemmererite, pink or colorless BERYL

2.80 Pink or colorless BERYL, LAPIS LAZULI (U), pseudophite, TURQUOISE (U), talc, pectolite (MG), pyrophyllite, beryllonite, wollastonite (MG), lepidolite (MG), prehnite, verdite, JASPER, pinite, MOLLUSK SHELL, kaemmererite, dolomite (G)

2.81 LAPIS LAZULI, wardite (MG), verdite, prehnite, lepidolite (MG), wollastonite (MG), beryllonite (G, U), pectolite (MG), MORGANITE, pseudophite, JASPER, kaemmererite, pinite

2.84 Pink PEARL, CONCH SHELL, verdite, prehnite, lepidolite (MG), wollastonite (MG), beryllonite, pectolite (MG), MORGANITE, pseudophite, LAPIS LAZULI, JASPER, pinite, kaemmererite

2.85 Pink PEARL, CONCH PEARL (U), verdite, prehnite (U), lepidolite (MG), wollastonite (MG), beryllonite, pectolite, MORGANITE, pseudophite, LAPIS LAZULI, pollucite, unakite, JASPER, pinite, kaemmererite

2.88 Pink PEARL, verdite, prehnite, lepidolite (MG), wollastonite (MG), pectolite, LAPIS LAZULI, unakite, pollucite, JASPER, kaemmererite

2.89 Pink PEARL, verdite, prehnite, lepidolite (MG), wollastonite (MG), LAPIS LAZULI, JASPER, unakite, pollucite, kaemmererite

2.90 LAPIS LAZULI, unakite, pollucite (U), verdite (U), prehnite, lepidolite, wollastonite, datolite, NEPHRITE, carbonado, JASPER, kaemmererite, anhydrite, tremolite

2.94 Carbonado, NEPHRITE, datolite, unakite, pollucite, verdite, prehnite, LAPIS LAZULI, aragonite (G, U), kaemmererite, anhydrite, tremolite

2.95 Phenakite, carbonado, NEPHRITE, datolite (G, U), unakite, verdite, prehnite, LAPIS LAZULI, kaemmererite, anhydrite, tremolite

2.96 Boracite, phenakite (G, U), carbonado, NEPHRITE (MG, U), datolite, unakite, verdite, LAPIS LAZULI, kaemmererite, anhydrite, tremolite

2.98 Tremolite, phenakite, carbonado, NEPHRITE, datolite, unakite, verdite,

LAPIS LAZULI, kaemmererite, anhydrite, tremolite

2.99 BRAZILIANITE (G, U), phenakite, carbonado, NEPHRITE, datolite (G), unakite, verdite, LAPIS LAZULI, kaemmererite, tremolite, DANBURITE

3.00 DANBURITE (G, U), herderite, magnesite, pink TOURMALINE, odontolite, phenakite, carbonado, NEPHRITE, datolite (G), unakite, LAPIS LAZULI, kaemmererite, synth. bromellite, tremolite, actinolite

3.02 Amblygonite (G, U = 3.03), TOURMALINE (red, pink), odontolite, magnesite, carbonado, NEPHRITE, actinolite, unakite, synth. bromellite

3.04 TOURMALINE (green, red, pink), amblygonite, odontolite, magnesite, carbonado, unakite, actinolite

3.05 TOURMALINE (green, red, pink, brown), odontolite, magnesite, carbonado, unakite, actinolite

3.06 TOURMALINE (brown, green, red (U)), odontolite, magnesite, carbonado, unakite, actinolite

3.07 Friedelite, TOURMALINE (brown, green), odontolite, magnesite, carbonado, unakite, actinolite

3.08 TOURMALINE (achroite, yellow, brown, green), odontolite, magnesite, carbonado, unakite, actinolite

3.09 TOURMALINE (blue, achroite, yellow, brown, green), odontolite, magnesite, carbonado, unakite, lazulite (G, U), actinolite

3.10 Chondrodite (G, U), EUCLASE (G, U), lazulite (G), ANDALUSITE, TOURMALINE (blue, achroite, yellow, green), odontolite, magnesite (G), carbonado, unakite, phosphophyllite (G), actinolite

3.11 ANDALUSITE, TOURMALINE (blue, achroite), odontolite, magnesite, carbonado, unakite, actinolite

3.12 ANDALUSITE, TOURMALINE (achroite), odontolite, magnesite, unakite, carbonado, zoisite (G, U), actinolite

3.15 APATITE, ANDALUSITE (G, U), odontolite, carbonado, unakite, actinolite

3.17 FLUORITE, SPODUMENE, APATITE, silicon carbide (G, U), actinolite, ANDALUSITE, odontolite, carbonado, unakite

3.19 SPODUMENE (G, U = 3.18), FLUORITE (G, U = 3.18), synth. fluorite, actinolite, APATITE, ANDALUSITE, odontolite, carbonado, unakite

3.20 Saussurite, chlorastrolite, DIOPSIDE, SPODUMENE, APATITE, ANDALUSITE, odontolite, carbonado, unakite, actinolite

3.21 APATITE (G, U), synth. fluorite, actinolite, DIOPSIDE, SPODUMENE, odontolite, carbonado, actinolite

3.22 DIOPSIDE, SPODUMENE, APATITE, odontolite, carbonado, actinolite

3.23 DIOPSIDE, SPODUMENE, odontolite, carbonado, actinolite

3.25 EPIDOTE, ZOISITE (thulite), clinozoisite, fibrolite (G, U), odontolite, carbonado, CALIFORNITE, actinolite, DIOPSIDE

3.26 Dumortierite, EPIDOTE, ZOISITE (thulite), clinozoisite, ENSTATITE, DIOPSIDE, carbonado, CALIFORNITE, actinolite

3.27 AXINITE, kornerupine, dumortierite, EPIDOTE, ZOISITE (thulite), clinozoisite, ENSTATITE (G, U), DIOPSIDE, carbonado, CALIFORNITE, actinolite

3.28 Ekanite (G, U), AXINITE (G, U), kornerupine, dumortierite, EPIDOTE, ZOISITE (thulite), clinozoisite, ENSTATITE, DIOPSIDE, carbonado, scorodite (G), CALIFORNITE, actinolite

3.29 AXINITE, dumortierite, EPIDOTE, ZOISITE, clinozoisite, ENSTATITE, DIOPSIDE (G, U), carbonado, CALIFORNITE, actinolite

3.30 Dioptase (G, U), JADEITE, kornerupine, dumortierite, EPIDOTE, ZOISITE, clinozoisite, ENSTATITE, DIOPSIDE, carbonado, GROSSULAR, CALIFORNITE, hypersthene, actinolite (G), bronzite

3.32 JADEITE, kornerupine (G, U), dumortierite, EPIDOTE, ZOISITE, clinozoisite, DIOPSIDE, carbonado, GROSSULAR, CALIFORNITE, hypersthene, actinolite, bronzite

3.34 PERIDOT (G, U), hypersthene, GROSSULAR, JADEITE (MG, U), dumortierite, EPIDOTE, ZOISITE, clinozoisite, DIOPSIDE, carbonado, actinolite, bronzite

3.35 IDOCRASE, hypersthene, GROSSULAR, JADEITE, dumortierite, EPIDOTE, ZOISITE, clinozoisite, carbonado, actinolite, bronzite

3.36 IDOCRASE, hypersthene, GROSSULAR, JADEITE, dumortierite, EPIDOTE, ZOISITE, clinozoisite, carbonado, actinolite, bronzite

3.37 Clinoenstatite, IDOCRASE (G, U = 3.38), hypersthene, GROSSULAR, JADEITE, EPIDOTE, ZOISITE, clinozoisite, actinolite, bronzite

3.40 CHLOROMELANITE, STAUROLITE, HYDROGROSSULAR ("South African jade"), RHODONITE, IDOCRASE, hypersthene, GROSSULAR, JADEITE, EPIDOTE, clinozoisite, carbonado, actinolite, bronzite

3.41 Uvarovite, RHODONITE, STAUROLITE, HYDROGROSSULAR ("South African jade"), IDOCRASE, GROSSULAR, JADEITE, EPIDOTE, clinozoisite, carbonado

3.43 Rhodizite, uvarovite, RHODONITE, STAUROLITE, HYDROGROSSULAR ("South African jade"), IDOCRASE, JADEITE, EPIDOTE, clinozoisite, carbonado

3.45 RHODOCHROSITE, STAUROLITE, rhodizite, uvarovite, RHODONITE, HYDROGROSSULAR ("South African jade"), IDOCRASE, GROSSULAR, JADEITE, EPIDOTE (G, U), clinozoisite, carbonado, SPHENE

3.47 SINHALITE, RHODOCHROSITE, STAUROLITE, uvarovite, RHODONITE, HYDROGROSSULAR ("South African jade"), GROSSULAR, JADEITE, EPIDOTE, clinozoisite, carbonado, SPHENE

3.49 SINHALITE (G, U), RHODOCHROSITE, STAUROLITE, uvarovite, RHODONITE, HYDROGROSSULAR ("South African jade"), GROSSULAR, JADEITE, EPIDOTE, clinozoisite, carbonado, SPHENE

3.50 TOPAZ (colorless, brown, pink), RHODOCHROSITE, STAUROLITE, uvarovite, RHODONITE, HYDROGROSSULAR ("South African jade") (U), GROSSULAR, JADEITE, EPIDOTE, clinozoisite, carbonado, SPHENE, realgar

3.51 DIAMOND, TOPAZ (colorless, brown, pink), RHODOCHROSITE,

STAUROLITE, uvarovite, RHODO-
NITE, HYDROGROSSULAR
("South African jade"), GROSSU-
LAR, SPHENE

3.52 DIAMOND (G, U), TOPAZ (colorless,
brown, pink), RHODOCHROSITE,
STAUROLITE, uvarovite, RHODO-
NITE, HYDROGROSSULAR
("South African jade"), GROSSU-
LAR, SPHENE

3.53 TOPAZ (colorless, brown, pink,
yellow (G, U), RHODOCHROSITE,
STAUROLITE, RHODONITE,
GROSSULAR, SPHENE (G, U)

3.54 TOPAZ (colorless, brown, pink,
yellow), RHODOCHROSITE,
STAUROLITE, RHODONITE,
GROSSULAR, SPHENE

3.55 TOPAZ (colorless, brown, yellow,
blue), RHODOCHROSITE, STAURO-
LITE, RHODONITE, GROSSULAR
(hessonite), SPHENE, synth. periclase

3.58 TOPAZ (brown, yellow, blue),
RHODOCHROSITE, STAUROLITE,
RHODONITE, GROSSULAR (hessonite), SPINEL (pink, purple, red),
synth. periclase

3.59 TOPAZ (brown, yellow, blue),
RHODOCHROSITE, STAUROLITE,
RHODONITE, GROSSULAR (hessonite), SPINEL (pink, purple, red),
synth. red spinel, synth. periclase

3.60 Taaffeite, TOPAZ (brown, blue),
RHODOCHROSITE, STAUROLITE,
RHODONITE (G, U), GROSSULAR
(hessonite), SPINEL (pink [G, U],
purple, red, blue), SYNTH. BLUE
SPINEL, synth. periclase

3.61 Taaffeite (G, U), SPINEL (blue,
purple, red), SYNTH. SPINEL,
RHODOCHROSITE, STAUROLITE,
RHODONITE, GROSSULAR (hessonite)

3.63 SPINEL (ceylonite, blue, purple, red),
SYNTH. SPINEL (G, U),
RHODOCHROSITE, STAUROLITE,
RHODONITE, GROSSULAR (hesso-
nite)

3.64 SPINEL (ceylonite, blue, purple, red),
SYNTH. SPINEL, RHODOCHRO-
SITE, STAUROLITE, RHODONITE,
GROSSULAR (hessonite)

3.65 SPINEL (ceylonite, blue, purple, red),
SYNTH. SPINEL, RHODOCHRO-
SITE, STAUROLITE, RHODONITE,

GROSSULAR (hessonite [G, U]),
PYROPE, benitoite

3.67 Benitoite (G, U), SPINEL (ceylonite,
blue), RHODOCHROSITE, STAURO-
LITE, RHODONITE, GROSSULAR
(hessonite), PYROPE

3.68 CHRYSOBERYL, SPINEL (ceylonite,
blue), RHODOCHROSITE, STAURO-
LITE, RHODONITE, GROSSULAR,
PYROPE

3.70 Shattuckite, CHRYSOBERYL,
SPINEL (ceylonite, blue), STAURO-
LITE, RHODOCHROSITE (G, U),
RHODONITE, GROSSULAR,
PYROPE (G, U)

3.72 Shattuckite, CHRYSOBERYL (G, U
= 3.71), SPINEL (ceylonite, blue),
STAUROLITE, GROSSULAR,
PYROPE

3.73 Azurite, shattuckite, CHRYSO-
BERYL, SPINEL (ceylonite, blue),
STAUROLITE, PYROPE

3.74 MALACHITE, azurite, shattuckite,
CHRYSOBERYL, SPINEL (ceylonite,
blue), STAUROLITE, PYROPE

3.75 MALACHITE, azurite, shattuckite,
CHRYSOBERYL, SPINEL (ceylonite,
blue), STAUROLITE, PYROPE

3.78 MALACHITE, azurite, shattuckite,
CHRYSOBERYL, SPINEL (ceylonite), STAUROLITE, PYROPE

3.80 ANDRADITE, MALACHITE (MG,
U), shattuckite, ceylonite, STAURO-
LITE, PYROPE, pyroxmangite,
siderite

3.83 DEMANTOID, ANDRADITE, MAL-
ACHITE, ceylonite

3.84 RHODOLITE, DEMANTOID, AN-
DRADITE, MALACHITE, ceylonite

3.85 ALMANDINE, DEMANTOID (G, U),
ANDRADITE, MALACHITE, ceylonite

3.88 Anatase (G, U), ALMANDINE,
ANDRADITE, MALACHITE, ceylonite

3.90 SPESSARTINE, gahnospinel, willemite, ALMANDINE, ANDRADITE,
MALACHITE, ceylonite, hodgkinsonite

3.95 Low (metamict) ZIRCON, willemite,
SPESSARTINE, gahnospinel, AL-
MANDINE, MALACHITE

3.96 CORUNDUM (yellow), low ZIRCON,
willemite, SPESSARTINE, gahnospinel, ALMANDINE

3.97 CORUNDUM (yellow, Burma ruby,

purple, pink, blue), celestite, low ZIRCON, willemite, SPESSARTINE, gahnospinel, ALMANDINE

3.98 SYNTH. CORUNDUM, CORUNDUM (yellow, Burma ruby, purple, pink, blue), celestite, low ZIRCON, willemite, SPESSARTINE, gahnospinel, ALMANDINE

3.99 SYNTH. CORUNDUM, CORUNDUM (colorless, green, Siam ruby, Burma ruby, purple, pink, blue, yellow), celestite, low ZIRCON, willemite, SPESSARTINE, gahnospinel, ALMANDINE, legrandite

4.00 SYNTH. CORUNDUM, CORUNDUM (colorless, green, Siam ruby, Burma ruby, purple, pink, blue, yellow), low ZIRCON, willemite, SPESSARTINE, gahnospinel, ALMANDINE, legrandite, goethite (MG), gadolinite

4.01 Painite, CORUNDUM (green, Siam ruby, Burma ruby, purple, pink, blue, yellow), low ZIRCON, willemite (G, U = 4.03), SPESSARTINE, gahnospinel, ALMANDINE, legrandite, goethite (MG), gadolinite

4.05 CORUNDUM (Siam ruby), low ZIRCON, willemite, SPESSARTINE, gahnospinel, ALMANDINE, calcium titanate, goethite (MG), gadolinite

4.06 Low ZIRCON, willemite, SPESSARTINE, ALMANDINE, gahnospinel, goethite, gadolinite

4.08 Sphalerite (G, U = 4.09), low ZIRCON, willemite, SPESSARTINE, ALMANDINE, goethite (MG), gadolinite

4.10 Intermediate ZIRCON, low ZIRCON, sphalerite, brookite, willemite, SPESSARTINE, ALMANDINE, goethite (MG), gadolinite

4.18 Brookite, intermediate ZIRCON, willemite, SPESSARTINE (G, U = 4.16), ALMANDINE, goethite (MG), gadolinite

4.20 Brookite, intermed. ZIRCON, SPESSARTINE, ALMANDINE (G, U), chalcopyrite, goethite (MG), gadolinite

4.21 Rutile, intermed. ZIRCON, samarskite, goethite (MG), gadolinite

4.25 Rutile, SYNTH. RUTILE (G, U), intermed. ZIRCON, goethite (MG), gadolinite

4.27 Witherite (MG), intermed. ZIRCON, gadolinite

4.29 Witherite (MG), intermed. ZIRCON, gadolinite

4.30 Smithsonite (MG), chromite, intermed. ZIRCON, gadolinite

4.35 Bayldonite (MG), smithsonite (MG, U), chromite, intermed. ZIRCON, gadolinite

4.40 Gahnite, smithsonite (MG), chromite, intermed. ZIRCON, gadolinite

4.45 Smithsonite (MG), chromite, intermed. ZIRCON, gadolinite

4.47 Barite, chromite, intermed. ZIRCON, gadolinite

4.50 Barite (G, U), chromite, intermed. ZIRCON, gadolinite

4.57 YTTRIUM ALUMINUM GARNET, chromite, intermed. ZIRCON

4.60 YTTRIUM ALUMINUM GARNET, chromite, intermed. ZIRCON, covellite

4.64 Lithium niobate, covellite

4.67 High ZIRCON (blue, colorless) (G, U), synth. zircon (4.68), covellite

4.70 High ZIRCON, euxenite, covellite

4.80 Euxenite, covellite

4.84 PYRITE, euxenite, yttrium oxide

4.85 Marcasite, PYRITE, euxenite

4.90 Marcasite, PYRITE (MG, U), bornite, synth. greenockite

4.95 HEMATITE, PYRITE, euxenite, bornite

5.00 HEMATITE, euxenite, bornite, pentlandite (MG, U = 5.05)

5.10 HEMATITE, pyrite, bornite

5.13 STRONTIUM TITANATE, HEMATITE, bornite

5.26 HEMATITE, bornite

5.40 Bornite, fergusonite (approx.)

5.56 Proustite

5.64 Zincite, proustite

5.66 Microlite (Amelia, Virginia), zincite

5.68 Zincite, synth. zincite

5.90 Barium titanate

5.96 Crocoite

6.00 Scheelite (G, U), crocoite, simpsonite (Brazil, approx.)

6.02 Scheelite, crocoite

6.06 Terbium aluminum garnet, scheelite

6.10 Scheelite, synth. scheelite, smaltite

6.11 Smaltite

6.12 Cuprite (G)

6.13 Phosgenite, cuprite (G) to 6.16

6.20 Dysprosium aluminum garnet

6.30 Holmium aluminum garnet

6.33 Cobaltite

6.39 Anglesite

6.43 Erbium aluminum garnet, niobium-doped potassium tantalate
6.48 Thulium aluminum garnet
6.50 Wulfenite
6.55 Wulfenite, cerussite
6.62 Ytterbium aluminum garnet, wulfenite
6.69 Lutecium aluminum garnet, wulfenite
6.80 Cassiterite, wulfenite
6.99 Cassiterite (G, U = 6.9), wulfenite
7.00 Wulfenite, cassiterite, mimetite
7.20 Domeykite, mimetite to 7.25
7.33 Niccolite, domeykite
7.35 Stibiotantalite to 7.46, niccolite, domeykite
7.54 Breithauptite, niccolite to 7.67, domeykite
7.70 Domeykite
7.90 Domeykite, stainless steel
8.00 Algodonite
8.04 Nickel-iron meteorite, algodonite
8.09 Cinnabar, nickel-iron, algodonite
8.39 Algodonite
10.31 Sterling silver, 10.50 pure silver
11.4 Gold (9k), 14.0 (15k), 15.4 (18k), 17.1 (22k), 19.32 (fine)
11.4 Palladium
12.3 Ruthenium
12.44 Rhodium
21.5 Platinum
22.41 Iridium
22.05 Osmium

Sources: R. Webster, *The Gemmologists' Compendium* 3d ed. rev. (London, 1964).

R. Webster, *Gems, Their Sources, Descriptions and Identification,* 2d ed. (London, 1970)

B. W. Anderson, *Gem Testing,* 7th ed. (London, 1964).

J. Sinkankas, *Gem Cutting,* 2d ed. (Princeton, N.J., 1962).

G. Vargas and M. Vargas, *Faceting for Amateurs* (Palm Desert, Calif., 1969).

Journal of Gemmology (London).

Gems and Gemology (Los Angeles, Calif.).

HARDNESS OF MINERALS AND GEMSTONES

Hardness is defined as that property which enables substances to scratch or abrade each other. In metallurgy it has been extended to include the ability of standard hard points to penetrate metals under test. In any case, hardness is a measure of the resistance of any substance to deformation under localized stress. Accurate measurements of hardness are difficult to obtain, especially in minerals where resistance to stress can and does vary remarkably according to crystallographic direction. As a test toward the identification of minerals it provides rough discrimination but is almost useless where hardnesses of a number of possible choices among minerals are nearly the same.

MOHS HARDNESS. A measure of *relative* hardness of minerals as determined by the ability of one species to scratch another.

MOHS HARDNESS SCALE

1. Talc (softest)
2. Gypsum
3. Calcite
4. Fluorite
5. Apatite
6. Feldspar
7. Quartz
8. Topaz
9. Corundum
10. Diamond (hardest)

Expanded Mohs Hardness Scale

1. *Talc:* Easily scratched by fingernail.
2. *Gypsum:* Scratched with pressure by fingernail; does not scratch copper coin.
2-1/2. *Fingernail:* Approximate hardness.
3. *Calcite:* Scratches and is scratched by copper; not scratched by fingernail.
3. *Copper:* About as hard as calcite; does not scratch fluorite.
4. *Fluorite:* Scratches copper; does not scratch apatite or glass.
5. *Apatite:* Scratches and is scratched by common glass.
5. *Glass:* About as hard as fluorite.
6. *Feldspar:* Scratches glass; scratched with difficulty by steel knife blade tip.
5-1/2-6. *Steel Knife Blade:* Just scratches feldspar; does not scratch quartz.
7. *Quartz:* Scratched with difficulty by file; easily scratches common glass.
7. *File:* Scratches quartz with difficulty.
8. *Topaz:* Scratches quartz.
9. *Corundum:* Scratches topaz, scratches quartz readily; scratches silicon carbide and is scratched by same.

9-1/2. *Silicon Carbide:* Black type barely scratches corundum.

10. *Diamond:* Not scratched by any other substance. See Tables B and C.

Source: H. Winchell, *Amer. Mineral.* 30 (1945): 583-95.

Hardness references: F. Auerbach, *Ann. d. Phys. u. Chem.* 43 (1891): 61-100.

P. Grodzinski, *Diamond Technology* (London, 1953), pp. 16-23.

T. A. Jaggar, *Amer. J. Sci.,* 4th ser., 4 (1897): 399-412.

T. A. Jaggar, *5th Special Report, Hawaiian Volcano Observatory* (1950), 43 pp.

P. Knoop et al., U. S. National Bureau of Standards Research Paper RP 1220 (1939).

C. G. Peters et al., *Metals and Alloys* 13 (1940): 292.

F. Pfaff, *Sitzungsber. Akad. d. Wiss.* (Munich, 1884), pp. 255-66.

H. Winchell, *American Mineral.* 30 (1945): 583-95.

MISCELLANEOUS HARDNESSES

BRINELL HARDNESS. An indentation hardness used mainly for testing metals by impressing a hardened ball into a selected surface of the test specimen. The "Brinell number" is calculated by the formula below:

$$\text{Brinell no. } (B_r) = \frac{P}{PiD/2} \times$$

$$(D - \sqrt{D^2 - d^2}$$

where P = load in kilograms, D = diameter of ball in mm, and d = diameter of depression made by the ball in mm.

ROCKWELL HARDNESS. An indentation hardness determined from the depth of penetration of a specially shaped standard hardness point into the material being tested. Test machines provide automatic readouts of values.

VICKERS HARDNESS. Similar to Brinell but uses an angular point of hard material instead of a ball. The formula is:

$$\text{Vickers (V)} = \frac{P}{0.5393d^2}$$

where P = load in kg, and d = length of the diagonal made by the angular point in mm.

SCLEROSCOPE (Shore). This device uses a small weight falling from a fixed

Table B.

COMPARISON OF VARIOUS MINERAL HARDNESS SCALES

Mineral	Mohs (S) (1820)	Franz (M) (1850)	Pfaff (M) (1874)	Pfaff (1884)	Auerbach (I) (1891-96)	Rosival (A) (1892)	Jaggar (A) (1897)	Knoop (I) (1939)	Peters (I) (1940)	Winchell (I) (1945)
Talc	1	—	—	—	—	—	—	—	—	—
Gypsum	2	—	14	12.03	12	0.3	0.04	32	32	46-54
Calcite	3	13.5	23	15.3	80	5.6	0.26	135	135	75-120
Fluorite	4	54	56	37.3	96	6.4	0.75	163	—	139-152
Apatite	5	235	141	53.5	197	8.0	1.23	360-493	—	—
Feldspar	6	392	310	191	210	59	25	490-560	—	—
Quartz	7	667	390	254	268	175	40	710-790	710-790	666-902
Topaz	8	843	705	459	456	194	152	1,250	—	1,040
Corundum	9	1,000	1,000	1,000	1,000	1,000	1,000	—	—	1,700-2,200
Diamond	10	—	—	—	2,170	140,000 (in 1916, 90,000)	>1,000	8,000-8,500	8,000-8,500	—

A = abrasion, I = indentation, M = machining, S = scratch.

Table C.

RECENT KNOOP HARDNESSES

Material	Knoop indentation hardness
Argentite	25
Gypsum	50; range 46-54
Galena	70
Calcite	100; range 75-120 (cleavage)
Fluorite	150
Sphalerite	177
Kyanite	200-1,700
Glass, slide	480
Magnetite	620-760
Quartz	660-900
Topaz (cleavage)	980-1,230
Spinel (synthetic)	1,110-1,230
Corundum (synthetic)	2,000; range 1,700-2,240
Silicon carbide (green)	2,675-2,825
Silicon carbide (black)	2,850-3,010

Source: H. Winchell, *Amer. Mineral.* 30 (1945): 583-95.

height upon the specimen. The rebound height is taken as a measure of hardness.

MOHS HARDNESS OF MINERALS

H	Species
1	Anthoinite, gamma sulfur, glauco-cerinite, griffithite, hoernesite, lawrenceite, lengenbachite, molysite, ozocerite, paralaurionite, pickeringite, plumbojarosite, sassolite, scacchite, sillenite, strigovite, tamarugite, todorokite, ulexite
1-1½	Embolite, epistolite, kermesite, melonite, molybdenite, nagyagite, natron, sternbergite, talc, thermonatrite, tyrolite
1-2	Albertite, aluminite, arseniosiderite, bischofite, brunsvigite, calomel, celadonite, collyrite, ferrimolybdite, graphite, guembelite, hydrobiotite, hydromuscovite, hydrophlogopite, iodoembolite, koenenite, molybdite, osteolite, prochlorite, teallite, vermiculite, wehrlite
1-2½	Nontronite
1-3	Garnierite, pyrophyllite
1½	Ammonia alum, andersonite, apjohnite, arsenolite, dimorphite, felsobanyite, iodoargyrite, isoclasite, jefferisite, lead, oruetite, rumpfite, stichtite, szmikite, teschemacherite
1½-2	Alunogen, bararite, barbertonite, covellite, gedanite, gypsum, hutchinsonite, maldonite, mirabilite, montroydite, orpiment, realgar, sal ammoniac, smithite, soda niter, sylvanite, tellurbismuth, tellurobismuthite, tetradymite, trechmannite, vivianite
1½-2½	Bieberite, erythrite, haidingerite, heliophyllite, hydroparagonite, luenebergite, mallardite, sulfur, tyuyamunite
2	Alaskaite, aphrosiderite, arsenolamprite, artinite, aurichalcite, beraunite, berzelianite, bilinite, bismuthinite, blakeite, boussingaultite, brugnatellite, cabrerite, cannizzarite, chalcophyllite, cyprusite, dietrichite, dundasite, emplectite, ferrinatrite, fizelyite, flagstaffite, gearksutite, gerhardtite, gilpinite, glauconite, gruenlingite, halotrichite, humboldtine, hydrotalcite, inyoite, joseite, kirovite, litharge, livingstonite, manasseite, melanterite, meyerhofferite, miersite, niter, parkerite, pisanite, portlandite, potash alum, pyrostilpnite, ramdohrite, rhomboclase,

schirmerite, selenium, stercorite, stibnite, struvite, sylvite, tachyhydrite, taylorite, tellurite, thomsenolite, tin, uranocircite, veatchite, zebadassite, zinc

2-2½ Acanthite, agalmatolite, aikinite, amber (succinite, etc.), anthracite, argentite, asbolane, autunite, bassettite, bismoclite, bismuth, bobierrite, boothite, borax, botryogen, brushite, chemawinite, cinnabar, clinochlore, coquimbite, daubreeite, daubreelite, epichlorite, epsomite, ettringite, fibroferrite, freieslebenite, goslarite, hydrozincite, johannite, kalinite, lanarkite, lecontite, lindackerite, liroconite, lorandite, mascagnite, mellite, metazeunerite, miargyrite, morenosite, nacrite, nantokite, nepouite, pennine, percylite, pharmacolite, proustite, pyrolusite, schwartzembergite, selen-tellurium, senarmontite, sepiolite, sideronatrite, stephanite, succinite, tellurium, torbernite, uintahlite, villiaumite, wapplerite, wittite, zeunerite

2-3 Alumian, auerlite, becquerelite, berthierite, beta sulfur, beyerite, carnotite, chiviatite, chlorites, chrysotile, darapskite, eglestonite, ferghanite, gaylussite, gladite, gonyerite, greenalite, hematophanite, hydroboracite, ianthinite, jamesonite, kaemmererite, lillianite, lubeckite, manandonite, massicot, melnikovite, minium, murmanite, pennantite, pitticite, platynite, polybasite, pyroaurite, radiophyllite, ripidolite, richellite, roesslerite, rossite, sahlinite, saleeite, schoepite, sharpite, spangolite, stilpnochlorane, terlinguaite, thenardite, trigonite, troegerite, uranophane, uranosphaerite, uranospinite, vashegyite, xanthoconite, xanthoxenite

2½ Aguilarite, alumohydrocalcite, amarantite, aramayoite, argyrodite, bandylite, bianchite, bloedite, bolivarite, bromargyrite, brucite, butlerite, calcioferrite, canfieldite, carnallite, chalcanthite, chalcoalumite, chalcophanite, chlorargyrite, chlormanganokalite, chlorothionite,

chloroxiphite, claudetite, clinoungemachite, codazzite, cookeite, copiapite, corundophilite, cotunnite, cryolite, cryptohalite, cumengeite, delafossite, delessite, delvauxite, devilline, diaboleite, donbassite, elpasolite, eriochalcite, eucairite, finnemanite, forbesite, fuloppite, galena, geocronite, gratonite, guildite, halite, hautfeuillite, hieratite, klaprothite, krausite, krennerite, kroehnkite, lansfordite, leadhillite, libollite, linarite, lizardite, lopezite, matildite, melanovanadite, meneghinite, metasideronatrite, metatorbernite, metavoltine, minnesotaite, mitridatite, mitscherlichite, muthmannite, nahcolite, naumannite, nesquehonite, onofrite, owhyeeite, oxammite, parabutlerite, paracoquimbite, paragonite, pascoite, pharmacosiderite, phosphoroesslerite, picromerite, plagionite, polyargyrite, pseudoboleite, pyrargyrite, pyrochroite, quenselite, quenstedtite, racewinite, ransomite, retgersite, roscoelite, samsonite, schroeckingerite, schultenite, semseyite, sengierite, spadaite, symplesite, syngenite, szomolnokite, tiemannite, trichalcite, trudellite, tungstenite, tungstite, ungemachite, whewellite

2½-3 Amarillite, amesite, anglesite, annabergite, biotite, boleite, boulangerite, bournonite, calaverite, caledonite, carminite, chalcocite, chalcomenite, chlorocalcite, chudobaite, clausthalite, clinoclase, coloradoite, connarite, copper, corvusite, cosalite, crocoite, crookesite, cryolithionite, cuprocopiapite, cylindrite, diaphorite, digenite, ecdemite, electrum, foshallasite, franckeite, glauberite, gold, gummite, hessite, heteromorphite, hopeite, iddingsite, kainite, kobellite, koettigite, langite, lanthanite, lavendulan, liebigite, magnesiocopiapite, margarosanite, marshite, matlockite, mendipite, muscovite, parsonite, penroseite, petzite, phlogopite, phosgenite, polyhalite, raspite, rezbanyite, siderophyllite, silver, stolzite, stromeyerite, taeniolite, trona,

	valentinite, vauquelinite, wulfenite, zincaluminite
2½-3½	Barite, gibbsite, guanajuatite, jarosite, loewite, soda alum
2½-4	Anthracite, lepidolite, lignite (jet), zinnwaldite, serpentine
3	Allophane, altaite, antlerite, arcanite, argentojarosite, arseno-bismite, astrophyllite, barysilite, baumhauerite, boehmite, bornite, buttgenbachite, cadmium oxide, cahnite, calcite, chamosite, connelite, cuprozincite, dawsonite, destinezite, diadochite, dolero-phane, dufrenoysite, duftite, enargite, englishite, ferruccite, fiedlerite, fluellite, foshagite, ganomalite, gillespite, guiterman-nite, hemafibrite, hohmannite, hulsite, hydrocalumite, inderite, jordanite, kamarezite, kernite, klockmannite, kurnakovite, lampro-phyllite, larsenite, leonite, leigh-tonite, lepidomelane, livingeite, lorettoite, loseyite, mackensite, melite, mendozite, metacinnabar, metavauxite, mooreite, mottramite, natrojarosite, niggliite, olivenite, pachnolite, paratacamite, paravaux-ite, pearceite, pilbarite, priceite, pseudolaueite, rathite, rinneite, riversideite, roeblingite, salesite, sartorite, seligmannite, shortite, spencerite, stewartite, stylotypite, sussexite, torreyite, umangite, vanadinite, viridite, weibullite, weissite, zaratite, zeophyllite, zippeite
3-3½	Amalgam, andorite, anhydrite, antimony, aphthitalite, atacamite, caryinite, celestite, cerussite, chlorophoenicite, churchite, collin-site, domeykite, empressite, gallite, gold amalgam, goldfieldite, greenockite, hanksite, hisingerite, kieserite, landesite, laurionite, lautite, lindstromite, luzonite, millerite, newberryite, phoenico-chroite, pirssonite, raimondite, reddingite, roemerite, spodiophyl-lite, teepleite, volborthite, wither-ite, zinkenite
3-4	Aerinite, antigorite, arseniopleite, ashcroftine, chalcostibite, colusite, dietzeite, dixenite, fourmarierite, galenobismutite, genthite, gyrolite,

	hammarite, hardystonite, hetero-genite, kalkowskite, kerstenite, langbeinite, laumontite, ludlamite, mixite, molybdophyllite, morden-ite, neotocite, parsettensite, phosphophyllite, pinnoite, prober-tite, soddyite, sphaerocobaltite, strengite, szaibelyite, tagilite, tenorite, truscottite, voltaite, warwickite, weinschenkite
3-4-3-	Atelestite, tennantite, tetrahedrite Adamite, akrochordite, allemontite, anapaite, arakawaite, arsenic, benjaminite, bermanite, borickite, burkeite, calciovolborthite, chalco-cyanite, cronstedtite, descloizite, dussertite, epigenite, fairfieldite, famatinite, fluoborite, gajite, georgiadesite, ginorite, gordonite, hematolite, hibbenite, howlite, hydrocerussite, hydromagnesite, inderborite, kempite, kleinite, leuchtenbergite, lime, mimetite, minyulite, monetite, moschellands-bergite, mosesite, penwithite, potarite, powellite, pyrobelonite, redondite, rhabdophane, rickardite, roselite, russellite, schafarzikite, schairerite, schapbachite, schulze-nite, searlesite, stilpnomelane, sulfohalite, sulvanite, thaumasite, tsumebeite, tychite, vauxite, vrbaite, walpurgite, weberite, wittichenite, zirklerite
3½-4	Alabandite, alunite, ankerite, aragonite, azurite, bastite, brochan-tite, chalcopyrite, chiolite, creedite, cubanite, cuprite, dickinsonite, dolomite, dufrenite, dyscrasite, euchroite, evansite, ferrierite, heulandite, kolbeckite, kutnahorite, laubmannite, lauterite, malachite, mansfieldite, metastrengite, nado-rite, northupite, overite, para-hopeite, pentlandite, poechite, pyromorphite, scorodite, siderite, sphalerite, stellerite, stilbite, strontianite, tarbuttite, veszelyite, wavellite, wurtzite
3½-4½	Beudantite, chenevixite, dufrenite, epistilbite, ferrisicklerite, magne-site, margarite, pyrrhotite, rhodo-chrosite, sampleite
3½-6	Clintonite
4	Aerugite, afwillite, algodonite, ampangabeite, andrewsite, arman-

gite, barytocalcite, bavalite, bellingerite, bindheimite, calcio-ancylite, corkite, coronadite, crandallite, crocidolite, ellsworth-ite, fluorite, germanite, hauerite, holdenite, johnstrupite, jurupaite, leucophane, libethenite, liskeardite, melanostibian, metavariscite, mont-gomeryite, morinite, mosandrite, nasonite, natroalunite, oldhamite, pholidolite, pucherite, renardite, retzian, riebeckite, salmonsite, sarcopside, seamanite, sicklerite, sphaerite, stannite, steenstrupine sulfoborite, troilite, vandenbrand-ite, vanthoffite, variscite, walther-ite, weddellite, xanthiosite, yeatmanite

4-
4½   Alstonite, austinite, bastnaesite, bismutite, carphosiderite, clarkeite, colemanite, dachiardite, edington-ite, ferberite, flinkite, ganophyllite, jarlite, lacroixite, levynite, phillip-site, platinum purpurite, roosevelt-ite, thorogummite, voltzite, wellsite, zincite

4-5   Apatite, berthonite, berzeliite, chabazite, cooperite, curite, fluocerite, friedelite, horsfordite, iron, kasolite, lithiophilite, manganite, paraurichalcite, phos-phoferrite, plumbogummite, pyros-malite, rosasite, samiresite, sarkinite, stibiconite, stibiopalladin-ite, triphylite, xenotime, yttrocerite

4-
5½   Limonite, triplite

4-6   Seybertite
4-7   Kyanite, pyroxenes
4½   Alamosite, allactite, alloclase, ancylite, bakerite, barrandite, bayldonite, bismite, brannerite, bultfonteinite, caracolite, cesaro-lite, chalcosiderite, conichalcite, cordylite, cornwallite, crednerite, cuprotungstite, davisonite, didy-molite, erinite, eulytine, fillowite, francolite, frondelite, gismondine, gmelinite, hagendorfite, harmo-tome, hedyphane, hinsdalite, kaliborite, kishtymite, lessingite, lindgrenite, mackayite, natrochal-cite, paramelaconite, parasite, polydymite, prosopite, ralstonite, renierite, rockbridgeite, roscherite, stottite, synadelphite, synchisite,

tornebohmite, valleite, villamanite, woodhouseite, yttrofluorite

4½-
5   Apophyllite, augelite, childrenite, corynite, erinite, gonnardite, hemimorphite, hodgkinsonite, man-ganberzeliite, natrophilite, okenite, orientite, palladium, parawolla-stonite, pectolite, pseudomalachite, safflorite, scawtite, schallerite, scheelite, smithsonite, thorite, triploidite, tripuhyite, wolfachite, wolfeite, wollastonite

4½-
5½   Ellestadite, emmonsite, legrandite, roweite

4-6   Hydronephelite, xanthophyllite
5   Adelite, akermanite, arandisite, arrojadite, attacolite, awaruite, beckelite, betafite, brewsterite, carbonate apatite, cebollite, chlorapatite, coeruleolactite, dahl-lite, dehrnite, derbylite, dioptase, durangite, eosphorite, faujasite, fermorite, florenceite, glaucodot, goyazite, graftonite, hainite, hatchettolite, hauchecornite, hea-zlewoodite, herderite, hilgardite, homilite, huhnerkobelite, hureau-lite, hydroxy-apatite, kataphorite, kentrolite, lepidocrocite, loranskite, ludwigite, maghemite, magnesio-kataphorite, maucherite, mesolite, nickel iron, obsidian, paigeite, parahilgardite, pararammelsbergite, plumboferrite, pseudowollastonite, pyrophanite, rinkite, sanbornite, sellaite, siegenite, spodiosite, spurrite, sterrettite, svabite, svanbergite, tilasite, torendrikite, trevorite, turanite, turquoise, varulite, violarite, wardite, whit-lockite, wilkeite

5-
5-1/2   Alluaudite, analcime, bismutotanta-lite, brandtite, carpholite, cobalt-nickel-pyrite, cornetite, cyrtolite, datolite, goethite, hausmannite, hiortdahlite, huebnerite, hyalote-kite, hydroxyl-herderite, kainosite, lazurite, loellingite, mangan-alluau-dite, melinophane, monazite, monticellite, natrolite, niccolite, plattnerite, pyrochlore, schizolite, scolecite, stibiotantalite, thomson-ite, titanite, ullmannite, wagnerite, wolframite, yttrialite, yttrotanta-lite, zwieselite

5-6   Actinolite, aeschynite, andesine,

arsenoclasite, augite, basaltic hornblende, cacoxenite, cancrinite, caryocerite, cirrolite, cobaltite, crossite, cuspidine, diopside, dysanalyte, edenite, ekermannite, eudialyte, eulite, ferroactinolite, ferroedenite, ferrohastingsite, ferrohypersthene, grunerite, hedenbergite, hetaerolite, holmquistite, hydrohetaerolite, hypersthene, ilmenite, ishikawaite, kaersutite, knopite, labradorite, lazulite, lithidionite, manganosite, melanocerite, melilite, mizzonite, monimolite, neptunite, omphacite, orthoferrosilite, polycrase, priorite, psilomelane, richterite, rosenbuschite, samarskite, scapolite, tanteuxenite, tremolite, urbanite, vishnevite, wernerite

5-6 Amphiboles, hematite, magnesiumorthite

5-7 Ephesite, olivine

5½ Aenigmatite, alleghanyite, alvite, arizonite, barkevikite, bavenite, bityite, blomstrandine, brazilianite, breithauptite, britholite, bronzite, bunsenite, carrollite, catoptrite, cenosite, cerite, chalcolamprite, chevkinite, chlorastrolite, chromite, clinohedrite, crichtonite, dannemorite, davyne, djalmaite, enigmatite, enstatite, epididymite, eschynite, fersmanite, gersdorffite, griphite, harstigite, hellandite, hillebrandite, hornblende, imerinite, joaquinite, koppite, lehiite, lewisite, lewistonite, linnaeite, magnesiochromite, microlite, millisite, nagatelite, nosean, pargasite, perovskite, plancheite, pumpellyite, rhoenite, rutherfordine, scheteligite, stibiocolumbite, taramellite, tritomite, trolleite, uhligite, uraninite, willemite, willyamite, zirkelite

5½-6 Allanite, anatase, anthophyllite, arfvedsonite, arsenopyrite, atopite, babingtonite, beryllonite, bravoite, brookite, chloanthite, cohenite, danalite, delorenzite, erikite, fergusonite, gedrite, gehlenite, guarinite, hauyne, heterosite, ilvaite, leucite, leucophoenicite, marialite, meionite, milarite, montebrasite, natromontebrasite,

nepheline, nickel-skutterudite, nordenskioldine, periclase, pisekite, pyroxmangite, rammelsbergite, roepperite, scorzalite, smaltite, sodalite, souzalite, stokesite, tephroite, titanaugite, wairikite, woehlerite, yttrocrasite

5½-6½ Bustamite, diallage, ferrosalite, formanite, franklinite, magnetite, opal, rhodonite, romeite, salite

6 Acmite, analbite, adularia, aegerine-augite, amblygonite, annerodite, banalsite, berlinite, bytownite, catapleiite, clinoenstatite, clinoferrosilite, clinohypersthene, cobalt pyrite, columbite, cummingtonite, dipyre, eichbergite, eudidymite, fassaite, fowlerite, geikielite, glaucochroite, gorceixite, gudmundite, hastingsite, hibschite, hollandite, inesite, jacobsite, johannsenite, kaliophilite, kalsilite, lavenite, lawsonite, leifite, lorenzenite, magnetoplumbite, merwinite, microsommite, paracelsian, picotite, pigeonite, pinakiolite, pistacite, pseudobrookite, ramsayite, sanidine, sarcolite, senaite, skutterudite, struverite, tantalite, tapiolite, thoreaulite, thulite

6-6½ Aegerine, albite, anorthite, anorthoclase, benitoite, bixbyite, braunite, cappelenite, celsian, chondrodite, clinohumite, ekanite, glaucophane, helvite, humite, hyalophane, ixiolite, magnesioferrite, manganotantalite, marcasite, microcline, mossite, nephrite, orthoclase, petalite, plagioclases, prehnite, pyrite, rutile, zoisite

6-7 Ardennite, bertrandite, cassiterite, chalcedony, cristobalite, epidote, forsterite, hancockite, iridosmine, jadeite, lechatelierite, mullite, oligoclase, ottrelite, platiniridium, siserskite, sperrylite, spodumene, tantalum, thortveitite, trimerite, ussingite

6-7½ Hydrogrossular, sillimanite

6½ Baddeleyite, bazzite, chloritoid, clinozoisite, eremeyevite, euxenite, fayalite, fuggerite, genthelvite, hoegbomite, hortonolite, idocrase, keilhauite, knebelite, kornerupine, kotoite, langbanite, leucosphenite,

	lyndochite, malacon, maskelynite, melanotekite, norbergite, piemontite, pollucite, polymignite, schneebergite, schreibersite, sinhalite, thalenite, thorianite, toddite, weslienite, xonotlite
6½-7	Andradite, axinite, chrysolite, diaspore, ferrohortonolite, gadolinite, grossular, hyalosiderite, melanophlogite, partschinite, serendibite, tinzenite
6½-7½	Uvarovite
7	Aurosmiridium, barylite, boracite, danburite, dravite, dumortierite, elbaite, elpidite, quartz, schorl, sjogrenite, tridymite, uvite, zunyite
7-7½	Almandine, cordierite, narsarsukite, pyrope, rhodolite, schorlomite, spessartine, staurolite, tourmaline
7½	Andalusite, chromohercynite, coesite, euclase, grandidierite, hambergite, laurite, manganspinel, naegite, painite, sapphirine, zircon
7½-8	Beryl, ceylonite, gahnite, hercynite, phenakite, simpsonite
8	Chrompicotite, galaxite, spinel, topaz, rhodizite, swedenborgite, taaffeite
8½	Chrysoberyl
9	Bromellite, corundum, moissanite
10	Diamond

HARDNESS OF MINERALS VERSUS CHEMICAL-CRYSTAL GROUP

Native elements: Metallics mostly soft. *Exceptions:* Some platinum group metals and iron. Nonmetallics soft. Outstanding exception is diamond (H-10).

Sulfides, sulfosalts: Soft but pyrite (H-6+) and others are exceptions.

Oxides, Hydroxides: Generally hard, with hydroxides tending to be softer; striking exceptions are noted.

Halides: Generally soft and brittle.

Carbonates, sulfates: Soft and brittle.

Nitrates: Soft and brittle.

Iodates: Soft.

Borates: Hydrous borates soft, anhydrous borates tend to be hard.

Phosphates, arsenates, vanadates: Generally soft, with some phosphates being appreciably harder.

Silicates: Generally hard to very hard.

HARDNESSES OF GEMSTONES

Entries under Sinkankas and Vargas are abrasive (gem cutting) values with ranges, where expressed, derived from noted differences in hardness according to crystallographic direction in the case of single crystals, or due to peculiarities of structure or aggregation, or inclusions in the case of massive materials. Primary entries represent scratch values accumulated over many years of experience by the authorities indicated as well as others.

Mohs	Anderson (1971), Webster (1970), and Others	Sinkankas (1962)	Vargas (1969)
1	Talc (pure), ulexite		
1½-2	Soapstone, pyrophyllite gedanite	Covellite	Vivianite, realgar
1½-2½			Sulfur
2		Ulexite	
2-2½	Gypsum, meerschaum, amber	Amber, proustite	Amber, cinnabar, proustite
2-3	Plastics, bone		Phosgenite
2-4	Chrysocolla		
2½	Whewellite, vegetable ivory, tortoiseshell, stichtite, pseudophite, proustite, ivory, albertite, amber		Inderite, kurnakovite

Mohs	Anderson (1971), Webster (1970), and Others	Sinkankas (1962)	Vargas (1969)
2½–3	Crocoite, wulfenite	Anglesite, cinnabar, crocoite, wulfenite	Anglesite, crocoite, wulfenite
2½–3½	Nacre, pearl		Barite
2½–4	Anthracite, jet, serpentine		Serpentine
3	Anglesite, anhydrite, barite, bornite, phosgenite, verdite	Barite, bornite, calcite, cerussite, verdite	Calcite, celestite
3–3½	Argillite	Celestite, domeykite witherite	Anhydrite, celestite, cerussite
3–4			Witherite
3–4½			Phosphophyllite
3½	Celestite, cerussite, coral, howlite, lepidolite, millerite, mimetite, pearl, phosphophyllite, witherite	Howlite, thaumasite	Ludlamite, cerussite
3-1/2–4	Algodonite, azurite, bastite, chalcopyrite, cobaltite, domeykite, magnesite, marble, pentlandite, siderite, sphalerite	Anhydrite, azurite, malachite, shattuckite, sphalerite	Aragonite, azurite, cuprite, dolomite, siderite, sphalerite
3½–4½		Rhodochrosite	Magnesite, rhodochrosite
3½–5½		Chiastolite	
4	Cuprite, fluorite, malachite, rhodochrosite, scorodite	Algodonite, aragonite, fluorite	Fluorite
4–4½	Zincite	Apatite, serpentine	Colemanite, zincite
4–5	Serpentine (bowenite)		Friedelite
4–7	Friedelite, kyanite		Kyanite
4½	Pseudomalachite, bayldonite, colemanite	Apophyllite, variscite	Hodgkinsonite
4½–5	Apophyllite, breithauptite, datolite (massive), scheelite, wollastonite	Wollastonite	Apophyllite, scheelite
4½–5½		Hodgkinsonite, magnesite	
5	Apatite, augelite, beryllonite, datolite, diopside, dioptase, durangite, herderite, legrandite, mesolite, obsidian, odontolite, pectolite, scheelite, smith-	Analcime, benitoite, cancrinite, colemanite, mesolite, natrolite, obsidian, phosphophyllite,	Apatite, dioptase, augelite, lazulite, legrandite

Mohs	Anderson (1971), Webster (1970), and Others	Sinkankas (1962)	Vargas (1969)
	sonite, variscite, wardite	smithsonite, zincite	
5–5½	Analcime, datolite, niccolite, thomsonite	Augelite, datolite, goethite (massive), scheelite, sphene	Analcime, datolite, natrolite, sphene
5–6	Chlorastrolite, glass, hypersthene, samarskite	Chlorastrolite, opal, tremolite, turquoise	Actinolite, diopside, obsidian, scapolite, tremolite
5–6½			Opal
5–7	Kyanite	Diopside	Feldspars
5–7½		Kyanite	
5½	Brazilianite, chromite, cobaltite, diopside, enstatite, idocrase (Calif.), lazulite, lazurite (lapis), microlite, moldavite, natrolite, smaltite, sphene, willemite	Amblygonite, breithauptite, lapis lazuli, stibiotantalite, tektites, willemite	Brazilianite, enstatite, microlite, obsidian, smithsonite, stibiotantalite, tektite
5½–6	Anatase, brookite, leucite, melinophane, sodalite, stibiotantalite, tremolite, turquoise	Anthophyllite, beryllonite, chondrodite, sodalite	Beryllonite, leucite, pyroxmangite, sodalite
5½–6½	Hauyne, opal, psilomelane	Rhodonite	Hematite, rhodonite
6	Amblygonite, cancrinite, columbite, hematite, lithium niobate, opal, orthoclase, periclase, prehnite, rhodonite, scapolite, pyrite, silica glass, strontium titanate, turquoise, zoisite	Actinolite, cassiterite (massive), clinozoisite, dioptase, enstatite, feldspars, leucite, microlite, sodalite, strontium titanate	Amblygonite, orthoclase, anatase
6–6½	Ekanite, marcasite, microcline, petalite, plagioclase, pyrite, rutile	Nephrite, peridot, prehnite, pyrite, zoisite	Benitoite, chondrodite, opal, petalite, prehnite, pyrite, rutile
6–7		Epidote, scapolite	Cassiterite, epidote, fibrolite, spodumene
6–7½		Axinite	

Mohs	Anderson (1971), Webster (1970), and Others	Sinkankas (1962)	Vargas (1969)
6½	Benitoite, cassiterite, chalcedony, chondrodite, demantoid, epidote, euxenite, hematite, idocrase, kornerupine, nephrite, peridot, pollucite, sinhalite, zircon (low), zoisite	Brazilianite, idocrase, jadeite	Idocrase, jadeite, kornerupine, pollucite, sinhalite
6½–7		Gadolinite, rutile	Axinite, peridot, spodumene
6½–7½		Euclase, garnets, hambergite, kornerupine	Zircon, garnet
6½–8		Spodumene	
7	Axinite, boracite, chalcedony, danburite, dumortierite, jadeite, quartz, spodumene, grossular, spessartine, iolite, tourmaline	Beryl, boracite, cassiterite, iolite, pollucite, quartz, sinhalite, tourmaline	Quartz, danburite
7–7½	Iolite, staurolite, tourmaline, zircon	Petalite, chalcedony	Andalusite, boracite, iolite, tourmaline
7¼	Hessonite, pyrope, rhodolite, spessartine		
7½	Almandite, andalusite, beryl, euclase, fibrolite, hambergite, painite, phenakite, uvarovite, zircon (high)	Fibrolite, periclase, spinel, topaz	Euclase, hambergite, zircon
7½–8	Gahnite, phenakite	Phenakite, simpsonite, zircon	Beryl, phenakite
8	Rhodizite, spinel, taaffeite, topaz		Topaz, rhodizite, spinel
8½	Chrysoberyl	Chrysoberyl	Chrysoberyl
9	Corundum	Corundum	Corundum
9½	Boron carbide	Silicon carbide	Silicon carbide
10	Diamond, borazon		Diamond

References: B. W. Anderson, *Gem Testing,* 8th ed. (London: Butterworth's, 1971).
J. Sinkankas, *Gem Cutting,* 2d ed., (New York: Van Nostrand Reinhold, 1962).
G. Vargas and M. Vargas, *Faceting for Amateurs,* (Thermal, Calif.: privately pub., 1969).
R. Webster, *Gems,* 2d ed. (London: Butterworth's, 1970).

MOHS HARDNESSES OF METALS, WOODS, AND MISCELLANEOUS SUBSTANCES

Substance	H. Mohs	Substance	H. Mohs
Anthracite	2.2	Osmium	7.0
Antimony	3.0-3.3	Palladium	4.8
Arsenic	3.5	Phosphor bronze	4
Asphalt	1-2	Phosphorus	0.5
Bell metal	4	Plastics	1.5-3
Bismuth	2.5	Platiniridium	6.5
Boron	9.5	Platinum	4.3
Brass	3-4	Potassium	0.5
Cadmium	2.0	Redwood	2
Calcium	1.5	Ross's metal	2.5-3.0
Cesium	0.2	Rubidium	0.3
Chromium	9.0	Ruthenium	6.5
Copper	2.5-3	Selenium	2.0
Emery	7-9	Silicon	7.0
Fingernail	2+	Silver	2.5
Gallium	1.5	Sodium	0.4
Gold	2.5-3	Steel	5-8.5
Indium	1.2	Steel file	6-7
Iridium	6-6.5	Steel, hi-speed tool	6.5
Iridosmium	7	Steel, machine	4
Iron	4-5	Steel, spring	5+
Iron, cast	6	Strontium	1.8
Lead	1.5	Tellurium	2.3
Lignum vitae	4+	Tin	1.5-1.8
Lithium	0.6	Tooth enamel	5
Magnesium	2.0	Wax	0.2
Manganese	5.0	Woods metal	3
Masonite, pressed wood	4+	Zinc	2.5

CLEAVAGE CHARACTERISTICS IN THE MINERAL SYSTEMS

Cleavages are the flat fractures in crystals that are guided by atomic structures and hence bear fixed geometrical relationships to such structures. When present, they provide valuable clues to identity. They are classified by (1) number of directions, (2) angular relationships to the axes and to each other, and (3) nature and quality of surface.

Cleavage planes may occur in sets analogous to the sets of natural faces called "forms." Like the latter, a larger number of like surfaces appear in crystals of higher symmetry and lesser numbers in crystals of lower symmetry. The same terminology is used as for face forms, e.g., "octahedral" for a cleavage that creates an eight-sided object of the same geometrical properties as the naturally-grown octahedron of the isometric system, "cube," "prism," "pinacoid," etc.

Several different cleavages may occur within the same crystal as is notably the case in the feldspars, but since each cleavage exposes a different atomic structure each is not developed with the same ease nor displays the same quality and markings on its surfaces. Examination must therefore carefully assess cleavage surface characters to determine if they belong to the same cleavage or to two or more different cleavages.

Possible Cleavage Sets: Isometric System

CUBIC. When fully developed, forms cubes; angles between surfaces 90°; all surfaces display like markings, luster, etc. Examples: *galena, halite.*

OCTAHEDRAL. Full development creates octahedrons, notably in *fluorite* which is commercially cleaved to produce interesting cleavage octahedrons. Angles between surfaces 109-1/2°. All surfaces are of like character.

DODECAHEDRAL. Full development creates rhombic dodecahedrons, comprised of twelve lozenge-shaped surfaces with angles of 120° between surfaces and angles of 70-1/2° and 109-1/2° within the corners of the surfaces. A rare cleavage. Example: *sphalerite*.

Tetragonal System

PRISMATIC. Four cleavage surfaces intersecting at 90° to each other and paralleling the principal or *c*-axis; there may be more than one set present in the same crystal, e.g., *scapolite*, in which the second set surfaces intersect the first at angles of 135°. If *both* sets are fully developed, an eight-sided prism would be formed. The surfaces within each of the sets are of the same character but different in character from the surface of the other set.

PINACOIDAL. (also called BASAL PINACOIDAL). Occurs at right angles to the principal or *c*-axis, hence at right angles to any prismatic cleavage surface also. When developed, cleaves the crystal into a number of thin to thick tabular segments. Common and often conspicuous, e.g., *apophyllite*.

PYRAMIDAL. Surfaces parallel to the faces of a square pyramid or dipyramid; when fully developed there can be four or eight such surfaces. Rare and usually poor in quality.

Hexagonal System

PRISMATIC. Cleavage surfaces parallel to the faces of the hexagonal prism, or the second order hexagonal prism; ideally developed forms six-sided prismatic objects but very rarely are the cleavages capable of providing such. Surfaces parallel to the principal or *c*-axis; angles between surfaces 120°. If second order prismatic cleavage is present, the angle between surfaces becomes 150°; example: *cancrinite*.

PINACOIDAL (also called BASAL PINACOIDAL). Occurs at right angles to the principal or *c*-axis, hence at right angles to any prismatic cleavage surface also. When developed, cleaves the crystal into a number of thin to thick tabular segments. The markings on the surfaces may intersect at angles of 120° or 60°. Examples: *graphite, molybdenite*.

PYRAMIDAL. Surfaces parallel to the faces of the hexagonal pyramid or dipyramid; rare and usually poor in quality.

RHOMBOHEDRAL. Three cleavage planes intersecting to form low three-surfaced pyramids; when fully developed, the three surfaces on one end of the crystal are matched by three below, yielding a six-surfaced cleavage fragment (rhombohedron). The conspicuous cleavage of *calcite* and other *rhombohedral carbonates;* also well-developed in *dioptase*. Commonly perfect and easily developed.

Orthorhombic System

PRISMATIC. Four cleavage surfaces meeting at various angles, not 90°, according to the species. Forms sections of lozenge-shaped cross section, e.g., *adamite*.

PINACOIDAL. Occurs at right angles to one of the axes; several may appear at once. In general, tabular crystals are likely to display this cleavage parallel to the broadest crystal faces. May be combined with prismatic cleavage, furnishing cleavage fragments of lozenge-shaped cross section (prismatic cleavage) terminated by two parallel pinacoidal cleavages at right angles, e.g., *barite*.

PYRAMIDAL. When fully developed, provides pyramids or dipyramids bounded by triangular (not equilateral!) surfaces. Very rarely observed.

Monoclinic System

PRISMATIC. Similar to the prismatic cleavages of orthorhombic.

PINACOIDAL. Similar to orthorhombic but the inclination of one of the axes in this system causes similar inclination of some cleavage surface pairs.

PYRAMIDAL. There are no cleavages of this type in this system.

Triclinic System

PINACOIDAL. Only pinacoidal cleavages occur; thus like cleavage surfaces can only be observed in pairs. None intersect at right angles although *microcline* and *rhodonite* are confusingly close to 90° intersections.

CLEAVAGES OF MINERALS ARRANGED BY SYSTEM AND TYPE

Cleavage Surface Quality

Abbreviations:
VP = Very perfect, eminent, extremely flat, shining and usually easily developed

PF = Perfect, close to the above in quality and ease of production

GD = Good, relatively flat overall but may be interrupted by slight steps, ripples, and other markings

FR = Fair, noticeably flat but smooth only in small areas

PR = Poor, generally flat with poor surface quality

TR = Cleavage occurs in traces only; merges into fracture

? = Insufficient information

ISOMETRIC CLEAVAGES

Cubic

Alabandite—PF
Altaite—PF
Analcime—TR
Argentite—PR
Beckelite—?
Bravoite—FR
Chloanthite—FR
Clausthalite—GD
Cobaltite—PF
Cuprite—FR
Galena—VP
Gersdorffite—PF
Halite—PF
Hauerite—PF
Hessite—PR
Iron—?
Linnaeite—GD
Maldonite—FR
Manganosite—FR
Moschellandsbergite—FR
Naumannite—PF
Oldhamite—PR
Penroseite—PF
Periclase—PF
Perovskite—GD
Petzite—PR
Pharmacosiderite—GD

Platiniridium—FR
Polydymite—GD
Pyrite—TR
Skutterudite—TR
Sperrylite—TR
Sulvanite—PF
Sylvite—PF
Thorianite—PR
Uhligite—?
Ullmannite—PF
Villiaumite—PF

Octahedral

Arsenolite—?
Bixbyite—TR
Bornite—TR
Chloanthite—FR
Cryptohalite—PF
Cuprite—TR
Diamond—PF
Digenite—PR
Faujasite—FR
Fluorite—PF
Helvite—TR
Hieratite—PF
Laurite—PF
Monimolite—PR
Mosesite—GD

Periclase—GD
Pyrite—TR
Pyrochlore—FR
Ralstonite—GD
Rhodizite—PR
Roemite—PR
Salammoniac—GD
Senarmontite—TR
Skutterudite—FR
Zunyite—PR

Dodecahedral

Argentite—PR
Chlacopyrite—TR
Chloanthite—TR
Cryolithionite—FR
Garnet—TR
Hauyne—PR
Lazurite—PR
Leucite—TR
Marshite—PF
Miersite—PF
Moschellandsbergite—FR
Nantokite—?
Penroseite—GD
Skutterudite—TR
Sodalite—GD
Sphalerite—PF

TETRAGONAL CLEAVAGES

Prismatic

Anatase—PF
Apophyllite—PR
Ashcroftine—PF

Autunite—PR
Boleite—GD
Cahnite—PF
Calomel—GD
Cassiterite—FR

Chiolite—GD
Cumengeite—2 GD
Edingtonite—PF
Gillespite—?
Hardystonite—?

Hausmannite–2 PR
Idocrase–PR, TR
Litharge–PF
Melilite–PR
Metazeunerite–FR
Narsarsukite–GD
Phosgenite–FR, PR
Pseudoboleite–GD
Pyrolusite–TR
Rutile–FR, PR
Saleeite–2 PR
Scapolite–GD, PR
Scheelite–FR
Schreibersite–2 GD
Sellaite–2 PF
Stannite–PR
Stolzite–PR
Thorite–FR
Xenotime–FR
Zircon–GD

Basal (Basal Pinacoidal)

Anatase–PF
Apophyllite–PF
Ashcroftine–GD
Autunite–VP
Bandylite–PF
Bismoclite–PF
Boleite–PF
Cassiterite–GD
Chiolite–PF
Cumengeite–PR
Daubreeite–PF
Diaboleite–PF
Gehlenite–GD
Gillespite–?
Hardystonite–?
Hausmannite–PF
Hematophanite–GD
Hetaerolite–PR
Idocrase–TR
Matlockite–PF
Melilite–FR
Metatorbernite–PF
Metazeunerite–PF
Phosgenite–PF

Pseudoboleite–PF
Saleeite–PF
Scheelite–PR
Schreibersite–PF
Schwarzembergite–FR
Stannite–FR
Stolzite–GD
Torbernite–VP
Wardite–PF
Wulfenite–PR

Pyramidal

Boleite–PR
Braunite–PF
Fergusonite–TR
Rutile–TR
Scheelite–PR
Wulfenite–FR
Zircon–2 PR

HEXAGONAL CLEAVAGES

Prismatic

Apatite–TR
Aphthitalite–FR
Bastnaesite–TR
Bismuth–2 GD
Bromellite–FR
Cancrinite–PF, GD
Coquimbite–PR
Delafosseite–GD
Ettringite–PF
Fluocerite–TR
Gmelinite–GD
Hedyphane–?
Kaliophilite–PR
Mimetite–TR
Nepheline–FR
Paratacamite–GD
Phenakite–FR
Pyromorphite–TR
Quartz–TR
Rinneite–GD
Selen-Tellurium–PF
Spangolite–FR
Tellurium–PF
Tourmaline–PR, TR

Zincite–PF
Zinkenite–PR

Pinacoidal (Basal Pinacoidal)

Allemontite–PF
Allopalladium–GD
Antimony–VP
Apatite–PR
Aphthitalite–PR
Arsenic–PF
Bararite–PF
Barbertonite–PF
Barysilite–FR
Beryl–TR
Beudantite–GD
Bismuth–PF
Bityite–?
Brucite–PF
Brugnatellite–PF
Chalcophanite–PF
Chalcophyllite–PF
Cordylite–FR
Covellite–VP
Crandallite–PF
Cronstedtite–PF

Dehrnite–PF
Eucryptite–FR
Eudialyte–PF
Fluocerite–FR
Friedelite–PF
Gmelinite–TR
Goyazite–PF
Graphite–VP
Greenockite–GD
Gyrolite–PF
Hanksite–GD
Hoegbomite–GD
Hydrocerrusite–PF
Hydrotalcite–PF
Iodyrite–PF
Iridosmine–PF
Jarosite–FR
Kaliphilite–PR
Kleinite–GD
Klockmannite–PF
Koenenite–PF
Lawrenceite–PF
Lewistonite–PF
Macgovernite–PF
Magnetoplumbite–PF
Manasseite–PF

Melonite—VP
Molybdenite—VP
Molysite—PF
Nepheline—PR
Nordenskioldine—PF
Penfieldite—FR
Plumboferrite—FR
Portlandite—PF
Pyraurite—PF
Pyrochroite—PF
Pyrosmalite—GD
Scacchite—PF
Schallerite—PF
Siserskite—PF
Spangolite—PF
Stichtite—PF
Synchisite—?
Tellurium—GD
Tellurobismuthite—PF
Tetradymite—PF
Trechmannite—FR

Tungstenite—PF
Ungemachite—PF
Wilkeite—GD
Willemite—FR
Woodhouseite—GD
Wurtzite—PR
Zeophyllite—PF
Zinc—PF

Pyramidal

Greenockite—FR
Wadeite—PR
Wurtzite—GD

Rhombohedral

Ankerite—PF
Benitoite—PR
Calcite—PF
Chabazite—FR

Cinnabar—PF
Cobaltocalcite—PF
Coquimbite—GD
Dioptase—VP
Dolomite—PF
Eudialyte—2 PR
Giekielite—FR
Levynite—FR
Magnesite—PF
Millerite—2 PF
Paracoquimbite—2 GD
Phenakite—PR
Proustite—FR
Pyrargyrite—FR, PR
Quartz—TR
Rhodochrosite—PF
Selenium—GD
Siderite—PF
Smithsonite—PF
Tachyhydrite—PF
Trechmannite—GD

ORTHORHOMBIC CLEAVAGES

Prismatic

Adamite—GD
Alstonite—GD
Andalusite—FR
Anglesite—FR
Anthophyllite—PF
Aragonite—2 TR
Ardennite—FR
Atacamite—FR
Austinite—GD
Banalsite—GD
Barite—GD
Becquerelite—PF
Berthierite—FR
Bertrandite—PF
Bismuthinite—GD
Brookite—GD
Caledonite—PR
Celestite—GD
Cerussite—2 FR, 1 TR
Chrysoberyl—FR
Dawsonite—PF
Diaspore—GD
Enargite—PF
Enstatite—GD
Epsomite—FR
Eriochalcite—PF
Erythrosiderite—PF
Galenobismutite—GD
Geocronite—FR
Gismondine—FR

Glaucodot—GD
Hemimorphite—PF, GD
Humite—FR
Hypersthene—GD
Ilvaite—PR
Kentrolite—FR
Kornerupine—PF
Kotoite—PF
Kremersite—PF
Larsenite—GD
Laurionite—FR
Lawsonite—PR
Lithiophilite—PR
Lorenzenite—FR
Mansfieldite—GD
Marcasite—FR, TR
Massicot—TR
Mendipite—PF
Natrolite—PF
Olivenite—2 PR
Orientite—PR
Rhomboclase—GD
Roweite—PR
Salesite—PF
Scorodite—GD
Staurolite—TR
Stephanite—GD
Stibnite—GD
Stokesite—PF
Strontianite—PF, PR
Sulfoborite—GD
Thenardite—FR
Thortveitite—FR

Tridymite—PR
Triphylite—PR
Tungstite—GD
Valentinite—VP
Wavellite—PF, GD
Weberite—PR
Witherite—GD

Pinacoidal

Adamite—PR
Andalusite—GD, TR
Anglesite—GD, TR
Anhydrite—PF, 2 GD
Anthophyllite—2 PR
Antlerite—PF, PR
Aragonite—FR
Ardennite—PF
Astrophyllite—PF
Atacamite—PF
Aurichalcite—PF
Banalsite—GD
Barite—PF, PR
Becquerelite—PF
Bertrandite—2 PF
Bismuthinite—PF, GD
Boehmite—?
Bournonite—GD, FR, PR
Brookite—PR
Caledonite—PF, PR
Celestite—PF, PR
Cerussite—TR
Chalcocite—PR

Chalcostibite–PF, GD, GD
Childrenite–PR
Chlorocalcite–3 FR
Chrysoberyl–2 PR
Cohenite–3 ?
Columbite–FR, PR
Cordierite–FR, PR
Cotunnite–PF
Diaspore–PF, TR
Dyscrasite–2 FR, GD
Emplectite–PF, GD
Enargite–2 FR
Eosphorite–PR
Epsomite–PF
Eriochalcite–?
Ferrierite–PF
Ferruccite–3?
Fibroferrite–PF
Flokite–2 PF
Fluellite–?
Fourmarierite–PF
Franckeite–PF
Frondelite–2 GD, FR
Gerhardtite–PF, GD
Glaucochroite–PR
Glaucodot–PF
Goethite–PF, GD
Goslarite–PF
Guanajuatite–FR, PR
Hambergite–PF, GD
Hemimorphite–TR
Heterosite–GD, PR
Hopeite–2 PF, GD
Hutchinsonite–GD
Hypersthene–PF, TR
Ianthinite–PF
Iddingsite–3 FR
Ilvaite–2 FR
Klaprothite–FR
Koechlinite–PF
Krennerite–PF

Langite–2?
Lanthanite–VP
Lautite–FR
Lawsonite–2 PF
Lepidocrocite–PF, 2 GD
Libethenite–2 PR
Liebigite–?
Lillianite–2 GD, PR
Lithiophilite–PF, GD
Loellingite–2 TR
Lorenzenite–FR
Mansfieldite–2 TR
Massicot–2?
Mendipite–2?
Meneghinite–PF, PR
Monticellite–GD
Montroydite–PF
Morenosite–FR
Nadorite–PF
Natrolite–GD
Norbergite–FR
Nordite–GD
Olivine–FR, PR
Pararammelsbergite–PF
Paravauxite–PF
Phosphoferrite–PR
Pinakiolite–GD
Polymignyte–2 TR
Prehnite–FR
Pseudobrookite–FR
Ptilolite–2?
Pucherite–PF
Purpurite–GD, PR
Reddingite–PR
Rhomboclase–PF
Rockbridgeite–2 GD, FR
Safflorite–FR
Schoepite–PF
Scorodite–2 TR
Seamanite–FR
Seligmannite–3 TR
Sengierite–PF

Serpierite–PF
Sicklerite–GD
Sillimanite–PF
Sklodowskite–PF
Staurolite–FR
Stephanite–GD
Sternbergite–PF
Stibiocolumbite–FR, PR
Stibiotantalite–FR, PR
Stibnite–PF, GD
Stokesite–PR
Strengite–GD, PR
Strontianite–TR
Sulfoborite–FR
Sulfur–3 PR
Tantalite–FR, PR
Teallite–PF
Tellurite–PF
Tephroite–3 FR
Thenardite–PF, PR
Thomsonite–PF, GD, TR
Topaz–PF
Triphylite–PF, GD
Tungstite–PF
Tyrolite–PF
Valentinite–GD
Variscite–GD, PR
Vrbaite–GD
Warwickite–PF
Wavellite–FR
Weberite–PR
Witherite–FR
Yttrotantalite–PR
Zoisite–PF

Pyramidal

Erythrosiderite–TR
Fluellite–PR
Geocronite–PR
Kremersite–TR

MONOCLINIC CLEAVAGES

Prismatic

Acmite–FR
Aenigmatite–FR
Amphibole–PF
Arfvedsonite–PF
Augelite–PF
Azurite–PF, TR
Baddeleyite–FR
Barytocalcite–PF
Borax–GD

Botryogen–GD
Chloroxiphite–PF
Claudetite–PR
Crocoite–FR
Didymolite–FR
Durangite–FR
Freieslebenite–GD
Gaylussite–PF
Glauberite–PR
Glaucophane–PF
Gypsum–PR

Herderite–PR
Heteromorphite–GD
Kaliborite–PF
Keilhauite–FR
Kernite–FR
Kroehnkite–TR
Laumontite–PF
Lauterite–GD, TR
Lazulite–GD
Liroconite–2 PR
Lorandite–GD

Manganite—GD
Mesolite—PF
Miargyrite—TR
Mirabilite—?
Nahcolite—PF, GD
Picromerite—PF
Plagionite—GD
Probertite—PF
Prosopite—PF
Pyroxene—PF, GD
Realgar—3 FR
Scolecite—PF
Scorzalite—GD
Semseyite—PF
Spodumene—PF
Syngenite—PF
Terlinguaite—PF
Thomsenolite—FR
Titanite—FR
Triploidite—FR
Trona—TR
Wolfeite—FR

Pinacoidal

Acmite—PR
Afwillite—PF
Alamosite—PF
Allactite—FR
Amphibole—2 PR
Arfvedsonite—GD
Arrojadite—GD, PR
Arsenopyrite—FR, TR
Augelite—GD, PR
Azurite—FR
Baddeleyite—PF, GD
Barytocalcite—GD
Baumhauerite—PF
Beraunite—GD
Beryllonite—PF, FR, PR
Borax—PF
Botryogen—PF
Boulangerite—GD
Brazilianite—PF, GD
Brewsterite—PF, TR
Brochantite—PF
Chlorites—PF
Chlorophoenicite—GD
Chloroxiphite—FR
Claudetite—PF
Clinoclase—PF
Clinohedrite—PF
Clinohumite—PR
Clintonites—PF
Colemanite—PF, FR
Cookeite—PF

Creedite—PF
Crocidolite—PF
Crocoite—2 PR
Cuspidine—FR
Dachiardite—2 PF
Darapskite—2 PF
Didymolite—FR
Dufrenoysite—PF
Emmonsite—PF
Epidote—PF, GD
Epistilbite—PF
Erythrite—PF, 2 PR
Euclase—VP, 2 PR
Ferberite—PF
Fiedlerite—GD
Ganophyllite—PF
Gaylussite—PR
Gibbsite—PF
Glauberite—PF
Graftonite—GD, FR
Gypsum—PF, FR
Harmotome—GD, FR
Heulandite—PF
Hilgardite—2 PF
Hodgkinsonite—PF
Huebnerite—PF
Hureaulite—GD
Hyalophane—PF, GD
Hydrocalumite—PF
Hydromagnesite—PF
Inderborite—GD
Inyoite, 2 GD
Jadeite—PF
Jamesonite—GD
Jezekite—PF, PR
Johnstrupine—?
Jordanite—VP
Kainite—PF
Kaliborite—PF, GD
Kasolite—PF, ?
Katoptrite—PF
Kermesite—PF, GD
Kernite—PF, GD
Koettigite—PF
Krausite—PF, GD
Kroehnkite—PF
Lamprophyllite—FR, PR
Lanarkite—PF, GD
Larnite—GD
Laubanite—GD
Laumontite—2 GD
Lauterite—TR
Lavenite—PF
Lazulite—PR
Leadhillite—PF
Legrandite—FR

Leucosphenite—FR
Linarite—PF, GD
Lindgrenite—PF
Livingstonite—PF, PR
Lorandite—PF, GD
Ludlamite—PF, PR
Manganite—VP, GD
Merwinite—PF
Metastrengite—GD, PR
Metavariscite—?
Miargyrite—2 GD
Micas—PF
Mirabilite—PF, 2?
Monazite—FR, PR
Montgomeryite—PF, PR
Mooreite—PF
Mordenite—PF
Nagyagite—PF
Nahcolite—FR
Neptunite—GD
Orpiment—PF, TR
Orthoclase—PF, GD, FR
Overite—PF, PR
Pachnolite—PR
Paralaurionite—PF
Parawollastonite—3 PF, PR
Petalite—PF, GD
Pharmacolite—PF
Phillipsite—2 FR
Phosphophyllite—PF, 2 FR
Polybasite—GD
Pseudomalachite—FR
Pumpellyite—2 PR
Pyrophyllite—PF
Pyrostilpnite—PF
Quenselite—PF
Raspite—PF
Rathite—PF
Realgar—GD, FR
Rinkite—FR
Roselite—PF
Sapphirine—3 PR
Sarkinite—FR
Sartorite—FR
Scawtite—2 PF
Schultenite—GD
Scorzalite—PR
Searlesite—PF
Smithite—PF
Stilbite—PF
Sylvanite—PF
Syngenite—PF, FR
Talc—PF
Thomsenolite—PF
Tilleyite—PF, 2 GD
Titanite—TR

Trimerite—FR
Triplite—GD, FR, PR
Triploidite—GD, PR
Trona—PF, TR

Veatchite—PF, GD
Vivianite—PF, 2 TR
Woehlerite—FR
Wolfeite—GD, PR

Wolframite—PF
Wollastonite—PF, GD
Xanthoconite—FR

TRICLINIC CLEAVAGES

Pinacoidal only

Alunogen—2 PF
Amblygonite—PF, GD, FR, PR
Aramayoite—PF, 2 FR
Axinite—FR, TR
Babingtonite—PF, GD
Bustamite—PF, 2 GD, PR
Chalcanthite—GD, TR
Chalcosiderite—PF, GD
Copiapite—PF. GD
Fairfieldite—PF, GD
Gordonite—PF, FR, PR
Guarinite—?

Inderite—PF, GD
Inesite—PF, GD
Johannite—GD
Kyanite—PF, GD
Margarosanite—PF, 2 ?
Meyerhofferite—PF, 2 TR
Microcline—PF, GD, PR
Okenite—PF
Parahilgardite—2 PF
Parahopeite—PF
Pectolite—2 PF
Plagioclase—PF; GD, PR
Polyhalite—PF
Pyroxmangite—PF, GD

Rhodonite—2 PF; GD
Roemerite—PF, VG
Rosenbuschite—PF
Sanbornite—PF, PR
Sassolite—PF
Schizolite—2 PF
Symplesite—PF
Tarbuttite—PF
Tinzenite—PF
Turquoise—PF, GD
Ulexite—2 PF; GD
Vandenbrandite—PF
Yeatmanite—PF

DISTINCTIVE MINERAL CRYSTAL HABITS

The lists below provide habits observed in most of the important species as well as those for many of the minor minerals. In many instances they are so characteristic that they provide invaluable clues to identity. Atomic structures tend to strongly influence habit, the cubelike or ball-like xls of the isometric system being especially remarkable. The following generalizations are therefore applicable to the xls in the systems named.

ISOMETRIC. Variations of the cube with increasing number of faces causing individuals to resemble faceted balls.

TETRAGONAL. Basically square prisms or tablets, with or without pyramids, and with corners of the square very commonly cut off to yield octagonal cross sections.

HEXAGONAL. Six-sided xl cross sections, with xls ranging from very thin hexagonal platelets to thin to thick tablets, and to very elongated prisms. Terminations commonly flat but also pointed by pyramids or with only some truncation of prisms by pyramidal faces. Some xls approach circular cross sections due to development of additional prism faces.

RHOMBOHEDRAL DIVISION. Characteristic is the rhombohedron, which resembles a distorted cube. Rhombohedrons may range from elongated, sharply pointed three-sided pyramidal shapes to those which are so close to the cube in shape and angles that they are commonly mistaken for same. Also form very low rhombohedrons which may resemble circular, sharp-edged disks.

ORTHORHOMBIC. Provides two distinct shape groups: (1) boxlike, and (2) lathlike to tabular. Xls in either group may be modified with faces but modifications of lathlike xls mostly tend to produce wedgelike or pointed terminations. A lozenge-shaped cross section is particularly characteristic of this group.

MONOCLINIC. Xls usually prismatic, similar to orthorhombic, commonly showing rectangular or lozenge-shaped cross sections and pointed or wedged terminations. Close examination usually shows one set of faces inclined at angles (unlike the orthorhombic) which results in terminal faces forming beveled, chisel-like terminations. Lozenge-shaped or boxlike individuals are common also. Particularly characteristic of xls in this system is their tendency to form elongated to acicular prisms, often in radiate sprays, tufts, etc.

TRICLINIC. The lack of obvious symmetry relationships in xls of this system is perhaps the best clue of all. Xls vary widely in habit, from boxlike to thick tabular to elongated prisms to acicular. Blunt to sharp wedge terminations are common.

Tables of Habits

The following tables are arranged according to the *first general impression* received upon observation of xls and not according to system, although the latter is indicated in parentheses for each species. Thus under cubic or cubelike xls may be found not only xls in the isometric system but others which look like cubes although belonging to other systems. Boldface species characteristically display the habit shown.

Abbreviations: (H) = hexagonal; (I) = isometric, (M) = monoclinic; (O) = orthorhombic; (R) = rhombohedral; (T) = tetragonal, (TRI) = triclinic.

Met. = metallic luster; SMet. = semi-metallic; NMet. = nonmetallic.

Shape	Luster	Species
Cubic	Met.	Silver (I), copper (I), **argentite (I)**, naumannite (I), **galena (I)**, stannite (T), pyrite (I), **sperrylite (I), cobaltite (I),** gersdorffite (I), ullmannite (I)
	SMet.	**Cuprite (I)**, hematite (R), **perovskite (M)**
	NMet.	Diamond (I), **bixbyite (I)**, uraninite (I), **halite (I), sylvite (I)**, cerargyrite-bromyrite (I), **fluorite (I), boleite (T), pseudoboleite (T)**, chlorocalcite (O), cryolite (M), thomsenolite (M), calcite (R), **borácite (O), voltaite (I)**, roemerite (TRI), **pharmacosiderite (I)**, beudantite (R), **corkite (R) hinsdalite (R)**, svanbergite (R), **woodhouseite (R)**, monimolite (I), quartz (H) uncommon, **pollucite (T)**, lazurite (I), **apophyllite (T), chabazite (R)**, analcime (I) rare
Cube-octahedrons	Met.	**Galena (I)**, argentite (I), skutterudite (I), smaltite (I)
	NMet.	Uraninite (I), hieratite (I), boracite (O), **sarcolite (T)**, **apophyllite (T)**
Octahedrons	Met.	**Gold (I)**, argentite (I), galena (I), linnaeite (I), pyrite (I), argyrodite (I), chalcophanite (R)
	SMet.	Cuprite (I), cassiterite (T), **anatase (T)** elongated, **magnetite (I), franklinite (I)**
	NMet.	Diamond (I), **hauerite (I)**, periclase (I), manganosite (I), arsenolite (I), **senarmontite (I)**, uraninite (I), **spinel (I), chromite (I), hausmannite (T)**, hetaerolite (T), **perovskite (M), microlite (I), pyrochlore (I)**, betafite (I), blomstrandine (I), samiresite (I), mendelyeevite (I), djalmaite (I), **fluorite (I)** rough, mosesite (I), kremersite (O), hieratite (I), fluellite (O) elongated, ralstonite (I), **northupite (I)**, ancylite (O), nitrobarite (I), voltaite (I), sulfohalite (I), xenotime (T), reddingite-phosphoferrite (O), variscite (O) rare, strengite (O), scorodite (O), **lazulite (M)** elongated, **romeite (I)**, monimolite (I), **scheelite (T), powellite (T)**, cristobalite (T), hauyne (I) rare, **danalite (I)**, idocrase (T), apophyllite (T) elongated, **faujasite (I)**

Shape	Luster	Species
Dodeca-hedrons	Met.	Moschellandsbergite (I)
	SMet.	Cuprite (I), magnetite (I)
	NMet.	Eglestonite (I), **rhodizite** (I), boracite (O), sulfohalite (I), sodalite (I) rare, **hauyne** (I) rare, **lazurite** (I), helvite (I), **garnet** (I), schorlomite (I)
Trapezo-hedrons	NMet.	Berzeliite (I), **leucite** (T), **garnet** (I), schorlomite (I), analcime (I)
Ball-Like, many faces	Met.	Hessite (I), **pyrite** (I), **cobaltite** (I), gersdorffite (I), **skut-terudite** (I), **smaltite** (I), **chloanthite** (I), **argyrodite** (I), **colusite** (I), miargyrite (M), smithite (M), tennantite (I)
	SMet.	**Sphalerite** (I), **cuprite** (I), hematite (R), perovskite (M), rutile (T), cassiterite (T), brookite (O), tapiolite-mossite (T)
	NMet.	Diamond (I), **sphalerite** (I), **microlite** (I), **pyrochlore** (I), **betafite** (I), sal ammoniac (I), fluorite (I), rare, eglestonite (I), terlinguaite (M), carnallite (O), calcite (R), **rhodizite** (I), boracite (O), bloedite (M), sulfohalite (I), conichalcite (O), pharmacosiderite (I), **eulytine** (I), **garnet** (I), **datolite** (M), humite-clinohumite (M), chabazite (R) twins
Pyrito-hedrons	Met.	**Pyrite** (I), cobaltite (I), gersdorffite (I)
Tetra-hedral	Met.	Metacinnabar (I), tiemannite (I), **chalcopyrite** (T), **tetra-hedrite** (I)
	SMet.	**Sphalerite** (I)
	NMet.	**Sphalerite** (I), miersite (I), marshite (I), iodyrite (H), rhodizite (I), cahnite (T), **tritomite** (R), **helvite** (I), eulytine (I)
Rhombo-hedral	SMet.	**Cinnabar** (R), hematite (R)
	NMet.	Chloraluminite (R), **paratacamite** (R), clinoclase (M), chlor-manganokalite (R), **calcite** (R), magnesite (R), **siderite** (R), **dolomite** (R), **rhodochrosite** (R), smithsonite (R), **ankerite** (R), **synchisite** (H), whitlockite (R), fillowite (M), dick-insonite (M), hematolite (R), **leadhillite** (M), soda-niter (R), colemanite (M), melanterite (M), **slavikite** (R), **goyazite** (R), **beudantite** (R), corkite (R), **svanbergite** (R), **eudialyte** (R), **caryocerite** (R), phenakite (R), **chabazite** (R), **gmelinite** (R)
Blocky, boxlike	Met.	Cubanite (O), sylvanite (M), bournonite (O), seligmannite (O)
	SMet.	Hematite (R), **yttrotantalite** (O), **columbite** (O)

Shape	Luster	Species
	NMet.	Stibiocolumbite (O), trona (M), gaylussite (M), **borax (M)**, inderborite (M), inyoite (M), barite (O), langite (O), kainite (M), triphylite (O), beryllonite (M), roselite (M), triplite (M), **orthoclase (M)**, **microcline (TRI)**, pyroxene, **spodumene (M)** kunzite, **rhodonite (TRI)**, idocrase (T), **andalusite (O)**, bertrandite (O), **harmotome (M)**
Square tablets or wafers	Met.	Nagyagite (I), **bournonite (O)**, teallite (O)
	SMet.	Anatase (T)
	NMet.	Claudetite (M), **matlockite (T)**, diaboleite (T), **torbernite (T)**, **phosgenite (T)**, teepleite (T), bandylite (T), **autunite (T)**, **uranocircite (T)**, **saleeite (T)**, **uranospinite (T)**, **metatorbernite (T)**, **metazeunerite (T)**, ecdemite (T), **wulfenite (T)**, koechlinite (O), **melilite (T)**, **gehlenite (T)**, thorite (T), **brewsterite (M)**, edingtonite (T)
Rect-angular tablets or wafers	Met.	Klaprothite (O), **miargyrite (M)**, **aramayoite (M)**, dufrenoysite (M), **andorite (O)**, baumhauerite (M), **plagionite (M)**, **semseyite (M)**
	SMet.	**Pseudobrookite (O), columbite-tantalite (O)**
	NMet.	Becquerelite (O), schoepite (O), vandenbrandite, diaspore (O), **lepidocrocite (O)**, **stibiotantalite (O)** striated, **laurionite (O)**, paralaurionite (M), avogadrite (O), erythrosiderite (O), beyerite (T), gerhardtite (O), darapskite (M), pinakiolite (O), hambergite (O), **barite (O)**, **anhydrite (O)**, antlerite (O), **celestite (O)**, roscherite (M), **copiapite (TRI)**, burkeite (O), **beryllonite (M)**, hopeite (O), strengite (O), metavariscite (M), metastrengite (M), **holdenite (O)**, allactite (M), flinkite (O), retzian (O), sarkinite (M), augelite (M), viszelyite (M), tsumebite (M), **sincosite (T)**, koechlinite (O), pectolite (M), **rhodonite (TRI)** wollastonite (M), leucophanite (O), olivine (O) peridot, epidote (M), allanite (M), **prehnite (O)**, **bertrandite (O)**, hemimorphite (O), heulandite (M), rinkite (M)
Lozenge-shaped tablets or wafers	NMet.	Rhomboclase (O), szomolnokite (M), **mooreite (M)**, **gypsum (M)**, chalcanthite (TRI), quenstedtite (TRI), linarite (M), kainite (M), schultenite (M), parahopeite (TRI), vivianite (M), phosphophyllite (M), erythrite (M), childrenite (O), **ludlamite (M)**, beraunite (M), paravauxite (TRI), catoptrite (M), pucherite (O), **raspite (M)**, **lindgrenite (M)**, **eudidymite (M)**, albite (TRI), **heulandite (M)**, **mica (M)**, barite (O)
Wedges, short	Met.	**Safflorite (I)**, **marcasite (O)**, **arsenopyrite (M)**, **glaucodot (O)**, freieslebenite (M), lorandite (M)

Shape	Luster	Species
	SMet.	wolframite (M)
	NMet.	Cerussite (O), shortite (O), pirssonite (O), monazite (M), struvite (O), gaylussite (M), azurite (M), kernite (M), colemanite (M), phosphophyllite (M), thenardite (O), anglesite (O), syngenite (M), barite (O), cornetite (O), chalcanthite (TRI), paracoquimbite (R), antlerite (O), vauquelinite (M), descloizite (O), herderite (M), trigonite (M), liroconite (M), sterrettite (O), whewellite (M), datolite (M), chondrodite (M), heulandite (M), titanite (M), keilhauite (M), clinohedrite (M)
Wedges, long	SMet.	Rutile (T) twinned, descloizite (O), huebnerite (M)
	NMet.	Azurite (M), colemanite (M), glauberite (M), vivianite (M), brazilianite (M), turquoise (TRI), axinite (TRI), titanite (M)
Pentagonal wafers	Met.	Marcasite (O) twinned
Disks	Met.	Chalcophanite (R)
	SMet.	Hematite (R), ilmenite (R)
	NMet.	Pyrochroite (H), calcite (R), siderite (R), dolomite (R), ankerite (R), phenakite (R), xanthophyllite (M), axinite (TRI)
Reticulated	SMet.	Rutile (T)
	NMet.	Cerussite (O)
Hex. prism, flat term.	Met.	Stephanite (O)
	SMet.	Hematite (R)
	NMet.	Corundum (R), simpsonite (H), penfieldite (H), malladrite (H), calcite (R), magnesite (R), witherite (O) striated, strontianite (O) striated, hanksite (H), vanadinite (H), aragonite (O) twinned; pyromorphite-mimetite (H), lewistonite (H), swedenborgite (H), nepheline (H), kaliophilite (H), milarite (H), beryl (H), cordierite (O), davyne (H), langbanite (H), tourmaline (R), staurolite (O), mica (M)
Hex. prism, pointed	Met.	Gratonite (R), zinkenite (H) striated
	SMet.	Pyrargyrite (R), proustite (R)
	NMet.	Iodyrite (H), kleinite (H), calcite (R), rhodochrosite (R), smithsonite (R), strontianite (O), parisite (H), cordylite (H), hanksite (H), apatite (H), pyromorphite-mimetite (H), hedyphane (H), armangite (H), finnemanite (H), quartz (H), svabite (H), beryl (H), cappelenite (H), cancrinite (H) rare, pyrosmalite (R), willemite (R), phenakite (R), dioptase (R), tourmaline (R), gmelinite (R)
Hex. prism, wedge term.	NMet.	Aragonite (O) twinned

Shape	Luster	Species
Hex. tablets or wafers	Met.	**Pyrrhotite** (H), breithauptite (H), sternbergite (O), **molybdenite** (H), **polybasite** (M), **pearceite** (M), stephanite (O)
	SMet.	Graphite (H), chalcocite (O), covellite (H), **xanthoconite** (M), **jordanite** (M), ilmenite (R), hematite (R)
	NMet.	Brucite (H), corundum (R), portlandite (H), pyraurite (H), sassolite (TRI), gibbsite (M), **chrysoberyl** (O) twinned, fluocerite (H), carnallite (O), bararite (H), **calcite** (R), **cerussite** (O) twinned, **hydrocerussite** (H), **bastnaesite** (H), **leadhillite** (M), nordenskioldine (R), **aphthitalite** (H), tamarugite (M), **spangolite** (R), devillite (M) **ungemachite** (R), **clinoungemachite** (M), **metavoltine** (H), dickinsonite (M), georgiadesite (M), **apatite** (H), **hedyphane** (H), bermanite (O), **roscherite** (M), **chalcophyllite** (R), **sengierite** (O), **tridymite** (O), **nepheline** (H), **albite** (TRI), **sanidine** (M), **beryl** (H) morganite, **eudialyte** (R), **catapleite** (M), **melanocerite** (R), caryocerite (R), **trimerite** (TRI), **chabazite** (R), **mica** (M), xanthophyllite (M), **chloritoid** (M), **chlorite** (M), **clinochlore** (M)
Hex. pyramids	SMet.	Brookite (O)
	NMet.	**Wurtzite** (H), **greenockite** (H), **zincite** (H), **corundum** (R), penfieldite (H), **aragonite** (O) elongated, **witherite** (O), striated, **alstonite** (O), hydrocerussite (H), **parisite** (H), cordylite (H), **coquimbite** (H), spangolite (R), **quartz** (H) amethyst, chlorite (M)
Pyramids, complexly faced	Met.	**Tetrahedrite** (I), vrbaite (O)
	SMet.	Hematite (R), **cassiterite** (T), **brookite** (O)
	NMet.	**Sulfur** (O), thenardite (O), durangite (M), brazilianite (M), **stolzite** (T), **datolite** (M)
Pyramids, square	SMet.	**Anatase** (T)
	NMet.	**Braunite** (T), **cumengeite** (T), szomolnokite (M), mackayite (T), **heliophyllite** (O), **cassiterite** (T), stolzite (T), idocrase (T), cyrtolite (T), wulfenite (T)
Prisms, wedge or chisel term.	Met.	**Loellingite** (O), marcasite (O), **arsenopyrite** (M), **glaucodot** (O), **gudmundite** (M), **krennerite** (O), sylvanite (M), meneghinite (O), klaprothite (O), **chalcostibite** (O) striated, **emplectite** (O) striated, dufrenoysite (M), cosalite (O), **baumhauerite** (M) striated, hutchinsonite (O), sartorite (M) striated, berthierite (O) striated
	SMet.	Brookite (O), **manganite** (M) striated, **goethite** (O), mossite (T), tapiolite (T), huebnerite-ferberite (M) striated, **eschynite-priorite** (O), **samarskite** (O), **euxenite-polycrase** (O)

Shape	Luster	Species
	NMet.	Realgar (M), orpiment (M), montroydite (O), valentinite (O), baddeleyite (O), stibiocolumbite (O) striated, delorenzite (O), cotunnite (O), terlinguaite (M), atacamite (O), aragonite (O), cerussite (O), pirssonite (O), malachite (M) rare, azurite (M), bellingerite (TRI), borax (M), meyerhofferite (TRI), inyoite (M), hambergite (O), thenardite (O), barite (O), celestite (O), anglesite (O), syngenite (M), bloedite (M), polyhalite (TRI), gypsum (M), lanarkite (M), linarite (M), parabutlerite (O), caledonite (O), brandtite (M), vivianite (M), chlorophoenicite (M), synadelphite (TRI), jezekite (M), clinoclase (M), conichalcite (O), olivenite (O), libethenite (O), adamite (O), liroconite (M), cornwallite, metavauxite (M), paravauxite (TRI), gordonite (TRI), orthoclase (M), microcline (TRI), pyroxene, spodumene (M), lavenite (M), hiortdahlite (TRI), actinolite (M), riebeckite (M), enigmatite (TRI), danburite (O), zoisite (O) striated, epidote (M) striated, allanite (M), ilvaite (O), ardennite (O), harstigite (O), ganophyllite (M), epistilbite (M), johnstrupite (M) striated, lawsonite (O), neptunite (M)
Prisms, pointed	Met.	Stibnite (O), calaverite (M), aikinite (O), diaphorite (O), andorite (O)
	SMet.	Polymignyte (O) striated, euxenite-polycrase (O)
	NMet.	Realgar (M), pachnolite (M), prosopite (M), salesite (O), sulfoborite (O), creedite (M), nahcolite (M), barytocalcite (M), mirabilite (M), krausite (M), gypsum (M), brochantite (M), ettringite (H), johannite (TRI), mackayite (T), crocoite (M), hureaulite (M) fairfieldite (TRI), roselite (M), parahopeite (TRI), koettigite (M), allactite (M), wagnerite (M), sarkinite (M), tarbuttite (TRI), childrenite-eosphorite (O), legrandite (M), wavellite (O), wulfenite (T), lavenite (M), babingtonite (TRI), monticellite (O), aegerine (M), euclase (M), cuspidine (M), kentrolite (O), inesite (TRI), phillipsite (M), harmotome (M), laumontite (M), natrolite (M)
Prisms, spear term.	NMet.	Laurionite (O), creedite (M), hydromagnesite (M), colemanite (M), natrochalcite (M), hopeite (O), herderite (M), brazilianite (M), titanite (M), hodgkinsonite (M)
Prisms, flat term	Met.	Enargite (O) striated
	SMet.	Manganite (M) striated, yttrotantalite (O), columbite-tantalite (O)
	NMet.	Thomsenolite (M), lauterite (M), hambergite (O), mirabilite (M), brochantite (M), metastrengite (M), triploidite-wolfeite (M), trippkeite (T), pyroxene, diopside (M), rhodonite (TRI), olivine (O) striated, idocrase (T), danburite (O), andalusite (O), lawsonite (O)

Shape	Luster	Species
Prisms, square or 8-sided cross sections	SMet.	Brookite (O), rutile (T)
	NMet.	Braunite (T), rutile (T) striated, pyrolusite (T), fergusonite (T), calomel (T), sellaite (T), **phosgenite (T)**, **amarantite (TRI)**, **xenotime (T)**, cornetite (O), **wardite (T)**, **nadorite (O)**, **babingtonite (TRI)**, **ganomalite (T)**, **wernerite (T)**, **idocrase (T)**, **zircon (T)**, **cyrtolite (T)**, **thorite (T)**
Cylinder, cross section	Met.	**Bournonite (O)** grooved
	SMet.	Rutile (T) striated
	NMet.	Beryl (H), **tourmaline (R)** striated, cerussite (O) striated, phosgenite (T), apatite (H), riebeckite (M) striated
Laths or thin blades	Met.	**Calaverite (M), lengenbachite (TRI), franckeite (O), galeno-bismutite (O)**
	SMet.	Goethite (O), columbite-tantalite (O)
	NMet.	**Kermesite (M), tellurite (O), fourmarierite (O)**, ianthinite (O), stibiotantalite (O) striated, **paralaurionite (M), fiedler-ite (M), loseyite (M), dawsonite (O), celestite (O)**, leighton-ite (TRI), **langite (O)**, felsobanyite (O), serpierite (O), metavariscite (M), **walpurgite (TRI)**, austinite (O), tyrolite (O), **sampleite (O)**, vauxite (TRI), xanthoxenite (M), montgomeryite (M), overite (O), spodumene (M), wollas-tonite (M), pectolite (M), hiortdahlite (TRI), **kyanite (TRI), hemimorphite (O), astrophyllite (O)**
Foliated, lamellar	Met.	Nagyagite (I), dyscrasite (I), stibnite (O), **bismuthinite (O)**, melonite (H), **teallite (O), franckeite (O)**
	SMet.	**Covellite (H), hematite (R)**
	NMet.	**Orpiment (M)**, zincite (H), **brucite (H)**, hydrotalcite (H), stichtite (H), manasseite (H), brugnatellite (H), diaspore (O), bischofite (M), tyrolite (O), englishite (M), **beraunite (M), ecdemite (T)**, petalite (M), barysilite (H), pyrosmalite (R), **kyanite (TRI), mica (M), margarite (M), talc (M), pyrophyllite (M)** radiate, **bementite** radiate, astrophyllite (O)
Foliated, cylindri-cally	Met.	**Cylindrite (unique!)**
Acicular or hairlike	Met.	**Stibnite (O), aikinite (O)** striated, boulangerite (M), **cosalite (O)**, livingstonite (M), **millerite (R), jamesonite (M)**
	SMet.	Rutile (T) striated, pseudobrookite (O)

Shape	Luster	Species
	NMet.	**Tellurite** (O), curite (O), nocerite (H), **aragonite** (O), strontianite (O), malachite (M), **chalcomenite** (O), fluoborite (H), **brochantite** (M), **connellite-buttgenbachite** (H), **crocoite** (M), annabergite (M), **austinite** (O), mixite (H), legrandite (M), metavauxite (M), pectolite (M), **byssolite** (amphibole or pyroxene), kaliophilite (H), microsommite (H), tourmaline (R), **laumontite** (M), **natrolite** (M), scolecite (M), **mesolite** (M), **uranophane** (O)
Fibrous, compact	Met.	Meneghinite (O), **boulangerite** (M), cosalite (O), **jamesonite** (M), berthierite (O), hollandite (T)
	SMet.	Hematite (R), **goethite** (O), coronadite (T)
	NMet.	Rutile (T)// fibers, cassiterite (T) wood tin, pyrolusite (T), cervantite (O), curite (O), stichtite (H), barbertonite (H), gibbsite (M), sellaite (T), mendipite (O), nocerite (H), trona (M), calcite (R) satin spar, gypsum (M) satin spar, **rhodochrosite** (R) banded, **cobaltocalcite** (R), **smithsonite** (R) banded, aragonite (O) banded, witherite (O) banded, hydrozincite (M), **malachite** (M) banded, **azurite** (M) banded, dietzeite (M), ludwigite-paigeite (O), priorite (T), **kernite** (M) // splintery, **ulexite** (TRI) // fibers, **veatchite** (M), hydroboracite (M), meyerhofferite (TRI), inderite (TRI), sussexite-szaibelyite (O), **kroehnkite** (M) // fibers, leightonite (TRI), mendozite (M), **chalcanthite** (TRI) // fibers, retgersite (T), melanterite (M), boothite (M), mallardite (M), **epsomite** (O), apjohnite (M), **alunogen** (TRI), antlerite (O), jarosite (R), fibroferrite (O), **botryogen** (M), **emmonsite** (M), haidingerite (O), erythrite (M), symplesite (TRI), **strengite** (O), erinite (O), pseudomalachite (M), andrewsite (M), laubmannite (O), **conichalcite** (O), volborthite (M), triploidite-wolfeite (M), olivenite (O), adamite (O), **frondelite-rockbridgeite** (O), **dufrenite** (M), dehrnite (H), leightonite (H), souzalite (M), **hemafibrite** (M), davisonite, wardite (T), millisite (T), lehiite, arseniosiderite (H), **wavellite** (O) radiate, quartz (H) various, **pectolite** (M) radiate, **wollastonite** (M), anthophyllite (O), actinolite (M), **crocidolite** (M) // fibers, hemimorphite (O), kornerupine (O), **fibrolite** (O), **piemontite** (M), **prehnite** (O) radiate, **dumortierite** (O), inesite (TRI), okenite (O), **mordenite** (M), **stilbite** (M) radiate, laubanite (M), **natrolite-scolecite-mesolite** (M) radiate, **thomsonite** (O) radiate, **pyrophyllite** (M) radiate, **thaumasite** (T)
Tufted or fibrous balls and crusts	Met.	Hutchinsonite (O)
	NMet.	**Kermesite** (M), tellurite (O), jarlite (M), **nesquehonite** (O), loseyite (M), **aurichalcite** (O), **rosasite** (M), **artinite** (M), dawsonite (O), dundasite, niter (O), nitrocalcite (M), **probertite** (M), ulexite(TRI), fluoborite (H), **halotrichite-**

Shape	Luster	Species
		pickeringite (M), connellite-buttgenbachite (H), **cyanotrichite** (O), **serpierite** (O), **sideronatrite** (O), **pharmacolite** (M), erythrite (M), **weinschenkite** (M), **carminite** (O), **mixite** (H), brackebuschite (M), **melanovanadite** (M), **hewettite** (O), metahewettite (O), **carpholite** (M), **ferrimolybdite**, **pectolite** (M), rosenbuschite (M), **ptilolite**, uranophane (O), **mesolite** (M), **scolecite** (M)

Part 8 / Chemical Testing of Minerals

BLOWPIPE FLAME COLORS

Observed when slender slivers of the minerals being tested are held in the blowpipe flame; also can be observed by crushing and dipping up powder in cleaned platinum or iron wire loop, first moistening the loop with conc. hydrochloric acid.

Color	Shade or tone	Element	Remarks
Red	Crimson	Lithium	
Red	Crimson	Strontium	Shown by carbonates and sulfates only
Red	Orangy	Calcium	Appears in only a few minerals; better when powder dipped up with acid
Yellow	Intense	Sodium	See note below
Green	Yellowish	Barium	Shown by carbonates and sulfates only
Green	Yellowish	Molybdenum	Shown by oxides and sulfide only
Green	Bright, yellowish	Boron	
Green	Pure hue	Thallium	Rarely observed
Green	Vivid	Copper	Oxides; moistening powder with acid gives blue
Green	Blue, pale	Phosphorus	Rarely observed except in some phosphates
Green	Bluish	Zinc	Usually occurs in bright flashes
Green	Pale	Antimony Lead Tellurium	Rarely observed
Blue	Bright	Copper	Powder dipped up with HCl
Blue	Azure	Selenium	
Blue	Pale	Lead	Flame tinged with green in outer parts
Blue		Indium	Rarely observed
Blue	Pale	Arsenic	
Blue	Greenish	Phosphorus Antimony	
Violet	Pale	Potassium Rubidium Cesium	Commonly observed in potassium minerals

Note: Sodium in the form of salt (sodium chloride) is such a widespread contaminant that unless care is used in handling and cleaning specimens and apparatus the sodium flame will appear in every test; avoid touching any specimen or loop with the fingers inasmuch as skin oils and perspiration contain sodium chloride.

SUBLIMATES IN GLASS TUBES: CLOSED

The "closed" tube is closed at one end only; size 3-4 mm (1/8"-3/16") inside diameter and 8 cm (3-1/4" long).

Sublimate	Substance	Remarks
Colorless liquid; easily volatilized	Water	From minerals containing water of crystallization or hydroxyl; may give acid reaction
Yellowish to colorless liquid; not easily volatilized	Tellurous oxide TeO$_2$	From Te and a few of its minerals
Red to dark yellow liquid; easily volatilized	Sulfur	From native sulfur and sometimes sulfides
Yellow solid	Sulfur	As above; obtained when tube cold
Dark red, nearly black liquid; easily volatilizes	Arsenic sulfides	From realgar and orpiment; also from arsenic sulfosalts
Reddish-yellow solid, transparent	Arsenic sulfides	As above; obtained when tube cold
Black to gray solid; partly crystalline	Arsenic	From arsenic and arsenides; brilliant luster
Black solid; not easily volatilized	Sb$_2$S$_2$O	Antimony oxysulfide from antimony sulfides and sulfosalts
Reddish-brown solid	Sb$_2$S$_2$O	As above; obtained when tube cold
Black solid, brilliant luster	Mercury sulfide HgS	From cinnabar; finely powdered sublimate turns red
Black fusible globules	Selenium	From native selenium and some selenides; crystals of selenious oxide (gray, small) are usually present also; powdered globules become red
Black fusible globules	Tellurium	From tellurium and some tellurides; usually with TeO$_2$ (see above)
Gray metallic globules	Mercury	From native mercury, amalgams; may be worked together into larger obviously metallic globules
White solid, fusible to yellow drops	Lead chloride	
White solid, fusible	Mercuric chloride	Sublimate is yellow when hot, white when cold
White solid, infusible	Mercurous chloride	As above
White solid, in acicular crystals; infusible	Antimony oxide	

SUBLIMATES IN GLASS TUBES: OPEN

Tubes are 5-7 mm (3/16″-1/4″) inside diameter and 15-17 cm (6″-6½″) long.

Sublimate	Substance	Remarks
Black, volatile	Arsenic or sulfide of mercury	Formed by excessively rapid heating; normal heating with adequate oxidation prevents formation
Brown	Antimony oxy-sulfide	ditto
Yellow, orange, easily volatilized	Sulfur or sulfides of antimony	ditto
Red, volatile	Selenium	May be accompanied by white selenious oxide crystals
Pale yellow	Molybdenum tri-oxide MoO_3	Turns white when cold
White, easily volatilized	Arsenious oxide As_2O_3	Forms ring around tube; forms small octahedral crystals
White, easily volatilized	Selenious oxide SeO_2	Forms radiating acicular crystals
White to pale yellow globules, slowly volatilized	Tellurous oxide TeO_2	
White, slowly volatilized	Antimonious oxide Sb_2O_3	From non-sulfur containing antimony minerals; two types of crystals in sublimate, octahedrons and prisms
Pale straw-yellow, infusible	Antimony oxide Sb_2O_4	From sulfides and sulfosalts of antimony; white when cold; no crystals
White, infusible; does not volatilize	Lead-sulfur compounds	From galena, usually as a meager deposit
Gray metallic globules	Mercury	Rubbed together the globules coalesce to form larger, obviously metallic globules
Brown, fusible	Bismuth oxide Bi_2O_3	Yellow when cold
White, does not volatilize	Bismuth sulfate $Bi_2(SO_4)_3$	Fuses to yellow droplets
White, partially volatile	Lead oxychloride $PbOCl_2$	Fuses to yellow droplets

ODORS PRODUCED IN HEATING MINERALS OR TESTING WITH ACID

Only three odors are common: the curious acrid "garlic" odor of arsenic when heated, the sulfurous or "burning match" odor of heated sulfur-containing compounds (sulfur dioxide), and the "rotten egg" odor of hydrogen sulfide produced when sulfide minerals are exposed to acid. All are characteristic and easily recognized.

SUBLIMATES ON CHARCOAL

Only the more common sublimates are included here.

Sublimate	Remarks
White	White sublimates form from numerous minerals containing arsenic, thallium, antimony, lead, mercury, etc. Arsenic, arsenides, and arsenic sulfides produce a volatile sublimate, usually at a considerable distance from the sample; garlic smell; a similar sublimate from thallium compounds but tinging the flame green at its edges. Dense white deposits near the sample are more likely to be oxides of antimony
Yellow, canary	Color observed while hot, changing to white when cold. Not volatile. Oxide of zinc
Yellow, faint	Color observed while hot, changing to white when cold. Not volatile. Oxide of tin
Yellow, pale	Color observed while hot, changing to white when cold. Volatile; may be distinctly crystalline. Oxide of molybdenum
Yellow	While hot, changing to straw-yellow when cold. Dense white sublimate with bluish-white border some distance away from sample. Volatile. Formed when galena and other lead sulfides very strongly heated
Yellow, dark	While hot, sulfur-yellow when cold. Volatile. Bluish white sublimate distant from sample. Lead oxide
Orange-yellow, dark	While hot, changing to orange-yellow when cold. Greenish-white sublimate away from sample. Bismuth oxide. Volatile
Black to reddish-brown	Yellow sublimate away from sample. Volatile. Cadmium oxide
Reddish to dark lilac	Silver + lead + antimony

Reference: For an extensive treatment with color plates illustrating numerous actual test results consult O. C. Smith, *Identification and Qualitative Analysis of Minerals* (New York: Van Nostrand).

Metallic Globules on Charcoal

Powder and mix mineral with sodium carbonate; heat in reducing flame.

Gold: Yellow, malleable globule.

Silver: Silver color, malleable.

Copper: Difficult to produce; bright color while molten but quickly covered with black oxide coating; malleable.

Lead: Accompanied by yellow oxide coatings near sample; malleable, gray.

Bismuth: Similar to lead in reactions and coating but brittle when hammered.

Tin: Produced with difficulty; white tin oxide coating near sample; malleable.

Sulfides and arsenides: Commonly form metallic globules but are very brittle when hammered.

Black semimetallic globules: A test for iron; magnetic. See Tables A and B.

SCALE OF FUSIBILITY

1. *Stibnite:* Fuses easily in luminous flame of a candle; fuses in closed tube; MP 977° F. (525° C.).

2. *Chalcopyrite:* Fuses easily in blowpipe flame; fusible with difficulty in luminous flame or in closed tube; MP 1,472° F. (800° C.).

3. *Almandine:* Fuses easily in blowpipe flame but not fusible in luminous flame or closed tube; MP 1,922° F. (1,050° C.).

4. *Actinolite:* Thin edges fuse easily in blowpipe flame; MP 2,192° F. (1,200° C.).

5. *Orthoclase:* Fuses on thin edges with difficulty in blowpipe flame; MP 2,372° F. (1,300° C.).

6. *Enstatite:* Fused and rounded on thinnest edges only in blowpipe flame; MP 2,552° F. (1,400° C.).

BEAD COLORS: BORAX

Oxidizing Flame			Reducing Flame		
Hot	Cold	Element	Hot	Cold	Element
Yellow, pale	Colorless to white	Antimony Bismuth Cadmium Lead Molybdenum Titanium Tungsten	Yellow, pale	Colorless	Antimony Cadmium Lead
			Yellow	Brownish	Tungsten
			Yellowish-gray	Brownish	Titanium
Yellow	Greenish-yellow	Cerium	Colorless	Colorless	Cerium Manganese
Yellow	Green	Chromium	Colorless to green	Brownish to opaque red	Copper
Yellow to yellow-orange	Greenish to brown	Iron	Bottle-green	Bottle-green	Iron
Yellow to yellow-orange	Yellow to brown	Uranium	Green	Green	Chromium
			Green, pale	Green	Uranium
Yellow	Green	Vanadium	Brownish to greenish	Yellow to green	Vanadium
Yellow to orange-yellow	Greenish to brown	Iron	Blue	Blue	Cobalt
Blue	Blue	Cobalt	Red, pale	Red, pale	Rare earths
Green	Blue	Copper	Brown	Brown to opaque black	Molybdenum
Red, pale	Red, pale	Rare earths	Gray	Gray	Bismuth
Violet	Brownish to reddish-violet	Manganese	Gray, opaque	Gray, opaque	Nickel
Violet	Reddish-brown	Nickel			

7. *Quartz:* Infusible even on extremely thin edges; MP over 2,552° F. (1,400° C.).

Note: Approximate limit of blowpipe flame is 2,732° F. (1,500° C.).

MISCELLANEOUS QUICK TESTS FOR ELEMENTS, RADICALS, AND CERTAIN MINERALS

ALUMINUM. To test for Al in pale-colored minerals: crush to powder, heat strongly, when cool add drops of cobalt nitrate, $Co(NO_3)_2$, sol.; reheat; powder turns blue but same reaction occurs when willemite and hemimorphite tested.

ANTIMONY. Native Sb and Sb-sulfides produce dense white smoke when strongly heated as on charcoal.

ARAGONITE Versus CALCITE. Powder mineral, boil in sol. cobalt nitrate, $Co(NO_3)_2$, for 15 minutes; wash thoroughly; pink stain in mineral indicates aragonite, no stain indicates calcite.

ARSENIC. Strongly heated gives off pungent disagreeable odor of garlic. Strong heating of native As, As-sulfides, or arsenides produces dense white coating arsenic oxide which deposits on cooler areas away from flame.

BARIUM. Flame test (green); use crushed sample, moisten first with HCl.

BERYLLIUM. No quick test is available.

BISMUTH. Powder Bi-mineral, usually

BEAD COLORS: PHOSPHORUS SALT*

Oxidizing Flame			Reducing Flame		
Hot	*Cold*	*Element*	*Hot*	*Cold*	*Element*
Yellow, pale	Colorless	Antimony Bismuth Cadmium Lead Niobium Tantalum Titanium Tungsten	Yellow, pale	Colorless	Cadmium Tantalum
			Yellow	Violet, pale	Titanium
			Yellow, pale, opaque	White	Cerium
			Green, dull	Yellowish-green	Molybdenum
Yellow	Yellowish-green to colorless	Uranium	Greenish to dull blue	Greenish-blue	Tungsten
Yellow	Greenish-yellow	Vanadium	Green, pale	Green	Uranium
Yellow, brownish	Yellow, pale	Cerium	Brown to dull green	Green	Vanadium
Yellow to brownish	Yellow, brownish	Iron	Red to dull green	Green	Chromium
Green, yellowish	Colorless	Molybdenum	Green, brownish	Red, opaque	Copper
Green, dark	Greenish-blue	Copper	Red or yellow to greenish-yellow	Violet, pale	Iron
Reddish to dull green	Yellowish-green to green	Chromium	Red, pale	Red, pale	Rare Earths
Red, pale	Red, pale	Rare earths	Reddish to brownish-red	Yellow to brown	Nickel
Reddish to brown-red	Yellow to brownish	Nickel	Brown	Red-brown	Niobium
Blue	Blue	Cobalt	Gray	Gray	Antimony Bismuth
Gray-violet	Violet	Manganese	Blue	Blue	Cobalt
			Colorless†	Colorless	Manganese

* Also known as microcosmic salt or salt of phosphorus; chemically it is sodium ammonium phosphate.

† Colorless beads also result when oxides of Ca, Sr, Ba, Mg, Be, Zn, Al, Th, Zr, Sn, and Si are tested. If beads are strongly saturated they may turn white upon cooling.

a sulfide or sulfosalt, mix with 3 parts anhydrous sodium carbonate, Na_2CO_3, moisten slightly to form pellet; place on charcoal and fuse. Produces metallic globules, pinkish white in color, which are *brittle* when hammered.

BORON. Many B-minerals give green flame coloration.

CALCIUM. Some Ca-minerals give red-orange flame coloration; helpful to moisten powder first with HCl.

CARBONATES. Many bubble when touched with acid, others require heating of acid to produce effervescence. This test does not distinguish calcite from aragonite (see ARAGONITE above). Some silicates containing carbonate do not diss. completely and leave white powdery residue.

CHLORIDES. Most sol. in water; add silver nitrate sol. to cause precipitation of white silver chloride; the precipitate is sol. in ammonia sol. Other chlorides sol. in nitric acid can be similarly tested.

CHROMIUM. See "Bead Tests" (p. 207-8). Commonly imparts distinctive "emerald-green" color to minerals.

COBALT. See "Bead Tests." Some dil. sols. with HCl color sol. pink.

COPPER. Native Cu distinctive, malleable. Cu-minerals color HCl sol. green; if some ammonia added sol. promptly turns blue. See also "Flame Tests."

FLUORINE. Crush mineral to powder, mix a little with conc. H_2SO_4 and place on glass slide; warm strongly from underneath. After several minutes cool and wash off slide, dry, and observe if glass etched by HF. Alternate method; repeat, leave slide with mixture for several days at room temp.

IRON. Crush mineral, heat very strongly; when cool, test for magnetism (iron oxides converted to magnetite). Some magnetism also observed in certain Co and Ni minerals also. Sols. Fe-minerals in HCl or HNO_3 color sol. yellow; also observed in oxalic sols. Add ammonia to acid sol. and note precipitate of iron hydroxide.

LEAD. Crush Pb-mineral, mix with 4 parts anhydrous sodium carbonate, Na_2Co_3; fuse and note formation metallic lead globules which are white in color and malleable. Also see "Sublimate Tests" and "Flame Tests."

LITHIUM. Gives fine red color in flame test.

MAGNESIUM. Use aluminum test but resulting color is pink. Sol. or partly water-sol. minerals taste bitter.

MAGNETITE. Only black mineral with strong attraction for magnet.

MAGNET TESTS. Use on magnetite; also pyrrhotite (dull brassy color) is decidedly attracted.

MANGANESE. See "Bead Tests." Sodium carbonate bead is colored blue-green in oxidizing flame, a specific test. Powdered Mn-oxide treated with hot conc. HCl produces choking fumes of chlorine.

MERCURY. Easily recognized when native. Hg-minerals produce Hg vapor when heated; use powdered Hg-mineral + powdered sodium carbonate; Hg forms silvery film on cold glass away from heated area, e.g., in the closed tube test.

MOLYBDENUM. See "Bead Tests." Molybdenite readily distinguished from graphite which is only mineral that resembles (molybdenite strong metallic luster, bluish color). Also wulfenite is distinctive in xls.

NICKEL. See "Bead Tests." Crush Ni-mineral, place powder in ammonia sol., add dimethylglyoxime and note resulting red precipitate. Some Ni-minerals crushed and strongly heated display weak magnetism.

NIOBIUM. Crush Nb-mineral to powder, fuse with anhydrous sodium carbonate, Na_2CO_3, or potassium sulfate, $K_2S_2O_7$; crush melt to powder, diss. in HCl, bring to boil and add scraps of tin at which time sol. turns blue, then brown.

NITRATES. Release oxygen when heated on charcoal, causing the latter to glow intensely white where in contact. If crushed and powder mixed with powdered charcoal, ignites readily and burns explosively.

PHOSPHORUS. Many P-minerals sol. HNO_3; add sol. ammonium molybdate to produce yellow precipitate of ammonium phosphomolybdate. Conc. HCl often etches phosphates, e.g., apatite, at fairly rapid rates.

POTASSIUM. See "Flame Tests." Use C-glass filter to cut off Na-flame which is usually present and disguises the violet flame of K.

SILICON. Some silicate minerals sol. in HCl and may leave either a gel or a powdery or skeletal residue of silica. Others sol. in HF form gas of SiF_4 which can deposit as a white powdery coating some distance away from acid sol. In sodium phosphate bead, silica is commonly separated and when bead is cool can be detected as slivery framework within glassy portions of bead.

SILVER. Native Ag distinctive; malleable as compared to As, Sb, Bi; brighter color than Pb. Diss. crushed Ag-mineral in conc. HNO_3 to form silver nitrate; decant and add sol. of common table salt to precipitate white silver chloride. White malleable bead produced by fusion silver minerals with anhydrous sodium carbonate on charcoal.

SODIUM. Distinctive brilliant yellow flame when Na-minerals heated in blowpipe flame.

STRONTIUM. Sr-minerals give distinctive red color to blowpipe flame.

SULFATES. Water-sol. sulfates detected by adding barium chloride sol. which precipitates white barium sulfate.

SULFIDES. Crush to powder, moisten with HCl, note distinctive "rotten egg" odor of hydrogen sulfide. Smell also appears when uncrushed mineral touched with conc. acid. Commonly appears merely in the act of crushing. Crush sample, mix with sodium carbonate and fuse on charcoal; cool and crush melt to powder, press and rub on silver coin and note blackening due to formation silver sulfides.

SULFUR. Native S easily recognized; burns with almost invisible blue flame.

TANTALUM. Usually associated with NIOBIUM, for which same test valid.

THORIUM. Test for radioactivity (also may be URANIUM).

TIN. Mix Sn-mineral powder with anhydrous sodium carbonate; fuse on charcoal to produce silver metallic bead of tin, malleable; when tested fails to respond to Ag tests, hence distinguished from silver.

TITANIUM. Fuse T-mineral powder on charcoal with anhydrous sodium carbonate; diss. crushed melt sol. conc. H_2SO_4 + water (50-50); add several drops hydrogen peroxide sol.; note appearance of yellow coloration.

Note: Ilmenite resembles magnetite but is not magnetic.

TUNGSTEN. Crush W-mineral to powder, mix with anhydrous sodium carbonate, fuse on charcoal; crush melt and add powder to HCl to diss.; now add scraps of zinc; note appearance of violet coloration to sol. when latter heated.

Note: Scheelite fluoresces; wolframite resembles cassiterite but has perfect cleavage and xls distinctive, also crushed powder fails to produce metallic bead as would be the case with tin.

URANIUM. Many U-species obviously fluorescent even in daylight, or brilliantly fluorescent under UV; also bright yellows, greens typical. Radioactivity unfailing test. Bright yellow fluorescence in beads fused from the U-mineral + borax + sodium fluoride.

VANADIUM. See "Bead Tests." Many V-minerals distinctive without testing.

ZINC. See "Flame Tests," e.g., coatings on charcoal when Zn-mineral heated, with yellow appearing when hot, and turning to white when cold. Some Zn-minerals turn HCl sol. blue.

ZIRCONIUM. Commonest Zr-mineral is zircon; note xl form, adamantine luster, and fluorescence under UV.

Simple Tests with Hydrochloric Acid

Mineral bubbles in acid: Carbonate, probably calcite, but also vigorous bubbling with aragonite, malachite, azurite, many others. If solid mineral fails to bubble crush to powder and note reaction; finally heat powder to observe if bubbles appear as may be necessary with some.

Solution turns green: A copper mineral is present; add a little ammonia and note that green promptly changes to blue (Cu).

Solution turns blue: Also due to copper.

Solution turns pink: Cobalt mineral present.

Solution turns yellow to dark yellow: An iron mineral is present.

Solution emits "rotten egg" odor: A sulfide mineral is present.

Solution emits choking greenish fumes: A manganese oxide is present, e.g., pyrolusite, manganite, psilomelane, hausmannite, braunite.

A rubbery transparent gel forms on mineral: This is a silica gel and forms on some zeolites, especially natrolite, also on anorthite, cancrinite, datolite, hemimorphite, nepheline, olivine, sodalite, willemite. When dry the gel is seen to be transparent to translucent, brittle, and cracked like dried mud.

A white porous to spongy residue is left on the mineral: This is also silica but forms a framework and not a gel. Observed on some zeolites, also on biotite, chrysocolla, garnierite, iolite, leucite, pectolite, rhodonite, scapolite, serpentine, wollastonite. Also noted on some specimens of olivine and willemite.

References: G. J. Brush and S. L. Penfield, *Manual of Determinative Mineralogy*, 16th ed., rev. (New York: Wiley, 1926.)

A. J. Moses and C. L. Parsons, *Elements of Mineralogy, Crystallography and Blowpipe Analysis*, 4th ed. (New York: Van Nostrand, 1911).

T. Richter and T. H. Cookesley, *Plattner's Manual of Qualitative and Quantitative Analysis with the Blowpipe* (London, 1875).

O. C. Smith, *Identification and Qualitative Analysis of Minerals*, 2d ed. (New York: Van Nostrand, 1953).

Part 9 / Mineralogical Miscellany

"SMOKING" CRYSTALS WITH AMMONIUM CHLORIDE

Where photographs of crystal specimens must emphasize aggregates, forms, twins, etc., it is necessary to eliminate glare from brilliant crystal faces. The following method employs the reaction of vapors of concentrated HCl and aqua ammonia (household, pure) to create a dense cloud of white ammonium chloride which settles as minute particles, like microscopic snowflakes, upon the specimen and quickly coats brilliant faces with an absolutely nonreflective layer.

The specimen is supported above a convenient working surface atop strips of thin wood laid over two coffee cans (about 8″ tall). Place beneath the wood two shallow glass or plastic dishes, one inside the other, the outer one to be filled to about 1/4″ deep with aqua ammonia, the inside one conc. HCl to about 1/2″ depth. Have ready a thin sheet plastic hood which covers the entire apparatus; this can be made from the exceedingly thin plastic used for protective bags for clothing or other similar articles. Place the specimen atop the wood strips, crystals *up!* Pour in acid into the inner container, and follow by pouring in ammonia in the outer container. At once the fumes will interact to form a dense white "smoke." Cover immediately with the plastic hood in such a way that the fumes can pass readily around the wood strips to the space above the specimen. "Smoke" for from 10 to 20 minutes, depending upon the density of coating desired. If the specimen is tilted, "shading" can be obtained, with the lower side uncoated, and the upper side heavily coated. After photography, remove coating by rinsing in water.

PRINTING FROM AGATES OR OTHER PATTERNED MINERALS OR ROCKS

By etching polished plates of agates, petrified wood, graphic granite, vein sections, etc., in which quartz is a prominent to major constituent, faithful reproductions can be obtained of the pattern or grain features displayed in such specimens. The method was first described by F. Leydolt.

Source: F. Leydolt, *Jahrb. Kais. K. Geologischen Reichs-Anstalt,* Jg. 2 (1851), pp. 124 ff. With plates.

Leydolt's method for producing the necessary hydrofluoric acid for etching quartz: Place powdered fluorite in the bottom of a lead vessel supplied with tight-fitting lid. Cover the powder with concentrated sulfuric acid. Place the specimen to be etched in a shallow vessel most conveniently made from sheet lead, and insert in the larger vessel. Cover the specimen to a depth of not more than about 1/8″ (3 mm) of water above surface to be etched. Put on the lid of the larger vessel and heat to generate hydrofluoric acid fumes which will dissolve in the water of the smaller vessel and etch the specimen. No time limit is set by Leydolt, but presumably at least 1/2 hr. would be required to obtain significant etching upon the specimen surface. Precaution: Do not heat so much that the acid or the water boils.

As an alternative and very satisfactory method, using commercial concentrated HF, dilute some acid with twice its volume of distilled water. Place specimen in the bottom of a suitable plastic container with side to be etched facing up. Pour in diluted acid and etch for 3 minutes. Pour off acid and wash off specimen carefully. Dry thoroughly and observe effect of etching. If the polish is now dull, the specimen can probably be printed; otherwise repeat treatment.

Another technique is to suspend specimen, face downward, over a shallow vessel filled with conc. acid; the specimen surface should be about 2-3″ (5-7.5 cm) above the liquid surface. Treat for 15 minutes; remove, wash, dry, and observe results. Repeat treatment as necessary.

Techniques using commercial acid require great care to avoid inhalation of fumes, contact with skin, and other dangers associated with hydrofluoric acid. Treatments are best carried out under a laboratory hood. On the other hand, Leydolt claims his method is very safe because of the weakness of the acid generated.

To "print" the specimens, one may use the specimen itself as follows. Using the ball-like ink applicator of the printer, or making one of stout tissue paper, ink the ball and apply to the agate using gentle rolling motion; avoid pressing ink into the etched recesses. Place paper over the specimen and rub with the fingernail, bottom of a spoon, burnisher, or similar instrument. Since all acid-resisting areas will be high these will print black while those lines or other features that etched more rapidly will be below the surface and hence will appear as white. Paper recommended is "Chinese" or "Japanese" print paper, available in art goods stores, or coated white paper used by printers. Another method of printing is that employed by copper-plate etchers where the specimen is heavily inked and the pigment forced into the etched recesses. The surplus is then carefully wiped off so that traces of ink remain only in the recesses. The specimen is now inserted over a slightly dampened sheet of paper in a printer's proof press and heavy pressure applied. If this is properly done, the paper is forced into the recesses, picks up the ink, and thus shows the pattern clearly when pulled off the specimen. Naturally this method exerts much force on the specimen and cannot be used for thin slabs or partly fractured specimens unless they are adequately supported in some fashion. Still another method of printing is to coat the etched specimen with a conductive layer and electroplate it. The copper is then stripped off and serves as the matrix for casting typemetal for formal press printing.

Among the kinds of materials that can be treated by Leydolt's technique are agates of all types, jaspers, ruin agates, opalized and silicified woods, graphic granites, and veins in quartz-bearing rocks; and also other materials in which silicates are present. Presumably similar results can be obtained with other classes of minerals by use of appropriate etchants.

STANDARD ROCK AND PARTICLE SIZE CLASSIFICATIONS

Rounded, Subrounded, Subangular Rocks

Size	Fragment	Aggregate
Over 256 mm (10")	Boulder	Boulder gravel; boulder conglomerate
64-256 mm (2-1/2 - 10")	Cobble	Cobble gravel; cobble conglomerate
4-64 mm (3/16 - 2-1/2")	Pebble	Pebble gravel; pebble conglomerate
2-4 mm (3/32 - 3/16")	Granule	Granule sand
1/16 - 2 mm (1/400 - 3/32")	Sand	Sand; sandstone
1/256 - 1/16 mm (1/6400 - 1/400")	Silt	Silt; siltstone
Under 1/256 mm (1/6400")	Clay	Clay; shale

Pegmatite Grain Sizes

Size	Term
Less than 1" (2.5 cm)	Fine grained
1 - 4" (2.5 - 10 cm)	Medium grained
4 - 12" (10 - 30.5 cm)	Coarse grained
Over 12" (30.5 cm)	Very coarse grained

METEORITES

Meteorites are divided into three groups: *stones* or *aerolites*, consisting of all or nearly all rocklike material; *irons* or *siderites*, all or almost all nickel-iron; and *siderolites*, which are mixtures of nickel-iron and rocklike material. A *fusion crust*, dull black in color and quite soft, is characteristic of all meteorites except those that have been in the ground a long time and have altered or rusted.

HOW TO RECOGNIZE METEORITES. Stony meteorites are much more difficult to recognize than the irons because they do not possess the "heaviness" of the latter and on the whole do not stand out among similarly colored fragments of earth rocks. The following are useful identification hints.

Shapes: Tend to be irregular to blocky, *not rounded.*

Surface features: Tend to display shallow scalloped places or depressions like the marks left in soft clay when it is pressed with the thumb; also miniature rills or canyons without sharp edges. Such sculpturing is due to the effects of erosion as the meteorite passes through the earth's atmosphere.

Surface color: Black to dark gray, but may be rusty if the meteorite has been buried for a long time.

Surface crust: The blackish crust is shallow, usually no more than 1/4" (3-4 mm) thick at the most and in most finds, much less. In many specimens it can be easily chipped away to reveal a paler interior which may range from nearly white to fairly dark gray in the case of the stony meteorites.

Heaviness: Stony specimens feel no more heavy than many earth rocks of the same general dark color, but iron or mixed types may be instantly recognized as being unusually heavy.

Specific gravity: Stones run from about 2.08 to 4.5; the mixed types higher; the irons between 7 and 8.

Fracture: The nickel-iron and some of the intermediate mixed types cannot be broken, only deformed or dented, but stones fracture readily. If a specimen is thought to be a meteorite any chip taken from it should be of the smallest size required to reveal the interior.

Fracture surface appearance: Practically all meteorites, including the stony types, show more or less nickel-iron when examined closely; magnification to 25x may be needed to see the smaller metal inclusions. Use a sharp steel point to test metallic inclusions for malleability; this test merely confirms that a malleable metal is present but is a very favorable sign that a meteorite is being dealt with. This test also excludes masses of ordinary sulfide minerals which may superficially resemble meteorites.

Abrasion test: Hold the stone against a grinding wheel for a few seconds; check surface to see if shining metallic areas have been exposed.

Henderson's Meteorite Recognition Hints

The following hints are offered by E. P. Henderson and A. S. Furcron (1956).

If the specimen is a stone, look for these features:

1. The presence of fused crust on the surface.
2. Small metallic inclusions which may be detected by a magnet, or by rubbing the fingers over a fresh break, in which case the metallic inclusions will feel jagged.
3. Metallic inclusions enclosing round silicate bodies.
4. Small rounded silicate bodies or chondrules.
5. Thin black veins within the specimen.

If the specimen is metallic, look for these features:

1. Is the object magnetic? All iron meteorites are strongly magnetic.
2. Is the iron malleable? The magnetic terrestrial minerals are brittle but meteoritic iron is malleable.
3. Remove the surface film from a small spot and note the color of the metal. Meteoritic iron is gray, similar in color to a five-cent coin.
4. Tap the object with something; metallic meteorites give a different sound than rock.
5. Is the specimen particularly heavy for its size?

REPORTING FINDS. To promote the science of meteorites all finds should be reported to either the U.S. National Museum, Washington, D.C., the Geological

Survey of Canada, Ottawa, or national museum in whatever country the specimen is found. Report where, when, and how, with as much detail on the appearance and properties of the find as possible. Some finds are of monetary value and are usually salable to mineral dealers.

Value of Meteorite Specimens

The following criteria are given by E. P. Henderson and A. S. Furcron (1956).

1. Size. May be too large to transport and slice or too small to divide. Specimens between 100 and 200 lb. are very desirable.
2. Type. Unusual type specimens are more valuable.
3. Degree of preservation. Specimens that are chemically stable offer less problems in preservation and hence are apt to fetch more from a knowledgeable buyer.
4. Unusual features. Flight markings, interesting inclusions, numerous cavities, or a witnessed fall increase value.
5. Witnessed falls and first finds. Collectors prefer witnessed falls, especially new ones.

ETCHING OF METEORITES. Used to reveal the characteristic patterns, or Widmanstätten figures, in the iron specimens. The simplest way to show the figures, but also the least satisfactory in many respects, is to place a slab of nickel-iron meteorite upon an asbestos fiber plate over a hot plate or Bunsen burner. As the metal oxidizes the surface takes on color which may be blue, purple, or yellow, and thus shows the crystallization pattern. Preliminary etching to show if a good pattern exists calls for swabbing the surface with nitric acid diluted to one-tenth its normal strength as it comes from the bottle. The surface should be clean and freshly filed or abraded. In about 4-5 minutes the pattern will be evident. This preliminary test is a useful one for field identification when it is possible that a fragment of man-made iron is at hand rather than a metallic meteorite.

FOOTE MINERAL COMPANY METHOD. (1) Wash specimen in benzine. (2) Lacquer unpolished portions and edges being careful to remove lacquer that creeps over the smooth surface to be etched. (3)

Carefully lacquer any nodular inclusions within the nickel-iron because these are very quickly attacked by the nitric acid used for etching. (4) Prop meteorite in horizontal position and wash surface with 5%-15% solution of chemically pure nitric acid for from 15 seconds to 4-5 minutes until the metal appears brilliant; longer washing causes darkening; apply acid with swab and keep moving over entire surface to ensure uniform etch; replace as soon as acid becomes discolored. (5) Place specimen in clean water heated to 120°-130° F. (50°-55° C.) for several minutes, rubbing with a brush. (6) Dry for a few seconds with blotting paper. (7) Thickly lacquer the surface at once.

Reference: O. C. Farrington, *Meteorites* (Chicago, 1915), pp. 127-29.

Farrington (cited above) also makes the following suggestions. Etching can be done by holding the specimen upside down to touch a basin of acid and thus obtain the desired uniform contact with the acid. Other etching agents include hydrochloric acid to which a small volume of antimony chloride is added to inhibit later rusting, also a solution of copper sulfate, the deposited copper being removed by ammonia, and other solutions such as mercury chloride, gold chloride, platinum chloride, or fused alkalies; or bromine water.

SMITHSONIAN METHOD. (1) prepare etchant solution of 2 parts by volume of conc. nitric acid and 5 parts by volume alcohol, made fresh for each etch, add 1 drop hide glue and stir thoroughly. (2) Place slab over suitable container and prop in horizontal position. (3) Pour on etchant covering all of the surface nearly at once as possible, distributing solution with clean swab. (4) Rinse off acid with alcohol brushing continuously, follow with rinse in running water and a final alcohol rinse. (5) Dry quickly under a fan. The treatment is repeated as necessary until figures are developed to desired degree. The treated surface may be coated with lacquer after it is completely dry.

PRESERVATION OF METEORITE SPECIMENS. Under ordinary room conditions, some meteorites disintegrate with distressing rapidity, largely due to the presence of moisture and active gaseous agents in the atmosphere. In some instances, careful treatment is required to dissolve sulfates, iron oxides, etc., from the specimens prior to placing in preservative storage in sealed containers. The latter may be plastic boxes, with seals, or glass jars with grease seals from which the air has been evacuated and/or replaced with nitrogen or some other inert gas. Silica gel desiccant bags may be placed inside to trap any moisture which may emanate from the specimens while in storage. Nickel-iron meteorites are least susceptible to deterioration, while certain stony meteorites are most likely to decompose in parts and disintegrate. In any case, specimens containing chlorides are most dangerous. Mere coating with lacquer is often only a stopgap measure.

References: E. P. Henderson and A. S. Furcron, "Meteorites in Georgia," *Georgia Mineral Newsletter* 9, no. 4 (1956): 126-35.

B. Mason, *Meteorites* (New York: John Wiley, 1962).

H. H. Nininger, *Our Stone-Pelted Planet* (Boston and New York: Houghton Mifflin, 1933).

H. H. Nininger, *Out of the Sky* (University of Denver Press, 1952; reprinted, New York: Dover Publications, 1959).

Tektites

Tektites are glassy objects believed to be extraterrestrial in origin. They are generally of small size as compared to other meteorites and commonly display characteristic surface markings, some due to ablation but most due to chemical weathering. In composition they do not resemble natural glasses found on earth and consist largely of silica (68%-82%) with relatively high contents of calcium, magnesium, and iron oxides, and relatively low contents of potassium and sodium oxides.

Collectors frequently confuse obsidian and man-made glasses for tektites, especially when the glasses mentioned occur in more or less rounded shapes with sandblasted or weathered exteriors. It now seems that most tektites by far, and the special glasses supposed to be due to the fusing of siliceous material during large meteorite impacts (impactites), occur in fairly well-defined areas known as *tektite strewn fields*. From the standpoint of collecting *they do not occur everywhere,* and when an object purporting to be a tektite is found well outside one of the fields mentioned below it can be justifiably regarded with suspicion. For example, and despite all of the vague and undocumented reports on tektite finds over much of the western United States, the only verified tektite occurrences in the United States are in Texas and Georgia, with one specimen reported from Martha's Vineyard, Massachusetts. All other finds prove to be obsidian, man-made glass, quartz, or even the bright green glasses thrown away by assayers of ore samples.

Tektite Strewn Fields

MOLDAVITES. Occur in two distinct areas of Czechoslovakia, one centered to the NW of Ceske Budejovice, Bohemia, and the other about 85 miles east, centered to the S and SE of Terbic (20 miles W of Brno), Moravia. Characteristically deep to very deep green in color, the so-called "bottle-green," and ranging in size from small splinters to several inches (c.7 cm) diameter. Maximum recorded weight for Moravian material 235 gm; for Bohemian, 87.5 gm. G = 2.303-2.367 (av. 2.3366); RI = 1.4798-1.49566 (av. 1.4888). Extensively "worm-tracked" sometimes very deeply; often extremely irregular and jagged in form. Large quantities have been cut into gems.

AUSTRALITES. Found over practically the entire Australian continent with the exception of the Northern Territory; greatest concentrations of finds in extreme S of New South Wales and in the S and S-central portions of Western Australia. Pitch black in color, but on thin edges or through flanges dark brown, greenish-brown, or dark olive-green. Shapes include buttons, lenses, ovals, boats, canoes, dumbbells, and teardrops, with flanges and rims on buttons being especially characteristic. Weights range from 0.15 to 218 gm, average 0.934 gm. G = 2.380-2.458 (av. 2.424); RI = 1.4981-1.520 (av. 1.509). Have been cut into gems and commonly offered for sale in the mineral and gem market.

DARWIN GLASS (Queenstownites; probably impactites). Occur in the Jukes-Darwin mining district of Tasmania. Dark smoky green to almost black, sometimes grayish-green, or nearly white when frothy. Contain numerous gas vesicles, much more so than other tektites or glasses. G = 2.275-2.296 (av. 2.288); RI = 1.474-1.4790 (av. 1.477).

JAVAITES. Occur around Sangiran, central Java, and near Mataloko, Flores Island. Dark color, nearly black. Sometimes show ablation markings; very deeply furrowed. G = 2.43-2.45 (av. 2.442); RI = c. 1.509.

BILLITONITES. From the island of Billiton, midway between Borneo and Sumatra. Furrowed black tektites. G = 2.457-2.512 (av. 2.494); RI = 1.5157-1.5305 (av. 1.5241).

INDOCHINITES. Occur in many places in North Vietnam, South Vietnam, Laos, Cambodia, Thailand, and in minor numbers on the mainland of China, on Hainan Island, and on the Malayan Peninsula. More or less deeply corroded black tektites, some with stream-wear markings. Black, yellowish, or brownish in thin sections. Shapes mostly spherical or nearly so, but lenticular, elongated, teardrop, and other forms are also abundant. G = 2.404-2.440; RI = 1.4972-1.5133. Recently collected in large numbers and sold in the amateur mineral and gemstone market.

PHILIPPINITES (RIZALITES). Scattered occurrences on the central islands of the Philippine Archipelago and more abundantly on Luzon. Essentially resemble tektites from the other SE Asia occurrences. G = 2.447-2.451; RI = c. 1.5130.

IVORY COAST TEKTITES. Very similar to billitonites in color and sculpture. G = 2.4-2.517; RI = 1.4991-1.5178.

LIBYAN DESERT GLASS (Impactite?). Pale greenish-yellow transparent glass found in a small area in the Libyan Desert. Fragments sometimes large, to 10 lb. (c. 4.5 kg). Irregular pieces, sometimes like twig or branch sections, ropy, etc., with smoothly rounded surfaces. Contain numerous fine inclusions forming veils and bands. G = 2.21; RI = 1.4624. Has been cut into gems.

BEDIASITES. Found in a narrow strip extending NE-SW from north Grimes County to NE corner of Gonzales County, Texas, corresponding to the outcrop of the Jackson group of formations. Black, but dark brown in thin sections. Approximately spherical in shape with little sculpture. The largest recorded specimen weighed 91.3 gm, with range of weights 0.5 to 59.4 gm for most specimens and average weight of 15.57 gm. G = 2.334-2.433 (av. 2.374); RI = 1.488-1.512. Sometimes cut into gems.

GEORGIA TEKTITES. Found very sparingly in an area SE of Empire, Dodge County. Discoidal to rounded in shape, with surfaces nearly covered with pits and furrows and resembling moldavites in this respect and also in color, a light olive-green. G = 2.330; RI = 1.485. The properties and appearance of the single tektite found on Martha's Vineyard, Massachusetts, are very similar.

How to Recognize Tektites

Shapes: Tend to be rounded, or ovoid, lenticular, discoidal, teardrop, etc.; also button-shaped, dumbbell-shaped, and rarely, with ablation flanges. Moldavites and the Georgia tektites tend to be extremely jagged upon their surfaces.

Sizes: Generally 2″ (5 cm) or less, with many not more than about 1″ (2.5 cm) diameter.

Surface features: Water-worn specimens with smooth surfaces but not bright; small surface fractures typically half-moon in shape with bright recesses. The external feature of greatest value in identification is the characteristic chemical erosion surface displaying the shallow to deep rills and furrows with lustrous sides and bottoms. Very rarely, ablation features, such as flanges, are observed and these are proof that a tektite is at hand.

Color: Most tektites appear coal-black, but some, like the green moldavites and Georgia specimens, are obviously colored. Shallow fracture edges or thin webs or splinters generally show dark brown, dark green, or various intermediate shades of these colors, commonly dingy in hue.

Surface crust: None.

Heaviness: Seem about as heavy in the hand as obsidian.

Specific gravity: Low, about 2.3 to 2.5.

Refractive index: Low, about 1.47 to 1.53.

Fracture: Glassy conchoidal, highly perfect.

Hardness: Harder than obsidian.

Toughness: Much less brittle than obsidian or man-made glasses.

Heat resistance: Very high; can be heated suddenly to bright red heat in the blowtorch flame without cracking and plunged into water while hot also without cracking (this test does not separate obsidian but does separate common artificial glasses which promptly crack at the first touch of the blowtorch flame).

References: G. Baker, "Tektites," *Memoirs National Museum of Victoria,* No. 23 (Melbourne, N.S.W., 1959), pp. 1-313.

V. E. Barnes, "North American Tektites," *University of Texas Publication* no. 3945 (1940), pp. 477-582.

G. A. Bruce, "Tektites in Georgia," *Gems and Minerals,* no. 264 (1959), pp. 22-23, 65-69.

R. S. Clarke, Jr., and M. K. Carron, "Comparison of Tektite Specimens from Empire, Georgia and Martha's Vineyard, Massachusetts," *Smithsonian Miscellaneous Collections* 143, no. 4 (1961), 18 pp., 6 plates.

Geochimica et Cosmochimica Acta, Second International Symposium on Tektites, 28, (1964): 753-1017.

B. Mason, *Meteorites* (New York: John Wiley, 1962), pp. 201-20.

J. A. O'Keefe, *Tektites* (University of Chicago Press, 1963).

L. J. Spencer, "Tektites and Silica-Glass," *Mineralogical Magazine* 25, no. 167 (1939): 425-40, with plates.

MINERAL SPECIMEN FAKES AND DECEPTIONS

The gentle art of faking, improving, or repairing specimens is of ancient lineage but has gained a special impetus in modern times because of the lively demand for specimens to satisfy the needs of the increasing body of mineral collectors. Many fakes are so crude that only a glance is needed to detect them, but others are so skillful that one is filled with admiration for the unsung "artist" and his work. The finest fakes contain no element which jars either the scientific or aesthetic sensibilities of the viewer, while the choice of components and their composition is exciting and absolutely true to nature.

Preceding the list below of minerals which for some reason or other require the critical examination of would-be buyers, appear definitions of fakes and the general instructions for their detection. It should be observed that "repairs" are not deceptions unless their presence in specimens is deliberately concealed from the buyer.

REPAIRED SPECIMENS. Portions of one specimen or xl reassembled with suitable cement and most commonly observed in brittle, friable, or cleavable minerals and matrices.

Detection: Look for cracks which extend entirely through the specimen or crystal; examine same under magnification for traces of cement or expose to UV to detect fluorescence which is common in many cements. Soaking in water may reveal conspicuous whitening of vinyl acetate water emulsion type cements; soaking in acetone can dissolve or loosen acetate or nitrate cements of the quick-drying type; in extreme cases, soaking in methyl ethyl ketone dissolves or softens cements which are unattacked by the previously mentioned solvents.

ASSEMBLED FAKES. Specimens assembled from components not originally belonging together. *Plausible fakes* are those in which the components are consistent with the nature of the deposit from which the specimen purportedly comes, e.g., colored pegmatite tourmaline attached to lepidolite or cleavelandite matrix. *Implausible fakes* are those in which the components are recognized as being from distinctly different types of deposits, or otherwise suspect, e.g., elongated prisms of pink tourmaline rising from biotite schist or native silver wires implanted in a sedimentary quartz geode.

IMPREGNATIONS AND COATINGS. Fragile specimens or those likely to crumble under handling or by loss or gain of water from the atmosphere are very commonly impregnated or sprayed with some sort of cementing material diluted by water or other solvent. Much can be said in favor of this practice providing the intent is to preserve rather than to artificially enhance the attractiveness of the specimen. In any case, like repairs, ethical dealers will state that spraying or impregnation has taken place. Common examples include laumontite groups from California or Brazil soaked in very dilute plastic solution to prevent disintegration due to loss of water; marcasite, sprayed to excluded atmospheric humidity and gases which may lead to decomposition of the marcasite; and native iron, sprayed to prevent corrosion. Unfortunately, spraying is all too often resorted to for xl specimens whose faces are dull in luster. The first washing usually removes the coating in portions and when the specimen is dried it becomes very unsightly.

Detection: Soakings may be difficult to detect if after soaking the specimen is rinsed in water to remove excess water-soluble cement, or similarly rinsed in solvent to remove excess plastic cement. Coatings are easier to detect because excessive use of spray results in bridging or covering of cracks or "veils" caused by slumping of the spray before it has dried. Coatings are also easily scratched off and often the fingernail, applied to an inconspicuous smooth xl surface, is enough to peel off the lacquer.

PLATINGS. In rare instances, precious metal platings are applied to specimens of a baser metal in a variation of the gold-brick swindle.

Detection: Cut below the surface with a file and examine the base of the cut under magnification.

A good general rule is to suspect any specimen in which delicate crystals or elongated crystals rise steeply from a matrix. The chances are that such crystals were broken off during late stages of formation, as is especially true in the "pocket" minerals of pegmatites and Alpine vugs, or they were broken off by the miner during removal from the ground. Examine very carefully for evidences of repair or for evidences of attachment at the bases of the crystals in the cases of assembled specimens. Clever assembled fakes always use bits of the same material as the matrix, carefully mixed with cement and applied to the base of the implanted crystal to provide support and to disguise the junction. A final touch may be the sprinkling of limonite dust on the joint, or even soaking the assembled specimen in a container filled with rusting nails to deposit a natural coating of limonite on portions that may look too new.

ACANTHITE. The mineral usually sold as "argentite" is actually the orthorhombic modification acanthite.

ADAMITE' Yellow acicular and transparent xls from Mapimi, Mexico, may be mistaken for the much rarer legrandite; adamite xl terminations are blunt wedges, legrandite terminations are sloped and steeper.

ALMANDINE. Euhedral xls tend to drop out of mica schist matrix and may be cemented back.

AMBER. Large clear lumps of yellowish kauri tree gum from New Zealand have been carelessly offered as true amber; they craze readily and quickly become sticky when rubbed with a little hydrocarbon solvent. Common inclusion-fakes in true or pressed amber include salamanders, lizards, frogs, and modern insects, although the smaller and fragile insects are usually real because they cannot be inserted into an amber fake without virtual destruction. Suspect all large and highly perfect inclusions.

AMPANGABEITE. Many xls of this mineral are betafite.

ANDALUSITE. Square prismatic xls of this species from the Tirol have been beautifully assembled into magnificent groups by using rusty mica flakes, limonite powder, and suitable cement; recent fakes require methyl ethyl ketone to dissolve the specimen. Signs of faking: mica flakes invariably about bases of protruding xls with filleting.

ANHYDRITE. Very easily cleaved; examine for repairs.

ANTIMONY. Large pot-melt masses have been broken up and offered as native Sb; usually the cleavage surfaces are very large, about 1″ (2.5 cm) or so; such specimens lack any trace of matrix rock and usually also any yellowish alteration products.

APOPHYLLITE. Very easily cleaved; examine for repairs.

ARAGONITE. Much coralloidal or slender prismatic calcite is sold for aragonite and in most instances is shown to be calcite by the presence of three intersecting *rhombohedral* cleavages typical of that species; aragonite cleavages are at right angles, i.e., orthorhombic. Further distinguishable by chemical test although effervescence in HCl not diagnostic.

ARGENTITE. See ACANTHITE. Very rarely argentite is sold for galena and vice versa; the best distinctions are perfect cubic cleavage in galena and the extreme softness (fingernail cuts) of argentite.

ASSAY GLASSES. Usually small (c. 1/2-1" (1.2-2.5 cm)) greenish transparent glass objects which may be approximately spherical or conical and may or may not have an iridescent whitish coating (somewhat like the perlitic coating on obsidian ("apache tears"); these are rejected from assay melts and typically show swirl marks inside; they rapidly deteriorate on the surface in damp atmospheres, forming whitish powdery coatings. They have been sold as "tektites," "green obsidian," and even as "peridot."

AUTUNITE. Loses water and becomes meta-autunite in ordinary room atmospheres; loss of water commonly causes disintegration and consequently many specimens are soaked in plastic solution or lacquer-sprayed.

BARITE. Xls readily cleave; examine for repairs.

BERYL. Emerald xls have been implanted in limestone matrix (Colombia) or cemented on such matrices with mixtures of crushed limestone, minute pyrite xls, and/or limonite; similar fakes on mica schist from Africa and Urals. Broken prismatic xls of aquamarine commonly cut squarely across and polished to form a basal face; detected by presence of parallel polishing marks and absence of spiral growths or etch figures characteristic of natural faces. Examine all matrix specimens showing elongated prismatic xls for repairs. Examine all Colombian emerald specimens for faking, especially when xls appear to grow from deep within small vugs where their bases cannot be easily seen entering matrix.

BISMUTH. Commonly occurs in beautiful xls in smelter flues and cooling chamber walls and sometimes offered as natural; suspect all specimens which are not attached to rock matrix.

BORATE MINERALS. Many alter readily when removed from the ground, commonly to opaque white tincalconite, and for this reason spraying or soaking is often resorted to to delay such changes.

BOULANGERITE. Commonly confused with jamesonite.

BRAZILIANITE. Excellent fakes have been made using small xls and attaching same to matrix from the same deposit with flakes of mica, grains of albite, and powdered limonite and glue. Close examination of points of attachment usually shows the mica-albite-limonite filleting; also examine under UV for fluorescence of the glue.

CACOXENITE. The "cacoxenite" in clear rock xls or amethystine quartz from Brazil is golden fibrous goethite.

CALCITE. Easily cleaved; examine for repairs. Cleavage rhombs can be dipped in dil. HCL to create interesting solution markings and such may be offered as natural xls. Many calcite xls from the Tri-State area of the U.S. are customarily dipped in dil. HCl to remove white powdery coatings which occur naturally, and to enhance luster of xls. Acid removal of calcite marble, e.g., as in the matrix of Franklin, New Jersey, specimens, reveals itself by glasslike luster, waving or curved surfaces, and obliteration of cleavage setbacks.

CELESTITE. Easily cleaved; examine for repairs.

CERUSSITE. May be mistaken for anglesite or phosgenite; cerussite very commonly twins while the others do not; furthermore, cerussite lacks the perfect basal cleavage of phosgenite. Examine all phosgenite specimens from Monteponi, Sardinia, with this in mind.

CHABAZITE. Very easily broken off matrices; examine for repairs.

CHALCANTHITE. Virtually all well-xled specimens purporting to be this mineral are actually natural matrices (commonly drusy quartz) upon which synthetic xls of copper sulfate (blue vitriol) have been grown from aqueous solution.

CHROMITE. Xls rare; test for magnetism to eliminate magnetite substitutions.

CHROMIUM. Not found native; artificial xl groups have sometimes been offered and display the typical brilliant color and luster of highly polished chromium.

CHRYSOCOLLA. A vaguely defined mineral at best and certainly most specimens of "chrysocolla" are mineralogically claylike coatings of clays, minor amounts of colloidal malachite and azurite, or the same included in small amounts in translucent chalcedony.

CLAY MATRICES. Usually soaked in

lacquer or vinyl acetate glue solution to prevent disintegration (e.g., kunzite in clay, Pala, California).

COBALTITE. Xls easily dislodged from matrix and usually cemented back.

COLUMBITE-TANTALITE. Often confused for each other but columbite ,black entirely opaque, while tantalite deep red translucent in thin splinters; columbite favors blocky habit, tantalite favors subparallel groups of tabular xls.

COPIAPITE. Readily alters in damp atmosphere and most specimens are sprayed with lacquer to prevent.

COPPER. "Native copper" taken in interesting wiry forms from copper-bath solutions has been offered as genuine; usually lacks distinct xls and is covered with a warty surface. Much genuine native copper is treated in acid baths to remove discolored films, adhering bits of matrix, etc.; the chief distinctive feature of such specimens is their bright luster and obliteration of fine striae and other markings on xls.

COQUIMBITE. Lacquer-sprayed, like copiapite.

CORUNDUM. Platy xl masses grown artifically from the vapor phase have sometimes been offered as genuine ruby; the xls do not resemble any natural ruby specimens and specimens usually are curved crusts 1/2-1″ (1.2-2.5 cm) thick, porous and vuggy, and without any trace of matrix rock. Hydrothermal rubies have now been grown and resemble high-quality tabular Burmese ruby xls but tend to be considerably flatter and of better quality; attachment points or remnants of metal clips may be present on such xls.

DANBURITE. Xls easily broken from matrix; examine for repairs.

DATOLITE. Specimens friable and may be repaired or reinforced along the base by impregnations of cement.

DIAMOND IN MATRIX. It is extremely rare that any diamond xl is found in matrix due to the modern mechanical methods of processing the ore which minimize visual examinations of the kimberlite rock. Kimberlite is usually grayish, soft, and studded with inclusions of other rock types as well as other minerals; some resembles a raisin pudding; a conspicuous constituent is brown phlo-

gopite mica, which, if absent, is cause for suspicion that the matrix is not genuine. Modern fakes, some frankly labeled as such, use genuine kimberlite but the diamond xls are cemented into carefully prepared depressions. The rusty conglomerate rock containing alluvial diamonds in certain Brazilian deposits is also a favorite material for faking because of the many deep recesses between the small pebbles that may receive a diamond cemented in with bits of sand, limonite, and glue. Regard *all* diamond matrix specimens with suspicion and buy only after careful examination.

EPIDOTE. Long prismatic xls from the Knappenwand, Salzburg, Austria, locality may be repaired but the fracture lines are usually obvious.

EUCLASE. Recent finds of euclase xls in Brazil produced some matrix fakes with loose xls cemented into recesses of vuggy albite-muscovite matrix.

FLUORITE. Readily cleaved and specimens may be repaired. The pink octahedra of Switzerland, usually found perched on quartz xls, are easily detached and therefore commonly cemented back in position. In some instances where Swiss pink fluorite xls are naturally coated with disfiguring chlorite, sellers have removed same by abrasives.

FRIEDELITE. Massive, fine granular material from Franklin, New Jersey, may be similarly colored serpentine.

GARNET. Grossular xls of orange hue have been sold as spessartine. Almandine xls may be cemented to mica schist matrix. Vivid green grossular in small xls, especially from Canada, has been sold as the much rarer demantoid variety of andradite. Almandine has been sold as pyrope but the latter has no xl faces.

GLASS. Chunks of glass have sold as unusually colored obsidian, e.g., green, blue, etc., but the colors of obsidian are dull and almost always black, brown, or sometimes red-brown. Sandblasted fragments have been sold as alluvial aquamarine, tektites, etc. See also ASSAY GLASS.

GOLD. The common fake is the implantation of small bits of native wire or flake gold into small inaccessible vugs in quartzose rock matrices using ordinary acetate cement which dries to a transparent colorless material. Examine all such specimens under powerful magnification. Washing in acetone dissolves the cement. If vinyl acetate water-emulsion glues have been used, soaking in water causes them to whiten and become visible. While wire, flake, and leaf gold does occur naturally in this manner, there is usually some place on the specimen where the gold can be seen entering the quartz; failure to find any trace of this feature is cause for suspicion as to authenticity of the specimen. Another fake, somewhat more crude, employs commercial leaf gold torn into small bits and forced into crevices or pressed against the matrix rock. The extreme and uniform thinness of the gold in such fakes should alert the prospective buyer to the possibility of fraud. Occasionally, native silver specimens have been gold-plated; cut a minute file groove at some inconspicuous point and examine under 25x to see if underlying silver appears; also check specific gravity by the immersion method, which should reveal the fake very quickly because of the much higher density of gold. Gold nuggets have been faked by melting a cheap gold alloy, puddling into irregular nuggetlike shapes until cool, and then subjecting to tumbling to simulate natural stream wear. Natural gold nuggets commonly contain bits of milky quartz, usually with the gold entering into crevices in the quartz or passing between fracture fragments of the quartz; limonite incrustations in deep recesses are also a very common feature of natural nuggets. See also TELLURIDE GOLD. Pyrite, or "fool's gold," offered as gold, is easily and certainly distinguished by crushing to a powder, which is not possible in the case of the real metal; in the field, the simplest test is to place a small sample on a flat smooth stone and hammer it with another stone; if it flattens, like lead, it is gold, if it shatters it is pyrite (or chalcopyrite). The same test can be applied more delicately on any specimen by scratching with a sharp piece of quartz, which leaves a dark powder trace on pyrite and a shining groove on gold.

GUMMITE. Not a distinct species but a mixture of uranium and other minerals found together in small to large masses in certain pegmatite occurrences.

Reference: C. Frondel, "Mineral Composition of Gummite," *American Mineralogist* 41 (1956): 125-32.

HALITE AND HALIDES. Commonly sprayed with transparent colorless lacquer to prevent attack by atmospheric moisture.

HANKSITE. Sprayed to prevent disintegration or alteration in damp atmospheres or dipped in oil to preserve.

HEMATITE. The famous shining "kidneys" of massive hematite from England were customarily rubbed with black shoe polish and then buffed to enhance the surface luster. Martite, the hematite pseudo after magnetite, is distinguished from the latter by being nonmagnetic and displaying a reddish or brownish streak (Utah). The hexagonal plates from which rutile grows in the famous rutilated quartz specimens of Minas Gerais, Brazil, are hematite and not rutile or ilmenite.

HEULANDITE. Xls very easily cleaved or dislodged from matrix; examine for repairs.

HUEBNERITE. Many specimens from Colorado, with the huebnerite blades solidly enclosed in quartz, are treated with hydrofluoric acid to expose them but are sold as such without attempt to deceive the buyer.

IRON. Native Fe in specimen grade appears on the market only from Greenland or Germany and shows the iron as irregular masses within basalt. Absence of matrix rock is cause to suspect authenticity. Most of the real specimens are sprayed heavily with lacquer to prevent rust.

IRON METEORITES. Pieces of deeply corroded agricultural iron or steel, or pieces of discarded machinery have been plowed up and thought to be meteorites. The nickel-iron meteorites are not brittle whereas cast iron can be easily fractured; however, to distinguish between steel and meteorite metal, sawing and etching of the metal is necessary to reveal the typical crystallization features of coarse grain in true meteorites and the much finer granular pattern in man-made steel.

IRON + STONE METEORITES. These are difficult to detect from external appearances when weathered or partly altered but if fractured, the interior shows nickel-iron in the form of rounded blebs within stony matrix, or webs of nickel-iron passing between fracture fragments of the stony material (see also "Meteorites," p. 213).

LAUMONTITE. Rapidly loses some water of crystallization and tends to quickly disintegrate; for this reason most specimens showing large xls (Brazil, California, India) are soaked in dilute glue or sprayed to hold them together.

LAZURITE (Lapis lazuli). Occasionally, fake dodecahedral xls have been prepared by cutting very uniformly colored pieces from among specimens of lapis lazuli and then smoothing the surfaces to a dull finish. The unnatural flatness of the surfaces of such "crystals" and the traces of abrasion marks usually distinguish the fakes.

LEAD. Found in quantity only at the Langban, Sweden, deposits; the typical form is sheets with rough surfaces, usually with whitish bits of alteration mineral in crevices, and with or embedded in dark brown granular hausmannite rock. The absence of any such rock in a specimen, or the presence of smoothness of surface upon the lead, are causes for suspicion.

LEGRANDITE. May be ADAMITE, which see.

LEUCITE. Trapezohedral xls from Italy readily dislodged from matrix; check for repairs.

LITHIOPHILITE. Many specimens of black color are largely impure masses of manganese oxides and various phosphates derived from the alteration of lithiophilite.

LUDLAMITE. Specimens from Idaho are fragile and the xls themselves very easily cleaved; check for repairs.

MAGNESIUM. Excellent crystals of artificially prepared magnesium have sometimes been sold as native magnesium, which element has never been found native in nature.

MAGNETITE. Specimens of the hematite pseudos (martite var.) from Utah and elsewhere are sometimes erroneously sold as magnetite; they are not magnetic nor do they provide the typical black streak of magnetite, although some specimens from these deposits are true magnetite.

MALACHITE. Fibrous masses or sprays of acicular xls are commonly mistaken for other copper minerals, e.g., brochantite.

The "malachite" pseudos after cuprite from Chessy, France, are largely cuprite with only a thin film or layer of malachite.

MANGANITE. Some specimens of manganite are actually psilomelane pseudos after this species.

MARCASITE. Many so-called marcasite concretions or radiate growths are pyrite, with or without some marcasite. Marcasite specimens are susceptible to alteration with formation of white efflorescences of melanterite; to prevent such alteration most specimens are soaked or heavily sprayed with plastic solutions in dilute form.

MESOLITE. Commonly confused with either scolecite or natrolite. There is no easy offhand way to distinguish these species; usually, optical tests are necessary.

MEYERHOFFERITE. Commonly replaces inyoite retaining the xl shapes of the latter.

MICROCLINE. Many early feldspar specimens from granitic pegmatites are still labeled "orthoclase" when actually most are perthitic microcline.

MICROCLINE (var. amazonite). Xl groups commonly break apart when being extracted; check for repairs.

MILLERITE. Loose tufts of acicular xls may be cemented into geode openings.

MOLDAVITE. Green transparent ASSAY GLASS (which see) has been frequently sold as the dark green tektite (moldavite) of Bohemia; the latter is characteristically sculptured with curving grooves, like worm marks, is glistening, and typical dark "bottle-green" in color whereas the glass objects lack the markings and are usually yellow-green in color, somewhat like peridot (see also Tektites, p. 215, 225).

MOLYBDENITE. This readily cleavable mineral commonly falls out of quartz matrix when specimens are cobbed; typical deceptions include cementing back into place or taking loose books of the mineral and cementing into crevices or vugs in massive milky quartz (Chelan, Washington).

NATROLITE. See remarks under MESOLITE.

NEPTUNITE. Many of the neptunite prisms associated with benitoite from the famous Dallas Gem Mine in San Benito County, California, are fractured during the growth of the enclosing white natrolite vein filling and consequently are found loose after the natrolite is removed with acid; these may be cemented back to their stubs.

NIOBATES-TANTALATES. Often confused for one another and may require careful testing to identify. See COLUMBITE.

OBSIDIAN. See ASSAY GLASS and GLASS.

OPAL. Some massive granular types of opal from Australia have been treated with sugar solution and concentrated sulfuric acid to impart an artificial blackening and then may be sold as true black opal.

ORPIMENT. Commonly sprayed with lacquer to prevent disintegration when associated with light-sensitive realgar. Many xl groups are exposed by dissolving enclosing calcite with hydrochloric acid.

PECTOLITE. "Pectolite" masses which are not fibrous but crumble readily into powder are replacements of pectolite by a clay mineral ("stevensite"). In some zeolite occurrences, notably around Paterson, New Jersey, pectolite sometimes forms groups of acicular xls which are commonly mistaken for natrolite. scolecite, or mesolite. Massive, very finely fibrous grayish to greenish pectolite has been confused with nephrite jade.

PERIDOT. See ASSAY GLASS for a material which is sometimes offered as genuine peridot.

PEROVSKITE. In the serpentine areas near the benitoite locality in California, small black cubes of magnetite are commonly mistaken for the much rarer perovskite; easily distinguished by the strong magnetism of magnetite and its absence in perovskite.

PHOSGENITE. Occasionally twinned tabular xls of cerussite from the Monteponi, Sardinia, locality are mistaken for phosgenite; usually twinning junctions and/or striae serve to distinguish the cerussites.

PLATINUM. May be imitated by steel shaped and suitably discolored into alluvial-type nuggets; strong magnetism of steel distinguishes, also rapid reaction to nitric acid. Platinum is infusible, unaffected by the borax bead, and soluble only in hot nitric-hydrochloric acid, but some natural nuggets are definitely magnetic. Insist on careful examination or pedigree before purchasing Pt nuggets.

PYRARGYRITE. May be offered as proustite but the latter is obviously red in hue and much more translucent to fully transparent.

PYRITE. Xls and balls, fans, disks, etc., obtained from sediments, are very likely to decompose into white powdery melanterite and for this reason are usually soaked or sprayed with dilute plastic solutions.

PYROPE. Well-formed garnet xls with good faces may be offered as pyrope garnet but the latter does not occur in euhedrons.

PYRRHOTITE. Certain specimens, particularly rosettes of numerous thin tabular xls piled one atop the other from the Yugoslavian-Romanian deposits, are susceptible to decomposition into melanterite; for this reason they may be soaked or sprayed with dilute plastic solution as a preservative measure. Pyrrhotite xls are commonly replaced wholly or in part by pyrite and may be offered as true pyrrhotites; chipping off a small fragment of such a pseudo usually reveals the bright, pale-hued surface of pyrite and not the duller and dingier color of pyrrhotite. Also check for the appreciable magnetism of pyrrhotite (none in pyrite).

QUARTZ (citrine var.). Sometimes rock xls acquire a very thin and uniform coating of iron oxide which imparts a yellow color like that of true citrine; scrape or rub some inconspicuous smooth surface to remove such coating; the coating is also easily removed by a drop of dil. oxalic or hydrochloric acid. Typically, coated xls are covered with the iron stain all over; this is seldom the case in true citrine, in which the yellow coloring tends to be confined to the tips of the xls. Recently much heat-treated amethyst in druse sections has been sold as citrine; it is distinguished by traces of carbon in crevices in the matrices and by a slight milkiness in the clear areas of the xl tips. Good xls of natural citrine are quite rare.

QUARTZ TWINS. Japanese twins are easily broken from their matrix; check for repairs.

QUARTZ, CRYPTOCRYSTALLINE. Agates are very commonly dyed to impart colors which rarely, if ever, appear in natural specimens, e.g., vivid reds, greens, yellows, and blues. Such colors seldom penetrate more than skin deep and removing a small chip from some inconspicuous place usually shows the naturally gray material underneath. Some agate nodules may be heat-treated to carnelian shades and in such cases the color passes all the way through. Look for carbonized matter in cracks along the exterior of the nodules as signs of heat treatment. In dyed nodules, traces of dye in exterior portions are usually convincing evidence that the nodule has been artificially colored.

REALGAR. Commonly sprayed with plastic lacquer to arrest alteration brought about by exposure to light.

RUTILE. Shining xls in matrix from California or Georgia are sometimes dislodged from matrix and cemented back in place.

SCOLECITE. See MESOLITE.

SERPENTINE. Extremely fine-grained serpentine has provided sharp replacements of various silicate mineral xls which sometimes are called "crystals" of serpentine. A beautiful pale yellow, greenish, or nearly white translucent form of serpentine (bowenite or "Soochow jade") is commonly used in China and Hong Kong as a jadeite substitute; it can be scratched with the sharp point of a steel knife whereas neither jadeite nor nephrite are touched by the knife, but heavy pressure must be used to obtain a definite scratch in the serpentine. The material occurs in very large flawless masses and is sold extensively in carved form to unwary tourists as genuine jade.

SILICA GLASS. Very few sources of natural silica glass are known, perhaps the most important being a small area in the Libyan Desert which provided sandblasted specimens of characteristic pale straw-yellow hue; all silica glass offered as genuine must be regarded with suspicion as to authenticity.

SILVER. Wire silver commonly occurs in nature in loose masses and numerous fakes have been prepared by cementing wire curls into recesses of suitable matrix pieces which may be vuggy sulfides, vuggy quartzes, or other minerals which are plausible associates of silver in veins and ore deposits. Look for points of attachment deep within vugs using a microscope lamp and at least 15x; the usual cement is acetate plastic which shrinks and becomes entirely transparent on drying. Gentle washing in acetone may dissolve such cement causing the wires to drop off. See GOLD for other pertinent remarks. Very rarely, native copper specimens are carefully cleaned by chemical means and then plated with silver. See GOLD for suggestions on detection of such fakes.

SMITHSONITE. At times xls of calcite from Tsumeb, South West Africa, are offered as smithsonite but can be detected by greater transparency, better cleavage, and much lower specific gravity as compared to smithsonite.

SPESSARTINE. May be confused with grossular.

SPINEL-FRANKLINITE-MAGNETITE. These three species form similar xls in the deposits of Franklin, New Jersey, but the spinel from this place is translucent greenish on thin edges or in splinters, while the other two are absolutely opaque; furthermore, only magnetite of the trio is magnetic. In gem gravel material, spinel is readily distinguished from sapphire by lacking dichroism and acquiring a generally much smoother surface upon the water-worn pebbles.

SPODUMENE (hiddenite var.). The pale green Brazilian spodumene is often sold as "hiddenite" but it is generally agreed that only the chromium-bearing spodumene from North Carolina should be called by that name.

SPODUMENE. Much kunzite is sold as "crystals," implying that they are euhedrons when such is very seldom the case. By far most fragments are cleavage pieces more or less etched upon the surfaces, none of which were the original crystal faces.

STAUROLITE. Many of the twinned xls ("fairy crosses") sold in the mountain districts of Virginia are altered staurolite, filed and smoothed to shape, and then oiled to improve color and luster. Unaltered staurolite is impossible to shape even with the hardest steel file.

STILBITE. Very easily dislodged from matrix; check for repairs.

SULFUR. At times beautiful but totally spurious specimens of sharp, transparent sulfur xls, usually on drusy quartz matrix, are sold to unwary buyers. They are prepared by crystallizing sulfur upon the matrices from solutions of sulfur in carbon disulfide.

SUSSEXITE. Many specimens of this mineral from Franklin-Ogdensburg, New Jersey, have been shown to be fibrous amphibole. True sussexite is soluble in hydrochloric acid and fuses in the blow-pipe flame.

TEKTITES. Glasses of various kinds, obsidian "apache tears," and even pieces of water-worn bottle glass have been sold as true tektites. Almost all tektites show characteristic surface markings and their absence is good cause for rejecting specimens offered as such or at least requiring proof of their nature.

TELLURIDE GOLD. Specimens of ore rich in surface coatings of gold tellurides (Colorado) become covered with small beads of gold when they are strongly heated to drive off the tellurium. Native gold is never found in such beadlike forms.

TENNANTITE. Tetrahedrite is sometimes offered as tennantite but usually the xls of the latter are small, around 1/8" (2-3 mm), whereas those of tetrahedrite are considerably larger.

THOMSONITE. When occurring as small spherical masses may be mistaken for scolecite, mesolite, or natrolite.

TINCALCONITE. Very commonly the whitish opaque coating or material found replacing various borate minerals, especially borax.

TOPAZ. The orange-yellow xls from the Ouro Preto deposits of Minas Gerais, Brazil, are easily heat-treated to pink although pink and red xls do sometimes occur in the same deposits; heat-treated xls are uniform pink throughout their length whereas naturally pink or red xls tend to exhibit these hues only near the termination with the remainder of the xls being the usual color. Some colorless xls have been turned to deep brown by X-ray irradiation. Uncleaved xls on matrix are very difficult to obtain; check for repairs. Matrix specimens from the Thomas Mountains, Utah, have been "improved" by cementing loose xls into the small vugs characteristic of the host rock; the joints are usually sprinkled with a "sand" derived from crushing the rock or obtained in the vicinity of the deposits.

TORBERNITE. Sometimes sprayed with plastic lacquer to preserve and more firmly attach the very fragile xls to matrix.

TOURMALINE. Colored tourmaline prisms are very commonly cemented to appropriate matrices by use of cement and fillets of lepidolite, albite, etc. In most examples the "buildup" of the cementing material around the bases of the xls is obvious. Broken prismatic xls are sometimes furnished with artificial terminations through the art of the lapidary; examine for lack of growth hillocks and other delicate markings typical of real terminal faces and for the parallel marks left by the lapidary's wheel. All very long prismatic xls should be examined for repair.

TRIPHYLITE. See remarks under LITHIOPHILITE.

TURQUOISE. May be soaked in oil or impregnated with very dilute plastic solution to decrease porosity and improve color.

ULEXITE. May be sprayed to prevent surface alteration.

UVAROVITE. The small bright green "uvarovite" garnet xls from Canada are usually grossular.

VIVIANITE. Large xls tend to spontaneously cleave; look for repairs. Many specimens are lacquer sprayed to improve appearance and, hopefully, to arrest destructive dehydration.

WILLEMITE. Often unrecognized as complex multiple crystalline masses from South West Africa and usually sold as "smithsonite." Typically colored tan or orange, translucent, and lacking the perfect cleavage of smithsonite; check under UV for fluorescence.

WOLFRAMITE. The splendid xls from Panasqueiras, Portugal, are surprisingly fragile and cleave very readily; check specimens for repairs.

WOLLASTONITE. White balls of crystallites suspended in man-made green glass have been sold as natural wollastonite.

ZIRCON. Natural zircons are usually some shade of tan to medium or dark brown, sometimes with reddish overtones; only rarely are other hues found as purplish; metamict zircon pebbles of a peculiar grayish-green hue and somewhat milky inside are common in the gem gravels of Ceylon and have been sold as peridot, sapphire, etc. Colorless or blue zircons are heat-treated.

ZOISITE. The fine blue gem xls from

Tanzania are usually heat-treated to drive off undesirable trichroic colors, usually greens or brownish-clarets.

FAKES, IMITATIONS, DECEPTIONS, AND SYNTHETICS AMONG GEMS AND GEMSTONES

The scarcity of some natural gem materials has resulted in greater use of synthetic materials which may or may not have natural counterparts. The various methods of synthesis now producing or capable of producing synthetic gem materials are briefly outlined below.

References: For the detection of gem fakes, substitutes, synthetics, etc., consult B. W. Anderson, *Gem Testing,* 7th ed. (London: Butterworths, 1971); R. T. Liddicoat, Jr., *Handbook of Gem Identification,* 6th ed. (Los Angeles: Gemological Institute of America, 1962); R. Webster, *Gems,* 2d ed. (London: Butterworths, 1970).

Methods of Synthesis

Flame fusion: Also called the Verneuil method after its French inventor. Powder of suitable composition is dropped through an intensely hot flame and melts, the droplets falling upon a refractory pedestal which is lowered in synchronization with the crystallization of the material as it cools. Forms more or less rounded conical solids called "boules." Extensively used to produce corundums and spinels, also rutile and strontium titanate.

Czochralski or pulling method: A flat plate of the desired crystalline solid, cut to preselected crystallographic orientation, is lowered to touch the surface of a melt of the same composition. When slowly withdrawn the molten material adheres to the bottom of the plate and crystallizes in the same orientation, thus forming a more or less smooth-walled cylindrical single crystal of very high quality. Used extensively to produce colorless and pink corundum, also yttrium aluminum and other rare-earth garnets, and lithium niobate.

Bridgman-Stockbarger method: A crucible containing a melt of desired composition is lowered into a somewhat cooler region of the furnace, whereupon the material crystallizes and forms large

crystals of excellent quality. Used to make scheelite and fluorite.

Hydrothermal autoclave: Seed wafers suitably oriented are fastened to a metal rack and inserted in a cylindrical metal pressure vessel; in the bottom are placed lumps of material of the same chemical composition as the seed crystals. The vessel is partly filled with water, sealed, and then heated on the bottom. At the proper pressure and temperature the nutrient material dissolves in the water and circulates upward around the seed crystals, depositing additional material on them and causing them to enlarge. Used primarily to grow large quartz crystals (colorless or colored), also corundum, beryl, magnetite, zincite, rare-earth garnets, and cadmium sulfide (greenockite).

An important variation of this method is used to synthesize diamond but the pressures are enormously higher; apparently a liquid phase of carbon develops from the graphite nutrient and by catalysis, converts into diamond. On a minute scale, the same may happen in the "shock" method of diamond synthesis where a rapid shock wave passing through metal saturated with carbon causes the latter to change to diamond. However, the change in crystal structure may also be explained as being direct modification due to application of pressure sufficient to cause collapse of the graphite structure.

Flux-melt or flux-fusion: Similar to the hydrothermal method in that a liquid, in this instance, a melted solid salt or salts, is the medium for dissolving the ingredients of the synthetic crystals and allowing them to migrate to seed crystals or spontaneously nucleate. Normally no pressure is applied. Used to grow beryl (emerald), corundums, spinels, and rare-earth garnets.

Sublimation: In this process a suitable solid is heated and its vapors cooled to force condensation during which crystals form, or several solids can be vaporized to react and form another compound which then crystallizes in a cooler region of the apparatus. The most important application produces silicon carbide abrasive crystals (sometimes of gem quality), but sphalerite and greenockite have also been produced in large fine crystals.

References: For a review of modern methods of crystal synthesis see J. J. Gilman, ed., *The Art* and *Science of Growing Crystals* (New York: John Wiley, 1963); K. Nassau, in a series of articles in *Lapidary Journal* 18, nos. 1-6 (1964).

ALEXANDRITE. Extensively imitated by synthetic corundums which also produce a color change between daylight and artificial light. Real alexandrite is enormously expensive and any gems offered at prices of a few dollars per stone, as is commonly done in Mexico, the Orient, and elsewhere, are almost certainly synthetics.

AMBER. Kauri gum, a geologically recent fossil resin from New Zealand, has been sold as true amber which it is not; kauri gum is softer, more brittle, crazes rapidly, and readily dissolves in common organic solvents. Much reddish, perfectly transparent and flawless bakelite resin has been carved into small to large objects which are sold to the unwary as "Burmese amber." This practice is common in the Far East.

BROMELLITE. This beryllium oxide has been synthesized in large colorless masses which are capable of being cut into faceted gems.

CACOXENITE. Transparent colorless, citrine, or amethystine quartz containing brilliant golden fibrous inclusions has been called "cacoxenite" or "cacoxenite quartz"; the inclusions are actually fine fibrous goethite.

CAMEOS AND INTAGLIOS. Imitations are made from pressed glass or sometimes from two-layer pressed glass to give fair simulations of onyx engraved gems; they are readily distinguished by untrimmed edges and lack of fine tool marks as well as slight shrinkage concavities along flat surfaces. Similar imitations have been prepared from plastics, especially simulating coral or ivory.

CHRYSOCOLLA. Applied indiscriminately to chalcedony stained blue to blue-green by copper minerals in colloidal form; among them may be chrysocolla but it is more likely that malachite and/or azurite are the coloring agents. True chrysocolla is an extremely brittle, opallike material whose exact nature is still in doubt.

COATED FACETED GEMS. Sometimes a low-index coating, possibly composed of fluorides, is deposited upon faceted gems to reduce surface reflections and permit light to pass into the gem to increase brilliance. Such coatings typically display a purplish iridescent "bloom" like that noted on camera lenses treated by the same process.

CORAL TREES IN MATRIX. These are coral branches crudely cemented into brownish rock bases and purporting to be coral as it grows on the sea floor. Real coral trees in situ show a mushrooming foot spreading over rock, usually accompanied by whitish limy deposits from other organisms.

CORUNDUM. The so-called "ruby" star stones of plum-red color from India are really red corundum rather than ruby; they do not compare in beauty or translucency to the star or cabochon rubies from classical sources. Hydrothermal synthesis of ruby produces tabular crystals with excellent growth markings similar to natural rubies, also the flux-melt process, but usually the crystals are uniformly dark red, excellent in quality, and may show cavities where attachment clips were present, or even pieces of the metal clips; they may be confused with natural crystals, especially those from Burma but the latter tend not to be so tabular in habit. The newer synthetics produced by the Czochralski method produce ruby and pink sapphire of much better internal perfection than those made by the flame-fusion method. Star rubies (and other colors) are made by introducing titanium to the starting powder in the flame-fusion method and then annealing the boules to encourage exsolution growth of rutile needles which form the star effect. The high degree of perfection of these stones and other signs prevent their being mistaken for real star stones when examined by an expert. The United States type shows very sharp reflective lines but a similar stone made in Germany displays much more diffuse lines. Synthetic corundums have been occasionally tumbled to simulate genuine alluvial stones.

DIAMOND. General Electric Company in the United States synthesized diamonds large enough to cut gems of 1 carat or less but at present they are far too costly to produce in quantity. Diamond doublet gems have been made in which the top of the gem is real diamond and the bottom some other gemstone material or even another piece of diamond. If mounted in rings which cover the junction of the two pieces they can be extremely difficult to distinguish.

DOUBLETS. The "false" type consists of two pieces, the upper or crown part being the genuine material but the bottom another material. A very common type uses a thin layer of almandine garnet for the crown and glass for the pavilion. They can be easily distinguished by the differences in luster of the two components and by the red gleams which reflect from the garnet when held in a certain position. The "true" doublet consists of sandwiches of genuine material cemented together for the purpose of cutting a larger gem than would be possible from either of the smaller pieces. Some cabochon gems are doubleted, notably opal, jade, star quartz, and some catseyes.

EMERALD. Large pieces of clean natural rough that are offered at cheap prices usually turn out to have thin color layers around the periphery of the crystal or crystal fragment and virtually colorless interiors. They are offered cheaply because some expert lapidary has already determined that a gem cut from the piece would be so pale in hue that it would be almost worthless. All emerald rough must be immersed in bromoform (R.I. = 1.594) to reveal the interior and determine the distribution of color. Hydrothermal and flux-melt emeralds tend to be flattened crystals which do not resemble natural emerald crystals in habit; however, when cut great care is required to identify them correctly. Lechleitner-type emeralds are thin veneers of emerald grown over preformed seeds of aquamarine; they must be faceted with care to prevent cutting through the emerald layers.

FLUORITE. Synthesized in large flawless masses.

GAHNITE SPINEL. Synthesized in flawless material suitable for gems.

GARNET. Demantoid or sometimes vivid green grossular may be offered for the much rarer uvarovite, which ordinarily occurs in crystals so small that it is not feasible to cut useful gems from them. One of the synthetic rare-earth garnets (see GARNETLIKE SYNTHETICS) has been made in a lovely green color, which along with other properties when cut, provides gems that are alarmingly like natural

demantoid. Spessartine and grossular of similar color are often confused but the latter usually displays characteristic "swirl" marks inside while spessartine lacks them completely. Rhodolite and almandine of similar hue cannot be easily distinguished without careful testing. Pyrope gems are seldom over several carats in weight; larger stones purporting to be this species are probably almandine. High quality, translucent bluish-green massive grossular from South Africa ("Transvaal jade") resembles fine jadeite but is generally distinguished by the presence of small black spots of chromite which are lacking in jadeite.

GARNETLIKE SYNTHETICS. Rare-earth elements have been combined with alumina in the Czochralski or flux-melt methods of synthesis to create large clear masses with the same structure as natural garnets; however, they lack the silicon present in natural garnets. High properties and attractive colors have won instant popularity for gem purposes. "Yag" is the term used for yttrium aluminum garnet, one of the most popular of the series of garnetlike synthetics. Colors include colorless, pink, green, and yellow.

GLASS GEMS. These are made in two types, the cheapest merely being melted glass pressed into suitable molds and the better class being molded first and then the facets polished in whole or in part. The pressed glass imitations always display unfinished girdles and slightly concave facets without any sign of lapidary tool marks. The better, fully cut glass imitations are not as easy to detect but usually display properties and internal features diagnostic of glass. Many dozens of types of glass have been used as the starting materials for glass gem imitations with their properties generally ranging between specific gravities of 2.3 to 5.0 and refractive indices between 1.47 and 1.8; some types for special purposes are higher. To increase brilliance, many are coated on the backs with silvery or golden metallic paints or platings. Favorite targets for imitation include aquamarines, amethysts, emeralds, and rubies. Cheap glass gems have also been coated to impart iridescent films which are quite striking in their beauty. Opal is imitated by a milky sandwich-type glass which emits feeble gleams of other colors from the backing material somewhat like that observed in very murky examples of white opal.

GREENOCKITE. Synthesized in gem quality material but seldom cut.

GREEN QUARTZ. The so-called "green quartz" carvings of China are actually green fluorite in which the octahedral cleavage planes are usually conspicuous. Carvings of this material are noticeably heavier in the hands than any kind of quartz carving of similar size because of the higher specific gravity of fluorite. The green quartz of Brazil is produced from certain types of amethyst by heat treatment.

IDOCRASE OR VESUVIANITE. Massive, fine-grained material from California ("californite") has been used as a jade substitute. A greenish-yellow translucent kind (Pulga, California) could be easily mistaken for serpentine.

JADEITE. Genuine Burma material has been dyed to improve color, sometimes preceded by heating to open pores for easier entry of the dye. Jadeite triplets of excellent color have been made and sold at high prices to the unwary. Some types of highly translucent serpentine resemble jadeite (see SERPENTINE); see also GARNET.

LAPIS LAZULI. Certain porous jaspers of Europe have been dyed blue to imitate genuine lapis lazuli but invariably lack the clean white patches of calcite and the specks of pyrite. They are called "Swiss lapis." Lapis lazuli has been closely imitated by a granular synthetic spinel + gold sintered material but it has not succeeded commercially and gems of this material are very rare.

LITHIUM NIOBATE. Synthesized in gem material in colorless, green, yellow, blue, and red.

OBSIDIAN. Greenish glass in which occur white ball-like aggregates of crystallites (wollastonite?) have been sold as "green obsidian"; also assay glasses from assay crucibles have been sold as obsidian or as "peridot" or "tektite." There is no green obsidian known.

OPAL. Poorly imitated by glasses but there is now some promise that synthetic opals may someday be manufactured in a process similar to that which produces natural material. Certain porous massive opal material from Australia has been found to accept black dye using the sugar solution–sulfuric acid method. The finished gems bear feeble resemblance to true black opal but the granular nature of the material and the appearance of black specks trapped in pores when viewed under high magnification quickly distinguishes the dyed gems. A similar black-dyeing method has also been used for Mexican opals but only very rarely. Opal doublets and triplets are now common on the market. Most doublets consist of thin veneers of black opal cemented to bases of opal potch, glass, or obsidian. The latest triplets, which are very handsome, add a third layer or top of clear rock crystal above the opal layer. The curving top provides both a magnifying effect and much better protection against wear.

PAGODA STONES. Tapered triangular prisms of rock crystal notched along the back to provide multiple reflections forming a pagoda image when viewed from the front. Commonly imitated in glass. The genuine stones usually show veils and inclusions typical of quartz while the imitations are either very perfect inside, or display rounded bubbles characteristic of glass.

PERICLASE. Colorless material has been synthesized and sometimes cut into faceted gems; no natural periclase occurs in facet grade material large enough to cut gems over about a millimeter or two in diameter.

POTASSIUM TANTALATE. Synthesized in colorless and colored transparent crystals suitable for gem purposes although there is no evidence that it has been so used.

PROUSTITE. A glass of approximately the composition of realgar and deep red in color has been made for infrared transmission lenses and prisms; it has sometimes been cut and offered as "proustite."

PSILOMELANE. A false name sometimes applied to a chalcedony from Mexico containing numerous small fibrous crystals of a black manganese oxide which may or may not be psilomelane. It has also been called "black malachite"!

QUARTZ. Much citrine is produced from amethyst by heat treatment; typical material sometimes shows opalescence. Green quartz is heat-treated amethyst from certain deposits, principally from one in

Brazil. Excellent green and blue synthetic quartz crystals of large size have recently appeared on the market from the USSR. Natural star quartz of good quality is rare but some occurs in the gem gravel of Ceylon, which not only shows a strong star but possesses the milky grayish or bluish-gray color of a very common type of star sapphire and is therefore sold as such. Most star quartz cabochons are so weakly asteriated that it is necessary to doublet them with backing of silvered glass which may be additionally colored red or blue to imitate corundum star gems. False star gems have also been made by ruling three sets of fine lines crossing at 60° angles on the bottom of a polished cabochon which may be glass or quartz; these may be further elaborated by attaching a mirror backing as noted above. Rose quartz carvings are imitated by cast plastics or glasses of appropriate color and trans-lucency. Spheres of glass are frequently sold to the unwary as quartz but are easily distinguished by the presence of bubbles, swirl marks, and by the absence of double refraction when the sphere is placed over a small ink mark and the mark observed from above through the sphere. Polished quartz spherical beads can often be easily identified by holding the bead to the northern sky light (polarized) and observing the uniaxial figure typical of this mineral; the same effect can be better seen if the bead is observed between two pieces of polaroid plastic in the crossed position.

RUTILE. Synthesized in boules which are heat-treated to produce a pale straw-yellow transparent material used for faceted gems. By varying the heat treatment, other colors can also be obtained but very little of this material has found its way into the market. Natural rutile is black to very dark red in color and seldom clear enough or light enough to afford more than very small faceted gems.

SCHEELITE. Synthesized in several colors, one of which is very close in hue to the brownish-orange natural material from the deposit in Sonora, Mexico, and which has been cut and sold as "natural" scheelite. Colorless scheelite has also been synthesized and would be difficult to distinguish in cut form from gems prepared from the colorless material of California. All large gems of scheelite, say over 10

carats, should be regarded with suspicion and tested thoroughly before they are accepted as natural.

SERPENTINE. Highly translucent serpentine, locally known as "Soochow jade," is regularly carved in China and offered in Hong Kong and elsewhere as jadeite. It is far more uniform in texture and of much higher translucency than most jadeite, especially in large masses, and possesses a peculiar yellowish-green hue which is distinctive when once examined. A scratch test on some inconspicuous spot on the base brings up a powder in the case of this material, but fails to affect either true nephrite or jadeite.

SILICON CARBIDE. Occasionally some tabular crystals of clear gem-quality silicon carbide are found among the large porous masses of this material which are produced in the electric furnace for abrasive purposes. Small gems of high properties have been cut in such colors as green, brown, and blue, but despite the suitability of silicon carbide for gem purposes no attempt has been made to produce it commercially in high optical quality.

SPHALERITE. Clear gem-quality sphalerite has been synthesized but its softness and brittleness have prevented its use for gems; natural sphalerite is abundant in gem quality but there is little demand for it except to cut an occasional collectors' gem.

SPINEL. Very commonly synthesized via the flame-fusion process and sold in large quantities. Recent syntheses have produced a fine red color suggestive of ruby or natural red spinel; some colorless synthetic spinel has been used as a diamond substitute in inexpensive jewelry.

SPODUMENE. The name "hiddenite," usually reserved for the chromium-bearing spodumene from North Carolina, has been indiscriminately applied to the pale yellow-green spodumenes of Brazil.

STRONTIUM TITANATE. Synthesized by the flame-fusion method into flawless and colorless boules with high optical properties. It has been used as a diamond substitute and could be sold to the inexpert as that gem.

TOPAZ. Certain topaz colors can be changed by heat treatment or by X-ray irradiation, namely, the yellow-orange crystals of Ouro Preto, Brazil, to pink by heat treatment, and the colorless or sherry crystals from Utah and Mexico to deep sherry or brown by X-ray irradiation.

TRIPLETS. Faceted gems (sometimes cabochons) composed of three layers of material which may be all genuine or only partly genuine. A typical triplet imitating emerald consists of an aquamarine crown, a thin layer of green plastic or glass, and a pavilion of quartz or glass.

Part 10 / Cleaning Mineral Specimens

WATER CLEANING METHODS

Most household water is slightly to significantly charged with mineral matter, the worst kinds being known as "hard" water, and those that are purer being known as "soft" water. However, some so-called "soft" waters contain considerable mineral matter, particularly salts of sodium, and while appearing "soft" insofar as laundering is concerned are as contaminated as the "hard" waters in which salts of calcium and magnesium cause the hardness. For minerals rather easily attacked by acids or other chemical agents, it is safer to use distilled water for cleaning, and certainly for rinsing, both to prevent chemical attack of brilliant crystal faces and to leave as little scum as possible after drying. Distilled water sold in grocery and hardware stores is completely satisfactory.

Soaking: Mere soaking is indicated for minerals covered with clays; this treatment allows maximum penetration of water which gradually forces apart the clay particles and makes them easier to remove. As much as possible of the clay should be picked off beforehand by any convenient method, then the specimen placed in the water to soak; allow at least 24 hours, and more is preferable. Remove, hose or spray, and reimmerse as necessary to expose clay deposits that have not softened.

Clay soaking additives: Clays are very commonly cemented together by minute amounts of iron oxides (reddish, brownish color), or calcite, or sometimes gypsum. Ordinary soaking is extremely slow in effect and therefore weak acid should be added to the bath to aid clay disintegration, e.g., weak HCl, or oxalic, the latter being very effective in attacking the iron oxides as well as calcite and gypsum; the action of the acid is noticeable in several hours when the clay surface layers become white or at least much paler in color. A pinch of powder or several drops of liquid detergent improves penetration of water.

Spray cleaning: For delicate specimens merely dribble water upon them; dislodge dirt by slender slivers of bamboo. For stronger specimens in which there is no fear of breakage, use garden spray nozzles to direct water against the specimen. The pistol-grip adjustable type spray nozzle is generally better than the ordinary twist-adjustment nozzle. A fine spray is more effective than heavy sprays or heavy streams of water which seldom get into crevices fully.

Single jet needle spray: Make this from a brass coupling which you can screw to the end of a garden hose. Solder or braze over the opening with a disk of brass in the center of which is a fine hole no larger than the diameter of an ordinary sewing needle. The single jet is very effective for aiming into deep recesses for cleaning out otherwise inaccessible deposits of clay and dirt.

Agitated water bath: This method is to be used for pegmatite pockets or other cavity deposits in which many small fragments, crystals, and matrix specimens are intimately mixed with clays, chlorites, or other such minerals; also for cavities near the surface filled with topsoil. Place material in a tub of appropriate size such that about half is filled with the material to be washed or just enough to allow a covering of about 4-6″ of water when the tub is filled. Use pistol-grip water-hose nozzle to spray contents and to fill tub. Keep directing spray below the surface to agitate contents. The strong water currents float off clays, soils, vegetable material, mica flakes, and other wastes. Also stir contents by hand to expose fresh material to the jet from the nozzle. When the water runs clean, drain tub and spread material over several thicknesses of newspaper to dry.

Quick concentration of heavy minerals: Use a household wire mesh strainer of at least 6 inches diameter, or make one from metal gauze. Fill about half full with the loose mineral grains that must be sorted. Immerse in a bucket of water and move up and down in short rapid strokes to cause the individual mineral grains to "float" momentarily. The motion allows heavy minerals to sift down through the lighter minerals until they concentrate at the bottom of the strainer. A double handful of loose material is usually well sorted after a minute or so of agitation. Discard lighter materials at top and save the heavier concentrates at the bottom. Repeat with the remainder of stock until all is processed. Repeat concentration of the "heavies" until nothing remains at the bottom of the strainer but the heaviest minerals of the lot. A cone screen for this purpose can be made easily from wire gauze and should be about 10″ to 14″ diameter at the top, and from about 6″ to 8″ deep. Useful for concentrating garnet, corundum, spinel, diamond, tantalite-columbite, and other heavy species which are likely to be found in gravels, sands, or within pegmatite or other mineralized pockets. Also very useful for gold but fines will be lost through the screen openings.

Gold panning: Steel gold pans are still available from miners' supply shops or lapidary shops, especially in the western United States. They are useful for concentrating heavy minerals such as gold, platinum, magnetite, and chromite by employing a rotary tipping action which causes the water in the pan to swirl the contents, and by being allowed to wash over one edge, to remove lighter minerals. Before washing a pan load, all pebbles should be removed by hand until only small stuff remains. Magnetite is usually concentrated with the gold but can be easily removed by an ordinary magnet.

ULTRASONIC CLEANING

A variety of small to large electronically operated ultrasonic baths are now available, from those which hold only several cupfuls of water to those which can be filled with several gallons of fluid. Read manufacturer's directions carefully to avoid damage to the crystal driving devices which are attached out of sight to the bottom of the tank. Stainless steel tanks may be used with water or mild acid solutions as desired.

General precautions: Never rest heavy mineral specimens directly upon the tank bottom because they may press directly over the driving crystals and place too much load on them. Fill to the level recommended by the manufacturer because the shock waves causing the cleaning action are most efficiently propagated at a certain filling level. Long, uninterrupted operation results in the water becoming warm to hot which may cause thermal shock damage to specimens either upon immersion or removal. Check frequently to see that the water is never more than lukewarm. If the power unit is separated from the tank (in larger models), allow adequate air circulation around the cooling vents. Prolonged immersion of finger joints in the tank may result in pain in the joint capsules and possible eventual damage to joint linings. In some models, a wire or plastic mesh immersion basket is provided; use this to immerse and remove specimens. If none is provided, make one, or suspend specimens by string from an overhead piece of wood. Clean tank frequently, especially if clay-covered minerals are being processed or minerals taken from acid baths are being cleaned. Use several drops of detergent, or a pinch of dry powder detergent to every quart of water.

Uses: Ultrasonic cleaners cannot perform miracles, as some are inclined to believe, but they are very effective for reaching into crevices on specimens which are physically impossible to clean. Best results occur with hard-surfaced minerals, such as quartz crystals, and poorest results with soft, flexible minerals like clays, cookeite, and chlorite. With the latter species it is usually necessary to remove as much as possible by mechanical means and then use the ultrasonic bath. Excellent results are obtained in cleaning minerals that have accumulated dust, dirt, and grime during storage or exhibit. If cooking grease or tobacco smoke are part of the dirt, the addition of a teaspoonful of straight household ammonia solution to each quart of bath is effective in dissolving these oily or greasy substances, if the ammonia itself is not otherwise harmful to the minerals. In general, distilled water is preferred in all ultrasonic cleaning, especially for chemically sensitive species.

Double baths for chemicals: While the unit in use may have a stainless steel tank it is generally preferable when using strong chemicals in conjunction with ultrasonic cleaning to make use of a double bath arrangement, the outer bath being the tank, and the inner bath being a suitable glass container holding both the chemical and the specimen. Avoid plastic containers because they absorb ultrasonic shocks rather than pass them through the walls as does glass.

MECHANICAL CLEANING TOOLS

DENTAL TOOLS. Obtain discarded dental picks, chisels, probes, and other stainless steel tools that may be discarded by the dentist. Sharpen as required on a 400 grit silicon carbide wheel with water spray to prevent "burning" of points, or rub down on oilstone.

JEWELERS' FILES AND RIFFLERS. These are all made of excellent steel and hardened at the "business ends." Sharpen as explained above. Must be used with care because they tend to snap easily but this is offset by their much superior hardness. Dental tools do not snap easily but on the other hand dull their points or edges quickly.

NEEDLES. Perhaps the best tool of all for fine work is the ordinary sewing needle inserted in a fine hole drilled into the end of a piece of 1/4″ birch dowel rod. They cost little, are suitably hard, can be sharpened a number of times before they get too short, are delicate, and can be had in many sizes. With care, they can also be bent into curves to reach around corners. Short lengths of piano wire can be used in lieu of needles but of course need to be sharpened.

BAMBOO SKEWERS. Obtainable from novelty or party shops and used as they come, or split into fine slivers. Blunt ends may be soaked in water, then hammered lightly to fray into short stiff miniature brushes. A great advantage of bamboo is its softness, which avoids scratching, yet sufficient stiffness to easily dislodge dirt and clay. Toothpicks of wood are also useful but less satisfactory on a number of counts. Plastic toothpicks or skewers are too brittle to use.

RAZOR BLADES. All types of discarded razor blades make excellent scrap-ing tools for the removal of adhering clays. They may be used as they come, or broken across into sharp-pointed sections. Hardware stores sell backed razor blades very cheaply ("industrial razor blades").

TWEEZERS. Various types of tweezers may be used to dislodge loose material from crevices but perhaps the best kind is the Swiss watchmakers' tweezer which is furnished in extremely fine tapering point models. It is eminently suited for removing and manipulating micromount specimens. Obtainable from jewelers' supply houses.

BRISTLE SCRUB BRUSHES. Obtainable in various sizes and shapes, mostly with nylon bristles. All are useful for vigorous scrubbing of nonfragile specimens. Toothbrushes are also useful, but it is generally better to cut off the rounded ends to enable the bristles to reach depressions.

ARTISTS' BRUSHES. Used for cleaning of very delicate specimens. Camelhair brushes are fairly good but sable brushes are better but also cost more.

WIRE BRUSHES. Sometimes used for fast removal of adhering clay from coarse mineral specimens or for brightening corroded or dirty native copper or native copper-silver specimens, especially those from Michigan.

LOOSE ABRASIVE CLEANING

Sometimes tenacious clay coatings can be removed more rapidly by using a stiff bristle brush in conjunction with a slurry of silicon carbide or alumina grit, mesh size 100, 220, or 400; alternative agents are pumice powder and ordinary toothpaste or scouring powder. Pick up slurry and scrub vigorously, and repeat as needed. Despite the hardness of the silicon carbide and alumina abrasives little damage is inflicted even on feldspar crystals (H-6).

SAND BLASTING

Has been used with considerable success with silicon carbide or alumina abrasives, or crushed feldspar, etc., for softer minerals. The "crow-foot" sprays of rubellite in lepidolite matrix prepared from specimens of Pala, California, material by Foote Company many years ago were processed in this manner.

MINERAL CLEANING AGENTS AND THEIR USE

WATER. H_2O. Dissolves many borates, sulfates, and complex carbonates. Sea water contains 3.5% by wgt. diss. salts (2.5% salt, NaCl). Hard water contains Ca and Mg ions which react with soaps to form curds. Soft water indicates either absence of diss. minerals or water treated by water-softening chemical to exchange Na ions for Ca ions. Hard water lathers poorly and very quickly washes off soap; soft water lathers profusely, and even when used without soap feels soapy. Rainwater is essentially soft but contains diss. gases CO_2, SO_2, and nitrogen oxides in addition to soot and other atmospheric dusts. It is slightly acidic. Boiling of rainwater and Ca-rich goundwater helps purify by ejection of gases or precipitation of Ca as insol. salts. Inexpensive distilled water is available for drinking and other purposes and should be used for cleaning mineral specimens.

HAND SOAPS. Only the alkali and acid-free types should be used, which are known as "castile" soaps (available in drugstores). Many other hand soaps are rich in free oil which forms oily scums on crystal faces; however, scums may be removed by rinsing in acetone or carbon tetrachloride. Oily scums attract and cement dirt.

DETERGENTS. Complex chemical formulations, many containing phosphates for strong attack against greases, oils, and waxes. Most contain fluorescent compounds which glow strongly blue in UV. Small quantities of either powder or liquid detergents may be used for the sake of the wetting agents within them as well as for their cleansing action. About 1 level teaspoonful of powder detergent is used to 3 gallons of water. Strong detergent sols. rapidly attack aluminum and slowly attack some minerals.

WETTING AGENTS. Sold by chemical and industrial supply houses in paste or liquid forms. Several drops per gallon greatly improve penetrating and cleaning action of water bath.

CHELATING AGENTS. Complex compounds added to water to entrap metal ions, notably iron, and help prevent remnants of iron compounds from appearing later and staining areas around fissures, cracks, and pores with disfiguring yellowish hues. Standard chelating agent is EDTA, also known as "versene" and chemically ethylene diamine tetra-acetic acid or ethylene dinitrilo-tetra-acetic acid, a white crystalline powder. Add to acid baths in the ratio of 1/4 of the total conc. acid required by wgt.

HYDROCHLORIC ACID (MURIATIC ACID). HCl. Cheap, yellowish conc. acid sold in hardware stores and useful for most calcite removals. Standard conc. 38%-39% by wgt. *Technical grade,* colorless, purer, and more expensive, and to be used for the cleaning of better specimens. *Chemically pure* (CP) is very seldom required. Conc. acid fumes when unstoppered with vapors highly corrosive to nearby metals, tools, etc. Pour slowly into water when diluting and stir with glass or plastic rod. Usual dil. ratio 1 volume conc. acid to 3 of water (strong); to 10 of water (weak). Conc. acid dangerous to skin and mucous membranes but dilute is less so. Spills on concrete floors are automatically neutralized by carbonates in the cement; upon other materials wipe up with newsprint, or flush with water, or neutralize with scattered marble or limestone powder, or flush with sol. household ammonia. Do not discard this or other acids via household plumbing because of active corrosion of piping even during brief intervals of contact. In using this acid for dissolution of carbonates, surround container with newspapers to catch small droplets of acid thrown out when sol. bubbles with release of CO_2 from carbonate. Plastic or glass containers indicated; do not use metal or earthenware of any type. Slowly evaporates through sides of plastic jug containers, releasing corrosive fumes. For long-term preservation transfer to stoppered glass bottles.

NITRIC ACID (AQUA FORTIS). HNO_3. Dangerous, readily evaporating and oxidizing acid which must be treated with great respect. Store in brown glass bottles because decomposed by light with formation of brownish fumes of nitrogen dioxide, or store in darkness. Do not store in plastic bottles, which permit acid to readily pass through the sides and into the room as corrosive vapors. Usual conc. 68%-70% by wgt. Dilute by pouring into water slowly. Strong acid attacks and ulcerates skin and flesh, causing painful slow-healing wounds. Weak acid stains skin yellow and while less dangerous is very irritating. Neutralize spills with baking soda or carbonate powder, flush with ammonia sol. Rapidly attacks many metals, usually releasing several nitrogen oxides, including the brown fumes of nitrogen dioxide which are poisonous and must not be inhaled. Perform cleaning operations under hood or outdoors in breeze. The oxidizing power of this acid requires care that wherever it is used spills must not fall upon finely divided organic matter such as newspaper or cloth, which may spontaneously ignite.

SULFURIC ACID (OIL OF VITRIOL, VITRIOLIC ACID). H_2SO_4. Thick, oily liquid. Colorless when pure, and noticeably heavy. Sold in various concentrations (see bottle label). When diss. in water liberates so much heat that explosions due to steam formation occur when water is poured *into* the acid. For this reason, the acid must always be poured into the water, preferably in a thin stream, stirring vigorously at the same time. After dilution do not lift or move the container without cautiously testing side for heat; it may be too hot to hold! The conc. acid attracts water from the atmosphere and automatically dilutes itself to a much larger volume; hence promptly clean up or neutralize spills with baking soda, carbonate, limestone powder, or ammonia sol., the carbonates being preferred. Should be stored in ground-glass stopper bottles and set into a plastic dish to catch any dribble which occurs as a result of attracting atmospheric water. Rapidly attacks organic materials, including living tissues, causing extraction of water and carbonization. Droplets on the skin must be promptly washed off with many volumes of water and the spots coated with a paste of baking soda. Chars paper, wood, decomposes sugar, etc. The strong affinity for water results in the removal of water of crystallization from hydrous minerals as gypsum and the zeolites. Hot conc. acid attacks many minerals, including some silicates.

AQUA REGIA. A mixture of 3 parts by vol. conc. HCl to 1 part by vol. conc. HNO_3. Very dangerous. Attacks and diss.

many of the less chemically active or "noble" metals, e.g., gold, platinum.

HYDROFLUORIC ACID. HF. No description of this acid could possibly overemphasize the dangers it offers to the human organism. Even the smallest droplets create painful ulcers upon the skin, signaled at first by no sensation whatever until it is too late to do anything about prompt removal. Bleaching of tissues occurs, followed by much pain. It is for this reason that the protective precautions discussed herein must be followed to the letter. The fumes are also extremely dangerous, with inhalation beyond trace amounts causing severe damage to lung tissues and even death due to incapacitation of the lining. *Serious contacts require the immediate attention of a doctor!* To prevent accidents, handle the acid under a laboratory hood under good ventilation. Protective clothing must include wrap-around plastic apron, rubber gauntlet gloves, and plastic face shield which covers *all* of the face. Tools for picking up specimens must be positive in their action to prevent splashing when placing specimens in the bath. May be used outdoors with long-handled plastic cups or scoops for specimens, standing away from the acid and ensuring that the breeze is taking away the fumes. It is to be noted that the latter attack vegetation in the vicinity and kill the leaves! It is always a good idea to have at hand a flushing hose and quick access to a shower in which the person can run in case of receiving clothing or skin contact with the acid. For small contacts, flush the spot with large volumes of water for at least 5-10 minutes; follow by applying a paste of baking soda. Despite its danger, this acid is unreplaceable for the dissolution of silicate minerals, especially clays, cookeite, chlorite, and other fine-grained minerals adhering to certain mineral crystals. It reacts with silicates to form the gas silicon tetrafluoride (SiF_4), but often leaves a white spongy residue which represents complex silico-fluoride-metallic ion compounds.

OXALIC ACID. COOHCOOH·$2H_2O$. A poisonous white crystalline powder; normally dil. sols. are safe to handle, providing none of the solution is accidentally ingested. Weak sols. only slightly irritate the skin but nevertheless should be washed off promptly. Used for the removal of rust stains (limonitic, goethitic), also attacks hematite, slowly attacks carbonates. Bleaches organic inks and dyes. Usual conc. 1/2 oz. avoir. to 2 oz. avoir. of powder to the gallon of water. With this acid it pays to use distilled water because it can react with Ca ions in hard water to form insol. Ca-oxalates (yellow stains).

SODIUM PYROSULFITE. A mild acid used in water for removing manganese oxide stains with little effect upon other minerals.

TARTARIC ACID. $HOOC(CHOH)_2COOH \cdot H_2O$. Similar to oxalic acid in chemical behavior but stronger, and not forming insol. compounds with Ca.

ACETIC ACID. CH_3COOH. The acidic ingredient in household vinegar with characteristic sour smell; vinegar may be used as an acid but the sugars and other substances contained therein are likely to introduce more problems than are solved by its use. Glacial acetic acid is the very pure form and highly concentrated; tends to congeal in cold weather. This acid is recommended by some for calcite removals from specimens in which associated minerals may be attacked by the stronger HCl. Intense, penetrating odor is disagreeable and persists; use in well-ventilated place. Dilute as with HCl. While vinegar is not regarded as a dangerous substance, conc. acetic acid is, and should be treated with the same care as HCl.

CITRIC ACID. $C_3H_4OH(COOH)_3$. The pleasantly acidic ingredient in soft drinks and fruit juices of the citrus group. Use like acetic acid. It has a much more acceptable smell. Useful for removals of calcite.

ORTHOPHOSPHORIC ACID. H_3PO_4. Conc. sol. 85% by wgt. Used to clean metals, e.g., copper.

SODIUM DITHIONATE. $Na_2S_2O_6 \cdot 2H_2O$. White-colorless crystals, readily sol. in water to form a mild acid bath useful for removing calcite from specimens in which other associated minerals may be attacked by stronger acids like HCl. Has been recommended for iron oxide stain removals from carbonates and phosphates, but eventually attacking the first. Usual sol. 1 teaspoonful per pint of water.

AMMONIA. NH_4. Usually supplied in conc. sol. 28% by wgt., or much less in the case of the pure household types (do not buy "detergent added" or "soapy" ammonias!). Helpful in dislodging vegetable matter from mineral specimens, as lichens and algae. Acrid choking odor, slippery feel. Attacks some carbonates, notably azurite and malachite. Conc. sols. attack skin and are dangerous; flush with large volumes of water. May be used for washing places dampened by acid to neutralize latter. Evaporates cleanly and gradually loses strength in storage.

ALCOHOLS. Methyl ("wood") alcohol is easily obtainable from hardware stores and may be used for rinsing specimens to (1) diss. greasy, oily deposits, or (2) to rapidly dry specimens after previous washing in water, or (3) to wash specimens that are readily water-soluble. Also useful are denatured ethyl ("grain") alcohol and isopropyl ("rubbing") alcohol although care must be taken that the last is not contaminated with scents and other ingredients. All are inflammable and poisonous.

ACETONE. CH_2COCH_3. Used like alcohol. Very rapidly evaporating and may present an explosion hazard if large amounts are spilled in closed room.

LIGHTER FLUID. This or other light petroleum distillates may be used to remove the white cement of surgical tape labels which adheres to specimens and is difficult to remove by other means.

SOLVENTS, METHODS OF CLEANING, PRESERVATION

Most minerals are attacked to some extent by the "mineral" acids hydrochloric (HCl), sulfuric (H_2SO_4), nitric (HNO_3), or hydrofluoric (HF), and the mixture of HCl and HNO_3 known as aqua regia (A.R.). They may also be attacked by organic acids like citric, oxalic, tartaric, and acetic. Rapidity of attack against any one mineral by any acid depends on the state of the mineral. Solid crystals without flaws are attacked most slowly but rate of attack rapidly increases as the mineral approaches granular or powdery form, or contains numerous fissures, cracks or pores. Thus shining near-perfect crystals of hematite may be only very slowly attacked by HCl but the same acid used against hematite in powdery or porous form results in much faster solution of the mineral.

The rate of attack is important in deciding whether acids can be used to selectively remove one species in the presence of another that is also attacked by the same acid. In cleaning clay minerals from tourmaline, beryl, or kunzite crystals, for example, the use of HF is satisfactory, even though it attacks all minerals mentioned, because it dissolves the clays so much faster that they can be almost entirely removed before appreciable damage is done to the species coated by the clays. On the other hand, the use of HCl to remove calcite enclosing crystals of rhodonite in specimens from the Franklin, New Jersey, deposit is *not* recommended because the rhodonite is also attacked to an unacceptable extent.

For these reasons it is always wise before engaging in any extensive use of acid to test reactions on some inconspicuous portion of the specimen unless the data given below indicate that the acid in question will not affect the species being cleaned. In any event, it is always good practice to use acids as dilute as possible consistent with good results.

The term "dilute" generally refers to any acid diluted with water, generally by mixing with an equal or greater part of water. "Concentrated" acid generally refers to the standard solution as obtained from the chemical supply house, or in the case of dry acids (e.g., oxalic), the addition of the acid to water to obtain a saturated solution. In only rare instances is acid ever used in concentrated form for normal cleaning purposes. For further information on acids and their properties see "Chemicals List" (p. 23).

SOLUBILITIES OF MINERALS GENERALIZED

METALS. Soluble in acids, the more "noble" requiring aqua regia.

SULFIDES, SULFOSALTS. Slightly sol. acids; insol. water.

OXIDES. Insol. water; in part sol. acids.

HYDROXIDES. Ammonium, potas-

sium, sodium sol. water, calcium slightly sol.; somewhat more sol. in acids than oxides.

HALIDES. Chlorides sol. water except lead, mercury, silver. Fluorides sol. acids; insol. water. Bromides and iodides insol. water or acids.

CARBONATES. Simple carbonates insol. water except ammonium, potassium and sodium; complex carbonates or minerals containing the carbonate radical in part, may or may not be easily sol. in water; most carbonates readily sol. acids.

BORATES. Containing water of crystallization easily sol. water, acids; others insol. water, most acids.

SULFATES. Sol. water, acids except those of lead, calcium, barium; rapidly sol. water when containing water of crystallization.

PHOSPHATES. Insol. in water except those of ammonium, potassium, sodium, but slightly sol. acids.

ARSENATES. Variable, some sol. water and readily sol. acids.

VANADATES. Insol. water; slowly sol. acids.

TUNGSTATES. Insol. water, acids.

MOLYBDATES. Insol. water; slightly sol. acids.

NITRATES. Sol. water, acids.

SILICATES. Insol. water, acids (except hydrofluoric), but many exceptions, notably among zeolites.

MINERALS: THEIR SOLUBILITIES, SPECIFIC CLEANING AGENTS AND METHODS, AND PRESERVATION

ACANTHITE. See ARGENTITE.

ACTINOLITE. Occurs cleaved and likely to disintegrate under vigorous scrubbing; not affected by acids except slowly by HF; rate of HF attack faster in fibrous forms. Avoid washing *amianthus, byssolite,* because fibers will mat. *Mountain leather, mountain cork* rapidly absorb impurities and liable to discolor in impure water sols.; use distilled water only for gentle rinsing or immersion in ultrasonic bath.

ADAMITE. Easily diss. or damaged by dil. acids, especially HCl, otherwise clean normally in water. Many matrix specimens

(Durango, Mexico) on powdery limonitic gossan which emits clouds of fine iron oxides when washed in ultrasonic bath but generally this does not harm specimens. Brittle, soft, heat-sensitive.

ADELITE. Sol. dil. acids, more rapidly in HNO_3.

ADULARIA. Dil. oxalic acid removes iron stains but avoid prolonged immersion and change sol. several times if first treatment fails to remove stains in first 6 hrs. Sols. may be used lukewarm. Rapidly diss. by HF. Commonly coated by green chlorite scales (Switzerland) which cannot be entirely removed due to partial embedment in surface layers of xls. Most removed by gentle scrubbing with toothbrush after removing largest masses by needle. Finally immerse in ultrasonic bath.

AEGERINE. Xls usually fractured, brittle, liable to disintegrate if handled roughly and may disintegrate in ultrasonic bath. Preliminary soak in vinyl acetate ("white") glue helps cement xls together prior to other treatment; let dry for several days before doing further work. Iron stains removed in dil. oxalic acid; slowly attacked by HF and v. slowly by HCl.

AENIGMATITE. Slightly attacked by warm conc. acids, more rapidly in HF.

AFWILLITE. Sol. HF or HCl.

AGARDITE. Sol. HCl.

AGATE. See CHALCEDONY.

AGUILARITE. Attacked by HNO_3.

AIKINITE. Attacked by HNO_3 or A.R.

AJOITE. Readily attacked by acids.

AKERMANITE. Rapidly attacked by HCl, forming gel.

AKROCHORDITE. Readily sol. H_2SO_4.

AKSAITE. Insol. water; readily sol. HCl.

ALABANDITE. Attacked by acids, especially HCl; also readily attacked by cold conc. citric acid sol. and completely sol. in this acid when warm. Sometimes unstable in storage, oxidizing in presence of moisture; light-sensitive.

ALABASTER (GYPSUM). Clean normally in water. Iron stains removed dil. sol. oxalic acid or ammonium oxalate; use cautiously and not overlong to prevent marring polished surfaces. Ultrasonic bath with some ammonia removes greases, oils.

Black organic stains removed with strong sol. H_2SO_4. Very soft, avoid all metal tools.

ALAMOSITE. Decomposed by HNO_3, forming gel.

ALBITE. Moderately to rapidly attacked by HF, the very thin bladed type with numerous cleavage cracks being most susceptible. Xl crusts fragile, xls easily broken off, especially by attempting to remove particles caught between. Remove soil, particles, etc. from between blades by needle water jet or flexible slivers bamboo; do not use metal or rigid tools. Iron stains removed by oxalic acid sol. used lukewarm but specimen removed at moment it is ready and thoroughly washed in several changes clean distilled water; allow to soak overnight in another change of clean dist. water. HCl can be used in lieu of oxalic. Dil. H_2SO_4 sometimes helpful in removing black organic stains.

ALEXANDRITE CHRYSOBERYL. Russian alexandrite xls are rather easily cleaned of adhering biotite mica using sharp steel tools. The latter do not scratch the xls but care must be exercised in their use to avoid breaking sharp corners or enlarging surface cracks. Much more difficulty is encountered in cleaning the xls from Rhodesia and the following method, worked out by John Patrick, is recommended.

Remove as much mica as possible using steel tools. Immerse xls in undiluted HF overnight or longer as experience dictates. Remove xls and soak in neutralizing sol. ammonia. If xls are allowed to dry it will be seen that a tenacious white residue on the mica adheres in many crevices and is not easily removed by tools or by ultrasonic bath. To remove this residue, place xls in warm oxalic acid solution and place container in ultrasonic bath, or if the latter is fitted with a stainless steel tank, place the acid and xls into the tank. Operate ultrasonic cleaner until residue disappears. Take out xls, wash, and neutralize as desired with dil. ammonia sol.

Conc. hot H_2SO_4 is also successful in dissolving the biotite mica but works considerably slower than HF. A white residue is also left and must be cleaned off by the oxalic acid step described above.

Sandblasting has been used to remove

the mica but the resilience of the scales makes the process a very slow one.

Matrix specimens should be cleaned with steel tools only because the white residue left by acid treatment is even more difficult to remove from the interstices of the remaining mica.

ALGODONITE. Attacked by acids; very readily tarnishes in ordinary atmosphere and cleaning is seldom worthwhile for this reason. Can be polished and surface protected by lacquer.

ALLACTITE. Rapidly sol. HCl or other acids.

ALLANITE. Very slowly attacked in conc. HCl with formation of gel but for practical purposes xls unaffected by acids except HF. Usually found "frozen" in matrix (commonly feldspar + quartz) and extremely difficult to extract without crumbling; to some extent crumbling may be prevented by coating exposed xl after thorough initial drying with dil. sol. vinyl acetate ("white") glue; let dry for at least several days; proceed to chip away matrix, but as more of the xl is exposed, repeat glue treatment. It seldom pays to attempt to remove xls entirely from matrix despite any preliminary treatment.

ALLEMONTITE. Slightly attacked by HNO_3, H_2SO_4, A.R. Tarnishes readily in ordinary atmosphere, hence clean only to remove grime. Brittle, cleavable, relatively soft.

ALLOPHANE. Readily attacked by HCl forming gel.

ALLUAUDITE. Slowly sol. conc. acids.

ALMANDINE GARNET. Very slightly attacked by conc. HF. Iron stains removed with oxalic sol. Adhering mica or chlorite removed with steel tools which will not scratch xls or by sandblasting with crushed feldspar or soaking in conc. HF, the latter acid also removing iron and manganese stains.

Note: Many xls badly fractured and actually cemented together with iron oxides whose removal allows xls to disintegrate. The large Salida, Colorado, xls, and others coated primarily by chlorite should generally be cleaned only with stiff scrub brushes to the point where the xl form is clearly defined; use of steel tools may result in unsightly whitened marks.

ALSTONITE. Sol. dil. HCl and other acids.

ALTAITE. Attacked by HNO_3.

ALUMIAN. Sol. acids.

ALUMINITE. Readily sol. acids.

ALUMOHYDROCALCITE. Decomposes in water and in alkali sols.; sol. acids.

ALUMS. The several alums are sol. in water and dil. acids; insol. in alcohols which may be used to rinse off dirt. Soft, fragile.

ALUNITE. Slowly sol. dil. H_2SO_4; insol. water and practically insol. HCl, HNO_3. Soft, fragile.

ALUNOGEN. Sol. water or acids; clean only with acetone or alcohols.

ALVANITE. Sol. HCl or HNO_3 but only in warm sols.

AMAKINITE. Rapidly alters in air; sol. HCl.

AMARANTITE. Attacked in water; sol. dil. HCl.

AMBATOARINITE. Sol. cold HCl.

AMBER. Attacked by ether alone from among all common organic solvents but to test properly the ether must be applied with a wad held in position for a minute or two to counteract the extremely fast evaporation of ether; a slight stickiness will be noted with true amber; other solvents readily attack amberlike resins. Clean with water and soap; avoid lyes, strong ammonia. Brittle, easily scratched.

AMBLYGONITE. Rapidly sol. HF, slowly sol. H_2SO_4, and slightly attacked by other acids. Normal water cleaning indicated but avoid hot water. Soft, do not use hard tools or metal implements; cleavable, heat-sensitive.

AMEGHINITE. Sol. water.

AMESITE. See CHLORITE.

AMINOFFITE. Insol. acids.

AMMONIOBORITE. Slowly sol. water; rapidly in dil. acids.

AMMONIOJAROSITE. Sol. HCl.

AMPANGABEITE. Readily sol. HCl and attacked by other acids. The usual tan earthy coating merges gradually into unaltered material beneath and it is useless to attempt its removal.

AMPHIBOLES. Slowly attacked by HF, the fibrous forms more rapidly.

ANALCIME. Rapidly attacked by HCl, forming gel, and very rapidly by HF or A.R. Luster of xls may be damaged by prolonged immersion in strong soap or detergent sols. Brittle, weak xls easily dislodged from matrix; avoid prolonged treatment in ultrasonic bath.

ANAPAITE. Sol. cold acids.

ANATASE. Insol. acids; iron stains removed with oxalic acid sol. Avoid use of metal implements which may damage sharp xl tips.

ANCYLITE. Rapidly sol. acids.

ANDALUSITE. V. slightly attacked by HF only. Clinging mica removed with steel points or needles, or rubbed off by abrasive grit slurry with vigorous brushing. *Chiastolite* very soft and damaged by steel tools.

ANDERSONITE. Easily sol. dil. acids or in water; unstable, store in sealed containers.

ANDESINE. Rapidly attacked by HF only.

ANDORITE. Sol. HCl, attacked by HNO_3 or A.R.

ANDRADITE. Slightly attacked by HF and very slightly by warm conc. HCl or A.R. HCl satisfactory for removing enclosing calcite.

ANGLESITE. Slightly sol. in conc. acids but their use may result in some loss of xl face luster. Slightly sol. ammonium citrate or acetate sols. Slowly sol. HNO_3. Soft, easily scratched, brittle.

ANHYDRITE. Slowly sol. cold acids, e.g., HCl, more so in warm; v. slightly sol. glycerine. Fragile, cleavable, avoid metal tools. Heat-sensitive.

ANKERITE. Slightly sol. cold acids but rapidly in warm, especially HCl. Brittle, cleavable, avoid metal tools. Unless carefully rinsed after acid treatment may develop severe surface rusting.

ANNABERGITE. Sol. acids which quickly destroy xl luster. Clean in dist. water only; ultrasonic bath satisfactory; avoid strong detergents, ammonia, lyes, etc. Porous types cannot be safely cleaned except by gentle immersion in warm distilled water.

ANORTHITE. Rapidly attacked by HF and moderately in HCl, forming gel, or in A.R. Iron stains removed by oxalic acid but prolonged immersion to be avoided and thorough cleaning afterward mandatory in warm dist. water; several changes are advisable.

ANTARCTICITE. V. readily sol. water; very hygroscopic.

ANTHONYITE. Sol. cold dil. acids.

ANTHOPHYLLITE. Attacked by HF only. Iron stains removed with oxalic acid sol. but soak thoroughly in several changes distilled water afterward.

ANTIGORITE. Slowly attacked by HF only; soft, avoid steel tools.

ANTIMONY. Sol. hot conc. H_2SO_4; decomposed in conc. HNO_3; v. slightly attacked by HCL or A.R. Brittle, cleavable, avoid metal tools. Fresh fracture surfaces (Mexico) retain luster indefinitely.

ANTLERITE. Readily attacked by dil. H_2SO_4; slightly by other acids. Weak, soft, avoid mechanical cleaning methods and hard tools but ultrasonic bath is satisfactory.

ANTOFAGASTITE. Sol. water.

APATITE. Many xls rapidly attacked by even brief immersion in sols. HCl, but others resist attack for hours. Sols. H_2SO_4 least active. Prolonged immersion HCl deeply etches xls, sometimes leaving bright surfaces with attractive etch patterns. Light iron stains removable with sodium dithionate sol., 1 teaspoon in 1 pint dist. water. Xls "frozen" in calcite are usually badly shattered and seldom extractable; soak exposed parts in dil. sol. vinyl acetate ("white") glue to enter cracks and cement them together; allow to dry for several days at least, then remove more matrix, etc. Soft, brittle, avoid use of metal tools.

APHTHITALITE. Sol. water, acids.

APJOHNITE. Sol. water.

APOPHYLLITE. Quickly attacked and bright xl faces dulled in even a few minutes exposure to HCl sol.; prolonged attack results in gel. V. rapidly sol. by HF; attacked by A.R. and other acids, including the organic. Very cleavable, soft, brittle; xls commonly cleave when trimming matrix. Ordinary cleaning with dist. water satisfactory; be careful with ultrasonic bath and probably best avoid its use.

ARAGONITE. Easily sol. all acids. Clean in dist. water and avoid strong detergents, lyes, soaps, ammonia, etc. Some coated xls (Bilin) cleaned by 1 minute dip in dil. HCl. Fragile, brittle, avoid use rigid or metal tools; clean recesses among prismatic xl groups by delicate slivers split bamboo.

ARAMAYOITE. Attacked by HNO_3 and A.R.

ARCANITE. Sol. water.

ARDENNITE. V. slightly attacked by H_2SO_4; not attacked by HCl or HNO_3; rapidly attacked by HF.

ARDUINITE. Rapidly attacked by HF or HCl. Normal cleaning in water.

ARFVEDSONITE. Attacked by HF only.

ARGENTITE. Rapidly sol. in HF; sol. HNO_3, slightly attacked by other acids; not attacked in cold conc. citric acid sol. Xls darken with exposure to light, eventually a sooty coating, which is easily removed by brief dip in ultrasonic bath using water + detergent. Very soft, sectile, avoid hard tools.

ARGYRODITE. Attacked by HNO_3 or A.R.

ARIZONITE. Decomposed in hot H_2SO_4.

ARMANGITE. Quickly attacked by HCl.

ARROJADITE. Sol. dil. acids.

ARSENIC. Slightly to moderately attacked by A.R., HNO_3, or H_2SO_4; sol. in HCl but slowly; not affected by HF which can be used to remove silicate minerals. Rapidly tarnishes in normal air and hence little point to cleaning past that needed to remove ordinary grime.

ARSENIOPLEITE. Sol. HCl.

ARSENIOSIDERITE. Sol. in acids.

ARSENOLAMPRITE. Etched by HNO_3.

ARSENOLITE. Sol. HCl and in some hydroxide sols.; very slightly sol. water.

ARSENOPYRITE. Unaffected by HCl or cold conc. citric acid sol., either of which may be used to remove sol. associated minerals as calcite (Trepca). Prolonged immersion is to be avoided and thorough rinsings in warm dist. water afterward are indicated, plus overnight soak in fresh water. Bright xls dulled after only few minutes exposure to conc. HNO_3. Naturally tarnished xls cannot be restored to brightness because they are etched rather than merely coated.

ARTINITE. Rapidly diss. dil. acids. Xls matted by dipping in water; recommend gentle dip in alcohol to remove soil.

ASBESTOS. Unaffected by normal cleaning treatments but attacked rapidly by HF. Scrubbing must be avoided because all it accomplishes is to tear off fibers which must then be removed by hand.

ASTROPHYLLITE. Readily attacked by HF; slowly attacked by conc. H_2SO_4 or HCl (forms gel).

ATACAMITE. Easily sol. acids, especially HCl; use dist. water without more than slight amount of wetting agent to clean; soft, brittle, xls easily damaged by any kind of hard or firm picks or tools.

ATELESTITE. Rapidly sol. HCl, attacked by HNO_3.

AUGELITE. Very slowly diss. hot conc. HCl; xl face luster likely to be lost by prolonged immersion in dil. acids. Brittle, heat-sensitive.

AUGITE. V. slowly attacked by HF only. Iron stains removed with oxalic.

AURICHALCITE. Readily diss. all acids and to lesser extent in strong ammonia sol. Typical sprays delicate needles cannot be cleaned mechanically and only gentle dip in dist. water satisfactory; avoid soaps or detergents.

AUSTINITE. Diss. by acids. Soft, brittle; avoid use of soaps and detergents in cleaning.

AUTUNITE. Sol. HNO_3 and rapidly attacked by HF and other acids whose use should be altogether avoided; in fact, use of any liquid should be avoided but it is safe to gently rinse in dist. water immediately after removal from ground. Rewetting thereafter must be avoided lest it accelerate crumbling of xls. If possible, store under glass or plastic cover to avoid airborne dirt. Very fragile and friable, especially after losing normal water present when in ground. Some specimens, especially the large thick curved books, tend to crumble due to loss of water. Various methods have been used to forestall such self-destruction including clear lacquer spraying or soaking in greatly diluted clear lacquer. Some success with these methods has been reported. Another method uses a v. dilute sol. of vinyl acetate ("white") glue to which some wetting agent has been added to hasten penetration of water into the xls. After soaking, specimen is toweled dry and allowed to dry further for several days in normal air. Others recommend placing specimens in boxes with dampened paper or other water-retaining material as soon as specimens are removed from ground, and then preserving thereafter in sealed transparent plastic boxes containing a small pad of water-soaked material to retain a moist atmosphere. In general, thin, tabular isolated xls of small size retain strength and do not crumble even without atmospheric control but the larger xls (Washington) may be much more troublesome.

AVICENNITE. Slightly attacked by acids.

AXINITE. Slowly diss. HF but scarcely attacked by other acids even when conc. HCl satisfactory for removal of enclosing calcite. Commonly accompanied by whitish prehnite which may resemble calcite but is removed only very slowly by HCl; in such specimens it is best not to use acid at all. Avoid use of metal tools because sharp xl tips are easily chipped. Often coated with greenish chlorite which is not easily removed (see ADULARIA for discussion).

AZOPROITE. Readily sol. dil. HCl; insol. in 1:3 sol. HNO_3.

AZURITE. Quickly attacked and diss. by acids and very slowly attacked by hot water; sol. in strong ammonia sols. Use dist. water and least amount of wetting agent to clean. Avoid prolonged immersions and exposure to strong detergent sols. Ultrasonic bath safe. Earthy or clayey types (Bisbee) should be immersed in dist. water only long enough to dislodge dirt. Xls very brittle and easily broken and chipped; use delicate slivers bamboo to dislodge foreign particles among xls.

BABEFPHITE. Insol. cold or warm HCl or HNO_3; sol. A.R. or HF.

BABINGTONITE. Slowly attacked by HF only; ultrasonic cleaning safe.

BADDELEYITE. Practically unaffected by cold acids; slightly attacked by hot conc. acids acting on powder; slowly decomposed by H_2SO_4.

BAEUMLERITE. Strongly hygroscopic.

BAKERITE. Attacked by HCl.

BANALSITE. Decomposed by HCl.

BANDYLITE. Slowly sol. HCl or HNO_3; easily sol. in ammonia sols.; slowly attacked by water.

BARITE. V. slowly attacked by conc. warm H_2SO_4 only, hence other acids may be used in cleaning. Soft, brittle, easily cleaved, heat sensitive. Remove iron stains with oxalic acid sol. Some English yellow barites are said to change hue when exposed to the sun.

BARKEVIKITE. Attacked by HF only.

BARNESITE. Slowly sol. dil. HCl.

BARTHITE. Readily sol. HCl or HNO_3; luster of xls damaged by brief exposure to acids. Brittle, soft. Ultrasonic bath safe.

BARYLITE. Insol. in usual acids; attacked by HF.

BARYSILITE. Decomposed by HCl, forming gel, easily sol. HNO_3, forming gel.

BARYTOCALCITE. Sol. dil. acids, especially HCl. Weak, cleavable, avoid metal tools. Normal water cleaning safe. Behaves like CALCITE, which see.

BASTNAESITE. V. slowly attacked by cold acids, more rapidly by warm, especially H_2SO_4.

BATISITE. Insol. HCl, HNO_3, or H_2SO_4.

BAUMHAUERITE. Attacked by HNO_3 and A.R.

BAVENITE. Rapidly sol. HF; decomposed by HCl. Fragile, easily damaged by any tools, brushes, etc. Gentle dip in dist. water only; may disintegrate in ultrasonic bath.

BAYLDONITE. Slightly attacked by HCl; soluble in HNO_3. Normal cleaning.

BAYLEYITE. Readily sol. water and acids.

BAZZITE. Sol. HF only, but slowly.

BEAVERITE. Insol. water; sol. HCl.

BECQUERELITE. Attacked by acids.

BEHIERITE. Insol. hot or cold acids.

BELLINGERITE. Rapidly sol. dil. HCl or other acids; slightly sol. water.

BEMENTITE. Readily attacked by HCl and rapidly by HF.

BENITOITE. Numerous trials show that benitoite is largely unaffected by HCl used to remove the enclosing white natrolite but some xls appear to dull if strong sols. of acid are used; recommend use of HCl dil. with at least 4 volumes of dist. water (see discussion under natrolite). Sol. HF.

BENSTONITE. Sol. acids.

BERAUNITE. Easily sol. HCl and attacked by other acids.

BERBORITE. Insol. HCl or HNO_3; sol. HF or conc. H_2SO_4 when warmed.

BERLINITE. Insol. cold acids, somewhat in warm; readily attacked by hydroxide sols.

BERMANITE. Sol. HNO_3.

BERTHIERITE. Sol. HCl, attacked by HNO_3, A.R.

BERTOSSAITE. V. slowly sol. HNO_3.

BERTRANDITE. Rapidly sol. HF and unaffected by other acids.

BERYL. Almost unaffected by any acid except HF which may be used to diss. clays from surfaces and recesses, especially on aquamarine and morganite xls.

Caution: In some morganite xls the color is enhanced by presence of iron-stained clays in recesses and its bleaching and removal by HF may cause considerable loss of attractiveness. Very slight etching of xl faces noted after several hours immersion in cold conc. HF. On the other hand, the use of HF, even prolonged use, in the case of aquamarines is recommended because iron-stain clays are extremely disfiguring.

BERYLLONITE. V. slowly sol. in acids but quick immersions are harmless. Cleaves but not readily; fairly hard.

BERZELIANITE. Sol. conc. HNO_3; usually tarnishes in air.

BERZELIITE. Rapidly sol. HNO_3 or HCl.

BETAFITE. Unaffected by acids to any significant degree. It is useless to try to remove brownish coatings occurring on some xls (Madagascar). Betafites from Bancroft, Ontario, may include apatite and this species will be damaged if acids are used.

BEUDANTITE. Sol. HCl.

BEYERITE. Rapidly sol. acids.

BIANCHITE. Loses water in air and crumbles.

BILINITE. Sol. in water.

BINDHEIMITE. Sol. HNO_3, HCl, or A.R.

BIOTITE. Decomposed by conc. H_2SO_4, more so when hot, causing bleaching and residue of porous silica; the same effects noted with cold conc. HF. When enclosing *alexandrite,* silica residue removed by an additional step, see ALEXANDRITE CHRYSOBERYL for details. As with most micas, prolonged immersion in any fluid is undesirable because exfoliation occurs; immerse only long enough to clean, promptly remove and blot dry, squeezing books to remove more water. Avoid anything except dist. water. Cleavage faces soft and easily scratched by metal tools.

BIRUNITE. Sol. HCl.

BISBEEITE. Attacked by acids and strong detergent sols. Dist. water used only.

BISCHOFITE. V. easily sol. water, alcohol, acids.

BISMUTH. Readily sol. HNO_3; slowly sol. hot conc. HCl or H_2SO_4. Slowly attacked by cold acids. Fresh fracture-cleavage surfaces usually remain bright.

BISMUTHINITE. Insol. dil. acids; attacked by conc. HNO_3.

BISMUTITE. Readily sol. in acids., especially HNO_3.

BISMUTOTANTALITE. Insol. in all acids, incl. HF (some state sol. HF).

BITYITE. Attacked by acids.

BIXBYITE. Slightly sol. in hot conc. HCl, otherwise unaffected by acids.

BLIXITE. Sol. dil. HCl, HNO_3, or H_2SO_4.

BLOEDITE. Rapidly sol. water or acids. Nearly pure xls last almost indefinitely in normal atmospheres without disintegration but many crumble due to admixtures of other less stable associated species. Rinse off with alcohols using gentle brushing to remove clays. Soft, brittle; avoid use of metal implements. Recommended for storage in sealed containers.

BOBIERRITE. Readily sol. acids.

BOEHMITE. Slightly sol. conc. H_2SO_4.

BOLEITE. Sol. conc. HNO_3; normal water cleaning harmless.

BORACITE. Slowly sol. conc. HCl and v. slightly sol. in water, but quick cleaning in dist. water harmless.

BORAX. Rapidly diss. in water, acids. Clean in alcohol. On exposure gradually alters to opaque white tincalconite layer which progressively thickens until entire xl altered; at this time, or before, the xls disintegrate. Long-range preservation requires storage in sealed containers with small pad moistened with water. Plastic sprays and soakings have been used to preserve borax xl groups but are seldom fully successful although alteration considerably delayed.

BORICKITE. Sol. acids.

BORNITE. Sol. HNO_3; slightly attacked by cold conc. citric acid sol.

BOTRYOGEN. Sol. HCl; insol. cold water.

BOULANGERITE. Decomposed in acids with hot conc. HCl being most effective. Acicular xls severely matted when dipped in water; a gentle dip in alcohol may be satisfactory but no washing at all is best.

BOURNONITE. Decomposed in acids, especially HNO_3; only slightly attacked in cold conc. citric acid sol. Normal cleaning. Brittle, easily damaged by metal tools.

BOUSSINGAULTITE. Sol. water and acids.

BRADLEYITE. Easily sol. HCl and attacked by other acids; slowly attacked by water.

BRAITSCHITE. Insol. water from $25°$-$100°$ C.; readily sol. dil. HCl, HNO_3, or H_2SO_4.

BRANDTITE. Sol. dil. acids especially HCl.

BRANNERITE. Sol. acids.

BRAUNITE. Sol. HCl or A.R. leaving gel residue. Normal water cleaning safe.

BRAVOITE. V. slightly attacked by conc. acids; sometimes unstable in storage, oxidizing in presence of atmospheric moisture. Ordinary pyrite specimens coated by bravoite (Colorado) are stable.

BRAZILIANITE. Slowly attacked in acids; rusty xls can be immersed in weak oxalic acid sol. to clean; strong sols. must be avoided. Brittle, cleavable; avoid metal cleaning tools.

BREITHAUPTITE. Sol. HNO_3 or A.R., but only slightly affected by other acids. Associated calcite may be removed with dil. HCl or one of the organic acids.

BREWSTERITE. Rapidly sol. in HF and appreciably by other acids, with HCl being most damaging. Avoid use of strong detergent sol.

BRIANITE. Insol. water.

BROCHANTITE. Readily sol. in acids, especially HNO_3. Use dist. water only, avoid use of detergents and other additives, especially ammonia. Delicate, easily damaged by strong water spray or flow; no tools should be used; probably harmed in ultrasonic bath.

BROCKITE. Decomposes in warm HCl, HNO_3 or H_2SO_4.

BROMYRITE. V. slightly attacked by HCl, cyanide sols., ammonia sols., or $Na_2S_2O_3$ sol.

BROOKITE. V. slightly attacked by H_2SO_4 only. Use normal cleaning methods.

BRUCITE. Rapidly sol. in acids, especially HCl. Very soft, easily damaged by hard implements and even by wood splinters. Avoid strong detergents or other additives to bath; ultrasonic cleaning safe.

BRUGNATELLITE. Rapidly sol. HCl and other acids, including citric and other organic acids. Almost impossible to clean due to fragility.

BRUSHITE. Sol. dil. acids.

BUDDINGTONITE. Decomposes in hot strong sol. NaOH.

BUKOVSKYITE. Readily sol. HCl.

BUNSENITE. Slowly sol. in acids.

BURKEITE. Sol. in cold water and in dil. acids; unstable, requires storage in sealed containers.

BUSTAMITE. Luster of xls damaged by prolonged immersion in dil. HCl used to remove enclosing calcite (Franklin, New Jersey); recommend use of dil. acetic, citric, or other organic acids instead. It is tedious but far better to mechanically remove calcite to preserve luster xls. Acid-treated xls further tend to darken to black upon exposure to sunlight, doing so far more rapidly than untreated xls.

BUTLERITE. Sol. acids, slightly sol. water.

BYTOWNITE. V. slightly attacked by HCl; rapidly by HF.

CACOXENITE. Extremely delicate tufts are best not cleaned at all, but if loose dirt must be removed do so by gentle laving in alcohol. Rapidly sol. in acids, especially HCl.

CAFETITE. Insol. HCl, HNO_3; decomposes in boiling H_2SO_4.

CAHNITE. Readily sol. in dil. HCl and attacked by other acids.

CALAVERITE. Decomposed in hot conc. H_2SO_4 or A.R. Normal cleaning safe.

CALCIBORITE. Insol. water but readily sol. warm acids.

CALCIOFERRITE. Decomposed by HCl.

CALCIOVOLBORTHITE. Sol. acids.

CALCITE. Readily sol. all acids with typical carbonate effervescence due to formation CO_2 gas. Mode of etching and resultant luster of xl faces depends on conc. of acid (usually HCl), and experimentation may reveal best dil. for purpose. Usual dil. from equal vols. water and acid, to 1 vol. acid to 8 of water. Dist. water decidedly preferable. To prevent grooving of surfaces by streams of bubbles move specimen about in acid bath frequently, or rotate to various positions with the hands (rubber gloves!). Most specimens Tri-State district coated with white porous coating which is customarily removed by dealers prior to offering specimens for sale. Crushed places or nicks on xls can be disguised effectively by use acid straight from bottle, applying with small artist's brush and taking care not to let acid dribble over remainder of xls. Carefully wipe off each application at the moment bubbling ceases; then reapply until minute crushed fragments dissolved. A good technique here is to hold specimen upside down so that acid remains on xl points, or, if dropping off, falls away from specimen. In all removals of calcite from other species check this list first to observe effect of acid (e.g., dioptase, rhodonite). According to Weinschenk, *Petrographic Methods* (New York: McGraw-Hill, 1912), a sol. of alum dissolves calcite readily without harming most associated minerals, "even dolomite." The use of sodium dithionate (see "Chemicals List," p. 23) has been recommended by other authorities as removing calcite without harming such normally susceptible minerals as apatite.

CALCIUM LARSENITE. Partly diss. by HCl, leaving whitish porous surface. Check Franklin, New Jersey, specimens for presence of this mineral before attempting treatment.

CALEDONITE. Rapidly sol. HNO_3; partly sol. HCl, and attacked by other acids. Delicate; avoid use of tools. Use dist. water only in ultrasonic bath but avoid strong detergents and ammonia.

CALOMEL. Sol. A.R.; insol. HCl; slightly attacked by other acids when warm. Sol. in silver nitrate sol., also in alcohol.

CALUMETITE. Sol. cold dil. acids; insol. water or ammonia sol.

CALZIRTITE. Partly sol. warm conc. H_2SO_4, H_3PO_4, or HCl.

CAMPYLITE (PYROMORPHITE). Sol. HNO_3; not affected by water.

CANASITE. Decomposed by acids.

CANCRINITE. Sol. HCl, forming gel; also in HF or A.R.

CANFIELDITE. Attacked by HNO_3 or A.R.

CAPPELENITE. Easily sol. HCl.

CARACOLITE. Partly sol. in water.

CARBOBORITE. Sol. water.

CARBOCERNAITE. Easily sol. HCl.

CARMINITE. Sol. HCl or HNO_3; attacked by other acids.

CARNALLITE. Rapidly sol. water or acids. Clean with alcohol or acetone. V. soft, brittle, avoid tools. Sealed container storage required.

CARNOTITE. Rapidly sol. acids. Fragile, avoid cleaning at all but quick dip in alcohol, or in dist. water, followed by alcohol rinse, is effective for loose dirt removal.

CARPHOLITE. Readily attacked by HF; unaffected by HCl.

CARPHOSIDERITE. Insol. water but sol. in HCl.

CARROLLITE. Attacked by HNO_3 but not HCl; tarnishes.

CARYINITE. Sol. HNO_3.

CARYOCERITE. Attacked by cold HF, hot HCl.

CARYOPILITE. Easily sol. strong acids.

CASSITERITE. Practically untouched by acids except the powder in hot conc. acids. Bolivian xls sometimes coated with thin translucent scum (clay?) which is removable with razor blades or by brief immersion in HF. Very hard and tough, and all metal instruments may be used with considerable safety.

CATAPLEIITE. Rapidly diss. HCl forming gel.

CEBOLLITE. Sol. HCl, forming gel.

CELESTITE. Slowly sol. as powder in hot conc. acids only. Brittle, cleavable, xls easily broken from matrix; avoid use of metal tools; bamboo slivers preferable for removing dirt between xl blades. Oxalic acid removes iron stains but first check for presence of calcite which will be attacked.

CELSIAN. Sol. HCl; also in HF.

CENOSITE. Slowly sol. acids, rapidly in warm.

CENTRALLASITE. Rapidly attacked by HCl and other acids.

CERARGYRITE. Sol. cyanide or ammonia sols. Surface decomposes, darkens with exposure to light. Soft, easily scratched by even wood tools.

CERITE. Slowly attacked and gelatinized in HCl; also attacked by other acids.

CERUSSITE. Quickly attacked by acids; only a few minutes contact with dil. HCl results in dulling bright xl faces; sol. dil. HNO_3. Avoid use of strong detergents in cleaning. Soft and brittle, heat-sensitive. Avoid use of hard or firm cleaning tools.

CERVANTITE. Attacked by HCl or A.R.

CHABAZITE. Rapidly attacked by HF or HCl, also A.R. Avoid use of strong detergent sols., ammonia, soap, etc. Brittle; fractured xls may disintegrate in ultrasonic bath.

CHALCANTHITE. Rapidly diss. water or dil. acids; nearly insol. in ethyl (grain) alcohol which can be used for washing of xls. Brittle, very soft; avoid use of firm or hard tools. Develops white alteration coating in dry atmospheres due to loss of water, while in wet climates attracts water; store in sealed containers if feasible.

CHALCANTHITE, COBALT. As above.

CHALCEDONY. Rapidly attacked by HF which etches bands selectively, the translucent bands being generally more rapidly dissolved than the opaque bands. Unaffected by other acids although impure ("commercial" grade) yellowish HCl has been used to dye yellow; conc. H_2SO_4 penetrates readily and has been used to carbonize sugar absorbed by soaking chalcedony slabs in conc. sugar sol. Also readily absorbs oils which may be removed in warm to hot baths containing phosphate detergents or lyes. Black types, especially certain petrified woods, are bleached by soaking in laundry bleach or in oxalic acid sol. Sometimes coated with calcite (removed with dil. pure HCl) or gypsum (also removed by dil. pure HCl).

CHALCOALUMITE. Attacked by acid; sol. HCl.

CHALCOCITE. Diss. HNO_3; not affected by cold. sat. sol. citric acid. Always forms sooty black coating as surface alters; this may be partly removed by water cleaning in ultrasonic bath but soon returns. Fragile, soft; avoid use of metal tools.

CHALCOMENITE. Sol. acids.

CHALCOPHANITE. Diss. HCl; attacked readily by other conc. acids.

CHALCOPHYLLITE. Diss. in acids, ammonia sols. Fragile and liable to damage

if allowed to soak in cleaning sols. Avoid use of tools or brushes.

CHALCOPYRITE. Sol. HNO_3 and attacked by other acids but all react slowly except against powder; not attacked by cold saturated sol. citric acid. Black alteration coating sometimes removable with cyanide sols. Brittle, avoid use of metal tools. Dil. HCl has been used to remove calcite (French Creek, Pennsylvania) without seriously affecting underlying chalcopyrite but in time an iridescent tarnish develops. After such acid treatment thorough washing in several changes of distilled water is required, followed by washing in slightly ammoniated water (1 tablespoonful household ammonia to 1 quart of water); rewash in distilled water until free of ammonia odor. Freshly fractured chalcopyrite specimens may be treated with conc. HCl to deliberately impart iridescent coating.

CHALCOSIDERITE. Slowly attacked by acids; sol. HCl.

CHALCOSTIBITE. Attacked by HNO_3, A.R.

CHALCOTRICHITE. Fibrous form of CUPRITE and treated similarly, but great care required in rinsing to avoid matting of fibers. In general, any type of washing should be avoided but gentle laving in alcohol or acetone may be preferable to water.

CHAMOSITE. Rapidly attacked by HF, slowly by HCl.

CHENEVIXITE. Easily sol. acids.

CHERNOVITE. Insol. acids.

CHEVKINITE (Tscheffkinite, etc.). Readily attacked by warm HNO_3; slowly attacked by HCl with formation of gel.

CHILDRENITE. Sol. in acids, especially HCl. It is best not to attempt removal of iron stains which commonly coat xls. Brittle, soft, easily damaged by tools. Recent large Brazilian xls fractured and may fall apart in ultrasonic bath.

CHIOLITE. V. slightly sol. conc. H_2SO_4. Normal cleaning safe.

CHKALOVITE. Sol. acids.

CHLOANTHITE. Sol. HNO_3; scarcely attacked by cold HCl which may be used to remove enclosing calcite. Some specimens reported unstable and oxidize in damp atmospheres.

CHLORALUMINITE. V. sol. water, dil. acids; deliquesces in air!

CHLORITES. Readily attacked and bleached (of iron) by HF; decomposed by conc. H_2SO_4 with bleaching. Generally removed by gentle lifting off of masses of minute xls, followed by brushing under water; however, seldom entirely removable since some chlorite is usually partly intergrown in the xl faces of the associated minerals (adularia, axinite).

CHLORITOID. Decomposed by H_2SO_4.

CHLORMAGNESITE. Sol. water; deliquesces!

CHLORMANGANOKALITE. Sol. water; deliquesces!

CHLOROCALCITE. Easily sol. water or dil. acids. Deliquesces!

CHLOROPHOENICITE. Sol. in acids.

CHLORXIPHITE. Sol. HNO_3 or A.R.

CHONDRODITE. Slowly attacked by HCl, forming gel; rapidly sol. HF. Sol. hot conc. H_2SO_4. Commonly fractured-granular and liable to disintegrate in ultrasonic cleaner. Enclosing asbestoslike mineral (Tilly Foster, New York) removed by careful picking away with needle and scrubbing with small stiff brush.

CHROMITE. Not affected by acids.

CHRYSOBERYL. Not affected by acids. Very tough and hard. See ALEXANDRITE CHRYSOBERYL for cleaning mica from xls.

CHRYSOCOLLA. Blue, green translucent chalcedony commonly called by this name should be treated like CHALCEDONY. Earthy varieties variable in behavior, but attacked by acids, rapidly by HF; porosity requires washing in pure distilled water, avoiding detergents, ammonia, etc.

CHRYSOPRASE. Treat like CHALCEDONY.

CHRYSOTILE ASBESTOS (SERPENTINE). Decomposed by HCl; HF rapidly attacks. Iron stains removed with oxalic but deep penetration may occur and thorough washing necessary to remove traces of iron salts created during the treatment. Avoid rubbing of specimens which merely fluffs fibers and requires hand picking later to remove.

CHURCHITE. Sol. acids.

CINNABAR. Diss. A.R. Not affected by cold conc. sol. citric acid. Tarnishes readily when exposed to strong light; rub xls gently with clean soft cloth or cotton swab; store in dark. Soft, brittle, easily damaged by metal implements.

CLARKEITE. Sol. HCl.

CLAUDETITE. Sol. HCl, some conc. hydroxide sols.

CLAUSTHALITE. Sol. HNO_3; completely sol. cold conc. sol. citric acid.

CLAYS. Silicates with micalike sheet structures formed from the alteration of other silicate minerals. Pure clays are pale colored, e.g., white, cream, pink, while browns, reddish-browns, etc., are usually impregnated with finely divided oxides of iron and are bleached when subjected to oxalic acid treatment. In some clays, the particles are held together with calcite, iron oxides, etc., and acid treatment serves to dissolve such contaminants and allow the clays to be picked away from the specimens they cover. Usually several such treatments are necessary, each one followed by washing and scrubbing to remove loosened clay. Thick deposits of clay should be allowed to thoroughly dry at which time shrinkage cracks form and the angular segments of dried clay easily dislodged. It may be necessary to rewet the clay and redry several times to remove as much as possible by this method. Sodium sulfite sol., 1 part to 4 parts by wgt. of water, has been used to remove clay, also addition of EDTA to the soak water. Clays adhering tenaciously to certain xls such as beryl and tourmaline can be removed with HF, but this acid also attacks other associated minerals, such as albite and microcline. While thin clay coatings are sometimes easily removed by dipping in ultrasonic bath, some coatings become flexible and yield under the vibrations instead of dislodging without any appreciable removal even after an hour of steady bath operation.

CLEAVELANDITE. See ALBITE.

CLIFFORDITE. Insol. dil. HCl but sol. in conc.; also slowly sol. in hydroxide sols.

CLINOCHLORE. Slowly attacked by hot conc. H_2SO_4, rapidly by HF. Treat like CHLORITE. Large books (Tilly Foster) should not be immersed for more than a minute or two during washing to prevent water entering the books and prying apart the leaves.

CLINOCLASE. Readily attacked HCl, HNO_3, H_2SO_4, A.R.; slightly sol. ammonia.

CLINOHEDRITE. Sol. HCl, forming gel.

CLINOHUMITE. Slowly attacked by acids with formation of gel; rapidly attacked by HF or conc. hot H_2SO_4.

CLINOZOISITE. Attacked by HF. Commonly fractured and cleaved, with xls liable to disintegrate in ultrasonic bath.

COBALTITE. Slowly decomposed in warm HNO_3, and v. slightly attacked by other acids. Dil. HCl can be used safely to aid in removal of enclosing minerals as calcite.

COBALTOCALCITE. Treat like CALCITE.

COERULEOLACTITE. Sol. acids, hydroxide sols.

COHENITE. Slightly attacked by acids.

COLEMANITE. Sol. warm acids, e.g., HCl, and v. slightly sol. in hot water. Use cold water to clean but avoid strong detergents and prolonged immersion. Sharp fragile xls easily damaged by any kind of hard or firm tool.

COLLINSITE. Sol. acids.

COLLOPHANE. Rapidly attacked by most acids.

COLLYRITE. Attacked by HCl with formation of gel.

COLORADOITE. Sol. HNO_3.

COLUMBITE. Only the powder is decomposed by hot conc. acids and for practical cleaning purposes, any acid may be used safely. Commonly fractured when completely enclosed in associated minerals and removal from matrix may be almost impossible (see ALLANITE for discussion of removal techniques). The most solid xls are those with shining flat faces while those liable to disintegrate are dull and ridged, or thin-bladed in habit.

COLUSITE. Attacked by HNO_3, A.R.

CONICHALCITE. Easily diss. HCl, HNO_3, A.R., and affected by others. Avoid acids, strong detergents, ammonia. Clean ultrasonically in dist. water to which trace of wetting agent has been added. Very delicate.

CONNELLITE. Insol. water, but sol. acids, ammonia.

COOKEITE. Commonly coats granitic pegmatite pocket minerals; sometimes easily scaled off by use of razor blades, needles, etc., but at other times requires removal with HF providing underlying

minerals not damaged in the process (e.g., quartz, albite, microcline, apatite). Seldom removable ultrasonically even after prolonged immersion. Bleached with oxalic acid sol. but thorough washing afterward required to remove iron compounds in solution. Attacked by H_2SO_4, rapidly in warm conc. sol.

COPAL. Brittle, soft tree gum which develops surface cracks (crazing) within weeks after polishing as volatile substances evaporate. Unlike true amber it is made sticky by contact with turpentine, acetone, and other common organic solvents.

COPIAPITE. Easily diss. water, acids. Absorbs water from atmosphere and long-term preservation requires storage in sealed containers.

COPPER. Readily attacked by acids, especially HNO_3, A.R. Dil. acids can clean but etch surfaces of xls and destroy their smoothness. Many collectors do not use more than normal water cleaning and claim that any other treatment destroys the natural appearance. In general, clean only those specimens consisting solely of copper because adhering rock fragments, clays, etc., tend to saturate with copper salts which later come to the surface and mar the appearance.

British Museum Formula

1 part by weight sodium hydroxide (soda lye)
3 parts rochelle salts (potassium sodium tartrate)
20 parts distilled water

This sol. diss. black copper oxides but does not attack the copper nor the cuprite commonly found associated with copper. Time in bath: from several minutes to 1 hour, as required.

Michigan (Keeweenaw) Formula

70 milliliters conc. sulfuric acid
90 milliliters glacial (conc.) acetic acid
30 grams sodium dichromate ($Na_2Cr_2O_9$)

Add sufficient distilled water to make 1 liter (approx. 1 gal.) Works very rapidly, producing brightening in several minutes; removes calcite.

To Remove Calcite From Copper

Make up a dil. sol. of sulfuric acid in dist. water, 1 vol. of acid to 4 vols. of water; removes calcite without seriously affecting the copper.

Acetic Acid Formulas

(1) One part by vol. glacial acetic acid to 10 parts dist. water, *or* (2) 1 tablespoonful household salt to 1/2 pint household white vinegar, *or* (3) Dil. acetic acid, or household white vinegar, mixed with cigar ashes to form a scouring compound.

After all chemical cleanings thoroughly wash specimens in several changes of lukewarm water; place under fan or in circulating air to dry as quickly as possible. For treatment of copper-silver masses ("half-breeds") with cyanide sol., see SILVER.

COQUIMBITE. Readily diss. water, acids. Brittle, soft. Rinse in alcohol to clean. Unstable, tending to lose water in dry air or become wet in moist air; store in sealed containers if possible.

CORDIERITE (IOLITE). V. slightly attacked by conc. acids, more rapidly by HF; for cleaning purposes ordinary acids are safe to use. Altered xls should not be treated with chemicals.

CORDYLITE. Partly decomposed by acids; sol. HCl.

CORKITE. Attacked by cold acids, more rapidly by warm.

CORNETITE. Sol. HCl.

CORNWALLITE. Attacked by acids.

CORONADITE. Attacked by HCl.

CORUNDUM. Unaffected by all acids, even when used hot and conc. Adhering micas removed mechanically with steel tools, sandblast, or with HF. Very hard, tough, and not heat-sensitive. Ultrasonic bath cleans water-worn xls and pebbles very effectively.

COSALITE. Sol. HNO_3, A.R.; attacked only slowly by conc. HCl.

COTUNNITE. Sol. water, dil. HCl, dil. HNO_3, sodium acetate sol.

COULSONITE. V. slowly sol. H_2SO_4.

COVELLITE. Sol. in hot conc. acids, especially HNO_3 or A.R.; also sol. cold cyanide sols. Easily cleaved and damaged by rough treatment or even overvigorous brushing. Alteration coating removed to some extent by ultrasonic detergent bath.

CRANDALLITE. V. slightly attacked by acids; slowly decomposed by A.R.

CREDNERITE. Diss. HCl; insol. HNO_3.

CREEDITE. Slowly sol. acids; avoid strong detergent sols. Sharp xls easily chipped by cleaning tools.

CRESTMOREITE. Rapidly attacked HCl and other acids.

CRISTOBALITE. Clean ultrasonically in water. Sol. HF.

CROCIDOLITE. Quickly diss. by HF but not attacked by other acids.

CROCOITE. Slightly attacked by acids. Brittle, weak, and easily damaged by stiff brushes; clean ultrasonically. Strong light gradually alters surface of xls causing darkening of color and increasing opacity.

CRONSTEDTITE. Decomposed by HCl with formation of gel; readily diss. by HF.

CRYOLITE. V. slightly sol. water or H_2SO_4; with latter acid the finely divided powder reacts to form gaseous HF! Soft and brittle; normal cleaning in water satisfactory.

CRYOLITHIONITE. Sol. H_2SO_4, with production of HF gas! V. slightly sol. warm water.

CRYOPHYLLITE. Attacked by HF; scarcely affected by other acids.

CRYPTOHALITE. Sol. hot water.

CUBANITE. Treat like CHALCOPYRITE.

CUMENGEITE. Sol. HNO_3. Not harmed by ordinary water cleaning.

CUMMINGTONITE. Affected only by HF.

CUPRITE. Diss. in conc. acids, including phosphoric; sol. pure H_2SO_4; readily and completely sol. dil. HCl; also sol. in warm ammonia or hydroxide sols; sol. in boiling conc. sol. citric acid. See COPPER for additional information. Affected by strong light which promotes formation of dark surface films and obscuration of reddish color and brilliant luster. See also CHALCOTRICHITE.

CUPROTUNGSTITE. Easily sol. acids.

CURITE. Easily sol. acids.

CURTISITE. Sol. hot benzol.

CUSPIDINE. Readily sol. HNO_3.

CYANOTRICHITE. Easily sol. acids; avoid use of water bath if possible, and certainly detergents, soaps, ammonia; however, brief immersion in dist. water in ultrasonic bath has not harmed some specimens.

CYLINDRITE. Attacked by hot HCl or HNO_3 but not other acids.

CYPRINE (IDOCRASE). Attacked by conc. HCl but scarcely in cold dil. sol.

CYRTOLITE. Unaffected even by conc. acids. Adhering clays, feldspars, etc., usually easily removed with needles and other steel implements to expose xls (Canada).

DACHIARDITE. Decomposed by acids, especially HCl and HF.

DANALITE. Rapidly decomposed by HCl with formation of gel; rapidly sol. HF.

DANBURITE. Slowly attacked by HF and very slightly by HCl which can be safely used to remove covering calcite. However, inspect carefully before use because some prisms fractured and cemented together by the calcite as at Charcas, Mexico. Also coated in part by small apophyllite xls or by quartz or chalcedony, neither of the last being removable without serious damage to the danburite xls. Presence of chalcopyrite should also be looked for because its attack by HCl can be followed by residual stains of green and blue unless acid bath is followed by careful rinsings in clean water.

DAPHNITE. Slowly decomposes in HCl, easily in warm; also in HF.

DARAPSKITE. Readily sol. water or dil. acids; slightly sol. acetone, alcohol, in the latter the xls turning white but remaining clear in acetone.

DATOLITE. Attacked by conc. HCl, forming gel, but only slowly and for practical calcite removal purposes HCl is safe to use. Avoid prolonged immersions. Sol. in hot conc. citric acid sol. Use extreme care in trimming specimens because xls very easily fly apart.

DAUBREEITE. Sol. HCl.

DAUBREELITE. Sol. HNO_3; unaffected by HCl.

DAVIDITE. Generally unaffected by acids. Do not attempt removal of usual alteration coatings of earthy material because you will not succeed.

DAVISONITE. Attacked by acids.

DAWSONITE. Sol. acids, especially in HCl.

DEHRNITE. Sol. acids.

DELAFOSSITE. Readily sol. HCl, H_2SO_4; insol. HNO_3.

DELESSITE. Easily sol. acids.

DELHAYELITE. Slowly attacked by acetic acid; and others?

DELRIOITE. Readily sol. water.

DELTAITE. Very slightly attacked by acids.

DENNINGITE. Easily sol. cold HCl; insoluble in hot or cold HNO_3; slightly sol. H_2SO_4.

DERBYLITE. Insoluble in the ordinary acids.

DESCLOIZITE. Rapidly attacked by acids and sol. in dil. HNO_3 with loss of xl face luster. Easily damaged by tools which should be altogether avoided. Clean ultrasonically.

DESPUJOLSITE. Sol. HCl; decomposed by HNO_3 with formation of brown to black stain; not attacked by cold acetic acid.

DESTINEZITE. Sol. HCl.

DEVILLITE. Sol. HNO_3; insol. water or conc. H_2SO_4.

DEWEYLITE. Rapidly attacked by HF, slowly by conc. HCl.

DEWINDTITE. Sol. acids; sol. in HNO_3.

DIABANTITE. Treat like CHLORITE.

DIABOLEITE. Completely sol. HNO_3 and attacked by other acids. Brittle, very easily damaged by brushing; rinse gently in water only and avoid detergents, soaps, and ammonia.

DIADOCHITE. Rapidly attacked by acids.

DIAMOND. Unaffected by any acid, base, or other ordinary chemical agent. Xls are usually cleaned by boiling in conc. acids, including HF, to remove coatings, Not heat-sensitive. Only damaged by prolonged ignition.

DIAPHORITE. Sol. HNO_3 or A.R.

DIASPORE. Not attacked by acids. Bladed xls easily dislodged and broken by rough cleaning, especially picking or brushing; may crumble in ultrasonic bath.

DICKINSONITE. Sol. acids.

DIDYMOLITE. Insol. except in HF.

DIETRICHITE. Sol. water.

DIETZEITE. Sol. hot water.

DIGENITE. Sol. in HNO_3 and slightly affected by other acids. Ordinary cleaning safe.

DIOPSIDE. Slowly attacked by HF and not affected by other acids. Clays removable with razor blades (New York State) or other suitable steel implements; immerse in oxalic acid bath as needed to bleach and loosen. Residual clays may be removed by brief dip in HF. Calcite removed with HCl.

DIOPTASE. Quickly etched and dissolved by the mineral acids but the rate of attack of the organic acids is much less and some may be used, with caution, to remove enclosing calcite. Try dil. acetic, citric, tartaric, etc.; also consult sodium dithionate in "Chemicals List" (p. 23) and CALCITE in this list for suggestions. Iron oxide stains are common on some African specimens and it is probably hopeless to attempt their removal without damage to the dioptase. Very soft, brittle, cleavable; avoid all hard tools; removal of calcite mechanically is almost impossible without damaging dioptase too.

DIXENITE. Decomposes in HCl.

DOLEROPHANITE. Sol. HNO_3.

DOLOMITE. Slowly sol. in cold acids (much less so than calcite), but more rapidly in warm acids. Very slowly attacked by cold conc. citric acid. See CALCITE for further information.

DOLORESITE. Slowly sol. HCl, HNO_3 and slightly in 40% KOH sol.

DOMEYKITE. Insol. HCl but sol. HNO_3 or A.R. or cyanide sols. Quickly alters and forms dull brown coat and thus there is little reason to chemically clean; suggest polishing if desired and coating surface with lacquer.

DOVERITE. Sol. HCl.

DRAVITE. V. slowly attacked by cold HF. Clinging mica scales easily removed with sharp needles or by immersion in HF. Calcite coatings removed with dil. HCl or by chipping method.

DRESSERITE. Rapidly sol. HCl.

DUFRENITE. Sol. dil. acids.

DUFRENOYSITE. Attacked by HNO_3 or A.R.

DUFTITE. Readily attacked by acids.

DUMONTITE. Sol. acids.

DUMORTIERITE. Unaffected by acids including HF; remove iron stains with oxalic acid.

DUNDASITE. Sol. dil. acids.

DURANGITE. Sol. H_2SO_4.

DUSSERTITE. Sol. dil. HCl.

DYPINGITE. Sol. dil. acids.

DYSANALYTE. Not affected by acids except attacked by hot conc. H_2SO_4.

DYSCRASITE. Decomposed in HNO_3.

DZHALINDITE. Attacked by HCl, H_2SO_4, but not by HNO_3, KOH, or KCN.

EAKERITE. Insol. acids or bases.

ECDEMITE. Sol. HNO_3, warm HCl, or hydroxide sols.

ECHELLITE. Decomposed in HCl with formation of gel; rapidly sol. HF.

EDENITE. Attacked only by HF.

EDINGTONITE. Decomposed in HCl with formation of gel; rapidly sol. HF.

EGLESTONITE. Attacked by acids; decomposed in HCl. Ordinary yellow material darkens when exposed to light.

ELLESTADITE. Attacked by acids.

ELLSWORTHITE. Slightly attacked by acids, more so when warm, especially warm conc. HCl.

ELPASOLITE. Attacked by conc. H_2SO_4 with release of gaseous HF. Soft and brittle, but normal water cleaning satisfactory.

EMERALD (BERYL). Iron stains on Chivor matrix material removed with oxalic but some deterioration of massive grayish limestone matrix occurs. Biotite flakes on xls (Urals, Austria, Transvaal) removable with needles; xls in biotite schist matrix can be exposed prominently by picking away the biotite flakes but avoid too much relief to prevent fractured xls from falling apart. Iron-stained clays in thin tubes in the xls can be removed by HF which is more penetrating than oxalic acid sol. See BERYL for further advice.

EMMONSITE. Attacked by weak acids, rapidly in conc. acids; sol. HCl.

EMPLECTITE. Attacked by HNO_3, A.R.

EMPRESSITE. Readily sol. HNO_3; not affected by HCl, KCN, KOH sols.

ENARGITE. Diss. A.R.; attacked by HNO_3. Many xls show dull black coating (Montana) which is firmly adherent and cannot be removed.

ENGLISHITE. Attacked by acids.

ENIGMATITE = AENIGMATITE.

ENSTATITE. Slowly attacked by HF only.

EOSPHORITE. Sol. acids; weak, fragile; use dist. water only in cleaning.

EPIDESMINE. Treat like STILBITE.

EPIDOTE. Only partly decomposed in hot conc. HCl; more rapidly attacked by cold HF. Use normal cleaning methods except where accompanied by byssolite

(Austria), for which treatment see ACTIN-OLITE.

EPISTILBITE. Decomposed by HCl with formation of gel; rapidly attacked by HF.

EPSOMITE. V. sol. water, acids. Unstable, requires storage in sealed containers to prevent loss or gain of water. Clean with alcohol.

EREMEYEVITE. Insol. acids.

ERINITE. Sol. acids; sol. HCl.

ERIOCHALCITE. Rapidly diss. water or acids.

ERIONITE. Rapidly decomposed by HCl with formation of gel; very rapidly diss. HF.

ERYTHRITE. Sol. acids, e.g., HCl; rapidly loses xl luster even in v. weak acid sols.; avoid use strong detergents, soaps, ammonia, etc. Cleaned without harm in dist. water ultrasonically. Xls very easily bent or split by stiff brushes and use of soft camel's hair brush recommended. Prolonged exposure to strong light alters surfaces of xls leading to loss of luster and darkening.

ERYTHROSIDERITE. Water sol.; very deliquescent!

ESCHYNITE. Not attacked by acids except when in powdered form.

ETTRINGITE. Rapidly sol. dil. acids; attacked in water.

EUCAIRITE. Slightly sol. cold conc. HNO_3, more so when warm.

EUCHROITE. Sol. acids, especially HNO_3.

EUCLASE. Slowly attacked only by HF; very cleavable and xls showing partly developed cleavages may split further in ultrasonic bath.

EUCRYPTITE. Attacked by HCl with formation of gel.

EUDIALYTE. Attacked by HCl with formation of gel; rapidly sol. in HF. Xls commonly cracked and may disintegrate if attempts made to remove from matrix.

EUDIDYMITE. Slightly attacked by acids.

EULYTINE. Attacked by acids, forming gel with HCl; attacked rapidly by HF.

EUXENITE. Unaffected by acids except hot conc. acids acting on powder. Usual brown coatings not readily removable and should be left undisturbed.

EVANSITE. Rapidly attacked by acids; completely sol. warm H_2SO_4.

EVEITE. Completely sol. HCl.

EZCURRITE. Sol. water; easily sol. acids.

FABIANITE. Nearly insol. water; easily sol. in HCl or HNO_3.

FAIRFIELDITE. Rapidly sol. in acids.

FAMATINITE. Attacked by HNO_3 or A.R.

FAUJASITE. Rapidly attacked by HF, also HCl, forming gel.

FAYALITE. Decomposed by HCl with gel formation; appreciable sol. in warm acid, less so in cold; more rapidly affected toward Mg-end member and less toward Fe-end member. Very rapidly attacked by HF and much less so by H_2SO_4. Iron stains removed with oxalic acid.

FEDORITE. Insol. in acids.

FELDSPARS. Listed also under species names. In general, all are rapidly attacked by HF, especially the perthitic types which quickly become cavernous due to differential sol. of component species. Anorthite, celsian, and sometimes others are appreciably attacked by other acids. Iron stains removed with oxalic acid but great care is required to thoroughly remove all traces of acid sol. afterward to prevent disagreeable yellow stains which creep from crevices and cleavage cracks. Yellow stains may be removed by fresh oxalic solution or HCl, again followed by thorough soakings in several changes dist. water.

FELSOBANYITE. Sol. acids.

FENAKSITE. Decomposed by acids.

FERBERITE. Slightly attacked by conc. hot acids. Porous quartz coatings (Colorado) or small drusy quartz xls may be removed by HF but the process is lengthy. Xls very fragile, easily broken off by use of any firm or hard implements during cleaning; use flexible slivers of bamboo.

FERGUSONITE. Attacked to some extent by conc. HF and only very slightly by other acids as conc. H_2SO_4. Typical pale brown earthy coatings cannot be removed and it is useless to try. Commonly fractured and easily crumbled by removal from matrix; may also crumble during ultrasonic cleaning.

FERNANDINITE. Sol. acids.

FERRIERITE. Very rapidly sol. HF and slowly attacked by other acids such as HCl.

FERRIMOLYBDITE. Sol. acids; decomposes in strong ammonia sol.

FERRINATRITE. Sol. water, dil. acids; unstable, requires sealed container storage.

FERRISICKLERITE. Slowly sol. acids.

FERRITUNGSTITE. Decomposed by acids.

FERROSELITE. Sol. HNO_3, but only slightly in HCl or H_2SO_4.

FERRUCCITE. Sol. water.

FERVANITE. Insol. water but attacked by dil. acids.

FIBROFERRITE. Sol. acids, attacked by water; unstable, store in sealed containers.

FIBROLITE (SILLIMANITE). Unaffected by acids.

FICHTELITE. Sol. in ether.

FIEDLERITE. Sol. HNO_3 or A.R.; slowly attacked by water.

FILLOWITE. Attacked by acids.

FLAGSTAFFITE. Sol. in warm alcohol.

FLINKITE. Sol. HCl.

FLOKITE. Attacked by HCl and other acids.

FLORENCEITE. Partly sol. HCl.

FLUELLITE. Attacked by H_2SO_4 and other acids; other authorities say it is unaffected by acids.

FLUOBORITE. Sol. HF.

FLUOCERITE. Sol. H_2SO_4; not attacked by other acids.

FLUORITE. Finely crushed powder attacked by warm H_2SO_4 with generation HF gas which is dangerous if large quantities are involved; however, treatment by cold acids only very slowly attacks this mineral and is safe for removal of adhering minerals, iron stains, etc. Coatings of calcite are removable with dil. HCl and iron stains with oxalic. Heat-sensitive, avoid placing in warm bath; easily scratches and cleaves, especially on edges and tips of xls; avoid metal implements! Some specimens change color when exposed to light.

FORSTERITE. Treat like FAYALITE.

FOSHAGITE. Attacked by HCl, forming gel; attacked by other acids.

FOURMARIERITE. Rapidly sol. in acids.

FOWLERITE. Treat like BUSTAMITE.

FRANCKEITE. Attacked by HNO_3; sol. in A.R.

FRANKLINITE. Variable in behavior toward acids, especially HCl which is commonly used to remove calcite; some xls totally unaffected and remain bright, others etch and dull. Not affected by cold saturated citric acid and this or sodium dithionate sol. have been recommended for calcite removals. See CALCITE for further advice. Xls usually fractured and mechanical removal of calcite, while advantageous from the chemical standpoint stated above, commonly results in disintegration of xls. As a general rule, those xls which seem to be sharper, brighter in matrix are more likely to hold together.

FREIBERGITE. Decomposed by HNO_3 or A.R.

FREIESLEBENITE. Attacked by HNO_3 and A.R.

FREIRINITE. Sol. HCl.

FRESNOITE. Insol. to slightly sol. in cold dil. acids or bases; decomposed by hot conc. HCl or cold glacial acetic acid.

FREUDENBERGITE. Only slightly attacked by HF.

FRIEDELITE. Readily sol. in HCl, forming gel.

FROLOVITE. Insol. water; readily sol. warm acids.

FRONDELITE. Sol. HCl, insol. HNO_3 or H_2SO_4.

FROODITE. Sol. HNO_3; stained by KCN or $FeCl_3$ sols.

GABRIELSONITE. Easily sol. cold dil. HCl.

GADOLINITE. Appreciably attacked by warm conc. HCl forming gel. The usual brownish coatings are seldom easily removed and should not be disturbed.

GAGARINITE. Decomposes in water; readily dec. HNO_3, HCl or conc. H_2SO_4.

GAGEITE. Rapidly attacked by HCl or HF; sol. dil. HNO_3.

GAHNITE. Not attacked by cold acids; v. slightly attacked by hot conc. H_2SO_4.

GALENA. HCl or HNO_3 rapidly attack and dull bright xl faces; sol. H_2SO_4; slightly sol. cold conc. citric acid sol. Brittle, v. easily cleaved even by use of soft implements. Covering calcite removable with dil. acetic acid but test first to observe effect on bright xl faces.

GALENOBISMUTITE. Sol. hot conc. HCl.

GANOMALITE. Readily sol. HNO_3 or HCl, with formation of gel.

GANOPHYLLITE. Readily sol. strong acids; sol. HCl, forming gel.

GARNETS. Attacked v. slowly by HF only. The demantoid of Italy enclosed in asbestos can be cleaned by mechanically removing asbestos fibers and further cleaned by treating with HF which acid is restricted in its use to the immediate vicinity of the xls. Many garnet xls are fractured and cemented together with Mn or Fe oxides whose removal by acids sometimes results in disintegration of the xls.

GASPEITE. Insol. water; v. slowly sol. HNO_3 or HCl.

GAYLUSSITE. Rapidly sol. dil. acids; v. slightly sol. water. Unstable, store in sealed containers.

GEARKSUTITE. Readily sol. dil. acids.

GEDRITE. Attacked by HF only.

GEHLENITE. Rapidly attacked by HF; sol. in HCl, forming gel.

GEIKIELITE. Slightly attacked by hot HCl.

GENTHELVITE. Sol. HCl, forming gel.

GENTHITE. Decomposes in HCl.

GEOCRONITE. Attacked by HNO_3, A.R., or warm HCl.

GEORGIADESITE. Sol. HNO_3.

GERHARDTITE. Sol. in dil. acids.

GERMANITE. Sol. HNO_3.

GERSDORFFITE. Attacked by warm HNO_3, otherwise nearly unaffected by acids.

GETCHELLITE. Sol. in mixture of $H_2SO_4 + HNO_3$.

GIBBSITE. Very slightly attacked by conc. H_2SO_4.

GILBERTITE. Treat like COOKEITE.

GILLESPITE. Attacked by HCl.

GISMONDITE. Rapidly sol. in HCl., forming gel; also rapidly sol. other acids.

GLAUBERITE. Sol. HCl and partly sol. in water.

GLAUCOCERINITE. Sol. HCl.

GLAUCOCHROITE. Sol. HCl, forming gel.

GLAUCODOT. Attacked by HNO_3 and slightly by HCl.

GLAUCONITE. Variably attacked and decomposed by HCl and other acids.

GLAUCOPHANE. More or less rapidly sol. in HF but unaffected by HCl; glaucophane in fibrous form accompanies the benitoite-neptunite of San Benito County, California.

GLUCINE. Slowly sol. in dil. HCl.

GMELINITE. Readily sol. HCl, forming gel; v. rapidly sol. HF and affected by other acids. Avoid strong detergents, ammonia, etc., during cleaning. Xls tend to crumble and use of ultrasonic cleaner may be harmful.

GOETHITE. Slowly attacked by cold conc. HCl and more rapidly by warm. Slowly attacked by oxalic acid, the rapidity of attack and degree of sol. of the goethite being much more pronounced when in earthy or spongy forms (limonitic). In contrast, bright xls of this species are only very slowly affected by HCl and it is possible to use this acid conc. and warm to dissolve the hematite flakes which occur upon the matrix specimens of amazonite-smoky quartz of Colorado. Furthermore, the Colorado goethite xls are cleaned to a brilliant luster by dil. HF (2 parts HF from bottle to 1 part water by vol.), but of course this acid rapidly attacks any feldspar present (private communication from Walter Miller, Yuma, Arizona).

GOETZENITE. Readily sol. hot dil. HCl.

GOLD. Sol. only in A.R., also in K and Na cyanide sols. Iron stains removed by any convenient acid; small amounts of quartz removed by HF in full strength; use of HF is common with certain wire forms imbedded in porous quartz (Colorado). Soft, malleable, easily scratched by firm tools not to mention metal tools.

GOLDICHITE. Sol. water.

GOLDMANITE. Decomposes in mixture $H_2SO_4 + HF$.

GONNARDITE. Readily attacked by acids, gelatinizing in HCl. Brittle, weak and requires delicacy in handling. Normal water cleaning harmless.

GORDONITE. Sol. acids.

GORGEYITE (GOERGEYITE). Slightly etched in hot water.

GOSLARITE. Readily sol. water and acids; rapidly dehydrates, store in sealed containers.

GOYAZITE. Very slightly sol. in acids.

GRAFTONITE. Easily sol. acids, especially in HCl.

GRANDIDIERITE. Insol. acids.

GRAPHITE. Unaffected by any acids or common reagents. Soft and easily disintegrated or scratched by even soft implements.

GRATONITE. Attacked by HNO_3, A.R., or HCl, quickly losing luster of xls.

GREENOCKITE. Slowly sol. conc. HCl.

GREIGITE. Very slowly sol. HF or HCl; stable in air.

GRIPHITE. Easily sol. acids, especially HCl.

GROSSULAR. Commonly found enclosed within coarsely xline calcite which is readily removed by HCl without affecting xl luster. However, in some deposits (Maine), cavernous xls occur which consist of thin concentric shells of grossular surrounding concentric cores of calcite; overtreatment with acid causes these to crumble or at least become less attractive. In most specimens it is better, despite the trouble, to remove calcite mechanically. Grossular is slightly attacked by HF.

GROTHINE. Attacked by H_2SO_4.

GRUNERITE. Unaffected by acids but readily attacked by HF.

GUDMUNDITE. Attacked by HNO_3.

GUETTARDITE. Forms black tarnish in HNO_3.

GUMMITE. Sol. in acids to some extent.

GUANJUATITE. Attacked by warm A.R.

GUNNINGITE. Easily sol. cold water.

GUSTAVITE. Apparently not affected by mineral acids.

GYPSUM. Sol. hot dil. HCl and very slowly sol. cold acid; somewhat sol. in glycerine. Conc. warm H_2SO_4 attacks by removing water of crystallization and thus decomposes. Extremely soft and no firm implements of any type can be used safely (scratched by the fingernail!). Soak off clays in water to which some ammonia has been added; iron stains removed with dil. oxalic or other organic acids.

GYROLITE. Attacked by HCl and other acids.

HAIDINGERITE. Insol. water but rapidly in acids as HNO_3.

HAINITE. Decomposed by HCl.

HALITE. Readily sol. water; attracts atmospheric moisture in damp climates; sol. in glycerine and slightly sol. in alcohols. Clean with saturated sol. table salt or with nearly pure alcohol. Very soft and brittle, easily fractured or cleaved.

HALLIMONDITE. Easily sol. HNO_3.

HALLOYSITE. Rapidly sol. HF and slowly decomposed by other acids, especially conc. H_2SO_4. Loosened by treating with HCl to dissolve calcite, or oxalic acid to dissolve iron oxides.

HALOTRICHITE. Very readily sol. water or dil. acids; loses water in drier climates and requires sealed container storage.

HALURGITE. Slightly sol. water, completely in hot.

HAMBERGITE. Sol. HF; iron stains removed with oxalic acid.

HAMLINITE. Insol. in acids.

HANKSITE. Very easily sol. in water or dil. acids; develops white coating due to dehydration, or conversely, in damp climates, may become moist on surface. Store in sealed containers or in jars to which light oil or other anhydrous fluid is added. Lacquer sprays effective only for short periods and usually are not worth the trouble.

HANNAYITE. Sol. water.

HARDYSTONITE. Sol. HCl, forming gel. Easily overlooked as a constituent of Franklin, New Jersey, matrix specimens which when treated by acid for calcite removal may be disfigured by the appearance of acid-attacked hardystonite.

HARMOTOME. Decomposes in HCl or A.R.; sol. in HF.

HARSTIGITE. Attacked by HF but not other acids.

HARTITE. Sol. in alcohols.

HATCHETTOLITE. Unaffected by acids; sol. in oils and other organic solvents.

HAUERITE. Sol. warm conc. HCl.

HAUSMANNITE. Sol. in conc. hot HCl but even dil. cold acids may harm luster of xl faces.

HAUYNE. Sol. acids; readily sol. HCl, forming gel.

HEDENBERGITE. Slightly attacked by HF only.

HEDYPHANE. Sol. HNO_3.

HELIOPHYLLITE. Sol. HCl, forming gel.

HELLANDITE. Sol. HCl.

HELVITE. Sol. HCl, forming gel.

HEMAFIBRITE. Sol. HCl.

HEMATITE. Very commonly appears on other species as a thin reddish coating while the brownish coatings are usually goethite. Slowly sol. in cold acids, faster in warm, with HCl being used most. Rate of dissolution dependent on fineness of particles, scales, dustings, etc., rapidly going into sol. and discoloring acid bath yellow to reddish-yellow, especially when warm. Large shining xls very slowly affected. Not affected by cold saturated citric acid sol. In hematite removals, use care in transfer of specimens in and out of warm baths to avoid thermal shock, especially to quartz xls. Wash carefully afterward to avoid yellowish stains of residual acid bath trapped in crevices.

HEMATOLITE. Sol. in acids.

HEMIHEDRITE. Decomposed in HNO_3 or HCl, and slowly decomposed in 20% sol. KOH; unaffected by 20% sol. ammonia.

HEMIMORPHITE. Readily sol. acids, especially HCl., forming gel. Also attacked by organic acids acetic and citric, and very rapidly by HF. Very slightly attacked by sols. of hydroxides. Use normal cleaning; ultrasonic bath safe. Care must be used to prevent breakage fragile xls, hence avoid any firm tools and use slender flexible slivers bamboo. Much powdery limonite is dislodged during ultrasonic cleaning of specimens from Durango, Mexico, but is harmless.

HENDERSONITE. Gradually alters in air, turning brown; sol. in H_2SO_4.

HENRITERMIERITE. Slowly sol. cold HCl, rapidly in warm.

HERDERITE. Sol. acids and rapidly sol. warm or conc. acids. Iron stains removed with mild oxalic acid, acetic, or citric acid sol.

HERRENGRUNDITE. Sol. HCl.

HERZENBERGITE. Readily sol. HCl or H_2SO_4.

HESSITE. Attacked by HNO_3.

HETAEROLITE. Attacked by acids; sol. in HCl.

HETEROSITE. Readily sol. HCl which can be used to remove dark alteration coating if used with care.

HEULANDITE. Rapidly sol. HF, less so in HCl. Easily cleaved, brittle, and commonly dislodged from matrix by rough trimming. Avoid use of strong detergents, ammonia, etc., when cleaning. Avoid prolonged immersion in water unless it is distilled.

HEWETTITE. Slightly attacked by water, rapidly by acids.

HIBONITE. Slowly sol. in mixture of H_2SO_4 and H_3PO_4.

HIERATITE. Sol. hot water.

HIGGINSITE. Sol. acids.

HILGARDITE. Insol. water; sol. HCl.

HILLEBRANDITE. Rapidly sol. HF, less so in HCl.

HINSDALITE. Almost untouched by any acid.

HIORTDAHLITE. Sol. acids with formation of gel.

HISINGERITE. Easily sol. HCl.

HODGKINSONITE. Sol. in acids with formation of gel.

HOERNESITE. Sol. acids.

HOHMANNITE. Insol. cold water; rapidly sol. dil. HCl. Unstable, requires sealed container storage.

HOLLANDITE. Sol. HCl.

HOMILITE. Sol. HCl, forming gel.

HOPEITE. Readily sol. HCl and attacked by other acids with loss of xl luster.

HORNBLENDE. Slowly attacked by HF only.

HORTONOLITE. Sol. HCl, with formation of gel.

HOWLITE. Easily sol. acids with gel formation and affected to some extent by strong detergents and soaps. Adhering clay (Tick Canyon) easily removed by washing and scrubbing.

HUANGHOITE. Rapidly sol. HCl.

HUEBNERITE. Treat like FERBERITE.

HUEHNERKOBELITE. Slowly attacked by acids.

HUEMULITE. Easily sol. in cold water.

HUMBERSTONITE. Sol. in water; insol. acetone or ethyl alcohol; sol. acids.

HUMBOLDTINE. Sol. acids.

HUMITE. Slowly attacked by acids with gel formation; rapidly sol. in HF; sol. in conc. warm H_2SO_4.

HUNGCHAOITE. Sol. water.

HUREAULITE. Easily sol. acids; avoid strong detergents. Tends to alter when exposed to strong light acquiring a dark coating.

HURLBUTITE. Attacked by acids; avoid strong detergents.

HYALITE (OPAL). Rapidly attacked by HF or by hot hydroxide sols only. Colorless transparent material on rhyolite relatively insensitive to heat.

HYALOPHANE. Readily sol. HF and only slightly sol. other acids if latter used hot. See FELDSPAR for general treatment remarks.

HYALOTEKITE. Rapidly sol. HF; insol. HCl or H_2SO_4.

HYDROBORACITE. Easily sol. acids; v. slightly sol. in water.

HYDROCALUMITE. Readily sol. dil. acids.

HYDROCERUSSITE. Easily sol. acids.

HYDROCHLORBORITE. Insol. cold water but readily in hot water and acids.

HYDROGLAUBERITE. Decomposes in water forming gypsum; readily sol. dil. acids.

HYDROHETAEROLITE. Readily sol. HCl.

HYDROMAGNESITE. Readily sol. acids.

HYDRONEPHELITE. Sol. HCl, forming gel.

HYDROPHILITE. Sol. water and very deliquescent!

HYDROTALCITE. Easily sol. dil. HCl.

HYDROTUNGSTITE. Insol. in acids or ammonia sols.

HYDROZINCITE. Rapidly sol. acids and may be attacked by strong detergents or soaps which are to be avoided in cleaning; use dist. water only.

HYPERSTHENE. V. slightly attacked by warm conc. HCl and more rapidly by HF.

IDDINGSITE. Slowly sol. conc. acids, rapidly in HF.

IDOCRASE. Partly decomposed in HCl or A.R. but removal of enclosing calcite with dil. HCl does little damage; avoid prolonged soak in acid to avoid damage to xl luster. Commonly associated with white fibrous or bladed WOLLASTONITE which may be confused with calcite, but latter promptly produces bubbles CO_2 when touched by HCl while former does not; prolonged acid treatment with view of dissolving the wollastonite usually results in severe marring of the idocrase xls. The "textbook" xls from Wilui, Siberia, are sometimes coated with a white brittle layer which detaches with needles or razor blades to uncover the lustrous xl beneath.

ILMENITE. V. slowly attacked by hot conc. HCl; enclosing calcite easily removed with dil. HCl without damaging xls.

ILMENORUTILE. Unaffected by acids.

ILVAITE. Fairly rapidly attacked and xls marred by acids including cold citric acid sol.; small xls or powders gelatinize in HCl, even the dil. acid causing rapid loss of xl luster. Brittle, and xls break off easily if enclosing quartz (Idaho) is disturbed or chipped. Not practical to attempt removal of rust stains due to attack of xls by acids.

INDERBORITE. Sol. acids; slowly sol. water.

INDERITE. Rapidly sol. dil. warm acids but insol. in cold water which can be used to wash specimens.

INDITE. Etched by conc. HNO_3; diss. in hot fuming H_2SO_4; other acids do not affect.

INESITE. Readily sol. acids.

INYOITE. V. rapidly diss. all acids; rapidly diss. cold to warm water.

IODARGYRITE. Insol. water; decomposes in hot conc. acids; sol. in conc. potassium iodide sol.; slightly sol. hot saline sols.

IODYRITE. Insol. water or dil. HNO_3; attacked by warm conc. HNO_3, H_2SO_4; slightly attacked warm chloride sols.; cyanide sols.; ammonia sols.

IOLITE. See CORDIERITE.

IOWAITE. Loses water and changes color on exposure; readily sol. mineral acids.

IRANITE. Sol. warm Na_2CO_3 sol.

IRIDOSMINE. Not attacked by acids.

IRIGINITE. Insol. hot or cold water but completely sol. strong acids, bases.

IRON. Rapidly diss. acids, especially HNO_3; slowly sol. acetic acid; insol. conc. H_2SO_4. In HNO_3 emits poisonous brownish fumes of nitrogen oxides which must not be inhaled. Native iron may oxidize rapidly in moist atmospheres and it is best to preserve specimens in sealed containers with small bag of dehydrated silica gel. See also special section on "Meteorites" (p. 213).

ISOCLASITE. Rapidly attacked by acids, expecially HCl.

ISOKITE. Sol. acids, slowly in cold HCl, rapidly in warm acids.

JACOBSITE. Slowly attacked by HCl.

JADEITE. Diss. by HF only.

JALPAITE. Stains brown HNO_3; iridescent stain with HCl.

JAMESONITE. Decomposed HNO_3 and attacked by other acids to some extent, especially warm HCl. Fibers mat easily in water and it is best to avoid washing altogether or to lave gently in alcohol or acetone. The more massive fibrous types can be gently washed in dist. water.

JARLITE. Sol. aluminum chloride sol.; attacked by H_2SO_4.

JAROSITE. Readily sol. HCl and by other acids; common constituent of limonite.

JEFFERISITE. Decomposes in HCl; slightly attacked by boil. saturated sol. citric acid.

JEFFERSONITE. Diss. by HF only. Care required in removing enclosing calcite (Franklin, New Jersey) to prevent crumbling of xls which are often internally fractured; generally dil. HCl used for this purpose although chipping methods can also be used; in general, the xls are stronger than the franklinite xls from the same locality.

JET. Attacked to some extent by strong organic solvents; resistant to all acids. Brittle, chips easily. Carvings cleaned with ordinary soap and water; do not use metal tools.

JEZEKITE. V. slightly attacked by acids.

JIMBOITE. Sol. HCl, HNO_3 or H_2SO_4.

JOAQUINITE. Found with benitoite-neptunite as small honey-yellow xls; not harmed by the HCl usually used to diss. the natrolite enclosing.

JOHANNITE. Sol. dil. acids; slightly sol. water.

JOHNSTRUPITE. Sol. HCl.

JORDANITE. Attacked by HNO_3 and A. R. Luster of xls liable to be harmed by prolonged exposure to HCl.

JOSEPHINITE (AWARUITE). Slowly sol. dil. HCl; slightly attacked by acetic.

JULIENITE. Readily sol. water or alcohol.

KAEMMERERITE. Treat like CHLORITE.

KAINITE. Easily sol. water or acids; attracts water, requiring storage in sealed containers.

KAINOSITE. Sol. HCl.

KALIBORITE. Readily sol. acids.

KALIOPHILITE. Sol. HCl, forming gel.

KALISTRONTITE. Insol. water; sol. warm HCl.

KAOLINITE. Treat like CLAY.

KARPINSKYITE. Insol. HCl, HNO_3, or H_2SO_4.

KASOLITE. Attacked by acids, forming gel.

KASSITE. Insol. acids.

KATOPTRITE. Insol. acids.

KEHOITE. Sol. in acids.

KEILHAUITE. Slightly attacked by HCl.

KELDYSHITE. Decomposed by HNO_3, HCl, and H_2SO_4.

KEMMLITZITE. Very resistant to mineral acids.

KEMPITE. Sol. HCl.

KENTROLITE. Rapidly sol. HCl, also in dil. H_2SO_4, HF, and A.R.

KERMESITE. Sol. strong alkali sols.; attacked by HCl. Avoid detergents in cleaning water. Fragile, easily cleaved or scratched by any tool.

KERNITE. Slowly sol. cold water, rapidly in dil. acids or hot water. Loses water in dry atmospheres; store in sealed container.

KIESERITE. Slowly sol. water; alters on surface in damp climate; store in sealed container.

KINOITE. Decomposed in dil. HCl.

KITKAITE. Sol. HNO_3; insol. in HCl.

KLAPROTHITE. Slightly sol. HCl, more so in HNO_3 or A.R.

KLEINITE. Sol. warm dil. HCl or HNO_3.

KLOCKMANNITE. Attacked by HNO_3 or A.R.

KNEBELITE. Readily sol. HCl, forming gel.

KOBEITE. Insol. hot conc. HCl; slightly attacked by hot conc. H_2SO_4 and more so by HF; warm conc. oxalic acid has no effect.

KOBELLITE. Sol. conc. HCl; attacked by HNO_3 or A.R.

KOECHLINITE. Sol. HCl.

KOENENITE. Decomposes in water.

KOETTIGITE. Attacked by acids; see ADAMITE for treatment.

KOKTAITE. Decomposed in water and precipitating gypsum.

KOLBECKITE. Slowly attacked by acids.

KONINCKITE. Sol. HCl.

KOPPITE. Decomposed in hot conc. H_2SO_4.

KORNERUPINE. Attacked v. slightly by HF only.

KOTULSKITE. Etched by HNO_3.

KOUTEKITE. Etched by HNO_3, HCl, or $FeCl_2$ sol.

KRAUSITE. Slowly sol. water, dil. acids, especially HCl.

KRAUSKOPFITE. Readily decomposes in cold dil. acids leaving silica residue; also affected by strong bases.

KRENNERITE. Decomposes in A.R. or hot H_2SO_4.

KROEHNKITE. Readily sol. water and dil. acids.

KTENASITE. Sol. dil. acids or ammonia.

KURNAKOVITE. Insol. water but easily sol. dil. HCl.

KUTNAHORITE. Rapidly sol. warm acids and only slowly in cold.

KYANITE. Unaffected by acids or other common agents. Iron stains removed with oxalic acid. Cleavable, wide hardness differences make it advisable to avoid metal tools in cleaning.

LABRADORITE. Treat like ALBITE; v. slowly attacked by HCl.

LABUNTSOVITE. Sol. with difficulty in HCl, HNO_3, or H_2SO_4.

LACROIXITE. Rapidly attacked by HCl and H_2SO_4.

LANARKITE. Sol. HNO_3 or KOH sol.

LANDAUITE. Very resistant to acids; sol. with difficulty in mixture of HNO_3 + H_2SO_4.

LANDESITE. Sol. acids.

LANGBANITE. Slightly attacked by HCl; rapidly by HF.

LANGBEINITE. Slowly sol. in water, rapidly in dil. acids; deliquescent! Store in sealed container.

LANGITE. Readily sol. acids or in ammonia sol.; insol. water.

LANSFORDITE. Readily sol. dil. acids. Loses water in dry air, requiring sealed container storage.

LANTHANITE. Sol. acids.

LAPIS LAZULI. Acids, including citric and other organic acids, readily attack the principal minerals calcite (white), hauyne, and lazurite (blue), but scarcely touch the pyrite. Thus acids cannot be used for exposing the xls of lazurite that occur in calcite matrix in the specimens from Afganistan; use mechanical methods only, and with great care because of the extreme fragility of the lazurite xls.

LARDERELLITE. Attacked by water; readily sol. in acids.

LARNITE. Slowly sol. in water; sol. in acids with gel formation.

LARSENITE. Slowly sol. dil. HCl, forming gel.

LATIUMITE. Decomposed by weak acids leaving silica residue.

LAUBANITE. Slowly sol. HCl, forming gel, and more rapidly in warm acid; v. rapidly sol. HF.

LAUMONTITE. Readily sol. HCl, forming gel, and v. rapidly in HF. Fresh xls clear and colorless but lose water immediately after removal and within minutes turn opaque white; all xls thereby become internally damaged and readily crumble when jarred or brushed, or spontaneously disintegrate in storage; restoration of water does not repair damage. Preservation in original state calls for immediate wrapping in wet paper and then transferring to containers in which free water is present. The usual alternative is to let xls dry, then spray heavily with lacquer or soak in dil. sol. vinyl acetate ("white glue") cement in order to impregnate and hold minute fragments together.

LAUNAYITE. Stained black by HNO_3.

LAURIONITE. Very slightly sol. in water, more so in hot; sol. HNO_3 or A.R. and attacked by other acids. Quick cleaning in dist. water is permissible but rapid drying afterward required; use no detergents or additives of any kind.

LAUSENITE. Sol. in water.

LAUTERITE. Sol. HCl.

LAUTITE. Sol. HNO_3.

LAVENITE. Sol. HCl.

LAWRENCEITE. Readily sol. water; hygroscopic, store in sealed container.

LAWSONITE. Sol. HF only. Adhering scaly minerals (glaucophane principally) removed with needles but care required since lawsonite prisms commonly cracked and may crumble when exposed or moved. Suggest application of dil. vinyl acetate ("white") glue sol. to xls and areas around xls after exposure.

LAZULITE. Readily attacked by hot acids and to some extent by cold but practically insol. in HCl. Xls very brittle and many contain numerous fractures which make them fall apart if matrix removal is attempted (see LAWSONITE above for recommendation on use of glue sol.). Many sharp xls can be easily exposed in the gritty quartz matrix of the Graves Mountain, Georgia, specimens merely by carefully picking away at the quartz with fine needles; however, removal of matrix by pinching methods may transmit shocks to xls causing them to fracture.

LAZURITE. Rapidly sol. HCl with formation of gel (see LAPIS LAZULI).

LEAD. Readily sol. HNO_3, with difficulty in conc. H_2SO_4; not affected by other acids or by cold or hot water. V. soft, malleable, easily scratched or grooved even by wood or plastic implements. Sometimes acquires white powdery alteration coating which mostly comes off in ultrasonic water bath. In the Langban specimens the matrix rock is usually easily detached from the lead.

LEADHILLITE. Exfoliates in hot water; diss. in HNO_3. V. soft and easily damaged; avoid any type of mechanical cleaning method or strong detergent bath.

LECONTITE. Sol. water.

LEGRANDITE. Treat like ADAMITE.

LEHIITE. Attacked by acids.

LEIFITE. Insol. in acids.

LEIGHTONITE. Sol. water, acids.

LENGENBACHITE. Attacked by HNO_3, A.R.

LEONHARDITE. See LAUMONTITE of which it is the desiccated form.

LEONITE. Rapidly sol. water.

LEPIDOCROCITE. Slowly sol. in HCl, rapidly in warm acid.

LEPIDOLITE. V. slowly attacked by HF only, which acid can be used to remove adhering clays, albite, etc., without much damage to the lepidolite. Books are very easily split and scratched upon the broad cleavage faces; avoid metal cleaning tools.

LEPIDOMELANE. Attacked by conc. HCl, otherwise treat like BIOTITE.

LETOVICITE. Sol. in water.

LEUCITE. Rapidly attacked by HF, less so by HCl. Brittle, xls may fall out of matrix if treated roughly.

LEUCOCHALCITE. Sol. acids.

LEUCOPHANITE. Readily attacked by HF only.

LEUCOPHOENICITE. Attacked and gelatinized by acids.

LEUCOPHOSPHITE. Sol. strong HCl.

LEUCOSPHENITE. Attacked by HF.

LEVYNE. Rapidly attacked by HCl or HNO_3 with formation of gel; v. rapidly attacked by HF.

LEWISITE. Insol. in ordinary acids.

LEWISTONITE. Sol. acids.

LIBETHENITE. Readily sol. acids or aqua ammonia; avoid use of detergents in water bath. Fragile, avoid use of brushes or picks.

LIEBIGITE. Sol. acids.

LIKASITE. Readily sol. dil. acids.

LIMONITE. Composed principally of goethite and jarosite and mostly removed from specimens by use of dil. sols. of oxalic acid, tartaric, or acetic acids; also attacked and diss. by HCl, HF. Earthy, porous types rapidly affected but very compact, hard types only slowly attacked but rate of attack can be increased by warming sol. Thick films on xls should be removed as much as possible by scraping or chipping if underlying xl is hard enough; otherwise treat in acid bath several times, changing to fresh acid sol. each time. Forms penetrating iron compounds which can enter crevices in specimens and later creep out to form disfiguring yellowish stains. For this reason, it is advisable to very thoroughly soak specimens after acid baths in several changes warm dist. water. Yellow stains can sometimes be removed by reimmersion in fresh oxalic sol.

LINARITE. Sol. dil. HNO_3; attacked more or less rapidly by other acids. Water cleaning generally satisfactory but avoid use of detergents, soaps, ammonia, etc.; also avoid prolonged soakings in water. Fragile, brittle, avoid use of tools.

LINDACKERITE. Sol. HCl.

LINDGRENITE. Readily sol. HCl, HNO_3, A.R. Rinse pure dist. water only; avoid strong detergents, soaps, ammonia, etc.

LINNAEITE. Attacked by HNO_3, A.R.; unaffected by HCl. Readily tarnishes.

LINTONITE. Massive form of THOMSONITE, which see.

LIROCONITE. Sol. acids, e.g. HNO_3. Avoid use of strong detergents, ammonia in water baths.

LISKEARDITE. Attacked by acids but insol. HNO_3.

LITHARGE. Slowly attacked by acids or alkalis; sol. HNO_3.

LITHIOPHILITE. Attacked by acids; avoid use of strong detergents in water baths.

LITHIOPHOSPHATE. Slightly sol. hot water; sol. in strong acids.

LIVINGSTONITE. Insol. most acids; sol. warm conc. H_2SO_4.

LOELLINGITE. Slightly sol. HNO_3;

completely sol. in cold saturated citric acid sol.; insol. HCl which may be used to remove covering calcite. Dull gray coatings are permanent surface blemishes and cannot be removed.

LOEWIGITE. Partly sol. HCl.

LOEWITE. Soluble in water.

LOMONOSOVITE. Decomposes in water.

LONSDALEITE. Treat like DIAMOND.

LOPEZITE. Soluble in water.

LORANDITE. Sol. in HNO_3 or A.R.

LORETTOITE. Sol. HNO_3.

LOSEYITE. Sol. HCl and attacked by other acids.

LOSSENITE. Sol. in acids.

LOTRITE. Attacked by acids, especially HCl.

LOUDERBACKITE. Soluble in water.

LOUGHLINITE. Slowly decomposed in water; sol. in HCl or H_2SO_4.

LUDLAMITE. Readily attacked by acids. Fragile, brittle, cleavable; easily dislodged from matrix (Idaho) by careless handling or shocks from trimming matrix. Avoid any hard tools. Use mild detergent only in bath; ultrasonic treatment safe when brief.

LUDWIGITE. Slowly attacked by acids; sol. HCl.

LUENEBERGITE. Sol. acids.

LUZONITE. Treat like ENARGITE.

MACDONALDITE. Insol. cold acids or bases; decomposed in boiling conc. HCl.

MACGOVERNITE. Attacked by HCl.

MADOCITE. Stained black by HNO_3.

MAGHEMITE. Treat like MAGNETITE.

MAGNESIOFERRITE. Very slightly attacked after prolonged immersion in warm conc. HCl; otherwise unaffected by acids.

MAGNESITE. Only slowly sol. in cold acids but rapidly in warm; insol. in acetic acid or in cold saturated citric acid. Care required in treating porous white masses which very readily absorb liquid and may become stained in acid-bearing baths.

MAGNESIUM CHALCANTHITE. Soluble in water; dehydrates, crumbling to powder and requiring storage in sealed container.

MAGNETITE. Slightly attacked by hot conc. HCl or by very long immersion in cold conc. HCl; otherwise nearly un-affected by acids. Xls from within rock usually crumbled if attempts are made to remove, but euhedrons in cavities are hard and tough (e.g., Switzerland, Tyrol). Note that some magnetites (Utah, Mexico) are altered wholly or in part to hematite (martite), in which event chemical attack is identical to HEMATITE, which see.

MAGNETOPLUMBITE. Slightly attacked by HCl.

MAKATAITE. Insol. water.

MALACHITE. Rapidly diss. in acids with vigorous production CO_2 gas bubbles. Decomposes v. slowly in hot water and diss. by conc. ammonia sol.; diss. in cyanide sols. Bruised places may be eradicated with judicious application dil. HCl, followed by thorough washing dist. water. If porous or cracked, wash in final bath dist. water to which several drops ammonia water are added and stirred in until a blue precipitate forms, at which time more water is added and the specimen allowed to soak for 1 hr. Pour off this sol. and resoak in clean dist. water. Soak for several hrs. Pour off water, drain, and then soak specimen in acetone, ethyl (grain), or methyl (wood) alcohol; drain; let dry. The last treatment removes traces of water which may contain slight traces of copper salts which may later "creep" from cracks and cause unsightly stains. Experimentation is required to obtain the desired results but it is possible to considerably improve the appearance of even badly marred specimens. This treatment should not be tried when azurite is present or when the malachite is earthy or porous.

MANANDONITE. Attacked by H_2SO_4.

MANGANESE OXIDES. These are commonly present as thin black, sooty films or as black dendrites on many mineral specimens and arise from weathering or alteration of manganese-containing minerals. Sol. in HCl, HF, or oxalic acid. Large amounts treated with HCl can generate dangerous volumes of greenish-brownish chlorine gas.

MANGANITE. Attacked by hot conc. acids, especially H_2SO_4 or HCl. Some large xls (Harz) tend to develop v. thin sooty coatings which disappear in ultrasonic water bath. Finely divided manganite reacts with HCl to form chlorine gas.

MANGANO-COLUMBITE. Treat like COLUMBITE.

MANGANOSITE. Slightly attacked by conc. HCl or H_2SO_4.

MANGANOSTIBITE. Sol. HCl.

MANGANOTANTALITE. Treat like COLUMBITE.

MANSFIELDITE. Sol. acids.

MARCASITE. Powder diss. HNO_3; not affected by cold saturated sol. citric acid. V. commonly unstable, tending to decompose and fall into powdery masses with formation of white iron sulfate (melanterite) with liberation of free sulfuric acid which attacks wood, paper, organic materials, metals, and even other minerals stored in the same space. For this reason, many collectors advise storage of marocasite in closed containers, or at least away from other specimens. Incipient decomposition often detectable by smelling specimen for typical sulfurous odor (SO_2). Various methods of preservation have been proposed but no assured preventative is known. In general, specimens are thoroughly washed by immersion for several hrs. in warm dist. water, after which a teaspoonful of conc. aqua ammonia is added to each gallon of water and the specimen resoaked for several more hours to neutralize acids. Drain, rinse in clean water, and towel dry; immerse and soak in alcohol or acetone to remove traces of water; drain and let dry. After thorough drying some authorities advise soaking specimen in thin sol. acrylic plastic to exclude air and moisture, preferably in vacuum under a bell jar to ensure removal of trapped air and deep penetration of the plastic sol. Thereafter, store in dry atmosphere. It is to be noted that not all marcasites deteriorate and some mineral dealers set aside all freshly mined specimens for a year and then sell only those that show no signs of alteration. The most likely specimens to deteriorate are those from the Tri-State district or nodular masses taken from clay and other sedimentary deposits.

Another preservative method calls for placing specimen in colorless conc. HCl, and soaking for 10-15 minutes, and repeating the process until the acid is no longer discolored by yellow stains. Drain, soak in ether until the acid is removed, using two separate soakings.

Preservation coating: 7% by wgt. of vinyl acetate in a mixture of equal parts of acetone and toluene. Another: 1 part balsam to 7 parts by weight of xylene; let dry for several days. This last is not favored because of the sticky nature of the balsam.

MARGARITE. Slowly attacked by HF; v. slowly attacked by boiling conc. HCl or H_2SO_4. May be safely cleaned by any normal method. Minerals enclosed in margarite can be revealed by picking off the margarite with sharp steel tools.

MARIALITE. See SCAPOLITE.

MARMATITE. Treat like DOLOMITE.

MARSHITE. Attacked by conc. HNO_3, H_2SO_4, sol. cyanide sols.

MARTHOZITE. Dehydrates at room temp. to a meta-phase; sol. dil. HNO_3 or HCl.

MASCAGNITE. Easily sol. water, acids; requires protection from moist atmosphere.

MASSICOT. Sol. HCl, HNO_3, attacked H_2SO_4.

MATILDITE. Sol. HNO_3, A.R.

MATLOCKITE. Diss. HNO_3, A.R., decomposed H_2SO_4, and attacked by other acids. Clean in pure dist. water only.

MAUCHERITE. Diss. strong HNO_3; attacked by other acids.

MAWSONITE. Not affected by acids.

MCALLISTERITE. Slightly sol. water, readily in acids.

MEERSCHAUM. Slightly softened after soaking in water; ingrained surface soiling removed by light sanding and refinished by burnishing with polished agate tool. Decomposed by HCl.

MEIONITE. See SCAPOLITE.

MELANOCERITE. Attacked by hot HCl, cold HF.

MELANOTEKITE. Slowly decomposed by HNO_3; attacked by HF, A.R.

MELANOVANADINITE. Sol. acids.

MELANTERITE. Readily diss. water, acids. Unstable, requires storage in sealed containers. Insol. alcohol.

MELILITE. Rapidly diss. HF; diss. by HCl with formation of gel.

MELIPHANITE. Readily diss. HF.

MELKOVITE. Readily sol. dil. acids.

MELLITE. Insol. water but decomposes in boiling water; alcohols; sol. HNO_3.

MELONITE. Sol. HNO_3.

MENDIPITE. Attacked by acids; sol.

dil. HNO_3, A.R. Clean with dist. water only.

MENDOZITE. Sol. in water.

MENEGHINITE. Attacked by HNO_3, A.R. Fibrous forms liable to mat in water; use alcohol or acetone for gentle washing.

MERCALLITE. Sol. in water.

MERCURY. Quickly diss. HNO_3; insol. dil. HCl. Crudely cleaned by forcing through a chamois leather. Native mercury usually as small droplets which can be dislodged by overvigorous cleaning or immersion in ultrasonic bath. The vapor is extremely poisonous and under no circumstances should distillation be attempted except under a laboratory hood with adequate forced draft ventilation; this also applies to roasting of cinnabar from which mercury issues in vapor form. Even spills of mercury upon floors or tables must be regarded as extremely hazardous, especially in a closed room, and breathing apparatus must be used to clean up.

MERRILLITE. Sol. HNO_3.

MERWINITE. Sol. HCl, forming gel.

MESOLITE. Rapidly sol. HF or HCl, with the last forming a gel; sol. in cold concentrated citric acid. Very fragile needles bar use of any mechanical cleaning but may be cleaned in an ultrasonic bath in dist. water to which a very little detergent has been added.

META-ALUMINITE. Sol. water but generally stable in normal atmosphere.

METABORITE. Slowly sol. water.

METACINNABAR. Sol. A.R. but insol. HNO_3.

METAHEWETTITE. Slightly sol. in water; sol. in acids.

METAROSSITE. Sol. water and dil. acids.

METASIDERONATRITE. Insol. cold water; rapidly sol. dil. acids.

METASTRENGITE. Sol. HCl; nearly insol. in HNO_3.

METATORBERNITE. Attacked by acids; sol. HNO_3.

METAVARISCITE. Sol. HCl.

METAVAUXITE. Readily attacked by HCl and other acids.

METAVOLTINE. Sol. in water; slowly sol. in acids.

METAZEUNERITE. Rapidly attacked by acids.

METEORITES. See special section (p. 213).

MEYERHOFFERITE. Rapidly sol. in acids and very slowly sol. in water but water can be used for cleaning provided it is distilled and cold; also can be cleaned in alcohol.

MIARGYRITE. Attacked by HNO_3 and A.R. Surface alters and darkens with exposure to strong light.

MICAS. Generally unaffected by all agents save strong, warm conc. acids. Some attack by acids occurs, especially by HF but it is possible to use acids in cleaning for considerable periods of time without serious harm. Problems are encountered in water baths due to the tendency for water to enter and pry apart the leaves, and for this reason prolonged immersions are to be avoided. Very easily scratched on the broad cleavage surfaces by steel tools.

MICHENERITE. Sol. HNO_3, unaffected by KCl, KCN, KOH; stained by A.R., $FeCl_3$.

MICROCLINE. Readily attacked by HF which exploits fractures and openings between the lamellae in perthite types and results in porous surfaces after treatment. Iron oxides removed by oxalic acid, specular hematite by conc. HCl used warm. Very careful washing in several changes of warm water is needed afterward to ensure removal of iron compounds in sol. which may later "creep" and stain the specimen during drying. Washings should consist of rinsing off acids, then soaking for several hours at least in warm dist. water, repeated several times. HCl, used conc. or cut by an equal vol. of dist. water, is the favorite for removal of the red hematite scales from the amazonites of Colorado. Prior to treatment, place specimens in clean warm water and soak for several hours to impregnate internal crevices and thus bar entry of acid. Then transfer to acid bath at same temperature. Upon removal, transfer to washing bath, again at same temperature, etc. Fresh, cool oxalic acid sol. sometimes effective in removing the yellow stains which creep out of improperly washed specimens. Avoid thermal shocks in all treatments, not so much for the amazonite as for the smoky quartz which is very liable to crack when suddenly changed in temperature.

MICROLITE. V. slowly attacked by H_2SO_4; not attacked by HCl. Xls usually fractured (Amelia, Virginia) and very likely to disintegrate if removed from matrix. May be impregnated with diluted vinyl acetate glue to prevent.

MICROSOMMITE. Sol. HCl, forming gel; readily attacked by HF.

MIERSITE. Sol. cyanide sols; attacked by conc. H_2SO_4 or HNO_3; not affected by dil. HCl.

MILARITE. Sol. in HF; not attacked by water or HCl.

MILLERITE. Sol. HNO_3 or A.R.; v. slightly by other acids. Hairlike xls should not be cleaned or else matting occurs; some suggest gentle laving in alcohol.

MILLISITE. Attacked by acids.

MILOSCHITE. V. slightly sol. HCl.

MIMETITE. Readily attacked by HNO_3 and slightly by other acids, while brief exposure to HCl causes xl face dulling. It is usually futile to try to remove associated calcite but one of the organic acids may be used; see CALCITE for recommendations. Brittle, readily fractured by rough handling.

MINASRAGRITE. Sol. water.

MINGUZZITE. Readily sol. water.

MINIUM. Sol. HCl, attacked by HNO_3.

MINYULITE. Sol. in acids.

MIRABILITE. Very sol. water and acids; dehydrates and falls to powder; preserve in sealed container.

MISENITE. Sol. water.

MIXITE. Attacked by acids; decomposes in HNO_3.

MOHAWKITE. Treat like DOMEYKITE.

MOHRITE. Sol. in water and acids.

MOISSANITE. Not attacked by acids or other common agents.

MOLDAVITE. Attacked and diss. by HF but scarcely affected by other acids. Very resistant to thermal shock; brittle, but fairly tough.

MOLYBDENITE. Decomposed in HNO_3; sol. A.R.; not affected by cold saturated sol. citric acid. Books fragile, easily scratched, bent, etc. Iron stains removable with oxalic acid.

MOLYBDOMENITE. Sol. cold HNO_3 in 1-acid to 10-water sol.

MOLURANITE. Sol. warm acids.

MOLYSITE. Very quickly sol. in water and acids. V. deliquescent; store in sealed container.

MONAZITE. V. slightly attacked by warm conc. HCl. Xls commonly fractured

and disintegrate when removed from matrix. Rust stains may be part of altered surface of xls and then should not be disturbed.

MONCHEITE. Not affected by acids.

MONETITE. Sol. acids.

MONTANITE. Sol. HCl.

MONTEBRASITE. Treat like AMBLYGONITE.

MONTGOMERYITE. Attacked by acids.

MONTICELLITE. Sol. strong HCl, forming gel.

MONTMORILLONITE. Treat like CLAYS.

MONTROYDITE. Easily sol. HCl or HNO_3; also in hydroxide sols.

MOOREHOUSEITE. Soluble in water.

MOOREITE. Sol. in acids.

MORDENITE. Sol. HCl with formation of gel; also stated as *insol.* HCl!

MORENOSITE. Sol. water and dil. acids. Rapidly dehydrates; store in sealed container.

MORINITE. Attacked by HCl.

MOSANDRITE. Decomposed in HCl.

MOSCHELLANDSBERGITE. Sol. in HNO_3.

MOSESITE. Attacked by cold HCl.

MOSSITE. Not attacked by acids.

MOTTRAMITE. Easily soluble in acids; sol. in dil. HNO_3.

MOURITE. Very slowly sol. conc. warm HCl; sol. conc. HNO_3; insol. H_2SO_4; sol. 20% hot sol. Na_2CO_3.

MUIRITE. Decomposed by dil. HCl or HNO_3; not affected by H_2SO_4 or acetic acid.

MURMANITE. Sol. H_2SO_4.

MUSCOVITE. See MICAS.

MUTHMANNITE. Sol. HNO_3 or HCl.

NADORITE. Attacked by HCl with xls quickly losing luster; also by HNO_3.

NAGYAGITE. Sol. HNO_3 or A.R.

NAHCOLITE. V. easily sol. water, acids, also glycerine; slightly sol. alcohols. Unstable, store in sealed container.

NANTOKITE. Slowly attacked by water; rapidly sol. HCl, HNO_3, or ammonia.

NARSARSUKITE. Attacked by HCl; sol. HF.

NATROCHALCITE. Rapidly sol. acids; slowly in water.

NATROJAROSITE. Slowly sol. HCl.

NATROLITE. Readily sol. HCl with

formation gel; attacked by other acids, including citric; rapidly sol. HF. Clay or opal-coated xls (Clear Creek, California) are not improved by immersion in dil. HCl which attacks and deeply etches the natrolite without affecting the coating. Massive white fibrous natrolite enclosing benitoite-neptunite in the same area is customarily removed by soaking entire specimen in dil. HCl, using 1 part conc. acid by vol. to 4 to 6 parts dist. water; greater conc. results in rapid formation thick coating silica gel which retards further chemical activity and presents problems in removal. A good system is to immerse specimens in dil. acid, leave overnight, and wash next morning, discarding old acid and replacing with fresh. Repeat as necessary to uncover xls. Selective "stopping off" to retard acid sol. in certain areas on specimens can be done with lacquer or beeswax applied to perfectly dry specimen. Long prismatic natrolites from zeolite occurrences (New Jersey; India) should not be treated with any kind of strong chemical but may be immersed in the ultrasonic bath water to which a little detergent has been added. Avoid use of any kind of tool or brush. Also see BENITOITE and NEPTUNITE.

NATRON. Rapidly sol. water or acids. Dehydrates; store in sealed container.

NATROPHILITE. Slowly sol. acids.

NAUMANNITE. Sol. hot HNO_3 and v. slightly sol. ammonia sol.

NEIGHBORITE. Insol. water.

NENADKEVICHITE. Readily sol. H_2SO_4, with difficulty in HNO_3 or HCl.

NEOTOCITE. Attacked by acids.

NEPHELINE. Readily sol. in acids, especially HCl, forming gel; attacked by cold conc. sol. citric acid. Associated calcite may be removed with the organic acids or chemicals; consult CALCITE.

NEPHRITE. Slowly attacked by HF only. Carvings efficiently cleaned by immersion in ultrasonic bath with strong detergent and/or ammonia to dissolve traces of grease and oil. Waxes may be removed but can be restored using any household polishing wax.

NEPTUNITE. Unaffected by usual dil. HCl sols. used to remove the massive natrolite enclosing neptunite-benitoite of California. Excessively strong HCl sols. may cause dulling of xl luster. Readily sol.

in HF. Xls may be broken and cemented together with natrolite, and excessive use of this acid in removing natrolite commonly causes detachment. After acid treatment some xls display a dull waxlike film which is probably a clay mineral; this may be removed by using slender wood or bamboo rods sharpened to chisel edges and used as scrapers.

NESQUEHONITE. Slightly sol. water, more rapidly in carbonated water and even more so in dil. acids.

NEWBERRYITE. Sol. HNO_3.

NEYITE. Slowly attacked and tarnished by HNO_3, and less so in HCl.

NICCOLITE. Sol. A.R. but unaffected by dil. HCl which can be used to remove calcite; not attacked by cold conc. sol. citric acid. Some specimens oxidize in damp air but this is rare and no special storage requirements are necessary.

NICKEL-IRON. Slowly sol. dil. acids; sol. HNO_3; slightly attacked by acetic acid. See section on "Meteorites" (p. 213).

NIFONTOVITE. Insol. water; slowly sol. dil. acetic acid or HCl; rapidly sol. in warm acids.

NISSONITE. Easily sol. dil. acids.

NITER. V. rapidly sol. water and acids; store in sealed containers.

NITRATINE. Sol. water; deliquescent!

NITROMAGNESITE. Sol. water.

NOBLEITE. Slightly sol. cold water, more so in hot, and rapidly in cold dil. acids or strong alkali sols.; v. sol. in methyl alcohol.

NOLANITE. Sol. H_2SO_4.

NONTRONITE. Sol. HCl with formation of gel; rapidly sol. HF.

NORBERGITE. Treat like CHONDRO-DITE.

NORDENSKIOLDINE. Sol. HCl.

NORDITE. Decomposes in acids.

NORSETHITE. Insol. water; decomposed in HCl.

NORTHUPITE. Rapidly sol. dil. acids; attacked by hot water.

NOSEAN. Rapidly sol. in HCl, forming gel.

NOVAKITE. Sol. conc. H_2SO_4.

OBSIDIAN. Rapidly sol. HF; unaffected by other acids except when used hot conc. against the powder.

OCHERS. Treat like LIMONITE.

OFFRETITE. Diss. HCl; rapidly diss. HF.

OKENITE. Readily sol. HCl with formation gel; attacked by other acids, rapidly by HF. Fragile, avoid brushing, use of strong detergents.

OLDHAMITE. Rapidly diss. HCl; decomposed by boiling water.

OLIGOCLASE. Treat like ALBITE.

OLIVENITE. Readily attacked by HCl, HNO_3, H_2SO_4, A.R.; slightly sol. ammonia sol. Normal water cleaning harmless.

OLIVINE. Rapidly sol. conc. HCl, forming gel; attacked by cold conc. citric acid.

OLSHANSKYITE. Easily diss. in acids.

ONYX. See CALCITE or CHAL-CEDONY. The chalcedony dyed onyxes, especially the black types, are discolored by prolonged immersions in acid or alkali baths, and especially in bleaching sols.

OPAL. All types rapidly diss. by HF; also attacked by strong alkali sols. Heat sensitive, brittle; some types rapidly lose water and develop shrinkage cracks but no method has yet been devised to halt this process. Certain porous types of peculiar granular structure from Australia have been impregnated with sugar and then treated with conc. H_2SO_4 to carbonize the sugar and hence impart a "black opal" background hue.

ORIENTITE. Sol. HCl.

ORPIMENT. Attacked by HNO_3, readily sol. A.R., sol. H_2SO_4. Partly attacked by hot water. Enclosing calcite (Manhattan, Nevada) customarily removed with dil. HCl without apparent harm to xls but probably safer to use dil. acetic. V. soft, easily damaged by stiff brushes, tools.

ORTHOCLASE. Treat like MICRO-CLINE.

OSARIZAWAITE. Insol. water, HNO_3 but sol. boiling HCl or H_2SO_4.

OTTRELITE. Treat like CHLORITE.

OVERITE. Attacked by acids; rapidly sol. hot conc. HNO_3.

OWYHEEITE. Sol. warm conc. HCl; attacked HNO_3, A.R.

OXAMMITE. Sol. water.

PACHNOLITE. Readily sol. H_2SO_4.

PAIGEITE. Slightly attacked by acids.

PALAITE. Sol. acids.

PALMIERITE. Decomposes in water; sol. in boric acid sol.

PALYGORSKITE. Treat like CLAYS.

PAPAGOITE. V. slowly diss. in hot HCl.

PARABUTLERITE. Insol. cold water; sol. dil. acids.

PARACOQUIMBITE. Readily sol. water, acids. Unstable, store in sealed containers.

PARAGONITE. Treat like MICAS. Iron stains removed with oxalic acid but careful and thorough washing afterward needed to eliminate residual yellow stains.

PARAHILGARDITE. Insol. water; attacked by HCl.

PARAHOPEITE. Easily sol. HCl and other acids.

PARALAURIONITE. Diss. HNO_3 and affected by other acids.

PARAMELACONITE. Easily sol. dil. acids, dil. hydroxide sols. or ammonium chloride sols.

PARARAMMELSBERGITE. Attacked by HNO_3; alters superficially to ERYTH-RITE.

PARATACAMITE. Easily sol. acids; use dist. water to clean.

PARAVAUXITE. Readily attacked by HCl and other acids; fragile, brittle, and requires care in cleaning to avoid breakage xls.

PARAWOLLASTONITE. Decomposed by HCl.

PARGASITE. Slightly attacked by HF only.

PARISITE. Sol. hot conc. acids but normal dil. cold acid sols. can be used to remove iron stains or calcite associated with parisite, beryl, albite in the specimens of Chivor, Colombia.

PARSONSITE. Sol. acids.

PARWELITE. Insol. cold 1:1 HCl sol.

PASCOITE. Sol. water, dil. acids.

PATERNOITE. Readily sol. acids; slightly sol. water.

PAXITE. Etched by HNO_3.

PEARCEITE. Attacked by HNO_3; surface alteration noted in some specimens exposed to strong light.

PECTOLITE. Diss. HCl with formation of gel; attacked by A.R. and rapidly by HF. The last acid can be used topically to diss. crushed surfaces on typical spheroidal aggregates but great care required. Completely sol. cold conc. citric acid. In general, avoid any brushing or scrubbing of upper surfaces because these are composed of numerous minute xls which can be easily crushed. Avoid excessive bare-hand handling because extremely slender xls readily embed in skin and cause considerable discomfort. Suggest use of plastic-coated gloves. Normal cleaning in ultrasonic water bath harmless.

PENDLETONITE. Burns; insol. acids but sol. in organic solvents.

PENFIELDITE. Decomposed prolonged immersion in water, more rapidly in hot; easily attacked by acids; sol. HNO_3, A.R.

PENNINITE. V. slowly attacked by warm conc. HCl, H_2SO_4; rapidly diss. HF. Fragile, xls easily bent; avoid use of hard or firm tools.

PENROSEITE. Easily sol. HNO_3.

PENTLANDITE. Almost unaffected by acids; v. slightly attacked by conc. HNO_3, A.R.

PERCYLITE. Slowly attacked by acids; sol. HNO_3.

PERICLASE. Sol. dil. HNO_3 or HCl; v. slightly sol. water; insol. alcohol. Bright surfaces gradually dull by reaction with atmospheric water.

PERIDOT. Readily sol. HCl, HF; attacked by conc. warm H_2SO_4. Iron stains may be removed with dil. oxalic acid but avoid prolonged immersion and best to avoid any acid treatment whatsoever.

PERISTERITE. Treat like ALBITE.

PERLITE. Porous, expanded OBSIDIAN surrounding nodules of same as the "Apache tears" of Superior, Arizona.

PEROVSKITE. Attacked by hot conc. H_2SO_4 or by cold HF.

PETALITE. Attacked only by HF.

PETZITE. Decomposed by HNO_3. Tarnishes.

PHARMACOLITE. Readily sol. acids but unaffected by water except when strongly ammoniated or when containing strong detergents.

PHARMACOSIDERITE. Attacked by acids; sol. HCl and even brief exposure to this acid results in loss of xl luster; attacked by ammonia sols.

PHENAKITE. Unaffected by acids and only slowly attacked by HF. Use oxalic to remove iron stains.

PHILLIPSITE. Readily sol. HCl forming gel and attacked by other acids; diss. HF.

PHLOGOPITE. Slowly decomposed by warm conc. H_2SO_4 or boiling saturated citric acid; attacked more or less rapidly by HF. See also MICAS.

PHOENICOCHROITE. Attacked by acids, diss. in HCl. Treat with care to avoid damage to fragile xls. Slowly alters on exposure to strong light.

PHOSGENITE. Readily sol. HCl, attacked by others, especially HNO_3; all quickly dull bright xl faces. Soft, brittle, easily scratched by tools. V. heat-sensitive.

PHOSPHOFERRITE. Sol. acids.

PHOSPHOPHYLLITE. Diss. acids. V. soft, cleavable, brittle. Heat-sensitive.

PHOSPHOSIDERITE. Sol. HCl.

PHOSPHOURANYLITE. Easily sol. acids, especially HCl.

PICKERINGITE. V. easily sol. water, acids; loses water in dry air, store in sealed containers.

PICROMERITE. Sol. water, acids.

PIEMONTITE. Slowly attacked HF only.

PIGEONITE. Slowly attacked HF only.

PINAKIOLITE. Sol. conc. HCl.

PINITE. Rapidly diss. by HF.

PINNOITE. Sol. acids.

PIRSSONITE. Sol. dil. acids; unstable, store in sealed containers.

PITCHBLENDE. Diss. HF, HNO_3, H_2SO_4; scarcely affected by HCl.

PITTICITE. Sol. HCl.

PLAGIOCLASES. Treat like ALBITE.

PLAGIONITE. Attacked by HNO_3, A.R.; sol. in hot HCl.

PLANCHEITE. Attacked by HCl and other acids.

PLATINIRIDIUM. Not attacked by any acid.

PLATINUM. Sol. only in A.R. although other acids can be used to remove clinging fragments of other species from the nuggets.

PLATTNERITE. Easily sol. HCl and attacked by other acids.

PLAYFAIRITE. Immersion in HNO_3 produces an iridescent coating.

PLAZOLITE. Attacked by HCl and HF.

PLEONASTE. Not attacked by acids or other agents.

PLUMBOFERRITE. Rapidly attacked by HCl and other acids.

PLUMBOGUMMITE. Attacked only by hot conc. acids, especially HNO_3.

PLUMOSITE. See BOULANGERITE.

POLIANITE. Treat like PYROLUSITE.

POLLUCITE. Attacked by HF and very slowly by HCl.

POLYBASITE. Attacked by HNO_3 only. Slowly alters on surface but sooty coating is removable in ultrasonic bath; avoid exposure to strong light to minimize alteration. Soft, easily scratched or chipped.

POLYCRASE. Treat like EUXENITE.

POLYDYMITE. Attacked by HNO_3; not attacked by HCl; tarnishes.

POLYHALITE. Sol. in dil. acids, and attacked slowly by water, faster in warm water.

POLYMIGNYTE. Slightly sol. conc. HF and otherwise unaffected by acids.

PORTLANDITE. Sol. in water and readily sol. in dil. HCl.

POSNJAKITE. Insol. in ammonia.

POWELLITE. Decomposed by HCl.

PRAVDITE. Slightly sol. in HCl, HNO_3, or H_2SO_4.

PREHNITE. Slowly attacked by HCl which whitens xl surfaces and renders them powdery, however quick immersions in dil. HCl to remove associated minerals not too harmful. Rapidly sol. HF; slightly attacked by boiling saturated sol. citric acid. In some specimens iron stains penetrate between xl fibers and these are impossible to remove.

PREOBRAZHENSKITE. Insol. water.

PRICEITE. Rapidly sol. acids, e.g., HCl, but insol. in water.

PRIORITE. Attacked only slowly in powder form by conc. acids.

PROBERTITE. Readily sol. dil. acids; partly attacked by water; dehydrates, store in sealed container.

PROCHLORITE. Slowly attacked by hot conc. H_2SO_4; rapidly by HF, and also attacked by saturated sol. citric acid. For removal, see CHLORITE.

PROSOPITE. Attacked by H_2SO_4 and by other acids.

PROTOLITHIONITE. Treat like MICAS.

PROUSTITE. Attacked by HNO_3. Alters when exposed to light, developing a dark film on the surface which increasingly masks the red color. This is removable by gentle swabbing with cotton, followed by immersion in an ultrasonic bath. Heat-sensitive, very soft, easily chipped.

PRSHEVALSKITE. Readily sol. acids.

PSEUDOBOLEITE. Sol. HNO_3. Normal cleaning safe.

PSEUDOBROOKITE. Slowly attacked by HF or hot conc. HCl or H_2SO_4.

PSEUDOCOTUNNITE. Sol. warm water.

PSEUDOMALACHITE. Sol. acids, especially in HCl; fragile, use great care in cleaning.

PSILOMELANE. Diss. HCl releasing poisonous chlorine gas; avoid treating large masses except in well-ventilated situations. Sol. oxalic acid, which can be used to remove from specimens ("manganese stains").

PTILOLITE. Insol. HCl but rapidly diss. HF; v. slowly attacked by H_2SO_4.

PUCHERITE. Sol. HCl, attacked by other acids.

PUMPELLYITE. Rapidly diss. HF; v. slowly diss. warm conc. H_2SO_4. Not affected by HCl.

PURPURITE. Readily sol. dil. HCl and attacked by other acids; remove dark alteration coatings with dil. HCl.

PYRARGYRITE. Treat like PROUSTITE.

PYRAURITE. Readily sol. dil. HCl and other acids.

PYRITE. Generally unaffected by acids including saturated sol. citric acid, but v. slightly attacked by conc. HNO_3, A.R. Iron stains removed with oxalic or HCl; calcite by dil. HCl; quartz coatings by HF. Brittle but not soft. Pyrite and marcasite often confused, but most specimens labeled "marcasite" are pyrite. Occasionally pyrite intergrown with marcasite, and such specimens liable to destructively alter (see MARCASITE), e.g., spherical nodules taken from clays and other sedimentary deposits.

PYROCHLORE. Decomposed slowly by hot conc. H_2SO_4; otherwise unaffected by acids.

PYROCHROITE. Readily sol. HCl and attacked by other acids.

PYROLUSITE. Readily sol. HCl, insol. HNO_3. See caution under PSILOMELANE on chlorine gas.

PYROMORPHITE. Sol. HNO_3 or HF and attacked to some extent by other acids. Fragile, soft, avoid use of hard tools in cleaning. It is generally impractical to attempt removal of enclosing calcite.

PYROPE GARNET. V. slowly attacked by HF only.

PYROPHANITE. Slightly attacked by hot HCl.

PYROPHYLLITE. Slightly attacked by warm conc. H_2SO_4. Iron stains readily removed with oxalic acid.

PYROSMALITE. Diss. HCl with formation gel.

PYROSTILPNITE. Attacked HNO_3.

PYROXENES. Slowly diss. by HF only.

PYROXMANGITE. Attacked rapidly by HF; very slowly attacked by HCl with subsequent dulling xl faces.

PYRRHOTITE. V. slowly attacked by HCl, A.R., or saturated sol. citric acid. May be cleaned with oxalic for iron stains, HCl for enclosing calcite without serious harm to xl luster. However, v. careful washing mandatory to remove all traces of acid which may remain between tabular xls and later cause slow alteration and disintegration. Most pyrrhotites which do alter, developing white powdery coatings and crumbling (Trepca, Yugoslavia), are probably altered in whole or in part to marcasite and may be recognized to some extent by a greenish cast or the rather brilliant white metallic luster typical of pyrite-marcasite replacement. Treatment of these should follow the lines suggested under MARCASITE. In any event, such specimens should be smelled for traces of sulfurous odors, which, if present, indicate incipient alteration. These specimens should be stored in sealed containers and kept away from other minerals in the cabinet. It seems evident that the pyrrhotites most likely to disintegrate are those of very thin tabular form, while those of stout prismatic form seem least likely to alter. Mexican specimens seem very stable as shown by preservation of typical xls over a period of at least 10 years. The Riondell, British Columbia, material is also stable. Mexican specimens often covered with brownish siderite which is removable with difficulty in acids, but such removal is not recommended.

QUARTZ. See CHALCEDONY for treatment of fibrous types. Crystalline quartz is more or less rapidly attacked by HF, slowly by dil. sols, and rapidly when warmed; also etched by warm sols. ammonium bifluoride which is safer to use but much less rapid in its activity. Speed of attack is greatest along fractures, inclusions, twin junctions, etc., which tend to rapidly disfigure specimens. Rubbed or abraded surfaces are very rapidly attacked. Aside from HF, all other acids have no effect on quartz. Many specimens cleaned in warm sols. of HCl or oxalic acid are cracked by being too rapidly cooled either by exposure to cold air or by plunging into rinse water which is not the same temperature as the acid bath. Thermal shocks are to be especially avoided with Japanese twins. Xls with large enclosures of clay or water should not be warmed under any circumstances, or frozen. Remove calcite with HCl, hematite with HCl (see MICROCLINE for procedure), iron stains with oxalic.

QUENSELITE. Easily sol. dil. acids, including acetic and other organic acids.

QUENSTEDTITE. Readily sol. water and dil. acids. Unstable, store in sealed containers.

QUETENITE. Partly sol. water.

RABBITITE. Slowly sol. water; sol. in HCl.

RAGUINITE. V. slowly attacked by dil. HNO_3.

RALSTONITE. Attacked by H_2SO_4.

RAMMELSBERGITE. Slightly attacked by HNO_3. Sometimes develops alteration coating of green annabergite in damp climates.

RAMSAYITE. Sol. HF only.

RANKINITE. Sol. in HCl, forming gel.

RASPITE. Attacked by HCl.

RASVUMITE. Sol. in acids.

REALGAR. Slightly attacked by HNO_3, more rapidly in A.R. and sol. in strong alkali sols. Covering calcite usually removed with dil. HCl without apparent harm. Rapidly alters in bright light to yellow orpiment, eventually crumbling to powder and grains. Preserve in light-tight box.

REDDINGITE. Sol. in acids.

REINITE. Treat like FERBERITE.

RENARDITE. Sol. in acids.

RETGERSITE. Sol. in water and in dil. acids; unstable, store in sealed containers.

RETZIAN. Sol. in acids.

RHABDOPHANE. Rapidly sol. in HCl and other acids.

RHODIZITE. Unaffected by acids. Xls usually badly fractured and likely to crumble if attempts made to remove from pegmatite matrix.

RHODOCHROSITE. Rapidly attacked by warm HCl and other acids, much less so in cold acids. Common massive material attacked unevenly by acids leaving porous skeletal surfaces. When exposed to weather + sunlight, this species quickly develops a black manganese oxide coating. Xls that are coated with a whitish powdery deposit are best left alone and no acid treatment directed against them.

RHODOLITE. Unaffected by acids except HF which very slowly attacks.

RHODONITE. Slightly but noticeably attacked by HCl, more so when strong, with dulling of bright xl faces on some but not all Franklin, New Jersey, specimens. Use of HCl seems to more rapidly produce black alteration coating of manganese dioxide. Rapidly attacked by HF and completely decomposed in saturated sol. citric acid. Xls brittle, very easily cleaved, both those from Franklin and from Broken Hill, New South Wales. Great care must be exercised in exposing xls in matrix. Suggest that xls, as exposed, be treated with vinyl acetate glue diluted to allow easy penetration into cracks. Let dry for several days, then continue matrix removal.

RHOMBOCLASE. Slowly sol. in water.

RICKARDITE. Sol. HNO_3.

RIEBECKITE. Treat like ASBESTOS.

RINKITE. Easily attacked by dil. acids, e.g., H_2SO_4.

RINNEITE. Sol. in water.

RIVADAVITE. Sol. water.

RIVERSIDEITE. Rapidly sol. HCl and other acids.

ROCKBRIDGEITE. Sol. HCl, insol. HNO_3 or H_2SO_4.

ROEBLINGITE. Sol. HCl, forming gel.

ROEMERITE. Sol. water and dil. acids. Unstable, store in sealed container.

ROESSLERITE. Slightly attacked by water; easily sol. dil. HCl.

ROMEITE. Insol. in acids.

ROQUESITE. Readily etched by HNO_3.

ROSASITE. Sol. in acids. Extremely delicate, requiring gentle rinsing only in dist. water; attacked by ammonia and strong detergents.

ROSCHERITE. Sol. in acids.

ROSCOELITE. Very slightly attacked by hot conc. acids; more so by cold HF. See MICAS.

ROSELITE. Readily sol. in acids.

ROSENBUSCHITE. Sol. HCl.

ROSSITE. V. slightly sol. water, more so in acids.

ROWEITE. Rapidly sol. dil. HCl, and attacked by other acids.

ROWLANDITE. Sol. HCl, forming gel.

RUBELLAN. Treat like BIOTITE.

RUSAKOVITE. Easily sol. cold dil. acids.

RUTHERFORDINE. Sol. in acids.

RUTILE. Practically unaffected by any acid but the powder is very slightly attacked by H_2SO_4. Associated silicates may be removed with HF and iron stains with oxalic.

SAFFLORITE. Attacked by warm HNO_3; practically unaffected by HCl.

SAKHAITE. Readily sol. acids, including acetic.

SAKURAIITE. Etched by conc. HNO_3.

SAL AMMONIAC. Rapidly sol. in water and dil. acids.

SALEEITE. Attacked by acids.

SALESITE. Rapidly sol. HNO_3 or A.R.; insol. in water.

SALMONSITE. Sol. acids.

SAMARSKITE. Slightly attacked by conc. acids only when in powder form; xls brittle, tending to crumble upon removal from matrix. Earthy outer coatings should not be disturbed since they are always firmly attached to the xls.

SAMPLEITE. Easily sol. acids.

SAMSONITE. Attacked by HNO_3 and A.R.

SANIDINE. Treat like ALBITE.

SANJUANITE. Readily sol. warm acids.

SAPONITE. Decomposed by H_2SO_4.

SAPPHIRINE. Slightly attacked by HF.

SARCOLITE. Rapidly diss. HF, diss. HCl with formation gel.

SARKINITE. Easily sol. acids, e.g., HCl.

SARMIENTITE. Rapidly attacked by acids.

SARTORITE. Attacked by HNO_3 or A.R.

SARYARKITE. Partly sol. HCl, HNO_3, or H_2SO_4.

SASSOLITE. Readily sol. water, acids, alcohols.

SATPAEVITE. Diss. readily cold dil. acids.

SCACCHITE. Rapidly sol. water, acids.

Attracts moisture from air, store in sealed containers.

SCAPOLITES. Slowly attacked by conc. HCl and slightly by dil. HCl which is commonly used to remove enclosing calcite (Canada, Mexico, Finland) without appreciable damage to the scapolite xls. Rapidly attacked by HF. Some Mexican (Oaxaca) scapolites develop dark-stained coatings which appear to be opal and which cannot be easily removed by any chemical or mechanical method; these are best left intact. Commonly somewhat altered and therefore likely to be powdery or crumbly in surface layers; avoid use of harsh cleaning methods, especially stiff brushes or tools. Iron stains removed with oxalic acid.

SCAWTITE. Attacked by dil. acids as HCl.

SCHAIRERITE. Slowly sol. in water.

SCHALLERITE. Decomposed by HCl.

SCHEELITE. V. slightly attacked by hot conc. acids only. Brittle, with xls tending to be fractured and crumbling with rough treatment.

SCHEFFERITE. Attacked only by HF.

SCHMITTERITE. Readily sol. dil. HCl and alkali sols.

SCHODERITE. Loses water in ordinary atmosphere, altering to metaschoderite.

SCHOEPITE. Attacked by acids.

SCHORLOMITE. Sol. HCl with gel formation.

SCHREIBERSITE. Slowly sol. HCl or HNO$_3$.

SCHROECKINGERITE. Sol. water, dil. acids.

SCHROETTERITE. Slowly sol. HCl.

SCHULTENITE. Attacked by acids.

SCHWARTZEMBERGITE. Sol. dil. HNO$_3$.

SCOLECITE. Sol. in HCl, forming gel.

SCORODITE. Sol. acids especially HCl, and attacked by strong detergents and ammonia. Fragile, cleavable, easily damaged by careless treatment. Clean with dist. water in ultrasonic bath.

SCORZALITE. Treat like LAZULITE.

SEAMANITE. Sol. cold dil. acids.

SEARLESITE. Attacked by HCl.

SEDOVITE. Sol. with difficulty in boiling HCl, HNO$_3$, or H$_2$SO$_4$.

SEIDOZERITE. Sol. with difficulty in HCl.

SELIGMANNITE. Attacked by HNO$_3$ or A.R.

SELLAITE. Attacked by conc. H$_2$SO$_4$.

SEMSEYITE. Attacked by HNO$_3$ or A.R.

SENARMONTITE. Rapidly sol. in HCl; also in tartaric or acetic acids.

SENGIERITE. Sol. acids.

SEPIOLITE. Slowly decomposes in HCl forming gel. See also MEERSCHAUM.

SERENDIBITE. Slowly sol. HF only.

SERICITE. Fine-grained MUSCOVITE but more rapidly attacked by HF. Usually removed with steel tools and sometimes, when impregnated with iron oxides, by immersions in oxalic acid followed by brushing, further immersion, etc.

SERPENTINES. Rapidly attacked by HF, v. slowly decomposed by conc. HCl or H$_2$SO$_4$ and attacked by cold saturated citric acid.

SERPIERITE. Rapidly sol. acids.

SEYBERTITE. Attacked only by HF. Treat like MUSCOVITE.

SHATTUCKITE. Readily attacked by HCl and rapidly by HF.

SHCHERBAKOVITE. Insol. HNO$_3$, HCl; partly sol. warm H$_2$SO$_4$.

SHELLS. Composed of aragonite or calcite prisms cemented together with v. thin layers organic material (conchiolin) and rapidly diss. by dil. acids, especially HCl, which tend to leave a brilliant, polished luster.

SHERWOODITE. Sol. in acids.

SHORTITE. Rapidly diss. in acids; attacked by water. Store in sealed containers.

SICKLERITE. Slowly sol. acids.

SIDERITE. Scarcely affected by cold acids as HCl or citric; but rapidly sol. in warmed acids.

SIDERONATRITE. Insol. cold water, readily attacked by acids.

SIDEROTILE. Sol. in water; rapidly dehydrates, crumbling to powder.

SIEGENITE. Attacked by HNO$_3$, unaffected by HCl. Tarnishes.

SILLIMANITE. See FIBROLITE.

SILVER. Readily sol. HNO$_3$, hot H$_2$SO$_4$, or A.R. Sol. cyanide sols. Insol. alkalies. A number of standard cleaning methods for removal of black tarnish have been devised.

Electrolytic method: Dissolve 20 grams each sodium chloride (NaCl, table salt) and baking soda (NaHCO$_3$, sodium bicarbonate) in 1,200 ml dist. water in aluminum pan large enough to allow specimen to be covered by sol. Warm sol. to increase activity, but do not boil, or use cool to lukewarm if heat-sensitive species associated (e.g., calcite). Immerse silver and ensure it contacts aluminum. In warm sols. tarnish begins to disappear in less than a minute and sometimes only several minutes needed to obtain satisfactory cleaning. Immediately remove and thoroughly rinse in warm clean water and towel dry. Recommended for quick results with specimens essentially pure silver but also useful for the half-Cu, half-Ag or "half-breed" specimens of Michigan, but note that the copper is not cleaned. Alternate formula: 1 teaspoonful each salt to 1 quart dist. water.

Another electrolytic method: To 1 gal. dist. water add 2 tablespoonfuls washing soda (Na$_2$CO$_3 \cdot 10H_2O$, sodium carbonate) and 1 tablespoonful trisodium phosphate, and trace table salt. Use aluminum pan or any other suitable container in which a piece of aluminum contacts the silver. Proceed as above.

Cyanide method: Diss. about 5 grams chemically pure potassium cyanide (KCN) or sodium cyanide (NaCN) in 5 liters dist. water in suitable glass or plastic container; do not use metal which reacts with the chemicals. Immerse specimen in sol. and check progress in 10 minutes; several hours may be needed to clean difficult encrustations. Increasing strength of sol. increases chem. activity.

Caution: All cyanides are extremely dangerous and rapid-acting poisons, and proper precautions must be taken to avoid inhalation of fumes or accidental ingestion. Alternative: Take specimen to silver-plating shop, explain problem and ask that they dip the specimen for you. Cyanide has the merit of cleaning both the copper and silver in the composite Michigan specimens.

Silver "dips": Various proprietary liquids sold in tall jars in grocery and hardware stores for very quick removal of tarnish. Satisfactory on the whole but leave surfaces that seem to be far more rapidly retarnished unless protected by lacquer coat. Not suitable for the Michigan specimens in which neither the silver nor the copper seem to be adequately cleaned.

Silver "polishes": These should not be used because a principal ingredient is an abrasive which seriously scores and erodes the silver. In any event, such polishes are difficult to apply and cannot reach crevices.

Mechanical cleaning: Michigan specimens have been cleaned by wire brushing, either worked by hand or by machine. Some surface rounding occurs but much of the clinging mineral matter is removed and specimens acquire an "antiqued" character which is fairly attractive, if one can excuse the damage which necessarily occurs. In any specimen, crystallizations or sharp details require avoidance of any mechanical method of cleaning.

Prevention of tarnish: The behavior of silvers in various cleaning solutions varies remarkably from specimen to specimen, and even among specimens from the same deposit. The return of tarnish is very directly connected to the place of storage or nearness to any possible emitter of sulfur compounds, some of these being: cheap sulfite newspaper, brown wrapping papers, matches, sulfide minerals, particularly marcasite and pyrite (check for typical sulfurous smell!), some foods preserved with sulfur compounds, and general nearness or exposure to cooking odors, tobacco fumes, automobile fumes, etc. In the mineral cabinet, it is safest to protect the silvers by enclosing them in plastic boxes with tight-fitting lids, or at least store them away from sulfide minerals.

Some authorities have recommended placing a small block of camphor wax in the same compartment as the silvers to prevent tarnishing. Various sprays and dips applied to freshly cleaned and dried specimens have also been recommended and many are effective, at least for a time. Acrylic sprays are useful, or acrylic-based clear lacquers, diluted with a suitable solvent and applied by brush. Collodion sol. also recommended, consisting of 5% collodion, 95% alcohol; also clear household fast-drying cements, diluted with suitable solvent such as amyl acetate or acetone, and proprietary metal lacquers obtainable in paint stores. It is highly important in applying coatings that the specimen be thoroughly dry beforehand, the lacquer applied in extremely thinned form, and that several coats be applied using great care to cover the entire specimen, including matrix. When tarnishing underneath such coatings occurs, steep specimen in an excess of the solvent to remove; reclean, and then relacquer.

SIMPSONITE. Unaffected by acids; iron stains removed with oxalic.

SINCOSITE. Sol. dil. acids.

SIPYLITE. V. slightly attacked by hot conc. sols. HCl, H_2SO_4.

SJOGRENITE. Easily sol. dil. acids.

SKLODOWSKITE. Readily attacked by acids; sol. dil. acids, forming gel; extremely fragile, use no tools, brushes, etc; rinse gently with alcohol to clean.

SKUTTERUDITE. Sol. HNO_3 but scarcely affected by other acids; HCl may be used to remove associated calcite; not affected by cold saturated citric.

SMALTITE. Treat like SKUTTERUDITE. Sometimes slowly alters in moist air.

SMITHITE. Attacked by HNO_3 or A.R.

SMITHSONITE. Rapidly sol. acids; slowly sol. in saturated cold citric acid; finely fibrous forms tend to acquire a gloss when treated in dil. HCl but coarsergrained types tend to become cavernous and rough-surfaced. Xls fragile, easily cleaved. Normal cleaning dist. water but avoid strong detergents.

SODALITE. Attacked with considerable rapidity by HCl and other acids, even acetic, forming gel.

SODDYITE. Sol. HCl with formation of gel; attacked by other acids.

SODIUM AUTUNITE. Readily sol. acids.

SODIUM URANOSPINITE. Readily sol. dil. acids or Na_2CO_3 sol.

SONOLITE. Decomposed in HCl with formation silica gel.

SONORAITE. Readily sol. HCl.

SORBYITE. Tarnishes brown to black in HNO_3.

SPADAITE. Sol. HCl, forming gel.

SPANGOLITE. Rapidly attacked by dil. acids but normal water cleaning harmless.

SPENCERITE. Sol. acids.

SPERRYLITE. Insol. in any acid.

SPESSARTINE. V. slowly attacked by HF which only can be used to remove micas, chlorite, albite, etc.

SPHALERITE. Bright xl faces more or less rapidly dulled by contact with HCl, but in some specimens the enclosing calcite can be removed with dil. HCl, acetic acid, citric acid, etc., before serious deterioration takes place. Brittle, easily cleaved, and quickly scarred by use of metal implements.

SPHENE. Slowly attacked by HF, warm conc. H_2SO_4, or A.R. V. slightly attacked by conc. warm HCl. There is no easy way to remove the chlorite scales which commonly coat xl faces (see ADULARIA for discussion of this problem). Dark brown xls of Canadian sphene are usually exposed in matrix by use of dil. HCl to dissolve enclosing calcite.

SPINELS. Unattacked by acids or other chemical agents and only the powder is slightly attacked by hot conc. H_2SO_4. Generally the xls are strong but some, as those at Franklin, New Jersey, are internally fractured and require care in exposing to avoid disintegration (see FRANKLINITE for discussion of techniques).

SPIROFFITE. Easily sol. HCl but insol. hot HNO_3 or H_2SO_4.

SPODIOSITE. Sol. acids.

SPODUMENE. Only v. slowly attacked by conc. HF which is safely used to remove iron-stained clays, even from the characteristic long, slender tubes in the gemmy material from California, Brazil, etc.

SPURRITE. Sol. acids, gel in HCl; and affected by atmospheric moisture which causes development of powdery whitish coating; store in sealed container.

STAINIERITE. Sol. HCl.

STANNITE. Attacked by HNO_3.

STANNOIDITE. Attacked only by HNO_3.

STAUROLITE. V. slightly attacked by conc. H_2SO_4 or HF; the latter can be used to remove mica scales. Partly altered types (Virginia) much more rapidly attacked by these acids.

STEATITE. See TALC.

STEENSTRUPINE. Attacked by acids.

STEIGERITE. Decomposed in mineral acids; insol. in water.

STELLERITE. Rapidly decomposed in HCl or HF.

STENONITE. Decomposed in HCl.

STEPANOVITE. Sol. in water.

STEPHANITE. Attacked by HNO_3 or A.R. Exposure to strong light causes formation of sooty film which is usually removed by ultrasonic cleaning.

STERNBERGITE. Sol. A.R.

STERRETTITE. Almost unattacked by acids.

STERRYITE. Unaffected by mineral acids.

STEWARTITE. Rapidly sol. acids.

STIBICONITE. Clean ultrasonically, avoiding acids, chemicals, etc., which may enter pores of usual pseudomorphs after stibnite (Mexico). The white coatings sometimes noted are also stibiconite and not affected by acids. Dark stains are usually inclusions within small stibiconite masses and are also unremovable.

STIBIOCOLUMBITE. Treat like STIBIOTANTALITE.

STIBIOTANTALITE. Readily attacked by HF but not other acids except when finely powdered.

STIBNITE. Diss. HCl; rapidly attacked conc. HNO_3, A.R. Fine surface luster also lost by contact with hydroxides; avoid strong detergents or soaps, ammonia, etc., in cleaning bath. Soft, cleavable, easily scratched; avoid rubbing or brushing of xls. Prolonged exposure to strong light promotes surface alteration and loss of brilliant luster.

STICHTITE. Rapidly sol. dil. HCl.

STILBITE. Rapidly attacked by HCl, other acids, especially HF. Typical "sheaves" easily dislodged from matrix during trimming or hammering. Clean in ultrasonic bath but avoid use of strong detergents or ammonia. Bruised spots sometimes "healed" by dissolving crushed bits of stilbite with strong HCl; see CALCITE for discussion of technique.

STILPNOMELANE. Rapidly attacked by HCl or HF.

STOLZITE. Diss. HCl and attacked by alkali sols., e.g., ammonia.

STRENGITE. Attacked by acids, especially HCl, HNO_3, A.R.

STRIGOVITE. Readily decomposed by acids.

STROMEYERITE. Sol. HNO_3.

STRONTIANITE. Diss. acids and only brief exposure seriously dulls luster of faces. Soft, fragile.

STRUVITE. Slightly sol. water, rapidly in dil. acids.

STUETZITE. Attacked by HNO_3, HCl.

SULFOBORITE. Slowly sol. water, rapidly in acids.

SULFOHALITE. Slowly sol. water, rapidly in acids.

SULFUR. Unattacked by acids except A.R. which v. slightly diss. Readily sol. carbon disulfide (CS_2) or toluene; slightly sol. alcohol, benzene, ether; considerably sol. methylene iodide. Fake specimens are made by diss. sulfur in carbon disulfide, and causing crystallization on matrix pieces of drusy quartz. Xls v. soft, brittle, and extremely heat-sensitive (heat of fingers causes cracking!). Affected by strong light, heat, and best stored in cool, dry place in dark; exposure to direct sunlight can cause cracking within minutes!

SULVANITE. Attacked HNO_3, A.R.

SUSSEXITE. Slowly sol. acids.

SVABITE. Attacked by acids.

SVANBERGITE. Insol. acids; also stated to be sol. in HCl.

SWARTZITE. Readily sol. acids.

SWEDENBORGITE. Insol. acids.

SYLVANITE. Decomposed by HNO_3, A.R. Alters on surface when exposed to strong light.

SYLVITE. Rapidly sol. water and acids. Deliquescent, store in sealed container.

SYMPLESITE. Sol. acids.

SYNADELPHITE. Easily sol. acids, especially in HCl; rapidly alters on surface when exposed to air.

SYNCHYSITE. Readily sol. acids.

SYNGENITE. Partly sol. in water.

SZAIBELYITE. Slightly attacked by acids as HCl.

SZMIKITE. Sol. in water.

SZOMOLNOKITE. Slowly sol. in water.

TACHARANITE. In air spontaneously breaks down to mixture tobermorite and gyrolite.

TACHYHYDRITE. Extremely deliquescent! Store in sealed container.

TAENIOLITE. Treat like MICAS.

TAGILITE. Sol. in acids.

TALC. Slowly attacked by HF, less so by hot conc. H_2SO_4. Softest of minerals, hence very easily scratched by any tool.

TAMARUGITE. Sol. in water.

TANTALITE. Not affected by acids. Xls commonly fractured and disintegrate when removed from matrix; those growing in cavities or those that are shining in luster are most likely to be free of cracks.

TAPIOLITE. Not affected by acids.

TARBUTTITE. Attacked by HCl and other acids.

TARNOWITZITE. Treat like ARAGONITE.

TATARSKITE. Sol. in boiling water or in cold dil. HCl.

TAVISTOCKITE. Slightly attacked by acids.

TEALLITE. Readily attacked by hot HCl, HNO_3, or A.R.

TEEPLEITE. Rapidly sol. in acids; easily sol. in water.

TEKTITE. Treat like MOLDAVITE.

TELLURITE. Readily sol. HCl, HNO_3; attacked by other acids; sol. ammonia.

TELLURIUM. Sol. warm conc. H_2SO_4 or HNO_3, A.R.; also by strong alkali sols., cyanide sols.; insol. HCl.

TENGERITE. Sol. in acids.

TENNANTITE. Slightly attacked by HNO_3, A.R.

TENORITE. Easily sol. dil. acids, especially HCl.

TEPHROITE. Easily sol. dil. acids; sol. HCl with formation of gel; attacked by cold saturated citric acid sol.

TERLINGUAITE. Attacked by HCl, HNO_3, acetic acid.

TERTSCHITE. Slightly sol. hot water, easily in dil. HCl.

TERUGGITE. Slightly sol. warm water; readily sol. HCl.

TETRAHEDRITE. Slightly attacked by HNO_3, A.R.; not affected by cold saturated citric acid sol.

THAUMASITE. Rapidly attacked by HCl, HF, and other acids.

THENARDITE. Sol. water, acids, glycerine, but insol. alcohol.

THERMONATRITE. Rapidly sol. water, acids. Loses water in dry air, requiring storage in sealed containers.

THOMSENOLITE. Readily sol. H_2SO_4.

THOMSONITE. Diss. by HCl with formation gel; rapidly attacked by HF; more or less seriously affected by other acids, including citric.

THORIANITE. Sol. conc. HNO_3, H_2SO_4; insol. HCl.

THORITE. V. slowly sol. HCl with formation gel.

THORTVEITITE. Insol. in HCl.

THURINGITE. Rapidly diss. HF; more slowly by HCl with formation gel.

TIEMANNITE. Attacked by HNO_3.

TILASITE. Rapidly sol. HCl, HNO_3.

TINAKSITE. Insol. acids.

TINCALCONITE. Treat like BORAX.

TITANITE. See SPHENE.

TOBERMORITE. Attacked by HCl; rapidly by HF.

TODOROKITE. Readily sol. warm conc. HCl.

TOPAZ. Practically unaffected by any acid, including HF which can be used to clean off clays and other adhering minerals; iron stains removed with oxalic acid. Brownish ("sherry") xls from various deposits lose color rapidly in direct sunlight or strong artificial light; in case of pegmatite brown xls the residual color is commonly pale blue. Matrix specimens usually cleaved near points of attachment to matrix and care should be taken in cleaning not to handle specimens roughly or otherwise cause such xls to detach. Blue xls from Urals originally coated with clays which scraped off with steel implements. Matrix xls from Mexico very easily detached during removal of tan clays associated with same.

TORBERNITE. Rapidly attacked by acids; iron stains removed by sol. sodium dithionate (1 tsp./pt. water); Fragile, cleavable; direct cleaning with brushes, tools inadvisable. Use pure dist. water, make immersions brief. Avoid use of ultrasonic bath which commonly dislodges the scaly xls.

TORREYITE. Sol. acids.

TOURMALINE. Xls slowly lose luster after immersion for some hours in conc. cold HF; unaffected by other acids. HF is commonly used to remove adhering albite, cookeite, clays, etc., but is advisable to remove as much of these minerals beforehand with tools in order to shorten acid bath time. Oxalic used to remove rust stains. Many schorl xls fractured, especially "frozen" types, and readily crumble when removed from matrix. Aggregates of jumbled prisms and clays should be handled cautiously because excessive removal of clays may result in disfiguring specimen through dropping out of tourmaline xls.

TRASKITE. Insol. dil. acids or bases.

TRAVERTINE. Massive, porous calcite

rock, v. easily diss. by HCl and other acids.

TREMOLITE. Slowly attacked by HF only, more rapidly when in fibrous form. Xls in calcite matrix exposed by immersion in HCl or by chipping away matrix.

Caution: Easily cleaved!

TREVORITE. Not attacked by acids.

TRICHALCITE. Easily sol. HCl.

TRIDYMITE. May be cleaned ultrasonically; insol. except in HF.

TRIGONITE. Sol. acids.

TRIMERITE. Rapidly attacked by HF, slowly by HCl.

TRIPHYLITE. Attacked by HCl and other acids.

TRIPLITE. More or less quickly attacked by acids.

TRIPLOIDITE. Sol. acids.

TRIPPKEITE. Rapidly attacked by HCl, HNO_3.

TRITOMITE. Diss. in HCl with formation gel.

TROEGERITE. Sol. in acids.

TROILITE. Treat like PHYRRHOTITE.

TRONA. V. rapidly sol. water, acids. Loses water in dry air, store in sealed containers.

TRUDELLITE. Soluble in water; very deliquescent! Store in sealed container.

TSUMEBITE. Easily sol. HCl, more slowly in HNO_3; attacked by other acids.

TUNGSTITE. Insol. acids but attacked in conc. alkali sols.

TUNELLITE. Insol. water but attacked by acids; soft, cleavable; remove clays with flexible bamboo slivers.

TUNISITE. Easily sol. conc. mineral acids except HNO_3; use of dil. acids results in formation of nearly insol. precipitate.

TURQUOISE. Slightly attacked by HCl. Clean only with dist. water to which a trace of wetting agent has been added; avoid ammonia, soaps, strong detergents. Rapidly absorbs oils, greases, etc., which are difficult to remove thereafter except by prolonged soaking in solvents as acetone, alcohol, heptane, etc. Do not use oxalic to remove rust stains.

TWINNITE. Tarnishes black in HNO_3.

TYCHITE. Sol. dil. acids; insol. water.

TYROLITE. Sol. acids or aqua ammonia.

TYUYAMUNITE. Rapidly attacked by acids; insol. dil. acetic acid.

ULEXITE. Slowly attacked by water,

rapidly in dil. HCl or other acids. Develops white coating even after being polished ("television stone") which is due to effect of water in atmosphere; recommend storage in sealed containers with silica gel desiccant. Very soft, very easily split along fibers.

ULLMANNITE. Slowly attacked HNO_3; not affected by cold conc. citric acid sol.

UMANGITE. Sol. HNO_3.

UMOHOITE. Insol. water.

UNGEMACHITE. Rapidly sol. dil. HCl.

URACONITE. Sol. acids.

URALBORITE. Slowly sol. dil. HCl.; insol. dil. acetic acid.

URALITE. Attacked fairly rapidly by HF only.

URAMPHITE. Easily sol. weak cold HCl or in weak warm HNO_3.

URANINITE. See PITCHBLENDE.

URANOCHALCITE. Sol. acids.

URANOCIRCITE. Sol. HCl and other acids.

URANOPHANE. Attacked by acids and sol. in HCl, forming gel. Delicately fibrous material requires great care in washing but may be rinsed in dist. water or alcohol.

URANOPILITE. Sol. in acids.

URANOSPINITE. Attacked by acids.

URANOTHALLITE. Sol. acids.

USOVITE. Sol. hot conc. HCl, HNO_3, or H_2SO_4.

USSINGITE. Sol. HCl, forming gel.

USTARASITE. Rapidly etched in HNO_3, slowly in HCl and turning to brown.

UVANITE. Insol. water but sol. in sol. ammonium carbonate.

UVAROVITE. Attacked slightly by HF; use HCl to remove calcite. The frozen xls of Finland are exposed with difficulty by removing matrix (quartz) but with care some good results may be obtained.

VALENCIANITE. Treat like ADULARIA.

VALENTINITE. Sol. HCl and attacked by other acids.

VANADINITE. Rapidly attacked by HNO_3 and A.R. but somewhat less so by HCl and other acids. Enclosing calcite removed by dil. organic acids or by sodium dithionate, but test first to observe effects. Brittle, very fragile and easily broken or chipped; the use of any firm tools is discouraged. Normal water cleaning ultrasonically harmless.

VANALITE. Easily sol. cold dil. HCl.

VANDENBRANDTITE. Slightly sol. cold acids, more so in warm.

VANTHOFFITE. Sol. in water.

VANURANYLITE. Easily sol. in acids.

VARISCITE. Slowly to rapidly attacked by HCl and other acids. Porous and easily absorbs chemicals dissolved in water; use dist. water only and avoid strong detergents, ammonia, etc.

VARULITE. Slowly attacked by acids.

VASHEGYITE. Sol. in acids.

VAUQUELINITE. Slightly attacked by HNO_3.

VAUXITE. Treat like PARAVAUXITE.

VEATCHITE. Attacked by acids and tends to disintegrate in any liquid.

VERMICULITE. Rapidly sol. HF and slowly attacked by HCl.

VERPLANCKITE. Slowly sol. dil. HCl or other acids.

VESUVIANITE. See IDOCRASE.

VESZELEYITE. Sol. in acids.

VIMSITE. Insol. water but easily sol. in acids.

VIOLARITE. Attacked by HNO_3, unaffected by HCl. Tarnishes.

VIVIANITE. Rapidly attacked by HCl and other acids; insol. in acetic acid. Very soft, fragile, cleavable; avoid use of any tools whatsoever except thin flexible slivers of bamboo for removing clays from around nodules and xl aggregates that have grown in clay. Changes color in light from green to dull dark purple or blue; this effect is noted more in some specimens than others, e.g., greens from Trepca and Poopo tend to stay green. Changes in color result in changes in xl structure causing stresses which often result in disintegration of very large xls, e.g., from the Cameroons. To some extent all of this is preventable by storage of xls in the dark and in a humidified atmosphere. Small xls and aggregates are more stable. On the whole, it seems that vivianite xls from clays and sedimentary deposits are far less stable than those from cavities within ore bodies.

VLADIMIRITE. Sol. in acids.

VLASOVITE. Nearly insol. in HCl or HNO_3; readily sol. in mixture HF + H_2SO_4.

VOGLITE. Sol. in acids.

VOLBORTHITE. Readily sol. acids.

VOLTAITE. Sol. dil. acids; attacked by water.

VOLTZITE. Readily sol. HCl.

VONSENITE = PAIGEITE.

VRBAITE. Sol. conc. H_2SO_4, HNO_3, or A.R.

WAD. Impure earthy manganese oxides; sol. in acids; react with HCl to generate poisonous fumes Cl.

WAGNERITE. Sol. acids, especially HCl.

WALSTROMITE. Not affected by bases; readily decomposed by cold dil. acids with silica residue.

WARDITE. Slightly attacked by acids.

WARDSMITHITE. Readily sol. in dil. acids; slightly sol. in hot water; very slightly sol. in cold water; insol. in methyl alcohol.

WARWICKITE. Attacked by H_2SO_4.

WATTEVILLITE. Sol. HCl.

WAVELLITE. Rapidly sol. in acids, especially in H_2SO_4, but any acid quickly causes loss of luster of spherical aggregate surfaces; also avoid strong detergents and ammonia in cleaning baths. Ultrasonic cleaning safe and a good way to remove clays.

WEBERITE. V. slightly sol. water; easily sol. aluminum chloride sols.

WEEKSITE. Decomposed by acids.

WEGSCHEIDERITE. Readily sol. hot water, more slowly in cold; rapidly decomposed in acids.

WEILERITE. Easily sol. HCl, more slowly in HNO_3.

WEINSCHENKITE. V. slightly sol. acids.

WELLSITE. Rapidly sol. HF; attacked by HCl with formation gel.

WELOGANITE. Sol. acids.

WERNERITE. See SCAPOLITE.

WHERRYITE. Slightly attacked by HCl or HNO_3.

WHEWELLITE. Insol. in water but sol. in dil. acids.

WHITLOCKITE. Readily sol. dil. acids.

WICKENBURGITE. Not affected by hot or cold acids or alkalies.

WIGHTMANITE. Slowly sol. cold dil. acids.

WILKEITE. Readily sol. HCl or HNO_3.

WILLEMITE. Quickly attacked by HCl which forms gel and destroys xl face luster; massive willemite becomes spongy under acid attack and surfaces whiten. Attacked by other acids, especially HF; completely decomposed by saturated citric. It is generally impractical to remove enclosing calcite (Franklin, New Jersey) except by mechanical means. See FRANKLINITE for techniques. The troostite variety is very brittle and xls easily disintegrate if specimens handled roughly; try use of thin vinyl acetate ("white" glue) + detergent sol. for cementing xls prior to removal of enclosing calcite. Let dry for several days before further work.

WILLIAMSITE. Slowly attacked by HF.

WITHERITE. Quickly attacked by acids which impart dull white coat to lustrous xls. Normal water cleaning satisfactory. Crushed spots on xls may be partly disguised by carefully dropping HCl on same (see CALCITE for discussion of technique).

WITTICHENITE. Sol. HCl, attacked by HNO_3.

WOEHLERITE. Rapidly attacked by warm to hot HCl or cold HF.

WOLFEITE. Sol. acids.

WOLFRAMITE. Slightly attacked by conc. acids but dil. acids may be safely used to remove calcite or iron stains. The superb xls from Panasqueiras, Portugal, cleave very readily under stress, especially when exposed to sudden temperature changes; some specimens have been ruined by merely immersing in hot water. It is quite possible that ultrasonic cleaning may cause enlargement of cleavage cracks.

WOLLASTONITE. Rapidly attacked by HF, slightly by conc. HCl or by saturated sol. citric acid.

WOODHOUSEITE. Almost unattacked by acids; also stated to be sol. HCl.

WULFENITE. Slowly attacked by HCl or HNO_3 or A.R.; dissolves in conc. H_2SO_4. Acids should be avoided because of damage to xl face luster. Use extreme care in handling because of fragility of usual thin tabular xls. Most effectively cleaned in ultrasonic bath to which a little wetting agent has been added.

WURTZITE. Attacked by HCl and other acids.

XANTHOCONITE. Attacked by HNO_3 and A.R.

XANTHOPHYLLITE. Treat like MICAS.

XANTHOXENITE. Sol. in acids.

XENOTIME. Not attacked by acids but slowly sol. in HF.

XONOTLITE. Attacked by HCl.

XYLOTILE. Decomposes in HCl.

YAVAPAIITE. Decomposed in boiling water; sol. in HCl.

YODERITE. Practically insol. in acids.

YTTRIALITE. Insol. in HCl, attacked by HF.

YTTROCALCITE. Sol. in acids.

YTTORCRASITE. Rapidly sol. HF but scarcely affected by other acids even when hot conc.; another ref. gives sol. H_2SO_4.

YTTROTANTALITE. Not affected by acids.

ZARATITE. Rapidly sol. dil. HCl; quickly attacked by other acids.

ZEBEDASSITE. Sol. in acids, forming gel.

ZEOLITES. All are more or less quickly diss. by HCl with or without formation of silica gel which has a rubbery texture when wet but becomes increasingly stiff as it dries, until finally it dries to a brittle glasslike solid which is very soft and friable. This can be easily dislodged from specimens by needles. Very rapidly attacked by HF and to varying extents by other acids. All zeolites are generally soft, fragile, many possess excellent and easily developed cleavages, and most are subject to damage if their matrices are hammered or broken. Calcite is a very common associate but cannot be removed by acids due to the great damage suffered by the zeolites in the process.

ZEUNERITE. Rapidly attacked by HNO_3 and other acids.

ZHEMCHUZHNIKOVITE. Easily sol. water.

ZINCALUMINITE. Sol. HNO_3.

ZINCITE. Fairly rapidly diss. by HCl and attacked by other acids; HCl tends to leave behind bright surfaces; dissolved in boiling saturated citric acid sol. Usually xls exposed by carefully working away enclosing calcite (Franklin, New Jersey). Brittle, cleavable.

ZINCSILITE. Dec. by acids, partly by Na_2SO_3 sol.

ZINKENITE. Diss. hot HCl, and attacked by other acids and A.R. Fibrous forms should not be washed in water but should be gently immersed in alcohol to clean in order to prevent matting of fibers.

ZINNWALDITE. Treat like MICAS.

ZIPPEITE. Insol. water, sol. dil. acids.

ZIRCON. Unaffected by acids or other chemical agents.

ZIRCOSULFATE. Easily sol. in water.

ZIRKELITE. Attacked only by hot conc. HF.

ZOISITE. Treat like EPIDOTE.

ZUNYITE. Attacked only by HF.

References: American Mineralogist 1-56 (1916-70).

H. C. Bolton, "The Application of Organic Acids to the Examination of Minerals," parts 1, 2, *Annals N.Y. Acad. Sci.* 50 (1877-80).

G. K. Czamanske and C. O. Ingamells, "Dissolution of Sulfides," *American Mineral.* 55 (1970): 2131.

J. D. Dana and E. S. Dana, *The System of Mineralogy,* 6th ed. with appendices 1-3 (New York: John Wiley, 1920).

E. S. Dana and W. E. Ford *A Textbook of Mineralogy,* 4th ed. (New York: John Wiley, 1932).

C. Frondel *The System of Mineralogy,* 7th ed. (New York: John Wiley, 1962). Vol. 3. *Silica Minerals.*

T. S. Hunt, *Systematic Mineralogy* (New York: Scientific Publishing Company, 1891).

C. Palache, H. Berman, and C. Frondel, *The System of Mineralogy,* 7th ed. (New York: John Wiley, 1944-51), vols. 1-2.

R. M. Pearl, *Mineral Collectors Handbook* (Colorado Springs: Mineral Book Company, 1949).

J. Sinkankas, *Prospecting for Gemstones and Minerals,* 2d ed. (New York: Van Nostrand Reinhold, 1970).

E. Weinschenk, and R. W. Clark, *Petrographic Methods* (New York: McGraw-Hill, 1912).

A. N. Winchell and H. Winchell, *Elements of Optical Mineralogy,* 4th ed. (New York: John Wiley, 1951), part 2.

Part 11 / Nomenclature

GREEK ALPHABET

Name	Capitals	Lower case	Equivalents
Alpha	A	α	A
Beta	B	β	B
Gamma	Γ	γ	G
Delta	Δ	δ	D
Epsilon	E	ϵ	E
Zeta	Z	ζ	Z
Eta	H	η	E
Theta	Θ	θ	Th
Iota	I	ι	I
Kappa	K	κ	K
Lambda	Λ	λ	L
Mu	M	μ	M
Nu	N	ν	N
Xi	Ξ	ξ	X
Omicron	O	o	O
Pi	Π	π	P
Rho	P	ρ	R
Sigma	Σ	σ, ς	S
Tau	T	τ	T
Upsilon	Υ	υ	U
Phi	Φ	ϕ	Ph
Chi	X	χ	Ch
Psi	Ψ	ψ	Ps
Omega	Ω	ω	O

RUSSIAN ALPHABET

Capitals	Lower case	Equivalent	Pronunciation
А	а	a	father
Б	б	b	book
В	в	v	vote
Г	г	g	good
Д	д	d	day
Е	е	e, ye	yes or yore
Ж	ж	zh	azure
З	з	z	zone
И	и	i	meet
Й	й	y	boy
К	к	k	kind
Л	л	l	well
М	м	m	man
Н	н	n	pen

Capitals	Lower Case	Equivalent	Pronunciation
О	о	o	*law*
П	п	p	*p*en
Р	р	r	er*r*or
С	с	s	ye*s*
Т	т	t	*t*all
У	у	u	sch*oo*l
Ф	ф	f	*f*ire
Х	х	kh	German: no*ch*
Ц	ц	ts	pan*ts*
Ч	ч	ch	*ch*ase
Ш	ш	sh	*sh*ort
Щ	щ	shch	ca*sh ch*eck
Ъ	ъ		"hard" sign
Ы	ы	y	h*i*t
Ь	ь		"soft" sign
Э	з	e	m*e*n
Ю	ю	yu	m*u*te
Я	я	ya	*ya*cht

COMMON COMBINING WORD FORMS APPEARING IN THE EARTH SCIENCES

The following forms are mainly Greek in origin; those from the Latin are designated by (L).

Form	Original word	Meaning
Acanth-	acantha	thorn
Achro-	achroia	colorless
Acm-	akme	point
Actino-	aktinos	ray
Adelph-	adelphos	brother
Aenigma-	ainigma	riddle
Aer	aerinos	sky blue
Aeschyn-	aischyne	shame
Agalm-	agalma	statue
Alb	albus (L)	white
Allac-	allaktron	change
Allo-	allos	different
Amarant-	amarantos	unfading
Ambly-	amblus	blunt
Amianth-	amiantos	undefiled (by fire)
Amphi-	amphi	on both sides
An-	an-	not
Ana-	ana	up, backward, again
Ancylo-	ankylos	curved
Anomal-	anomalos	irregular
Antho-	anthos	flower
Anthophyllo-	anthophyllum (L)	clove (color)
Anthra-	anthrax	glowing coal
Anthraco-	anthrakos	coal

Form	Original word	Meaning
Aphan-	aphanes	obscure
Aphr-	aphros	foam
Apth-	aphthitos	unalterable
Aphtho-	aphthonos	abundant
Aplo-	haploos	simple
Apo-	apo-	from, away, off
Aqua-	aqua (L)	water
Argent-	argentum (L)	silver
Argyro-	argyros	silver
Aster-	aster	star
Astro-	astron	star
Atop-	atopos	unusual
Aug-	auge	luster
Aur-	aurum (L)	gold
Automol-	automolos	deserter
Axin-	axine	axe
Bary-	barys	heavy
Basan-	basanos	touchstone
Bi-	bis (L)	2, twice, double
Botryo-	botrys	grape bunch
Brachy-	brachus	short
Caco-	Kakos	bad
Carpho-	karphos	straw
Caryo-	caryon	nut
Cata-	kata	with
Cer-	keras	horn
Cer-	keros	waxy
Chalco-	chalkos	copper
Chalyb-	Chalybes	ancient iron makers, hence iron
Chiasto-	chiastos	crosswise
Chio-	chion	snow
Chlo-	chloe	verdure
Chlor-	chloros	green
Chondro-	chondros	grain
Chrom-	chroma	color
Chryso-	chrysos	gold, gold color
Clase-	klasis	fracture, cleavage
Cleio-	kleios	fame
Clino-	klinein	slope, incline
Cocco-	kokkos	grain
Coll-	kolla	glue
Con-	konia	lime (mineral)
Crase-	krasis	combination
Crepto-	crepitare (L)	crack
Croco-	krokos	saffron color
Cron-	kronos	Saturn, or Pb, Sb
Cryo-	kryos	ice
Crypto-	kryptos	concealed
Cubo-	kubos	cube
Cupro-	cuprum (L)	copper
Cyano-	kyanos	blue

Form	Original word	Meaning
Cym-	kyma	wave
Cyrt-	kyrtos	curved
Dat-	datysthei	divide
Deca-	deka	10
Desm-	desme	bundle
Di-	dis	2, twice, double
Dia-	dia	through, apart, between
Didym-	didymos	twin
Dodeca-	dodeka	12
Dym-	dymos	fold
Dys-	dys	hard, ill
Elaeo-	elaion	oil
Enantio-	enantios	opposite
Endo-	endon	within
Enigma-	enigma	riddle
Epi-	epi	upon, near
Erythro-	erythros	red
Eu-	eu-	good, well, favorable
Ferro-	ferrum (L)	iron
Fibro-	fibra (L)	fibrous
Fluo-	fluere (L)	flow
Gala-	galactos	milk
Galeno-	galene	lead
Gano-	ganos	luster
Gen-	gennan	make
Geo-	ge	earth
Glauco-	glaukos	gray, greenish-blue
Gonio-	gonia	angle
Gramm-	gramme	line
Grano-	granum (L)	grain
Graph-	graphein	write
Griph-	griphos	enigma
Gyro-	gyros	ring, round
Haema-	haima	blood (color)
Halo-	hals	salt
Harmo-	harmos	joint
Hecto-	hekatron	100
Helio-	helios	sun
Hema-	haima	blood (color)
Hemi-	hemi	half
Hepat-	hepar	liver (color)
Hepta-	hepta	7
Hetero-	heteros	other, different
Hexa-	hex	6
Holo-	holos	whole, entire
Homo-	homos	same
Hyalo-	hyalos	glass
Hydro-	hydro	water
Hyper-	hyper	over, above
Hypo-	hypo	under
Icosa-	eikosi	20

Form	Original word	Meaning
Idio-	idios	inherent, peculiar to
Ido-	eidos	form
Ines-	ines	flesh fiber
Iodo-	iodes	violetlike (containing I)
Ion-	ion	violet
Iso-	isos	equal, similar
Kaino-	kainos	recent
Kali-	kalium (L)	potash; containing potassium
Kilo-	chilioi	1,000
Kyano-	kyanos	blue
Lampro-	lampros	shining
Lazur-	lazur (L)	blue stone
Lepido-	lepis	scale
Leuco-	leukos	white
Liro-	leiros	pale
Lithio-	lithos	stone; also Li
Macro-	makros	large
Malaco-	malakos	soft
Margaro-	Margaritis	pearl
Mela-	melas	black
Melan-	melanos	black
Meli-	meli	honey
Meso-	mesos	middle
Meta-	meta	between, with, after
Micro-	mikros	small; also, one-millionth
Mime-	mimetis	imitator
Molybd-	molybdos	lead; now also containing Mo
Mono-	monos	1, alone, sole, only
Morph-	morphe	form
Myria-	myrias	10,000
Natro-	nitron	native soda; now also containing Na
Neo-	neos	fresh, recent, young
Nitro-	nitron	native soda; also containing N
Octa-	octo-	8
Oligo-	oligos	little
Ortho-	orthos	right, straight
Para-	para-	near
Penta-	pente	5
Peri-	peri-	about, around, beyond, near
Phane-	phanein	appear, seem
Pharmaco-	pharmakos	poison
Phos-	phos	light
Phyllo-	phyllon	leaf
Picro-	pikros	bitter
Piezo-	piezein	press
Plagio-	plagios	inclined
Pleio-, pleo-	pleion	more, several
Plumbo-	plumbum (L)	lead
Poly-	polys	many, much
Praseo-	prasos	leek (green)
Pro-	pro	before

Form	Original word	Meaning
Proto-	protos	earlier
Pseudo-	pseudes	false, spurious
Pycno-	pyknos	dense
Pyr-, pyro-	pyr	fire
Pyrrho-	pyrrhos	flame (colored)
Retin-	retine	resin
Rhabdo-	rabdos	rod
Rhodo-	rhodon	rose (color)
Sarco-	sarkos	flesh (color)
Scol-	skolex	worm
Selen-	selene	moon; containing selenium
Sider-	sideros	iron
Soda-	soda (L)	headache; containing Na
Sphen-	sphen	wedge
Sphere-	sphaira	ball
Spod-	spodios	ash (color)
Stanno-	stannum (L)	tin
Staur-	stauros	cross
Sthen-	sthenos	strength
Stibio-	stibium (L)	antimonial, Sb
Stilb-	stilbein	shine
Stilpno-	stilpnos	shining
Tachy-	tachys	quick
Tephro-	tephros	ash color
Tetra-	tetrakis	4
Thermo-	thermos	heat
Tri-	tris	3
Tribo-	tribos	rubbing
Trich-	trichos	hair
Xantho-	xanthos	yellow
Xen-	xenos	stranger
Xylo-	xylon	wood

GERMAN MINERALOGICAL NAMES AND THEIR ENGLISH EQUIVALENTS

Names have been selected on the basis of their dissimilarity to corresponding English names or for appearing in older German works on minerals or gemstones and no longer being used in modern German literature.

Elements

Blei. Lead
Eisen. Iron
Jod. Iodine

Kalium. Potassium
Kohlenstoff. Carbon
Kupfer. Copper
Natrium. Sodium
Sauerstoff. Oxygen
Schwefel. Sulfur
Stickstoff. Nitrogen
Wasserstoff. Hydrogen
Wismut. Bismuth
Wolfram. Tungsten
Zinn. Tin

Minerals

Achat. Agate
Agtstein. Amber, jet, or obsidian

Alaun. Alum
Alaunstein. Alunite
Alumogel. Bauxite
Ammoniakalaun. Tschermigite
Antimonblende. Kermesite
Antimonblüte. Valentinite
Antimonfahlerz. Tetrahedrite
Antimonglanz. Stibnite
Antimonit. Stibnite
Antimonnickel. Breithauptite
Antimonnickelglanz, Antimonnickelkies. Ullmannite
Antimonocker. Stibiconite in part
Antimonsilber. Dyscrasite
Antimonsilberblende. Pyrargyrite or proustite
Arsenantimonnickelglanz. Corynite
Arsenblende. Realgar or orpiment
Arsenblüte. Arsenolite, pharmacolite
Arseneisen, Loellingite
Arsenfahlerz. Tennantite
Arsenikalkies. Arsenopyrite, loellingite
Arsenikblüte. Arsenolite
Arsenikeisen. Loellingite
Arsenikfahlerz. Tennantite
Arsenikies, Loellingite
Arsenikkobaltkies. Skutterudite
Arsenikkönig. Arsenic metal
Arseniknickel. Niccolite
Arsenit. Arsenolite
Arsenkies. Arsenopyrite
Arsennickelglanz, Arsennickelkies. Gersdorffite
Arsenomelan. Scleroclase
Arsensilberblende. Proustite
Atlasspat. Chatoyant massive calcite or gypsum
Augenachat. Eye agate
Augenstein. Chalcedony with eyelike markings
Auripigment. Orpiment
Bandachat. Banded agate
Bandjaspis. Banded jasper
Bariumuranit. Uranocircite
Barytkreuzstein. Harmotome
Baryturanglimmer. Uranocircite
Baryumuranit. Uranocircite
Baumachat. Tree agate
Beintürkis. Odontolite
Bergblau. Lapis lazuli
Bergflachs, Bergwolle. Mountain flax, wool, or byssolite
Berggrün. Chrysocolla or malachite
Bergholz, Bergleder. Mountain wood, leather, or byssolite or amphibole
Bergkristall. Rock crystal

Bergwachs. Bitumen
Bernstein. Amber
Biegsamer Stein. Itacolumite
Bildstein. Agalmatolite, pyrophyllite
Bimsstein. Pumice
Bittersalz. Epsomite
Bitterspat. Dolomite, magnesite
Blätteraugit. Diallage
Blättererz. Nagyagite
Blätterserpentin. **Antigorite**
Blättertellur. Nagyagite
Blätterzeolith. Heulandite
Blättriges Olivenerz. Libethenite
Blaubleierz. Galena pseudo after pyromorphite
Blaueisenerde, Blaueisenerz. Vivianite
Blaueisenstein. Crocidolite
Blauspat. Lazulite
Bleiantimonglanz. Zinckenite
Bleiarsenglanz. Scleroclase
Bleiglanz. Galena
Bleiglas. Anglesite
Bleihornerz. Phosgenite
Bleilasur. Linarite
Bleimolybdat. Wulfenite
Bleiniere. Bindheimite
Bleischwärze. Cerussite
Bleischweif. Compact galena
Bleispat. Cerussite
Bleivitriol. Anglesite
Bleiweiss. Cerussite
Bleiwismutglanz. Galenobismutite
Blende. Sphalerite
Blutjaspis. Bloodstone, heliotrope
Blutstein. Hematite
Boromagnesit. Szaibelyite
Boronatrocalcit. Ulexite
Bouteillenstein. Moldavite
Braunbleierz. Pyromorphite
Brauneisenerz, Brauneisenstein. Limonite ore
Brauner Glaskopf. Goethite
Brauner Yttrotantalit. Fergusonite
Braunkohle. Lignite
Braunmanganerz. Manganite
Braunsalz. Tecticite
Braunspat. Dolomite, ankerite, siderite
Braunstein. Pyrolusite
Braunsteinblende. Alabandite
Braunsteinrahm. Earthy manganite
Bromsilber. Bromargyrite
Büchsenstein. Flint
Bündelzeolith. Stilbite
Buntbleierz. Pyromorphite
Buntkupfererz, Buntkupferkies. Bornite
Carminspath. Carminite

Chalkolith. Torbernite
Chalkosin. Chalcocite
Chalzedon. Chalcedony
Chlorkalium. Sylvite
Chlornatrium. Halite
Chlorquecksilber. Calomel
Chlorsilber. Cerargyrite
Chrombleierz. Crocoite
Chromeisenerz. Chromite
Cobaltin. Cobaltite
Coelestin, Cölestin. Celestite
Demant. Diamond
Demantspat. Corundum
Desmin. Stilbite
Diamantspat. Corundum
Disthen. Kyanite
Doppelspat. Calcite
Dunkles Rotgültigerz. Pyrargyrite
Dunkles Weissgüldigerz. Freibergite
Edelopal. Precious opal
Edler Spinell. Precious, i.e., magnesian spinel
Einaxiger Glimmer. Biotite
Eisenalaun. Halotrichite
Eisenapatit. Zwieselite
Eisenblau. Vivianite
Eisenblüte. Coralloidal aragonite
Eisenchlorit. Delessite
Eisenglanz. Hematite
Eisenglimmer. Specular hematite, later Fe-mica
Eisenkies. Pyrite
Eisenkiesel. Quartz colored by limonite, goethite, etc.
Eisennickelglanz, Eisennickelkies. Pentlandite
Eisenpecherz. Stilpnosiderite
Eisenrose. Hematite "iron rose"
Eisensinter. Pitticite
Eisenspat. Siderite
Eisenstein. Iron ore
Eisentongranat. Almandine
Eisenvitriol. Melanterite
Eisspat. Sanidine
Eisstein. Cryolite
Erdkobalt. Asbolane
Erdpech. Asphalt
Erdwachs. Ozocerite
Eugenglanz. Polybasite
Fahlerz. Tetrahedrite
Falkenauge. Falcon's-eye
Fasergips. Fibrous gypsum
Faserzeolith. Natrolite, scolecite
Fasriges Olivenerz. Olivenite
Federalaun. Any alum of feathery growth habit

Federerz. Plumosite
Festungsachat. Fortification agate
Fettstein. Elaeolite
Feuerblende. Pyrargyrite
Feueropal. Fire opal
Feuerstein. Flint
Fischaugenstein. Apophyllite
Fliegenstein. Arsenic
Flusspat. Fluorite
Fraueneis. Gypsum
Gagat. Jet
Galmei. Zinc carbonate or silicate ores
Gelbbleierz. Wulfenite
Gelbe Arsenblende. Orpiment
Gelbeisenerz. Copiapite
Gelbeisenstein. Limonite
Gelbnickelkies. Millerite
Gelenkquarz. Itacolumite
Giftkies. Arsenopyrite
Gips. Gypsum
Glanz. Galena
Glanzbraunstein. Hausmannite
Glanzeisenerz. Hematite
Glanzkobalt. Cobaltite
Glanzkohle. Lustrous coal
Glasachat. Obsidian
Glaserz. Argentite
Glaskopf. Goethite
Glasopal. Hyalite
Glaubersalz. Mirabilite
Glimmer. Mica
Goldstein. Touchstone
Granat. Garnet
Griesstein. Sandstone, nephrite
Graubraunstein. Manganite
Graugültigerz. Freibergite
Graumanganerz. Pyrolusite
Grauspiessglanz. Stibnite
Grauspiessglanzerz, Grauspiessglaserz. Stibnite or jamesonite
Grünbleierz. Pyromorphite or mimetite
Grüneisenerz, Gruneisenstein. Dufrenite
Grünerde. Celadonite
Grüner Glaskopf. Dufrenite
Grünstein. Greenish fine-grained rocks in general
Gur, Guhr. Earthy or powdery mineral substances
Haarkies. Millerite
Haarsalz. Alunogen, epsomite, or halotrichite
Haarstein. Clear quartz with hairlike inclusions
Halblasurblei. Caledonite
Halbopal. Impure opal, jaspopal
Halbvitriolblei. Lanarkite

Hartbraunstein. Braunite
Hartkobalterz. Skutterudite
Hartmanganerz. Braunite, psilomelane
Hartspat. Corundum
Himbeerspat. Rhodochrosite
Himmelstein. Benitoite
Hohlspat. Chiastolite
Holzopal. Wood opal
Holzstein. Silicified wood
Holzzinn. Wood tin
Honigstein. Mellite
Hornblei. Phosgenite
Hornerz. Cerargyrite
Hornsilber. Cerargyrite
Hornstein. Jaspery quartz
Jaspachat. Jaspagate
Jaspis. Jasper
Jodargyrit, Iodit, Jod Silber, Jodyrit.
Iodargyrite
Jolith. Iolite
Kalialaun. Kalinite
Kalifeldspat. Potassium feldspar
Kaliglimmer. Muscovite
Kalk. Calcite, lime
Kalkchromgranat. Uvarovite
Kalkeisengranat. Andradite
Kalkfeldspat. Plagioclase
Kalkgranat. Grossular
Kalkharmotom. Phillipsite
Kalkkreuzstein. Phillipsite
Kalksinter. Calcareous sinter
Kalkspat. Calcite
Kalkstein. Limestone
Kalktongranat. Grossular
Kalkuranglimmer. Autunite
Kalkuranit. Autunite
Kalzit. Calcite
Kallainit. Variscite (?)
Kallait. Turquoise
Kallochrom. Crocoite
Kaneelstein. Hessonite
Kaprubin. Pyrope
Karbonat. Carbonado diamond
Karfunkel. Carbuncle
Karneol. Carnelian
Karstenit. Anhydrite
Kascholong. Cacholong opal
Katzenauge. Cat's-eye
Katzengold, Katzenglimmer. Finely divided
mica
Katzenzinn. Cassiterite
Kerasin. Phosgenite
Kerat. Cerargyrite
Kies. Pyrite, sulfide
Kiesel. Quartz or siliceous stone
Kieselarten. Silicates

Kieselerde. Silica
Kieselgalmei. Hemimorphite
Kieselguhr. Diatomaceous earth
Kieselkupfer. Chrysocolla
Kieselmalachit. Chrysocolla
Kieselmangan. Rhodonite
Kieselwismuth. Eulytine
Kieselzincerz. Hemimorphite
Kobaltarsenkies. Danaite, glaucodot
Kobaltbeschlag. Erythrite
Kobaltglanz. Cobaltite
Kobaltin. Cobaltite
Kobaltkies. Linnaeite
Kobaltmanganerz. Asbolane
Kobaltnickelkies. Siegenite
Kobaltvitriol. Bieberite
Kohle. Coal
Kohlengalmei. Smithsonite
König. Regulus, arsenic, bismuth, or
antimony
Koralle. Coral
Korallenachat. Agatized coral
Korund. Corundum
Kreide. Chalk
Kreuzstein. Chiastolite, staurolite, or
harmotome
Krokydolith. Crocidolite
Kupferantimonglanz. Chalcostibite
Kupferfahlerz. Tetrahedrite
Kupferglanz. Chalcocite
Kupferglimmer. Chalcophyllite
Kupfergrün. Chrysocolla
Kupferindig. Covellite
Kupferkies. Chalcopyrite
Kupferkiesel. Chrysocolla
Kupferlasur. Azurite
Kupferlebererz. Cuprite
Kupfermanganerz. Lampadite
Kupfernickel. Niccolite
Kupfersammterz. Cyanotrichite
Kupferschaum. Tyrolite
Kupfersmaragd. Dioptase
Kupferuranglimmer. Torbernite
Kupferuranit. Torbernite
Kupfervitriol. Chalcanthite
Kupferwismutherz, Kupferwismuthglanz.
Wittichenite
Kymophan. Cymophane chrysoberyl
Lasur. Azurite
Lasurit. Azurite, lazurite
Lasurstein. Lazurite, lapis lazuli
Lavezstein. Talc
Leberblende. Fine granular sphalerite ore
Leberkies. Marcasite
Lichtes Fahlerz. Tennantite
Lichtes Rotgültigerz. Proustite

Lilalith. Lepidolite
Linsenerz. Liroconite
Lithionglimmer. Lepidolite, zinnwaldite
Luchssaphir. Cordierite gem
Lydischer Stein. Touchstone
Magnesia Alaun. Pickeringite
Magnesiaglimmer. Biotite, phlogopite
Magnesiatongranat. Pyrope
Magnesitspat. Magnesite
Magnet. Magnetite
Magneteisenerz. Magnetite
Magnetkies. Pyrrhotite
Magnetopyrit. Pyrrhotite
Manganalaun. Apjohnite
Manganblende. Alabandite
Manganepidot. Piemontite
Manganglanz. Alabandite
Manganvitriol. Mallardite, ilesite
Manganschaum. Wad
Marmor. Marble
Mehlzeolith. Scolecite
Melanglanz. Stephanite
Mergel. Marl
Merkurblende. Cinnabar
Merkursilber. Amalgam
Milchopal. Milk opal
Milchquarz. Milky quartz
Mildglanzerz. Polybasite
Mimetesit. Mimetite
Misspickel. Arsenopyrite
Molybdänbleierz, Molybdänbleispat. Wulfenite
Molybdänglanz. Molybdenite
Mokkastein. Dendritic agate
Mondstein. Moonstone
Moosachat. Moss agate
Nadeleisenerz. Goethite
Nadelerz. Aikinite
Nadelsteine. Clear quartz with acicular inclusions
Natronalaun. Mendozite
Natronglimmer. Paragonite
Natronmesotyp. Natrolite
Natron Salpeter. Nitratine
Nickelblüte. Annabergite
Nickelgrün. Annabergite
Nickelin. Niccolite
Nickelkies. Millerite
Nickelocker. Annabergite
Nickel Smaragd. Zaratite
Nickelspiessglanzerz. Ullmannite
Nickelvitriol. Morenosite
Nickelwismuthglanz. Polydymite
Nierenkies. Botryoidal massive chalcopyrite
Nierenstein. Nephrite

Ocker. Ocher
Olivenerz. Olivenite
Operment. Orpiment
Oxalsäurer Kalk. Whewellite
Pagodit. Pyrophyllite
Pechblende. Pitchblende
Pecherz. Pitchblende
Pechstein. Obsidian rock
Pechuran. Pitchblende
Perlglimmer. Margarite
Perlmutter. Nacre
Perlspat. Dolomite
Perlstein. Perlite
Phosphorkupfererz. Pseudomalachite
Phosphorochalcit. Pseudomalachite
Porzellanerde. Kaolinite
Probierstein. Touchstone
Punamu, Punamustein. New Zealand nephrite
Punktachat. Agate with dots of color
Quecksilberfahlerz. Schwatzite
Quecksilberhornerz. Calomel
Rädelerz. Bournonite
Raseneisenstein. Limonite ore
Rauchkalk. Dolomite
Rauchquarz. Smoky quartz
Rauchtopas. Smoky quartz
Rauschgelb. Orpiment
Rauschrot. Realgar
Regenbogenquarz. Iris quartz
Regulus. Antimony
Rheinkiesel. Stream-worn quartz crystal of the Rhine R.
Röhrenachat. Tube agate
Rotbleierz. Crocoite
Rote Arsenblende. Realgar
Roteisenerz -Stein. Hematite
Rötel. Rouge
Roter Erdkobalt. Erythrite
Roter Glaskopf. Hematite kidney ore
Rotgültigerz. Proustite, pyrargyrite
Rotkupfererz. Cuprite
Rotnickelkies. Niccolite
Rotspiessglanzerz. Kermesite
Rotzinkerz. Zincite
Rubin. Ruby
Rubinblende. Red sphalerite
Rubinglimmer. Lepidocrocite
Rubinspinell. Ruby spinel
Ruinenmarmor. Ruin marble
Salmiak. Sal ammoniac
Salniter. Saltpeter
Salz. Salt
Salzkupfererz. Atacamite
Sammetblende, Samtblende. Goethite
Saphir. Sapphire

Saphirquarz. Blue quartz
Sappar. Kyanite
Saualpit. Zoisite
Schalenblende. Banded massive ore of sphalerite-wurtzite
Scharfmanganerz. Hausmannite
Schaumkalk, Schaumspat. Porous aragonite
Scheel, Scheelerz, Scheelspat. Scheelite
Scheelbleierz. Stolzite
Scherbenkobalt. Arsenic
Schiefergrün. Chrysocolla
Schilfglaserz. Freieslebenite
Schillerspat. Bastite
Schmirgel. Emery
Schrifterz. Sylvanite
Schrifttellur. Sylvanite
Schwarzeisenstein. Psilomelane
Schwarzer Erdkobalt. Asbolane
Schwarzer Glaskopf. Botryoidal psilomelane
Schwarzer Spinell. Ceylonite
Schwarzer Yttrotantalit. Yttrotantalite
Schwarzerz. Alabandite
Schwarzgültigerz. Stephanite
Schwarzspiessglanzerz, Schwarzspiessglaserz. Bournonite
Schwefelarsen. Orpiment
Schwefelkies. Pyrite
Schwefelsilber. Argentite
Schwerspat. Barite
Schwerstein. Scheelite
Seifenstein. Saponite
Selenblei. Clausthalite
Selenbleikupfer. Mixture
Selenkobaltblei. Mixture
Selenkupfer. Berzelianite
Selenkupferblei. Mixture
Selenquecksilber. Tiemannite
Selenschwefelquecksilber. Onofrite
Selensilber. Naumannite
Selensilberblei. Mixture
Selenwismutglanz. Guanajuatite
Silberantimonglanz. Miargyrite
Silberfahlerz. Freibergite
Silberhornerz. Cerargyrite
Silberkupferglanz. Stromeyerite
Silberwismutglanz. Maltidite
Smaragd. Emerald
Sonnenstein. Sunstone
Spargelstein. Apatite
Spat. Spar
Spateisenstein. Siderite
Speckstein. Steatite
Speerkies. Marcasite
Speiskobalt. Safflorite
Spiegelglanz. Specular hematite

Spiegelstein. Specular hematite
Spiessglanzbleierz. Bournonite
Spiessglanzsilber. Dyscrasite
Spiessglas. Antimony
Spiessglaskönig. Antimony
Sprödglaserz. Stephanite
Sprödglimmer. Brittle mica
Sprudelstein. Calcareous sinter
Stahlerz, Stahlstein. Siderite
Steinsalz. Halite
Stephanstein. Point agate
Sternrubin, Sternsaphir. Star ruby, sapphire
Stiblith. Stibiconite
Stinkfluss, Stinkspat. Antozonite fluorite
Strahlenblende = Schalenblende
Strahlerz. Clinoclase
Strahlglimmer. Massive mica
Strahliger Graubraunstein. Pyrolusite
Strahlkies. Radiate marcasite
Strahlstein. Actinolite
Strahlzeolith. Stilbite
Tafelspat. Wollastonite
Talkspat. Magnesite
Tellurblei. Altaite
Tellurgoldsilber. Petzite, sylvanite
Tellurige Säure. Tellurite
Tellur Ocker. Tellurite
Tellurquecksilber. Coloradoite
Tellursilber. Hessite
Tellurwismut. Tetradymite
Ternärbleierz. Leadhillite
Tesseralkies. Skutterudite
Thon, Ton. Argillite, alumina
Thumerstein. Axinite
Tigerauge. Tigereye
Tinkal. Borax
Titaneisen. Ilmenite
Titanmagneteisen. Ilmenite, titanomagnetite
Toneisengranat. Almandine
Tonkalkgranat. Grossular
Tonmangangranat. Spessartine
Topas. Topaz, also citrine
Topfstein. Steatite
Tripel. Tripoli
Tropfstein. Stalactitic calcite
Trümmerachat. Ruin agate
Tungstein. Scheelite
Türkis. Turquoise
Uranblüte. Zippeite
Uranglimmer. Micaceous uranium minerals
Urangrün. Uranocircite
Uranin. Uraninite
Uranit. Autunite, uraninite
Uranocker. Uraconite, uranopilite

Uranpecherz. Pitchblende
Uranotantal. Samarskite
Uranvitriol. Johannite
Vanadinbleierz. Vanadinite
Venushaare. Venus hair quartz
Verkieselte Holz. Silicified wood
Vitriol. Sulfate; melanterite
Vitriolbleierz. Anglesite
Wasserblei. Molybdenite
Wasserchrysolith. Moldavite
Wasserkies. Marcasite
Wasseropal. Water opal
Wasserstein. Enhydro
Weichmanganerz. Pyrolusite
Weissbleierz. Cerussite
Weissgültigerz. Freibergite, freieslebenite
Weissnickelkies. Chloanthite, rammelsbergite
Weisspiessglanzerz, Weisspiessglaserz. Valentinite
Weisstellur. Krennerite
Weltauge. Hydrophane opal
Wismutblende. Eulytine
Wismutglanz. Bismuthinite
Wismuthkobaltkies. Skutterudite
Wismutkupferblende. Wittichenite
Wismutocker. Bismite
Wismutspat. Bismutite
Wolframerz. Wolframite
Wolkenachat. Cloud agate
Würfelerz. Pharmacosiderite
Würfelzeolith. Chabazite
Ytterspat. Zenotime
Yttroilmenit. Samarskite

Zahntürkis. Odontolite
Zeilanit. Ceylonite
Zinkblende. Sphalerite
Zinkblüte. Hydrozincite
Zinkspat. Smithsonite
Zinkspinell. Gahnite
Zinkvitriol. Goslarite
Zinnkies. Stannite
Zinnober. Cinnabar
Zinnstein. Cassiterite
Zitrin. Citrine
Zölestin. Celestite
Zweiaxiger Glimmer. Muscovite

References: M. Bauer, *Lehrbuch der Mineralogie,* 2d ed. (Stuttgart, 1904).

A. H. Chester, *A Dictionary of the Names of Minerals* (New York: Wiley, 1896). Contains many names and synonyms.

K. F. Chudoba and E. J. Gübelin, *Edelsteinkundliches Handbuch,* 2d ed. (Bonn: Stollfuss Verlag, 1966).

C. Ehlers, *Nomina der Kristallographie und Mineralogie* (Hamburg: Boysen & Maasch Verlag, 1952).

M. H. Hey, *An Index of Mineral Species and Varieties,* 2d ed. rev. (London: British Museum, 1962). Much more complete list than the above list of German synonyms.

F. von Kobell, *Die Mineral-Namen und die Mineralogische Nomenklatur* (München, 1853).

H. Lüschen, *Die Namen der Steine* (Thun and München: Ott Verlag, 1968). Numerous derivations and explanations for old German terms.

C. W. Schmidt, *Wörterbuch der Geologie, Mineralogie und Paläontologie* (Berlin and Leipzig: Walter de Gruyter, 1928).

Part 12 / Optical Properties of Minerals and Gemstones

OPTICS

Frequency-Wavelength-Velocity Relationship

$$c = f\lambda$$

c = velocity of light in vacuum
f = frequency of light
λ (lambda) = wavelength of light

Wavelength Changes During Passage from One Medium to Another

$$\frac{c_1}{c_2} = \frac{\lambda_1}{\lambda_2}$$

c_1 = light velocity in first medium
c_2 = light velocity in second medium
λ_1 = wavelength in first medium
λ_2 = wavelength in second medium

Refractive Index (n)

$$n = \frac{c_v}{c_m}$$

n = refractive index of medium m
c_v = velocity of light in vacuum
c_m = velocity of light in medium m

$$\text{also, } n = \frac{\sin i}{\sin r}$$

n = refractive index
$\sin i$ = sine of the angle of incidence i
$\sin r$ = sine of the angle of refraction r

Refractive Index Versus Wavelength

$$\frac{\lambda_1}{\lambda_2} = \frac{n_1}{n_2}$$

λ_1 = wavelength of light in first medium
λ_2 = wavelength of light in second medium

Snell's Law (Refraction)

A light ray passing from a medium of certain refractive index into another of differing refractive index is refracted at an angle according to the relationship shown below:

$$n_1 \sin i = n_2 \sin r$$

n_1 = refractive index of first medium
n_2 = refractive index of second medium
i = angle of incidence of light ray
r = angle of refraction of light ray

$$\text{or, } \sin r = \frac{n_1}{n_2} \sin i$$

In the above it is assumed that the first medium is optically less dense, and for most mineralogical and gemological purposes is air with a refractive index very nearly 1.0. Hence the formula above becomes:

$$\sin r = \frac{\sin i}{n_2} \text{ and further,}$$

$$n_2 = \frac{\sin i}{\sin r} = \frac{\text{refractive index of}}{\text{second (denser) medium}}$$

Critical Angle

The angle at which a light ray traveling in a denser medium is *totally reflected* when it strikes a flat boundary with an optically less dense medium is expressed by:

$$\sin i_m = \frac{n}{n_m}$$

$\sin i_m$ = sine of the angle of *internal* incidence
n = refractive index of *external* medium
n_m = refractive index of *denser* medium

Brewster's Law on Polarization of Light

Light rays are partly polarized when reflected or refracted according to the following relationship:

$$\tan i = \frac{n_1}{n_2}$$

$\tan i$ = tangent of the angle of incidence in a less dense medium

n_1 = refractive index of the less dense medium

n_2 = refractive index of denser medium

Refractive Index Symbols in Mineralogy

n = refractive index of isotropic substances, or arithmetical mean of doubly refracting substances (see below)

O, o; or

ω (omega) = refractive index of the ordinary ray in uniaxial minerals

E, e; or

ϵ (epsilon) = refractive index of extraordinary ray in uniaxial minerals

α = (alpha) the lowest value of refractive index in biaxial minerals

β = (beta) the intermediate value of refractive index in biaxial minerals

γ = (gamma) the highest value of refractive index in biaxial minerals

Arithmetical Mean of Refractive Indices in Doubly Refracting Minerals

$$n = \frac{2o + e}{3}$$

For uniaxial minerals (tetragonal, hexagonal)

$$n = \frac{\alpha + \beta + \gamma}{3}$$

For biaxial minerals (orthorhombic, monoclinic, and triclinic)

Refractive Index of Medium Versus Refractive Index of Refractometer Prism

The following relationship holds where the refractive index of the refractometer prism glass is known:

$$n_m = \sin r \times n_g$$

n_m = refractive index of medium

r = angle of refraction within glass prism

n_g = refractive index of glass prism

Dispersion

The dispersive power of a mineral is usually stated as follows:

$$\text{disp.} = n_F - n_C$$

n_F = refractive index using F (4,861 A) light

n_C = refractive index using C (6,563 A) light

Also the following formula may be used and is claimed to be somewhat more expressive of the mineral's dispersive powers:

$$\text{disp.} = \frac{n_F - n_C}{n_D - 1}$$

n_F = refractive index using F

n_C = refractive index using C

n_D = refractive index using D (5,893 A)

LIGHT

VELOCITY OF LIGHT (c), in vacuum = about 300,000 km/sec. or 186,000 miles/sec., or more accurately = 299,776 ± 4 km/sec.

ÅNGSTROM UNIT (Å or simply A) = 10^{-8} cm = 0.00000001 cm = $\dfrac{1}{100,000,000}$ cm = 10^{-7} mm = $\dfrac{1}{10,000}$ micron (μ) = $\dfrac{1}{10}$ millimicron (mμ)

VISIBLE SPECTRUM (generally) 3,900-7,700 A.

CALIBRATION WAVELENGTHS

Produced by inserting a suitable compound containing the element in an intensely hot flame but difficulty is encountered in preventing the appearance of brilliant sodium lines because of the nearly universal presence of sodium chloride. Vapor lamps are available (Osram) for emission wavelengths for a considerable number of elements, the one most used in

Color Spectrum (A)

Color and standard λ	Limits	
Invisible Ultraviolet (UV), less than	4,000 A	*Bouma (1947)*
Visible Violet (4,100 standard value)	4,000-4,240	3,800-4,360
Visible Blue (4,700 st.)	4,240-4,912	4,360-4,950
Visible Green (5,200 st.)	4,912-5,750	4,950-5,660
Visible *Best visibility*	5,560 (5,600	
	Pringsheim 1942	
Visible Yellow (5,800 st.)	5,750-5,850	5,660-5,890
Visible Orange (6,000 st.)	5,850-6,470	5,890-6,270
Visible Red (6,500 st.)	6,470-7,000	6,270-7,800
Invisible Infrared (IR), greater than	7,000	

Fraunhofer Lines (A)

A (oxygen)	7,621 A		F (hydrogen)	4,861*
A (oxygen)	7,594*		G (hydrogen)	4,340
B (oxygen)	6,870*		G (calcium)	4,308*
C (hydrogen)	6,563*		G (iron)	4,308*
D_1 (sodium)	5,896* }	5,893 av.	H (calcium)	3,968
D_2 (sodium)	5,890* }		K (calcium)	3,934
E_2 (iron)	5,270*			

* Major lines.

mineralogy and gemology being the twin for sodium (5,890, 5,896 A). The mercury vapor lamp is also rich in sharp emission lines which may be used for calibration and mensuration of refractive indices.

Flame Spectra (Persistent Lines)

Barium	5,535 A	(yellow-green)
Boron	5,481	(green)
Calcium	6,182	(orange)
Calcium	6,203	(orange)
Potassium	7,699	(deep red)
Potassium	7,665	(deep red)
Rubidium	4,202	(violet)
Rubidium	4,216	(violet)
Sodium	5,890	(yellow)
Sodium	5,896	(yellow)
Strontium	6,060	(orange)
Strontium	4,608	(blue)
Thallium	5,351	(green)

Mercury Vapor Lamp Emissions

In the invisible UV region strong lines are emitted at 2,537, 2,652/2,655, 3,126/3,132 and 3,650/3,662 A; in the visible region strong lines appear at 4,017 (violet) and 4,358 (blue) and then lines at 5,461 (green-yellow) and a doublet at 5,770/5,791 A (yellow).

References: B. J. Bouma, *Physical Aspects of Colour* (Eindhoven, Netherlands, 1947).

P. Pringsheim and M. Vogel, *Luminescence of Liquids and Solids* (New York: Interscience Publishers, 1943).

R. Webster, *Gems,* 2d ed. (London: Butterworths, 1970).

PERCEPTION OF COLOR

The response of the human eye to colors of the spectrum is not uniform. Colors (or wavelengths) in the central region of the visible spectrum are much more easily detected and correctly interpreted than those toward either end. Best vision occurs in the yellow-green at about 5,600 A with rapid falling off toward the shorter wavelengths approaching violet and somewhat less rapid toward the deep red of the longer visible wavelengths. Taking response at the yellow-green at 100%, the responses elsewhere are as shown below.

Wavelength band	Color	Response (approximate)
4,000-4,400 A	Violet	2%-3%
4,400-4,800	Blue	3%-15%
4,800-5,000	Blue-green	15%-30%
5,000-5,300	Green	30%-85%
5,300-5,600	Yellow-green	85%-100%
5,600-5,700	Yellow-green	100%-95%
5,700-5,900	Yellow	95%-80%
5,900-6,200	Orange	80%-40%
6,200-6,400	Orange-red	40%-18%
6,400-6,800	Red	18%-ca. 0%

COLORING IONS IN MINERALS AND GEMSTONES

The causes of color in minerals and gemstones are many and complex. Chudoba (1969) summarizes causes as follows.

Idiochromatic: May be due to structural changes or transformations.

Achromatic to idiochromatic: May be colored by (1) pigments, (2) isomorphous substitution of elements in trace amounts, (3) irradiation, or (4) lattice disturbances.

Further color changes may be induced by heating and mechanical stress.

Isomorphous substitutions appear to provide much of the color observed in minerals and gemstones, particularly by the transition elements: scandium, atomic no. 21; titanium, 22; vanadium, 23; chromium, 24; manganese, 25; iron, 26; cobalt, 27; nickel, 28; and copper, 29. The table below gives examples of color believed caused by these and other ions. "Colorless" ions are those which do not ordinarily produce color in their compounds, e.g., aluminum, barium, calcium, potassium, sodium, and lithium.

Chromium, 24   Commonly imparts pale to strong blue-green color in beryl (emerald), or red in corundum (ruby); many others are colored by this ion, e.g., spodumene (hiddenite), diopside, demantoid and uvarovite garnet, red spinel, pyrope garnet, red topaz, chrysoberyl (alexanderite), jadeite, green kyanite, enstatite, some euclase.

Cobalt, 27   Imparts pink in erythrite, cobaltocalcite, roselite, and bieberite, but blue in glasses and in synth. spinels.

Copper, 29   Imparts green or blue in many species, among them malachite, azurite, turquoise, atacamite, boleite, diaboleite, rosasite, aurichalcite, dioptase, brochantite, linarite, and chalcanthite.

Fluorine, 9   May in part be responsible for purple coloration of fluorite.

Iron, 26   Commonly produces intense yellows, greens, browns, reds, and black in a very large number of minerals but is also considered responsible for blue in spinel and with Ti for blue in sapphire; also for purple in spinel. E.g.: green in corundum, epidote, olivine, aquamarine, diopside, enstatite, idocrase, tourmaline; yellow in corundum, citrine, orthoclase, chrysoberyl, sinhalite, spodumene; red in almandine; brown in axinite, blue in kyanite.

Manganese, 25   Typically produces pink in rhodonite and rhodochrosite but its function in producing purple in amethyst is unproved; while present in spessartine it is more likely that the orange coloration is produced by traces of iron. Manganese imparts purple in glasses.

Molybdenum, 42 Probably causes intense coloration in powellite and wulfenite.

Nickel, 28 Imparts a yellow-green color of a considerably warmer quality than the green of Cr; e.g., garnierite, zaratite, genthite, connarite.

Scandium, 21 Blue in bazzite?

Silver, 47 Dark colors appearing in certain silver salts (and minerals) are attributed to the dissociation of the metal resulting in un-combined ions strongly absorptive of light; this property is made use of in the manufacture of ordinary photographic film.

Sodium, 11 Believed to impart blue coloration to halite when some ions of this element are uncombined; also may be present in fluorite and responsible for some coloration in that mineral.

Sulfur, 11 Responsible for intense coloration in certain organic dyestuffs and is believed to be the cause of blue in sodalite, lazurite, and hauyne.

Thorium, 90 Indirectly responsible for much dark coloration, generally brown or black, in minerals in which it is present, by virtue of the destructive effects of its radioactivity on crystal lattices.

Titanium, 22 Imparts, with iron, blue in corundum; probably responsible in part for blue of benitoite.

Uranium, 92 See THORIUM above; probably imparts vivid greens and yellows in uranium minerals.

Vanadium, 23 Role in coloring minerals uncertain but probably responsible for rich colors of vanadinite; recent investigations indicate warmer greens noted in certain emerald beryls is due to this element instead of Cr.

References: K. F. Chudoba and E. Gübelin, *Edelsteinkundliches Handbuch,* 2d ed. (Bonn: Stollfuss Verlag, 1966).

K. F. Chudoba, "Über die bedeutung ... der Edelsteinfarben, im geschichtlichen Rückblick," *Zs. d. Deutschen Gemm. Ges.,* Sonderheft 3 (Idar-Oberstein, 1969), p. 37.

DICHROSCOPES

Calcite type–homemade: Cleave a piece of transparent, colorless calcite into a rhomb measuring approximately 1.5″ x .5″ x .5″ (3 x 1.5 x 1.5 cm) or somewhat larger. The small faces at the ends of rhomb should be quite flat; the quality of the sides is unimportant. Paint the sides with black paint or cover with black paper or other kind of tape. On one of the end faces left open temporarily fasten a small cover of black pasteboard with a pinhole in the center. Place this pinhole next to the specimen to be tested and observe dichroism. If the two circular patches are far apart, carefully enlarge the hole until they touch; now enlarge the hole on corners to form a rectangular opening. When properly done the opening in the pasteboard will show two square patches of colored light, each just touching the other.

Polaroid type–homemade: From any convenient scrap of Polaroid film, cut in two, and turn one piece 90° to the other. When properly done both pieces will fit tightly against each other. Mount in thin cardboard frame.

ABSORPTION SPECTRA OF GEMSTONES AND MINERALS

The following data have been assembled from a number of sources as indicated in references below. Figures are given from 7,000 A at the red end of the visible spectrum to 4,000 A at the opposite, violet end. Symbols used are as follows:

0,000 = in ordinary type, normal strength lines or bands

0,000 = in boldface, strong lines or bands

(0,000) = in parens, weak lines or bands

[0,000] = in brackets, bands only

[(0,000)-(0,000)] = weak band

. . . = continuous to limit shown

// = virgules, to indicate doublet lines

Example: 7,000 ← fading 6,800)], [(6,200 . . . **[6,050]** . . . 5,730)], (5,500//), [4,200 . . . 4,000.

Explanation: A continuous weak band of absorption from 6,800 toward 7,000, fading toward 7,000; another continuous weak absorption band from 6,200 to 5,730 but with a strong line at 6,050; a weak doublet at 5,500; another normal strength absorption band beginning at 4,200 and continuing to the 4,000 end of the spectrum.

Note: Some values are given without symbols and therefore indicate merely the position of the lines.

Brown Stones

Axinite. 5,320, **5,120**, **4,920**, **4,660**, 4,400, **4,150**.

Diamond. Brown generally shows: (5,040), (5,370), (4,980).

Diamond. Brown: [5,770-5,760], [5,390-5,370]; both are fluorescent bands.

Diamond. Bombarded to green, annealed to brown or yellow: (5,940), (5,040), (4,970).

Diamond. Brown, yellow fluorescent: 7,000 . . . 6,800)] faint; 5,410, **4,870**, [4,150], [4,100 . . . darkening → 4,000.

Diamond. Red-brown, treated: **6,340**, **6,215**, **6,105**, [5,670-5700 fluorescent], [c. 5,000 . . . 4,000.

Diamond. Yellow-brown, fluorescent: **5,635**, [5,500-5,480], **5,060**, 4,790, [4,170].

Diamond. Yellow-brown, natural: 7,000 . . . 6,850], **5,680**, (5,500), [4,770], (4,640), [4,550 . . . [4,160-4,140] . . . 4,000.

Diamond. Dark greenish-brown. Fluorescent band at [**6,300**].

Enstatite, brown (Fe): **5,475**, 5,090, **5,060**, 5,025, 4,830, 4,720, 4,590, 4,490, 4,250. The 5,060 line is very strong.

Greenockite. Synthetic, orange-brown (Cd). 7,000 . . . fading → 6,700)], [**5,160** . . . 4,000.

Hypersthene. Brown: 5,510, **5,475**, **5,060**, 4,820, 4,485.

Scheelite. Synthetic, red-brown: 7,000 . . . fading → 6,700], 6,000, [5,905 . . . **[5,850]** . . . 5,700], 5,450, [**5,360**], [5,360 . . . 5,300], **5,300**, [(5,215-5,175)], [5,000 . . . darkening - 4,000.

Staurolite. Brown, transp., St. Gotthard: 7,000 . . . 6,650], [5,780-5,750], [5,500-5,430], 5,270.

Willemite. Brown cat's-eye, Franklin, New Jersey: [(5,000 - 4,850) very faint], [(4,730) faint], [(4,480 ← fading [**4,270**] . . . [4,205-4,160] 4,160)], [(4,080 ← fading . . . 4,000.

Red Stones

Almandine. (Fe): [6,170], [**5,760**], [**5,270**], [**5,050**], 4,760, [4,620], 4,380, 4,280, 4,040, 3,930.

Corundum. Ruby, natural or synthetic: **6,942//6,928** usually seen as a single bright band, 6,680, 6,595, [**6,100** . . . fading at each end . . . **4,900**], **4,765**, **4,750**, **4,685**, c. **4,100** . . . **4,000**.

Corundum. Synthetic sintered, massive, pink: 7,000 . . . 6,900], [**5,505** . . . fading → 4,360], [**4,200**], [4,040 . . . 4,000.

Cuprite. Red, transp.: 7,000 . . . 6,800], **6,800**, [(6,250-5,650)], [(4,750 . . . 4,000.

Diamond. Orange-red, treated: (6,350), (6,150), **5,930**, [5,670-5,700 fluorescent], (5,115), **5,040**, [5,040 . . . [4,600-4,420 a lighter band] . . . 4,000.

Fluorite. Synthetic, dark red: 7,000 . . . 6,600], **6,570**, **6,310**, (6,100), [5,860 . . . **5,495** . . . 5,300], 5,300, **5,200**, [5,000-4,950], [4,950-4,400], [faint (4,300 . . . darkening → 4,000.

Garnet, Rare-Earth. Y, Ga type, pink: 7,000 . . . 6,800 very faint], **6,650**,

[6,400], 5,490, [5,295], [5,220], [4,950-4,000], 4,630//, 4,530//, 4,470, 4,100, 4,080, [4,200 ... 4,000. Many fine lines between 7,000 and 4,350.

Glass. Selenium, red: [5,400-5,200], [4,150 ← fading ... 4,000.

Glass, Fabergé red "purpurine": 7,000 ... fading → 6,700], [6,310], [6,260-6,200], [6,000 → fading 4,500 → darkening → 4,000.

Pyrope. (Cr, Fe): 6,870, 6,850, 6,710, 6,500, [6,200-5,200], [5,050].

Rhodochrosite. Pink, transp., Colorado: 7,000 ... 6,800 very weak], [5,650-5,300 very weak], [4,750-4,440 very weak], [4,200 ... 4,000 very weak.

Rhodochrosite. (Mn): 5,520, 4,490, 4,100.

Rhodonite. (Mn): 5,030, (4,550), 4,120, 4,080.

Scapolite. Pink: 6,580, 6,570, [(5,970-5,370)], [(4,100 ... 4,000.

Smithsonite. Transp. pink: [5,500-5,300 faint], [4,800].

Spinel. Synthetic, red: 6,855, 6,750.

Spinel. Nat. red. (Cr): 6,855, 6,840, 6,750, 6,650, 6,560, 6,500, 6,420, 6,320, [5,950-4,900], 4,650, 4,550.

Topaz. Pink (Cr): fluorescence at 6,820.

Tourmaline. Red (Mn?): 5,370, [5,370-4,800], [4,580], [4,500].

Yttrium Aluminate. Synthetic, orthorhombic, pink: Many lines 6,850-6,680, c. 6,800, 6,000-6,100, very dense concentration [5,950-5,750], [5,300-5,230], 5,150, 5,125, 4,750//, 4,565, 4,360, 4,340, 4,310.

Zircon. Red: 6,910, 6,890, 6,625, 6,605, 6,535, 6,210, 6,150, 5,895, 5,620, 5,375, 5,160, 4,840, 4,600, 4,330.

Orange Stones

Corundum. Sapphire, synthetic, orange (Cr): [6,942-6,928], (6,680), (6,592).

Crocoite. [5,560-5,500], [4,700 ← fading ... all faint ... 4,000.

Grossular. Orange (Mn): 5,470, 4,900, 4,350.

Scheelite. Brown-orange, natural: 7,000 ... 6,900 fading → 6,700], [5,960 ... 5,900 ... 5,850], 5,780, 5,360, 5,300, (5,210), (5,190), [(4,890)].

Scheelite. Orange, natural (Nd, Pr): fluorescent at 6,500, 6,200, 5,580 (synth. shows no fluor.).

Scheelite. Synthetic, orange; may exhibit some of these rare-earth lines:
Nd: 7,320, 5,940, 5,920, 5,890, 5,850, 5,800, 5,780, 5,735, 5,690, 5,310, 5,280.
Pr: 5,890, 5,830, 4,850, 4,770, 4,490.
Er: 6 well defined bands between 6,750 and 6,410; many fine bands between 5,590 and 5,290; 5 strong bands between 5,240 and 4,840; strong bands at 4,490 and 4,410.

Spessartine. Orange (Mn): 5,050, 4,950, 4,850, [4,620], [4,320], 4,240, 4,120.

Spessartine-almandine. Red-orange, Tanzania: (6,190), [(5,760)], 5,040, [5,040-4,860], (4,630), [4,330-4,320], 4,220, [4,145-4,090], [4,020 ... 4,000.

Willemite. Orange, transp., Franklin, New Jersey: [(5,380-5,330)], [(4,750) faint], [(4,580-4,550) very faint], [4,180 ... 4,000.

Yellow Stones

Apatite. Yellow, Durango, Mexico (Dy): 6,053, 6,025, 5,975, 5,840, 5,780, 5,740, 5,335, 5,295, 5,270, 5,250, 5,210, 5,140, 4,690, 4,425.

Carnotite. Massive, yellow (Fe): 7,000 ... 6,700], [(4,860-4,840)].

Chrysoberyl. Yellow (Fe): 5,050, 4,950, 4,850, [4,480-4,370].

Corundum. Yellow, natural (Fe): [4,710], [4,600], [4,500].

Danburite. Yellow (?), Burma (?): 5,900, 5,860, 5,845, 5,840, 5,830, 5,820, 5,805, 5,780, 5,760, 5,730, 5,710, 5,680, 5,645, 5,615.

Diamond. Greenish-yellow, treated: 7,000 ... 6,800 faint], 5,920, (5,120 very faint), (5,020), 4,980, [(4,980-4,250) weak], [4,250 ... stronger → 4,000.

Fluorite. Yellow, natural: 5,450, 5,150, 4,900, 4,700, 4,520.

Orthoclase. Yellow, Madagascar (Fe): [4,480], [4,200].

Orthoclase. Yellow, Madagascar (Fe): [4,495-4,425], [4,215-4,185].

Scheelite. Synthetic, pale yellow: 6,050, 4 strong bands between 5,960 and 5,750, 2 faint lines c. 5,415, 3 strong lines between 5,360 and 5,260, 5,170, **5,120**, 5,040, faint lines between 4,800 and 4,700.

Scheelite. Synthetic, pale yellow: 7,000 ... 6,600 faint], (4,880), 4,680//. [4,200 ... (4,190) ... 4,170 ... **4,095** ... 4,000.

Serpentine. Greenish-yellow, transl.: [[**4,170-4,100**] ... [4,430-4,410] ... [4,095 ... 4,000.

Sinhalite. Yellow (Fe): 5,270, 4,930, 4,750, [4,630], 4,500, [4,360 ... 4,000.

Sphalerite. (Cd): 6,900, 6,650, **6,510**.

Spodumene. Yellow (Fe): **4,380**, 4,325.

Willemite. Pale yellow, transp., Franklin, New Jersey: 7,000 ... fading → 6,850], [(5,800-5,700) very weak], [5,400], [(5,050-4,850) faint], [4,670 ... [4,370 - dark ... 4,000.

Zircon. Yellow (U): **6,910, 6,625, 6,590, 6,535, 5,895, 5,625, 5,375, 5,150, 4,840, 4,325**.

Zoisite. Yellow: [4,600-4,550].

Green Stones

Actinolite. Green, transp.: 4,310.

Andalusite. Greenish, Brazil: 7,000 ... 6,550)], [(6,550-6,300) weak], (4,530), 4,395.

Andalusite. Greenish (Mn): (5,525), **5,495, 5,175**, (4,550), [4,500 ... 4,000.

Andalusite. Olive-green, transp.: 7,000 ... 6,800], [4,550], 4,360, [4,230 ... 4,000.

Andradite, Demantoid. (Fe, Cr): 7,010//, 6,930, (6,400), (6,210), 4,850, 4,640, [**4,430**], also in dark specimens: [4,470 ... 4,000.

Beryl. Emerald (Cr): **6,835, 6,805**, 6,620, 6,460, **6,370**, (6,060), (5,940), [**6,300-5,800**], 4,774, 4,725.

Beryl. Aquamarine, green (Fe): **5,370**.

Beryl. Emerald, synthetic (Gilson) (Cr): **6,860**, (6,660), [**6,450**], [[6,200] ... 5,950], [4,600 ... [4,280] ... 4,000.

Chrysoberyl. Green (Fe): 5,050, 4,950, 4,850, [**4,480-4,370**].

Clinozoisite. Green (Fe): **4,750, 4,550**, [4,350 ... 4,000.

Corundum. Sapphire, green (Fe): [**4,710**], [**4,600**], [**4,500**].

Corundum. Synthetic sapphire, "peridot" type (Cr): 6,880, 6,780, 6,450.

Diamond. Dark yellow-green, treated: 7,000 ... fading → 5,700], **5,140, 5,050**, [**4,260** ... **4,000**.

Diamond. Blue-green, treated: **7,350, 7,230**, [**7,000**], **6,700**, (4,300), [4,100 ... 4,000.

Diopside. Chrome (Cr, Fe): **6,900//, 5,470**, 5,080, **5,050, 4,930**, 4,560.

Dioptase. (Cu): 5,700, 5,600, [4,650 ... 4,000.

Enstatite. Chrome, San Carlos, Arizona (Cr, Fe): [**6,800**], (6,500), [**5,500**], **5,070**, [4,900 ... 4,000.

Enstatite. Green (Fe): **5,475**, 5,090, **5,060**, 5,025, 4,830, 4,720, 4,590, 4,490, 4,250.

Enstatite. Green (Cr, Fe): as above, but with strong doublet **6,870**.

Epidote. 4,560.

Epidote. (Fe): **4,750, 4,550**, [4,350 ... 4,000.

Fluorite. Synthetic, green: 7,000 ... 6,850], [6,500 ... [**6,400-6,050**]], [4,500-4,270], [**4,270-4,100**], [4,100 ... 4,000.

Fluorite. Green: 6,400, 6,005, **5,850**, 5,700, 5,530, 5,500, 4,520, 4,350.

Fluorite. Green: (6,340), (6,100), (5,820), (4,460), (4,270).

Garnet, Rare-earth. Yttrium-aluminum, Cr-doped green: 7,000 ... c. 7,300], 3 strong lines between 5,950 and 5,900, **5,370, 5,330, 4,870**; many fine lines between previous limits.

Hydrogrossular. (Cr): broad band centered at 6,300.

Idocrase. Green: [4,640].

Idocrase. Transp. yellow-green: 5,295, [4,625], [4,430 ... 4,000.

Idocrase. 5,910, 5,880, **5,845**, 5,820, 5,775, 5,745.

Idocrase. Californite, green (Fe): 5,300, **4,610**.

Idocrase. 5,280, [**4,610** ... 4,000.

Jadeite. Dark green: [**7,000 - 6,000**], [**5,000** ... 4,000.

Jadeite. Dyed green: Broad absorption band in red.

Jadeite. (Cr, Fe): **6,915**, (6,940), **6,550, 6,300**, 4,950, 4,500, **4,375**, 4,330, [**violet** ... 4,000.

Kornerupine. [5,400], [5,030], [4,630], [4,460], [4,300].

Kyanite. (Cr): 7,060, 6,890, 6,710, 6,520.

Olivine. Peridot (Fe): (6,530), (5,530), 5,290, 4,970, 4,950, 4,930, 4,730, 4,530.

Prehnite. Massive, green: [4,300 weak],

Quartz. Aventurine (Cr?): [6,990-6,750].

Quartz. Chalcedony, green-dyed (Cr): 7,050, 6,700, 6,450.

Quartz. Chalcedony, natural green (Cr): [6,400 . . . 4,000.

Quartz. Chrysoprase (Ni): (6,320), (4,440).

Quartz. Chalcedony, natural (Cr): 6,320//.

Quartz. Synthetic, dark green: 7,000 . . . 6,700)], [(4,200 . . . 4,000.

Scheelite. Synthetic, pale green: 7,000 . . . 6,800) faint], 6,000, 5,890, 5,760, [4,920], 4,780, [4,570 . . . 4,560 . . . 4,515], [← fading . . . 4,250 . . . darkening → . . . 4,000.

Serpentine. Green (Cr): 7,000 . . . 6,800], [6,800-6,590], [← fading 4,950 . . . darkening → . . . 4,000.

Serpentine. Williamsite (Cr): 7,000 . . . 6,700) very faint], [(6,400-6,300)], [4,960 faint], (4,600 faint), [(4,600 very faint . . . 4,000.

Sinhalite. Green (Fe): 5,270, 4,930, 4,760, 4,630, 4,520, [4,360 . . . 4,000.

Sphene. 5,900, 5,860, 5,820, 5,800, 5,750, 5,340, 5,300, 5,280.

Spinel. Synthetic, green "tourmaline" type: 4480.

Spinel. Synthetic, yellow-green: 4,900, 4,450, 4,220.

Spodumene. Hiddenite, green (Cr): 6,905, 6,860, 6,690, 6,460, 6,200, 4,375, 4,330.

Tourmaline. Green, Tanzania (Cr): 6,810, [6,450-5,780], [(4,900-4,800)], [4,800 . . . darkening → . . . 4,000.

Tourmaline. Green (Fe): 7,000 . . . 6,400], 4,970, (4,610), (4,150).

Uvarovite. Green, Orford, Quebec (Cr): 7,000 . . . 6,700], [6,220-5,750], [4,900 . . . 4,000.

Variscite. Green: [6,850], 6,500, [← fading 4,600 . . . darkening → . . . 4,000.

Variscite. Green, transl.: 6,920, [6,700-5,750 fading →], [4,400 . . . 4,000.

Vivianite. Dark green:
X-direction; 7,000 . . . 6,300) faint], [(6,300-5,900) very faint],

[(5,200-4,940) faint], [(4,940 . . . 4,795 . . . [4,550] . . . 4,500], [4,170 . . . very faint . . . 4,000.
YZ direction: 7,000 . . . 6,500) faint], [(5,030) very faint], (4,810 faint, [(4,575-4,540) faint], [4,180 . . . faint . . . 4,000.

Zircon. Green (U): 6,910, 6,625, 6,590, 6,535, 5,895, 5,625, 5,375, 5,150, 4,840, 4,325, all bands indistinct on borders.

Zircon. Green, metamict (U): [(6,530)], (5,200).

Zircon. Green, metamict: [6,560-6,360], [5,200] . . . 4,000.

Blue Stones

Apatite. Blue: 6,310, (6,290), 6,220, 5,110, 4,900, [4,640].

Azurite. (Cu): 5,000.

Beryl. Aquamarine, blue (Fe): 5,350, [4,560], [4,270], [4,200 . . . 4,000.

Beryl. Aquamarine, Maxixe Mine, Brazil, blue: 6,970, 6,570, 6,280.

Corundum. Sapphire, blue (Fe): [(5,900-5,600)], [4,710], [4,600], 4,550, [4,500].

Diamond. Dark blue, treated: 7,000 — darkening . . . 6,210 . . . 5,930], [5,040], (4,980), 4,780//, (4,500).

Glass. Cobalt (Co): [6,800-6,400], [6,000-5,800], [5,490-5,270], [4,950].

Iolite. (Fe): [6,500], 5,930, 5,850, 5,350, [4,920], [4,560], [4,370], [4,250 . . . 4,000.

Kyanite. Blue, Tanzania: c. 7,100, 6,910, [6,500-5,400 fading at each end but very dark at 6,000], [4,530 . . . 4,000.

Lazurite. Transl.: [5,600-4,800], [4,400 . . . fading → 4,000.

Odontolite. 7,000 . . . 6,400], [6,400-6,170 a blank band], [6,170 . . . fading → 4,400 darkening → 4,000.

Phenakite. Pale greenish-blue:
O-ray: 7,000 . . . 6,600 faint], [5,800 . . . [5,760-5,600] . . . 5,530].
E-ray: 7,000 . . . 6,700], [6,280 6,100].

Quartz. Synthetic blue (Co): [6,800-6,400], [6,000 - 5,800], [5,490-5,270].

Quartz. Synthetic blue, USSR: [6,560-6,480], [5,940-5,900], [(5,560-5,500) . . . [4,450 . . . 4,000.

Scorodite. Blue, Tsumeb, South West Africa: [5,980-5,350) fading →], [4,415-4,170].

Sillimanite. Blue, Burma: 7,000 . . . 6,200 fading →], [(4,630)], [4,380], [→ fading (4,180 . . . [4,100] . . . 4,000.

Spinel. Natural, blue (Fe): [6,350], [5,850], 5,550, 5,080, 4,780, [4,620-4,520], 4,430, 4,330, [4,300 . . . 4,000.

Spinel. Natural, blue: [5,900-5,595], [5,595-5,500], (5,090 faint), [4,800], [4,640-4,560], [4,320 . . . 4,000.

Spinel. Natural, blue: [6,400-6,230], [5,980 . . . [5,580]], 5,510, 5,495, 4,800, [(4,650-4,550)], [4,300 . . . 4,000.

Spinel. Synthetic, blue, aquamarine (Co): 4,230.

Spinel. Synthetic, blue, aquamarine (Fe): 5,370, 4,560, 4,270.

Spinel. Synthetic, blue (Co): [6,480-6,300], [5,900-5,680], [5,460-5,350], (4,850), [4,780], (4,490).

Tourmaline. Blue (Fe): [4,970], (4,600).

Turquoise. (Cu): [(4,600-4,500)], [[4,320] . . . (4,200) . . . 4,000.

Zircon. Blue (U): 6,590, 6,535.

Zoisite. Blue: [5,950 broad band], [5,280 broad band], [(4,550) broad band].

Zoisite. Blue, transp., Tanzania, trichroic:
Yellow direction: 7,000 . . . 6,500], [(6,000 - 5,750) faint], [5,150 . . . 4,000.
Purple direction: 7,000 . . . 6,800) faint], [(6,000 - 5,750) very faint], [(5,400-5,200) very faint], [(4,620-4,550) very faint].
Blue direction: 7,000 . . . 6,600], [(6,000-5,800) extremely faint], [(5,400) extremely faint].

Violet

Jadeite. Lavender-dyed: 7,000 . . . 6,600 fading →], [5,800-5,580], [4,370-4,360], [4,300 . . . 4,000.

Scapolite. Violet: see pink scapolite under Red Stones.

Scheelite. Synthetic, purple: [6,770], (6,250), [5,995-5,700], 5,430,

5,410, [5,395-5,100], 4,915, 4,850, 4,370, 4,670, [4,330].

Scheelite. Synthetic, lavender (Nd): 7,000 . . . [6,700]], (6,300), (6,010), [6,000 . . . [5,800 open band] . . . 5,740], 5,400, 5,345, 5,305, [5,240], [5,200], [4,820], [(4,370)], [4,370 . . . 4,000.

Spinel. Natural, violet: see blue natural under Blue Stones.

Stichtite. Purple: 7,000 . . . 6,600], (6,180), (5,800), [← fading 5,700 . . . 5,100], [← fading 4,300 . . . [4,050 . . . dark . . . 4,000.

Taafeite. Dark brownish-purple, Ceylon: 7,000 . . . 6,800) faint], (5,900 very faint]. [(5,600-5,550)], [(4,200 . . . 4,000.

Taafeite. Purplish: 5,580, 5,530, 4,780.

Yttrium Aluminate. Synthetic, orthorhombic, pale blue-violet: similar to same, pink, which see under Red Stones.

Essentially Colorless Stones

Calcite. 5,820.

Diamond. "Cape" type: 4,780, [4,650), (4,510), [4,350], (4,230), 4,155.

Diamond. Usual type: 4,155.

Rutile. Synthetic, faint yellowish: (6,500 very faint), [[4,215-4,190] . . . 4,000.

Zircon. Colorless (U): 6,590, 6,535, (5,895), (5,625).

Alexandrite and Alexandrite Type Stones

Chrysoberyl. Alexandrite (Cr): 6,805, 6,775, 6,650, 6,550, 6,490, 6,450, [6,400-5,550], 4,730, 4,680, [4,660 . . . 4,000.

Corundum. Synthetic, alexandrite-type (V): 4,750, 6,870, [(6,100 . . . (5,700) . . . 5,600)]. Emission spectra: 6,942, 6,928.

Spinel. Synthetic alexandrite-type: 7,000 . . . 6,680 fading →], 6,620, [(6,750)], [(5,800)], [(5,400)].

Spinel. Synthetic alexandrite-type (Co): [6,470-6,250], [5,890 - 5,730], [5,450-5,330].

Miscellaneous

Diamond. Gray: 5,480.

Pearl. Natural, "black": 7,000 . . . 6,550],

[6,310-6,350], [[5,800-5,750] ...
[5,510-5,490] ... [5,170-5,130] ...
4,000.
Willemite. Color unstated: 5,830, 5,400,
4,900, 4,425, 4,315, 4,210.

References: B. W. Anderson, *Gem Testing,*
8th ed. (London: Butterworths, 1971).

K. F. Chudoba and E. J. Gübelin, *Edelsteinkundliches Handbuch,* 2d ed. (Bonn: Stollfuss
Verlag, 1966).

G. R. Crowningshield, various contributions
in *Gems and Gemology,* vol. 9 (1957) to present.

R. T. Liddicoat, Jr., various contributions in
Gems and Gemology, vol. 9 (1957) to present.

R. Webster, *Gems,* 2d ed. (London: Butterworths, 1970).

REFRACTIVE INDICES OF
GEMSTONE MATERIALS
ARRANGED ACCORDING TO
INCREASING INDEX

References: For the determination of refractive indices consult any one of the following
standard works: B. W. Anderson, *Gem Testing,*
8th ed. (London, 1971; a translation in German
was published in 1952); J. Bolman, *Handboek
voor Edelsteenkunde* (Amsterdam, 1950); S.
Cavenago-Bignami, *Gemmologia* (Milan, 1965);
R. T. Liddicoat, Jr., *Handbook of Gem
Identification,* 6th ed. (Los Angeles, 1962); C. J.
Parsons, *Practical Gem Knowledge* (San Diego,
1969); K. Schlossmacher, *Edelsteine und Perlen*
(Stuttgart, 1969); G. F. H. Smith and F. C.
Phillips, *Gemstones* (London, 1958); H. L.
Tardy, *Les Pierres Precieuses,* 4th ed. (Paris,
1965); R. Webster, *Gems* (London, 1970).

Singly Refractive Materials

Note: All indices in sodium light.

1.42　(glass: to 1.96, usual range
　　　1.50-1.70)
1.434　Fluorite, (glass)
1.435　Fire opal, (glass)
1.44　Opal, fire opal, (glass)
1.445　Opal, fire opal, (glass)
1.46　Opal, silica glass, (glass)
1.48　Sodalite, obsidian, moldavite, (glass)
1.487　Analcime, obsidian, moldavite,
　　　(glass)
1.49　Tektites, obsidian, moldavite, (glass)
1.496　Hauyne, obsidian, tektites, (glass)
1.50　Obsidian, tektites, glass
1.51　Leucite, obsidian, tektites, glass
1.517　Pollucite, tektites, glass
1.525　Pollucite, tektites, glass

1.53　Tektites, glass
1.539　Amber, glass
1.54　Copal, amber, glass
1.545　Amber, glass
1.595　Ekanite, glass
1.60　Ekanite, glass
1.66　Rhodolite, glass
1.69　Rhodizite, rhodolite, glass
1.70　Arandisite, rhodolite, glass
1.715　Spinel, rhodolite, (glass)
1.724　Spinel (synth.), rhodolite, (glass)
1.729　Spinel (synth.), rhodolite, (glass)
1.73　Pyrope, rhodolite, (glass)
1.738　Periclase (synth.), pyrope, rhodo-
　　　lite, (glass)
1.74　Gahnospinel, pyrope, rhodolite,
　　　(glass)
1.742　Hessonite, pyrope, rhodolite, gahno-
　　　spinel, (glass)
1.748　Hessonite, pyrope, rhodolite, gahno-
　　　spinel, (glass)
1.75　Pyrope-almandine, pyrope, rhodo-
　　　lite, gahnospinel, (glass)
1.76　Almandine, pyrope-almandine,
　　　rhodolite, (glass)
1.77　Almandine, pyrope-almandine,
　　　rhodolite, (glass)
1.78　Spessartine, pleonaste, almandine,
　　　pyrope-almandine, rhodolite, (glass)
1.80　Spessartine, pleonaste, almandine,
　　　rhodolite, (glass)
1.81　Spessartine, almandine, rhodolite,
　　　(glass)
1.83　Yag (yttrium aluminum garnet),
　　　rhodolite, (glass)
1.834　Yag, demantoid, rhodolite, (glass)
1.86　Demantoid, rhodolite, (glass)
1.87　Uvarovite, demantoid, (glass)
1.89　Demantoid, (glass)
1.93　Microlite, (glass)
1.96　(Glass)
2.368　Sphalerite
2.371　Sphalerite
2.41　Strontium titanate
2.418　Diamond
2.85　Cuprite

Uniaxial Gemstones

1.486　Calcite
1.500　Dolomite, calcite
1.515　Magnesite, dolomite, calcite
1.535　Apophyllite, magnesite, dolomite,
　　　calcite
1.537　Apophyllite, magnesite, dolomite,
　　　calcite

1.540 Scapolite, magnesite, dolomite, calcite

1.544 Quartz, scapolite, magnesite, dolomite, calcite

1.553 Quartz, scapolite, magnesite, dolomite, calcite

1.560 Beryl, scapolite, magnesite, dolomite, calcite

1.568 Beryl, scapolite, magnesite, dolomite, calcite

1.570 Beryl, magnesite, dolomite, calcite

1.577 Beryl, magnesite, dolomite, calcite

1.593 Melinophane, beryl, magnesite, dolomite, calcite

1.594 Melinophane, beryl, magnesite, dolomite, calcite

1.597 Rhodochrosite, melinophane, magnesite, dolomite, calcite

1.612 Rhodochrosite, melinophane, magnesite, dolomite, calcite

1.616 Tourmaline, rhodochrosite, magnesite, dolomite, calcite

1.63 Apatite, tourmaline, rhodochrosite, magnesite, dolomite, calcite

1.633 Siderite, apatite, tourmaline, rhodochrosite, magnesite, dolomite, calcite

1.64 Siderite, apatite, tourmaline, rhodochrosite, magnesite, dolomite, calcite

1.644 Dioptase, siderite, rhodochrosite, magnesite, dolomite, calcite

1.654 Phenakite, dioptase, siderite, rhodochrosite, magnesite, dolomite, calcite

1.658 Phenakite, dioptase, siderite, rhodochrosite, magnesite, dolomite, calcite

1.670 Phenakite, dioptase, siderite, rhodochrosite, magnesite, dolomite

1.679 Dioptase, siderite, rhodochrosite, magnesite, dolomite

1.691 Willemite, dioptase, siderite, rhodochrosite, magnesite

1.705 Idocrase, willemite, dioptase, siderite, rhodochrosite, magnesite

1.709 Idocrase, willemite, dioptase, siderite, rhodochrosite, magnesite

1.71 Idocrase, willemite, siderite, rhodochrosite, magnesite

1.718 Taaffeite, willemite, siderite, rhodochrosite, magnesite

1.72 Taaffeite, willemite, siderite, rhodochrosite

1.722 Taaffeite, siderite, rhodochrosite

1.755 Benitoite, siderite, rhodochrosite

1.760 Corundum, benitoite, siderite, rhodochrosite

1.779 Corundum, benitoite, siderite, rhodochrosite

1.78 Zircon (low), benitoite, siderite, rhodochrosite

1.787 Painite, zircon (low), benitoite, siderite, rhodochrosite

1.804 Painite, zircon (low), benitoite, siderite, rhodochrosite

1.81 Painite, zircon (low), siderite, rhodochrosite

1.816 Painite, siderite, rhodochrosite

1.820 Siderite, rhodochrosite

1.873 Siderite

1.918 Scheelite

1.925 Zircon, scheelite

1.937 Zircon, scheelite

1.984 Zircon

2.001 Cassiterite

2.013 Zincite, cassiterite

2.029 Zincite, cassiterite

2.101 Cassiterite

2.114 Phosgenite

2.120 Mimetite, phosgenite

2.135 Mimetite, phosgenite

2.140 Phosgenite

2.304-2.402 Wulfenite

2.493-2.554 Anatase

2.61-2.90 Rutile (nat. and synth.)

2.65-2.69 Silicon carbide

2.79-3.09 Proustite

2.905-3.256 Cinnabar

Biaxial Gemstones

1.480 Natrolite

1.486 Inderite, natrolite

1.487 Kurnakovite, inderite, natrolite

1.490 Whewellite, kurnakovite, inderite, natrolite

1.493 Whewellite, kurnakovite, inderite, natrolite

1.504 Petalite, whewellite, kurnakovite, inderite

1.515 Magnesite, petalite, whewellite, kurnakovite, inderite

1.516 Magnesite, petalite, whewellite, kurnakovite, inderite

1.517 Magnesite, whewellite, kurnakovite, inderite

1.52 Orthoclase (moonstone), magnesite, whewellite, kurnakovite

1.522 Orthoclase (moonstone, yellow (Fe)), microcline, magnesite, whewellite, kurnakovite

1.527 Orthoclase (moonstone, yellow

(Fe)), microcline, magnesite, whewellite, kurnakovite

1.53   Orthoclase (moonstone), microcline, magnesite, whewellite

1.537 Iolite, orthoclase (moonstone), magnesite, whewellite

1.54   Albite (peristerite), iolite, orthoclase (moonstone), magnesite, whewellite

1.542 Oligoclase, iolite, whewellite

1.549 Oligoclase, iolite, whewellite

1.55   Iolite, whewellite

1.553 Beryllonite, hambergite, whewellite

1.560 Labradorite, beryllonite, hambergite, whewellite

1.562 Labradorite, beryllonite, hambergite, whewellite

1.564 Bytownite, labradorite, hambergite, whewellite

1.565 Bytownite, labradorite (+ yellow), hambergite, whewellite

1.570 Bastite, bytownite, labradorite (+ yellow), hambergite, whewellite

1.571 Anhydrite, bastite, bytownite, labradorite (yellow), hambergite, whewellite

1.573 Anhydrite, bastite, bytownite, labradorite (yellow), hambergite, whewellite

1.574 Augelite, anorthite, anhydrite, bastite, bytownite, hambergite, whewellite

1.576 Augelite, anorthite, anhydrite, bastite, bytownite, hambergite, whewellite

1.58   Augelite, anorthite, anhydrite, bastite, hambergite, whewellite

1.586 Colemanite, augelite, anorthite, anhydrite, hambergite, whewellite

1.588 Colemanite, augelite, anorthite, anhydrite, hambergite, whewellite

1.589 Colemanite, anorthite, anhydrite, hambergite, whewellite

1.59   Chondrodite, colemanite, anhydrite, hambergite, whewellite

1.591 Herderite, chondrodite, colemanite, anhydrite, hambergite, whewellite

1.595 Phosphophyllite, herderite, chondrodite, colemanite, anhydrite, hambergite, whewellite

1.60   Tremolite, phosphophyllite, herderite, chondrodite, colemanite, anhydrite, hambergite, whewellite

1.603 Brazilianite, tremolite, phosphophyllite, herderite, chondrodite, colemanite, anhydrite, hambergite, whewellite

1.61   Topaz (colorless, blue), brazilianite, tremolite, phosphophyllite, herderite, chondrodite, colemanite, anhydrite, hambergite, whewellite

1.612 Amblygonite, topaz (colorless, blue), brazilianite, tremolite, phosphophyllite, herderite, chondrodite, colemanite, anhydrite, hambergite, whewellite

1.614 Amblygonite, topaz (colorless, blue), brazilianite, tremolite, phosphophyllite, herderite, chondrodite, colemanite, anhydrite, hambergite, whewellite

1.615 Lazulite, amblygonite, topaz (colorless, blue), brazilianite, tremolite, phosphophyllite, herderite, chondrodite, hambergite whewellite

1.616 Lazulite, amblygonite, topaz (colorless, blue), brazilianite, tremolite, phosphophyllite, herderite, chondrodite, hambergite, whewellite

1.62   Lazulite, amblygonite, topaz (colorless, blue), brazilianite, tremolite, herderite, chondrodite, hambergite, whewellite

1.621 Lazulite, amblygonite, brazilianite, tremolite, herderite, chondrodite, hambergite, whewellite

1.623 Lazulite, amblygonite, brazilianite, tremolite, chondrodite, hambergite, whewellite

1.625 Datolite, celestite, lazulite, amblygonite, tremolite, chondrodite, hambergite, whewellite

1.628 Pargasite, datolite, celestite, lazulite, amblygonite, tremolite, chondrodite, whewellite

1.630 Topaz (yellow, brown, pink), danburite, pargasite, datolite, celestite, lazulite, amblygonite, tremolite, whewellite

1.631 Topaz (y, b, p), danburite, pargasite, datolite, celestite, lazulite, amblygonite, tremolite, chondrodite, whewellite

1.634 Andalusite, topaz (y, b, p), danburite, pargasite, datolite, celestite, lazulite, amblygonite, tremolite, chondrodite, whewellite

1.635 Andalusite, topaz (y, br, p), danburite, pargasite, datolite, celestite, lazulite, amblygonite, tremolite, chondrodite, whewellite

1.636 Andalusite, barite, topaz (y, br, p), danburite, pargasite, datolite, lazulite, amblygonite, tremolite, chondrodite, whewellite

1.638 Andalusite, barite, topaz (y, br, p), pargasite, datolite, lazulite, amblygonite, tremolite, chondrodite, whewellite

1.64 Andalusite, barite, pargasite, datolite, lazulite, tremolite, chondrodite, whewellite

1.642 Andalusite, barite, pargasite, datolite, lazulite, tremolite, whewellite

1.645 Andalusite, barite, pargasite, datolite, lazulite, whewellite

1.648 Andalusite, barite, pargasite, datolite, whewellite

1.65 Ludlamite, pargasite, datolite, whewellite

1.651 Ludlamite, pargasite, datolite

1.652 Euclase, ludlamite, datolite

1.654 Peridot, euclase, ludlamite, datolite

1.658 Fibrolite, peridot, euclase, datolite

1.660 Spodumene, fibrolite, peridot, euclase, ludlamite, datolite

1.662 Durangite, spodumene, fibrolite, peridot, euclase, ludlamite, datolite

1.663 Enstatite, durangite, spodumene, fibrolite, peridot, euclase, ludlamite, datolite

1.665 Kornerupine, enstatite, durangite, spodumene, fibrolite, peridot, euclase, ludlamite, datolite

1.67 Diopside, hypersthene, sinhalite, bronzite, kornerupine, enstatite, durangite, spodumene, fibrolite, peridot, euclase, ludlamite, datolite

1.672 Diopside, hypersthene, sinhalite, bronzite, kornerupine, enstatite, durangite, spodumene, fibrolite, peridot, euclase, ludlamite, datolite

1.673 Diopside, hypersthene, sinhalite, bronzite, kornerupine, enstatite, durangite, spodumene, fibrolite, peridot, ludlamite, datolite

1.675 Axinite, legrandite, diopside, hypersthene, sinhalite, bronzite, kornerupine, durangite, spodumene, fibrolite, peridot, ludlamite, datolite

1.678 Axinite, legrandite, diopside, hypersthene, sinhalite, bronzite, kornerupine, durangite, spodumene, fibrolite, peridot, ludlamite, datolite

1.680 Axinite, legrandite, diopside, hypersthene, sinhalite, bronzite, kornerupine, durangite, peridot, ludlamite, datolite

1.684 Axinite, legrandite, diopside, hypersthene, sinhalite, bronzite, durangite, peridot, ludlamite, datolite

1.685 Axinite, legrandite, diopside, hypersthene, sinhalite, durangite, peridot, ludlamite, datolite

1.689 Legrandite, diopside, hypersthene, sinhalite, durangite, peridot, ludlamite, datolite

1.69 Legrandite, diopside, hypersthene, sinhalite, durangite, ludlamite, datolite

1.691 Zoisite, legrandite, diopside, hypersthene, sinhalite, durangite, datolite

1.70 Zoisite, legrandite, diopside, hypersthene, sinhalite, durangite, datolite

1.702 Legrandite, diopside, hypersthene, sinhalite, durangite

1.71 Legrandite, hypersthene, sinhalite, durangite

1.712 Legrandite, hypersthene, durangite

1.715 Kyanite, legrandite, hypersthene

1.72 Rhodonite, clinozoisite, kyanite, legrandite, hypersthene

1.724 Hodgkinsonite, rhodonite, clinozoisite, kyanite, legrandite, hypersthene

1.73 Azurite, hodgkinsonite, rhodonite, kyanite, legrandite

1.732 Azurite, hodgkinsonite, rhodonite, kyanite, legrandite

1.735 Azurite, hodgkinsonite, rhodonite, legrandite

1.736 Epidote, azurite, hodgkinsonite, rhodonite

1.739 Staurolite, epidote, azurite, hodgkinsonite, rhodonite

1.74 Scorodite, staurolite, epidote, azurite, hodgkinsonite, rhodonite

1.745 Chrysoberyl, scorodite, staurolite, epidote, azurite, hodgkinsonite, rhodonite

1.746 Chrysoberyl, scorodite, staurolite, epidote, azurite, hodgkinsonite, rhodonite

1.747 Chrysoberyl, scorodite, staurolite, spidote, azurite, rhodonite

1.75 Pyroxmangite, chrysoberyl, scorodite, staurolite, epidote, azurite

1.76 Pyroxmangite, chrysoberyl, scorodite, staurolite, epidote, azurite

1.762 Scorodite, staurolite, epidote, azurite

1.770 Scorodite, epidote, azurite

1.804 Cerussite, scorodite, azurite
1.81 Cerussite, scorodite, azurite
1.84 Cerussite, azurite
1.877 Anglesite, cerussite
1.88 Sphene, anglesite, cerussite
1.894 Sphene, anglesite, cerussite
1.958 Sulfur, sphene, cerussite
2.05 Sulfur, sphene, cerussite
2.06 Euxenite, sulfur, cerussite
2.078 Euxenite, sulfur, cerussite
2.21 Samarskite, lithium niobate, euxenite, sulfur
2.30 Lithium niobate, euxenite, sulfur
2.31 Crocoite, euxenite, sulfur
2.39 Stibiotantalite, crocoite, euxenite, sulfur
2.245 Stibiotantalite, crocoite, euxenite, sulfur
2.26 Stibiotantalite, crocoite, euxenite, sulfur
2.46 Stibiotantalite, crocoite
2.538 Realgar, crocoite
2.583 Brookite, realgar, crocoite
2.66 Brookite, realgar, crocoite
2.704 Brookite, realgar
2.705 Brookite

Massive Gemstones

These are considered separately because in most of the species the fine-fibrous or fine-grain structure affords only a diffuse and weak reading upon the refractometer, which is commonly worsened by the tendency of lapidaries to polish cabochons with less attention to surface perfection than is usually the case in faceted gems. Curvature of surfaces also permits only a small tangential area of the gem to influence the light rays as they pass through the refractometer and the method of "spot reading," explained in modern gem identification books, must be employed. Some coarse-grained massive species may, however, provide double readings, notably calcite and other rhomobohedral carbonates; the possible readings for these are therefore spread over a considerable number of entries.

1.48 Natrolite
1.50 Mesolite, lapis lazuli, calcite
1.51 Ulexite, cancrinite, calcite
1.52 Gypsum, alabaster, witherite, calcite
1.53 Thomsonite, meerschaum, chalcedony, witherite, calcite
1.54 Stichtite, chalcedony, jasper, quartz, talc, steatite, bone, ivory, vegetable ivory, tortoise shell, lepidolite. witherite, calcite
1.55 Pyrophyllite, agalmatolite, quartz, steatite, witherite, calcite
1.56 Variscite, serpentine (bowenite), deer horn, black coral, pyrophyllite, agalmatolite, steatite, witherite, calcite
1.57 Pearl, coral, pseudophite, black coral, serpentine (williamsite), ophicalcite, odontolite, pyrophyllite, agalmatolite, steatite, witherite, calcite
1.58 Verdite, odontolite, pyrophyllite, agalmatolite, steatite, witherite, calcite
1.59 Wardite, howlite, odontolite, pyrophyllite, agalmatolite, steatite, witherite, calcite
1.60 Rhodochrosite, wardite, odontolite, pyrophyllite, agalmatolite, witherite, calcite
1.61 Prehnite, pectolite, rhodochrosite, odontolite, agalmatolite, witherite, calcite
1.62 Wollastonite, nephrite, prehnite, rhodochrosite, odontolite, agalmatolite, witherite, calcite
1.63 Lazulite, wollastonite, turquoise, nephrite, odontolite, prehnite, rhodochrosite, witherite, calcite
1.64 Barite, jet, friedelite, prehnite, rhodochrosite, witherite, calcite
1.65 Datolite, jet, friedelite, rhodochrosite, witherite, calcite
1.66 Jadeite, jet, rhodochrosite, witherite, calcite
1.67 Fibrolite, jadeite, jet, rhodochrosite, witherite
1.68 Dumortierite, diopside (violane), jet, rhodochrosite, witherite
1.69 Diopside (violane), rhodochrosite, witherite
1.70 Idocrase (californite), saussurite, zoisite (thulite), chlorastrolite, smaragdite, rhodochrosite, witherite
1.71 Willemite, idocrase (californite), saussurite, zoisite (thulite), rhodochrosite
1.72 Grossular, rhodochrosite
1.73 Rhodonite, rhodochrosite
1.75 Epidote, rhodochrosite
1.77 Leucosphenite, malachite, rhodochrosite
1.78 Azurite, shattuckite, malachite, rhodochrosite
1.79 Malachite, rhodochrosite

1.80 Malachite, rhodochrosite
1.81 Rhodochrosite (to 1.82)
1.97 Bayldonite
2.00 Cassiterite ("wood tin")
2.12 Mimetite

Plastics

1.30- Teflon (polytetrafluorethylene)
1.40
1.43 Polytrifluorochloroethylene
1.46 Cellulose acetate butyrate, cellulose acetate
1.48 Methyl methacrylate, acetal, cellulose acetate butyrate, cellulose acetate
1.49 Polypropylene, methyl methacrylate (Lucite, Plexiglas, Perspex), cellulose acetate butyrate, cellulose acetate
1.50 Celluloid (also slightly lower and higher), polyethylene, methyl methacrylates, cellulose acetate
1.53 Nylon, polyethylene
1.54 Polyvinylchloride, vinylchloride acetate, polyethylene
1.55 Casein, bakelite
1.56 Polystyrene-acrylonitrile, casein, bakelite
1.57 Polystyrene-acrylonitrile, bakelite
1.58 Epoxy, bakelite
1.59 Polystyrene, bakelite
1.60 Vulcanite, polycarbonates, polystyrene, bakelite
1.61 Vulcanite, bakelite
1.63 Vulcanite, bakelite

BIREFRINGENCES OF UNIAXIAL AND BIAXIAL GEMSTONES WITH OPTIC SIGNS

Birefringence values are often useful in quickly narrowing possible choices during identification work. Careful rotation of the gemstone upon the refractometer will usually provide the maximum spread between indices which is then equal to the birefringence.

0.002 Apophyllite (±U)
0.003 Apatite (−U)
0.004 Taaffeite (−U), apatite (−U)
0.005 Idocrase (yellow, −U), orthoclase (yellow, Fe, −B), beryl (aquamarine, yellow, some pinks, −U), beryl (emerald, −U)
0.006 Danburite (−B), beryl (aquamarine, yellow, some pinks, −U), beryl (emerald, −U)
0.007 Oligoclase (±B), danburite (−B), beryl (emerald, −U)
0.008 Topaz (yellow, −B), orthoclase (moonstone, −B), labradorite (yellow, −B), iolite (−B), microcline (−B), chrysoberyl (+B), beryl (colorless, some pinks, −U), corundum (−U), zoisite (+B)
0.009 Iolite (−B), chrysoberyl (+B), beryl (colorless, some pinks, −U), zoisite (blue, +B), bytownite (−B), andalusite (−B), beryllonite (−B), scapolite (pink, −U), quartz (+U), celestite (+B)
0.010 Iolite (−B), chrysoberyl (+B), bytownite (−B), andalusite (−B), celestite (+B), axinite (−B), rhodonite (+B), labradorite (+B), pyroxmangite (+B), enstatite (+B), topaz (colorless, blue, +B), clinozoisite (+B)
0.011 Albite (peristerite, +B), euxenite (+B), iolite (−B), andalusite (−B)
0.012 Kyanite (−B), hypersthene (−B), staurolite (+B), petalite (+B), barite (+B), kornerupine (−B), iolite (−B)
0.013 Kyanite (−B), hypersthene (−B), kornerupine (−B), natrolite +B), rhodonite (±B)
0.014 Kyanite (−B), hypersthene (−B), bronzite (+B), augelite (+B), tourmaline (−U)
0.015 Kyanite (−B), hypersthene (−B), spodumene (+B), mimetite (−U), tourmaline (−U), anorthite (−B), phenakite (+U)
0.016 Scheelite (+U), zincite (−U), mimetite (−U), tourmaline (−U), phenakite (+U)
0.017 Anglesite (+B), scheelite (+U), mimetite (−U), tourmaline (−U)
0.018 Willemite (+U), mimetite (−U), tourmaline (−U)
0.019 Melinophane (−U), willemite (+U), tourmaline (−U)
0.020 Scorodite (+B), tremolite (−B), brazilianite (+B), scapolite (yellow, −U), euclase (+B), fibrolite (+B), willemite (+U), tourmaline (−U)
0.021 Scorodite (±B), tremolite (−B), phosphophyllite (+B), willemite (+U), tourmaline (−U)
0.022 Scorodite (±B), tremolite (−B),

hodgkinsonite (−B), willemite (+U), tourmaline (−U)
0.023 Scorodite (±B), tremolite (−B), pargasite (−B), willemite (+U)
0.024 Scorodite (±B), tremolite (−B), willemite (+U)
0.025 Scorodite (±B), tremolite (−B), chondrodite (+B), willemite (+U)
0.026 Scorodite (±B), tremolite (−B), chondrodite (+B), amblygonite (+B), phosgenite (+U), willemite (+U)
0.027 Scorodite (±B), tremolite (−B), chondrodite (+B), inderite (−B), willemite (+U)
0.028 Scorodite (±B), tremolite (−B), chondrodite (+B), herderite (−B), colemanite (+B), willemite (+U)
0.029 Scorodite (±B), tremolite (−B), chondrodite (+B), painite (−U)
0.030 Diopside (+B), scorodite (±B), tremolite (−B), chondrodite (+B)
0.034 Epidote (−B), chondrodite (+B)
0.036 Kurnakovite (−B), lazulite (−B), peridot (+B), chondrodite (+B)
0.038 Sinhalite (−B)
0.040 Ludlamite (+B)
0.043 Anhydrite (+B), silicon carbide (+U)
0.044-0.045 Datolite (−B)
0.047 Benitoite (+U)
0.050 Durangite (−B)
0.053 Dioptase (+U)
0.059 Zircon (+U)
0.060 Legrandite (+B)
0.061 Anatase (−U)
0.070 Stibiotantalite (+B)
0.072 Hambergite (+B)
0.090 Lithium niobate
0.098 Wulfenite (−U), cassiterite (+U)
0.110 Azurite (+B)
0.120 Sphene (+B)
0.122 Brookite (+B), sphene (+B)
0.135 Sphene (+B)
0.160 Whewellite (+B)
0.166 Realgar (−B)
0.172 Calcite (−U)
0.179 Dolomite (−U)
0.202 Magnesite (−U)
0.220 Rhodochrosite (−U)
0.240 Siderite (−U)
0.274 Cerussite (−B)
0.287 Rutile (+U)
0.290 Sulfur (+B)
0.300 Proustite (−U)
0.350 Crocoite (+B)
0.351 Cinnabar (+U)

REFRACTIVE INDICES OF MINERALS ARRANGED ACCORDING TO INCREASING INDEX

Singly Refractive Minerals

1.326-1.328 Villiaumite
1.339 Cryolithionite, hieratite
1.370 Cryptohalite
1.403 Termierite
1.406 Opal
1.427 Ralstonite, opal
1.434 Yttrocerite, fluorite, opal
1.44 Hisingerite, opal
1.454 Sulfohalite, hisingerite, opal
1.456 Alum, hisingerite, opal
1.457 Yttrofluorite, hisingerite, opal
1.459 Tschermigite, hisingerite, opal
1.46 Hisingerite, opal
1.461 Melanophlogite, hisingerite
1.462 Lechatelierite, hisingerite
1.47 Neotocite, allophane, nosean, hisingerite
1.479 Analcime, allophane, nosean, hisingerite
1.48 Obsidian, moldavite, faujasite, analcime, allophane, nosean, hisingerite
1.483 Sodalite, obsidian, moldavite, analcime, allophane, nosean, hisingerite
1.485 Evansite, obsidian, moldavite, analcime, allophane, nosean, hisingerite
1.486 Cristobalite, obsidian, moldavite, analcime, allophane, nosean, hisingerite
1.487 Hackmanite, obsidian, moldavite, analcime, allophane, nosean, hisingerite
1.49 Sylvite, tektites, obsidian, moldavite, allophane, nosean. hisingerite
1.495 Tektites, obsidian, nosean, hisingerite
1.496 Hauyne, bolivarite, tektites, obsidian, hisingerite
1.50 Lazurite, stevensite, hauyne, tektites, obsidian, hisingerite
1.505 Vashegyite, hauyne, tektites, obsidian, hisingerite
1.508 Tychite, hauyne, tektites, obsidian, hisingerite
1.509 Leucite, hauyne, tektites, obsidian, hisingerite
1.51 Cimolite, hauyne, tektites, obsidian, hisingerite
1.514 Northupite, tektites, hisingerite
1.517 Planerite, meerschaum, tektites, hisingerite

1.518 Pollucite, tektites, hisingerite
1.525 Pollucite, tektites, hisingerite
1.53 Kehoite, tektites, hisingerite
1.533 Langbeinite, hisingerite
1.535 Succinite, hisingerite
1.54 Neotocite, cornuite, succinite, hisingerite
1.541 Ajkaite, succinite, hisingerite
1.542 Telegdite, halloysite, succinite, hisingerite
1.544 Halite, halloysite, succinite, hisingerite
1.555 Halloysite, hisingerite
1.558 Serpentine, hisingerite
1.565 Traversoite, hisingerite
1.569 Collophane, zaratite, hisingerite
1.572 Nitrobarite, manganlangbeinite, collophane, zaratite, hisingerite
1.58 Koninckite, collophane, zaratite, hisingerite
1.584 Schroetterite, koninckite, collophane, zaratite, hisingerite
1.59 Garnierite, kochite, koninckite, collophane, zaratite, hisingerite
1.596 Zunyite, ekanite, koninckite, collophane, zaratite, hisingerite
1.60 Stibiconite, borickite, zunyite, ekanite, koninckite, collophane, zaratite, hisingerite
1.602 Voltaite, stibiconite, borickite, zunyite, koninckite, collophane, zaratite, hisingerite
1.605 Grodnolite, stibiconite, borickite, koninckite, collophane, zaratite, hisingerite
1.61 Diadochite, allanite, stibiconite, borickite, koninckite, collophane, zaratite, hisingerite
1.63 Allanite, stibiconite, borickite, koninckite, collophane, hisingerite
1.635 Pitticite, allanite, stibiconite, borickite, koninckite, hisingerite
1.638 Hydrothorite, allanite, stibiconite, borickite, koninckite, hisingerite
1.639 Sal ammoniac, allanite, stibiconite, borickite, koninckite, hisingerite
1.64 Picite, griphite, homilite, allanite, stibiconite, borickite, koninckite, hisingerite
1.65 Egueiite, tritomite, greenalite, griphite, allanite, stibiconite, borickite, koninckite, hisingerite
1.653 Lovchorrite, tritomite, greenalite, griphite, allanite, stibiconite, borickite, hisingerite
1.66 Tritomite, greenalite, griphite,

allanite, stibiconite, borickite, hisingerite
1.67 Hibschite, tritomite, greenalite, allanite, stibiconite, hisingerite
1.674 Tritomite, greenalite, allanite, stibiconite
1.675 Plazolite, tritomite, allanite, stibiconite
1.69 Rhodizite, orangite, tritomite, allanite, stibiconite
1.70 Polycrase, tritomite, allanite, stibiconite
1.702 Arandisite, tritomite, allanite, stibiconite
1.705 Pyrope, arandisite, tritomite, allanite, stibiconite
1.707 Berzeliite, pyrope, arandisite, tritomite, allanite, stibiconite
1.710 Uranothorite, berzeliite, pyrope, arandisite, tritomite, allanite, stibiconite
1.715 Spinel, berzeliite, pyrope, arandisite, tritomite, allanite, stibiconite
1.716 Delvauxite, berzeliite, pyrope, arandisite, tritomite, allanite, stibiconite
1.718 Spinel, berzeliite, pyrope, arandisite, tritomite, allanite, stibiconite
1.720 Spinel, berzeliite, pyrope, arandisite, tritomite, allanite, stibiconite
1.725 Rowlandite, spinel, berzeliite, pyrope, arandisite, tritomite, stibiconite
1.735 Grossular, spinel, berzeliite, pyrope, arandisite, tritomite, stibiconite
1.736 Periclase, grossular, spinel, berzeliite, pyrope, arandisite, tritomite, stibiconite
1.739 Helvite, grossular, spinel, berzeliite, pyrope, arandisite, tritomite, stibiconite
1.74 Pilbarite, caryocerite, grossular, spinel, berzeliite, pyrope, arandisite, tritomite, stibiconite
1.742 Grossular, spinel, berzeliite, pyrope, arandisite, tritomite, stibiconite
1.748 Grossular, spinel, berzeliite, arandisite, tritomite, stibiconite
1.75 Grossular, spinel, berzeliite, arandisite, tritomite, stibiconite
1.754 Danalite, grossular, berzeliite, arandisite, tritomite, stibiconite
1.755 Arsenolite, grossular, berzeliite, arandisite, tritomite, stibiconite
1.757 Grossular, berzeliite, arandisite, tritomite, stibiconite

1.758 Yttrialite, grossular, berzeliite, aran-disite, stibiconite
1.760 Rhodolite, grossular, berzeliite, arandisite, stibiconite
1.763 Grossular, berzeliite, arandisite, stibiconite
1.766 Almandine, berzeliite, arandisite, stibiconite
1.77 Melanocerite, mackintoshite, pleo-naste, almandine, berzeliite, aran-disite, stibiconite
1.779 Almandine, berzeliite, arandisite, stibiconite
1.780 Gadolinite, almandine, arandisite, stibiconite
1.782- Gahnite, almandine, arandisite,
1.79 stibiconite
1.80 Hercynite, spessartine, gahnite, almandine, arandisite, stibiconite
1.805 Hercynite, spessartine, gahnite, almandine, arandisite, stibiconite
1.812 Beckelite, hercynite, spessartine, almandine, arandisite, stibiconite
1.815 Hercynite, spessartine, almandine, arandisite, stibiconite
1.818 Naegite, hercynite, almandine, aran-disite, stibiconite
1.82 Hercynite, almandine, arandisite, stibiconite
1.826 Malacon, hercynite, almandine, stibiconite
1.83 Romeite, hercynite, almandine, stibiconite
1.838 Lime, uvarovite, romeite, stibiconite
1.84 Uvarovite, romeite, stibiconite
1.86 Bindheimite, uvarovite, romeite, stibiconite
1.865 Andradite, romeite, stibiconite
1.87 Andradite, chalcolamprite, romeite, stibiconite
1.88 Chevkinite, andradite, stibiconite
1.89 Ellsworthite, chevkinite, andradite, stibiconite
1.895 Chevkinite, andradite, stibiconite
1.90 Chevkinite, andradite, stibiconite
1.92 Betafite, samiresite, chevkinite, andradite, stibiconite
1.923 Galaxite, samiresite, chevkinite, andradite, stibiconite
1.925 Microlite, samiresite, chevkinite, andradite, stibiconite
1.94 Microlite, samiresite, chevkinite, andradite, stibiconite
1.96 Neotantalite, pyrochlore, microlite, samiresite, chevkinite, stibiconite

1.965 Microlite, samiresite, chevkinite, stibiconite
1.97 Djalmaite, microlite, stibiconite
1.98 Hatchettolite, schorlomite, micro-lite, stibiconite
1.99 Microlite, stibiconite
2.02 Microlite
2.05 Percylite
2.07 Mosesite
2.071 Cerargyrite
2.087 Senarmontite
2.13 Ampangabeite
2.142 Priorite
2.15 Yttrotantalite
2.19 Manganosite
2.20 Miersite
2.22 Polymignyte
2.24 Euxenite
2.248 Polycrase
2.26 Eschynite
2.35 Marshite
2.37 Bunsenite, sphalerite
2.42 Diamond, sillenite, sphalerite
2.47 Sphalerite
2.49 Eglestonite
2.69 Hauerite
2.85 Cuprite

Uniaxial Minerals

Note: To the left of virgules (//) = (+); to right = (−).

1.34 //Soda niter
1.46 Tincalconite, chrysocolla // thauma-site, hanksite, gmelinite, soda niter
1.47 Laubanite, gmelinite, hatchettite, tincalconite, chrysocolla // beidellite, thaumasite, loeweite, ettringite, hanksite, gmelinite, soda niter
1.48 Chabazite, laubanite, hatchettite, chrysocolla // beidellite, thaumasite, loeweite, ettringite, cristobalite, hanksite, chabazite, gmelinite, soda niter
1.49 Aphthitalite, laubanite, hatchettite, chrysocolla // calcite, beidellite, nocerite, thaumasite, levyne, loe-weite, ettringite, analcime, cristob-alite, gmelinite, soda niter
1.50 Liskeardite, aphthitalite, douglasite, hatchettite, chrysocolla // trudellite, pholidolite, calcite, dolomite, beidel-lite, hydrotalcite, nocerite, can-crinite, thaumasite, levyne, gmelinite, soda niter

1.51 Ozocerite, leucite, liskeardite, chrysocolla // magnesite, brugnatellite, mellite, slavikite, tachyhydrite, trudellite, pholidolite, calcite, dolomite, beidellite, hydrotalcite, nocerite, cancrinite, thaumasite, soda niter

1.52 Natrodavyne, microsommite, koenenite, davyne, chrysocolla // ankerite, magnesite, fluoborite, stichtite, brugnatellite, mellite, dipyre, slavikite, tachyhydrite, trudellite, pholidolite, calcite, dolomite, beidellite, cancrinite, soda niter

1.53 Apophyllite, fibroferrite, natrodavyne, microsommite, koenenite, chrysocolla // ankerite, magnesite, fluoborite, stichtite, brugnatellite, mellite, apophyllite, dipyre, chalcedony, milarite, kaliophilite, nepheline, slavikite, trudellite, pholidolite, dolomite, calcite, soda niter

1.54 Quartz, ashcroftine, coquimbite, apophyllite, fibroferrite, koenenite, chrysocolla // jefferisite, gyrolite, ankerite, magnesite, fluoborite, stichtite, brugnatellite, marialite, mellite, apophyllite, dipyre, chalcedony, nepheline, trudellite, pholidolite, dolomite, calcite, soda niter

1.55 Vaterite, quartz, ashcroftine, coquimbite, fibroferrite, koenenite, chrysocolla // chalcophyllite, chloraluminite, parsettensite, mizzonite, wernerite, jefferisite, gyrolite, ankerite, magnesite, fluoborite, dipyre, trudellite, pholidolite, dolomite, calcite, soda niter

1.56 Chlorite, brucite, ferrinatrite, julienite, vaterite, ashcroftine, coquimbite, fibroferrite, chrysocolla // cordylite, chalcophyllite, chloraluminite, meionite, connarite, uranospinite, parsettensite, mizzonite, beryl, wernerite, zeophyllite, jefferisite, ankerite, magnesite, fluoborite, dipyre, trudellite, dolomite, calcite, soda niter

1.57 Ekmanite, penninite, alunite, pinnoite, chlorite, brucite, ferrinatrite, julienite, vaterite, ashcroftine, coquimbite, fibroferrite, chrysocolla // cordylite, chalcophyllite, chloraluminite, meionite, metavoltine, connarite, parsettensite, calcioferrite, mizzonite, beryl, wernerite, ankerite, magnesite, zeophyllite, fluoborite,

dipyre, dolomite, calcite, soda niter

1.58 Alumian, cacoxenite, coeruleolactite, ekmanite, penninite, alunite, pinnoite, chlorite, brucite, ferrinatrite, julienite, vaterite, fibroferrite // szaibelyite, troegerite, cordylite, chalcophyllite, chloraluminite, meionite, torbernite, metavoltine, connarite, penninite, parsettensite, calcioferrite, mizzonite, ankerite, beryl, magnesite, dolomite, calcite, soda niter

1.59 Manganbrucite, wardite, rinneite, alumian, cacoxenite, coeruleolactite, alunite, brucite, ferrinatrite, julienite, vaterite // meliphane, dennisonite, dehrnite, szaibelyite, troegerite, cordylite, chalcophyllite, chloraluminite, meionite, torbernite, metavoltine, connarite, uranospinite, mizzonite, beryl, ankerite, magnesite, dolomite, calcite, soda niter

1.60 Sarcolite, amesite, manganbrucite, wardite, alumian, cacoxenite, ferrinatrite, julienite, vaterite // siderite, rhodochrosite, stilpnomelane, bementite, meliphane, dahllite, dennisonite, dehrnite, szaibelyite, troegerite, cordylite, chalcophyllite, chloraluminite, meionite, mizzonite, beryl, ankerite, magnesite, dolomite, calcite

1.61 Pseudowollastonite, narsarsukite, eudialyte, sarcolite, amesite, cacoxenite, ferrinatrite, julienite, vaterite // dravite, bazzite, lewistonite, fluocerite, siderite, rhodochrosite, stilpnomelane, bementite, meliphane, dahllite, dehrnite, chalcophyllite, szaibelyite, troegerite, cordylite, meionite, ankerite, magnesite, dolomite, calcite

1.62 Metatorbernite, goyazite, churchite, pseudowavellite, pseudowollastonite, narsarsukite, cacoxenite, ferrinatrite, julienite, vaterite // smithsonite, friedelite, tourmaline, zeunerite, uvite, mitscherlichite, dravite, podolite, francolite, bazzite, merrillite, lewistonite, eucolite, gillespite, siderite, rhodochrosite, stilpnomelane, bementite, dahllite, dehrnite, szaibelyite, troegerite, cordylite, chalcophyllite, ankerite, magnesite, dolomite, calcite

1.63 Akermanite, svanbergite, metatorbernite, goyazite, churchite, pseudowavellite, pseudowollastonite, narsarsukite, cacoxenite, ferrinatrite, julienite, vaterite // smithsonite, friedelite, tourmaline, zeunerite, uvite, mitscherlichite, dravite, fluorapatite, voelckerite, melilite, podolite, francolite, bazzite, siderite, rhodochrosite, stilpnomelane, bementite, dahllite, dehrnite, szaibelyite, troegerite, cordylite, ankerite, magnesite, dolomite, calcite

1.64 Dioptase, akermanite, deltaite, svanbergite, goyazite, churchite, pseudowavellite, pseudowollastonite, cacoxenite, julienite, vaterite // spangolite, smithsonite, schallerite, pyrosmalite, friedelite, daphnite, gehlenite, tourmaline, apatite, zeunerite, uvite, wilkeite, strontianapatite, mistcherlichite, dravite, stilpnomelane, rhodochrosite, siderite, bementite, dahllite, dehrnite, szaibelyite, cordylite, ankerite, magnesite, dolomite, calcite

1.65 Rhabdophane, plumbogummite, phenakite, dioptase, churchite, pseudowollastonite, cacoxenite, julienite, vaterite // freirinite, smithsonite, spangolite, schallerite, pyrosmalite, ellestadite, friedelite, daphnite, gehlenite, tourmaline, apatite, wilkeite, siderite, rhodochrosite, stilpnomelane, bementite, szaibelyite, cordylite, ankerite, magnesite, dolomite, calcite

1.66 Cahnite, rhabdophane, plumbogummite, phenakite, dioptase // freirinite, smithsonite, spangolite, schallerite, sincosite, pyrosmalite, hardystonite, ellestadite, friedelite, gehlenite, tourmaline, apatite, wilkeite, siderite, rhodochrosite, stilpnomelane, cordylite, ankerite, magnesite, dolomite, calcite

1.67 Hinsdalite, rabdophane, plumbogummite, phenakite, dioptase // freirinite, smithsonite, spangolite, ferroakermanite, svabite, schallerite, sincosite, pyrosmalite, hardystonite, gehlenite, tourmaline, apatite, siderite, rhodochrosite, stilpnomelane, cordylite, ankerite, magnesite, dolomite, calcite

1.68 Florencite, parisite, hinsdalite, rabdophane, plumbogummite dioptase // pyrochroite, freirinite, smithsonite,

spangolite, svabite, ferroakermanite, schallerite, sincosite, pyrosmalite, gehlenite, tourmaline, stilpnomelane, rhodochrosite, siderite, cordylite, ankerite, magnesite, dolomite, calcite

1.69 Willemite, florencite, parisite, hinsdalite, rabdophane, dioptase // pyrochroite, freirinite, smithsonite, spangolite, ferroakermanite, svabite, schallerite, gehlenite, tourmaline, stilpnomelane, rhodochrosite, siderite, cordylite, ankerite, magnesite, dolomite, calcite

1.70 Willemite, parisite, rabdophane, dioptase // pyrochroite, ferroschallerite, idocrase, freirinite, smithsonite, svabite, schallerite, tourmaline, stilpnomelane, rhodochrosite, siderite, cordylite, ankerite, magnesite, dolomite, calcite

1.71 Willemite, parisite, dioptase // hematolite, pyrochroite, ferroschallerite, idocrase, freirinite, smithsonite, svabite, cordylite, ankerite, magnesite, stilpnomelane, rhodochrosite, siderite, dolomite, calcite

1.72 Connellite, xenotime, bromellite, bastnaesite, idocrase, willemite, parisite // jarosite, ferritungstite, hematolite, melanocerite, pyrochrosite, ferroschallerite, idocrase, smithsonite, freirinite, cordylite, ankerite, magnesite, siderite, rhodochrosite, stilpnomelane, dolomite, calcite

1.73 Mixite, connellite, xenotime, bromellite, bastnaesite, willemite, parisite // carphosiderite, jarosite, borgstromite, ferritungstite, hematolite, melanocerite, idocrase, smithsonite, freirinite, siderite, rhodochrosite, stilpnomelane, cordylite, ankerite, magnesite, dolomite

1.74 Mixite, connellite, xenotime, bastnaesite, parisite // carphosiderite, jarosite, borgstromite, ferritungstite, idocrase, freirinite, smithsonite, cordylite, ankerite, siderite, rhodochrosite, stilpnomelane, dolomite

1.75 Abukamalite, buttgenbachite, mixite, connellite, xenotime, bastnaesite, parisite // natrojarosite, carphosiderite, jarosite, borgstromite, ferritungstite, ammoniojarosite, freirinite, smithsonite, cordylite, ankerite, stilpnomelane, rhodochrosite, siderite, dolomite

1.76 Benitoite, buttgenbachite, mixite, xenotime, bastnaesite, parisite // natrojarosite, carphosiderite, jarosite, borgstromite, molybdophyllite, ferritungstite, ammoniojarosite, smithsonite, corundum, cordylite, stilpnomelane, rhodochrosite, siderite, dolomite

1.77 Benitoite, buttgenbachite, mixite, xenotime, bastnaesite // natrojarosite, carphosiderite, jarosite, borgstromite, molybdophyllite, ferritungstite, ammoniojarosite, smithsonite, britholite, swedenborgite, corundum, dolomite, rhodochrosite, ankerite

1.78 Conichalcite, benitoite, mixite, xenotime, bastnaesite // plumbojarosite, natrojarosite, carphosiderite, jarosite, borgstromite, molybdophyllite, ferritungstite, ammoniojarosite, smithsonite, britholite, rhodochrosite, siderite

1.79 Arseniopleite, conichalcite, benitoite, mixite, xenotime, bastmaesite // argentojarosite, plumbojarosite, arseniosiderite, natrojarosite, carphosiderite, jarosite, borgstromite, molybdophyllite, ferritungstite, ammoniojarosite, smithsonite, siderite, rhodochrosite

1.80 Thorite, arseniopleite, conichalcite, benitoite, mixite, xenotime, bastnaesite // argentojarosite, plumbojarosite, arseniosiderite, hoegbomite, natrojarosite, carphosiderite, jarosite, borgstromite, molybdophyllite, ferritungstite, ammoniojarosite, rhodochrosite, siderite, smithsonite

1.81 Thorite, mixite, xenotime, bastnaesite // argentojarosite, plumbojarosite, arseniosiderite, hoegbomite, natrojarosite, carphosiderite, jarosite, borgstromite, molybdophyllite, ammoniojarosite, smithsonite, rhodochrosite, siderite

1.82 Xenotime, bastnaesite // bismite, argentojarosite, plumbojarosite, arseniosiderite, hoegbomite, natrojarosite, carphosiderite, jarosite, borgstromite, molybdophyllite, ammoniojarosite, smithsonite, siderite, rhodochrosite

1.83 Xenotime // bismite, argentojarosite, plumbojarosite, arseniosiderite, hoeg-

bomite, natrojarosite, ammoniojarosite, smithsonite, siderite, rhodochrosite

1.85 // Bismite, argentojarosite, plumbojarosite, dussertite, arseniosiderite, hoegbomite, siderite

1.87 // Bismite, argentojarosite, plumbojarosite, dussertite, arseniosiderite, siderite

1.88 // Bismite, argentojarosite, plumbojarosite, arseniosiderite, siderite

1.90 Trippkeite // bismite, argentosiderite, arseniosiderite

1.91 Nasonite, ganomalite, trippkeite // bismite, argentojarosite

1.92 Scheelite, nasonite, ganomalite, trippkeite // bismite

1.93 Zircon, scheelite, nasonite, ganomalite, trippkeite // bismite

1.94 Zircon, scheelite, nasonite, ganomalite, trippkeite // bismutosphaerite, hydrocerussite, bismite

1.95 Hedyphane, zircon, nasonite, trippkeite // giekielite, bismutosphaerite, hydrocerussite, bismite

1.96 Hedyphane, zircon, nasonite, trippkeite // giekielite, bismutosphaerite, hydrocerussite, bismite

1.97 Powellite, calomel, zircon, nasonite, trippkeite // giekielite, bismutosphaerite, cumengeite, hydrocerussite, bismite

1.98 Powellite, calomel, zircon, trippkeite // giekielite, bismutosphaerite, cumengeite, hydrocerussite, bismite

1.99 Cassiterite, calomel, zircon, trippkeite // beyerite, giekielite, bismutosphaerite, cumengeite, armangite, hydrocerussite, bismite

2.00 Calomel, zircon, trippkeite // beyerite, giekielite, bismutopshaerite, pseudoboleite, cumengeite, armangite, hydrocerussite, bismite

2.01 Zincite, cassiterite, calomel, zircon, trippkeite // matlockite, beyerite, giekielite, bismutosphaerite, pseudoboleite, cumengeite, hedyphane, armangite, hydrocerussite, bismite

2.02 Cassiterite, zincite, calomel, zircon, trippkeite // matlockite, beyerite, giekielite, bismutosphaerite, pseudoboleite, cumengeite, hedyphane, hydrocerussite

2.03 Voltzite, zincite, cassiterite, calomel, trippkeite // boleite, matlockite, beyerite, giekielite, bismutosphaerite, pseudoboleite, cumengeite, hedyphane, hydrocerussite

2.04 Cassiterite, calomel, trippkeite // boleite, pyromorphite, matlockite, beyerite, giekielite, bismutosphaerite, hydrocerussite

2.05 Cassiterite, calomel, trippkeite // barysilite, boleite, matlockite, pyromorphite, beyerite, giekielite, bismutosphaerite, hydrocerussite

2.06 Simpsonite, cassiterite, calomel, trippkeite // barysilite, matlockite, beyerite, giekielite, bismutosphaerite, hydrocerussite

2.07 Cassiterite, calomel, trippkeite // barysilite, matlockite, beyerite, giekielite, bismutosphaerite, hydrocerussite

2.09 Cassiterite, calomel, trippkeite // matlockite, beyerite, giekielite, bismutosphaerite, hydrocerussite

2.10 Cassiterite, calomel, trippkeite // hydrohetaerolite, hetaerolite, matlockite, beyerite, giekielite, bismutosphaerite

2.11 Phosgenite, calomel // hydrohetaerolite, hetaerolite, matlockite, beyerite, giekielite, bismutosphaerite

2.12 Phosgenite, calomel // hydrohetaerolite, hetaerolite, matlockite, mimetite, beyerite, giekielite, bismutosphaerite

2.13 Penfieldite, phosgenite, calomel // mimetite, hydrohetaerolite, hetaerolite, matlockite, beyerite, giekielite, bismutosphaerite

2.14 Penfieldite, phosgenite, calomel // bellite, mimetite, hydrohetaerolite, hetaerolite, matlockite, giekielite

2.15 Penfieldite, calomel // hausmannite, bismoclite, bellite, hydrohetaerolite, hetareolite, matlockite, giekielite

2.16 Penfieldite, calomel // hausmannite, bellite, hydrohetaerolite, hetaerolite, giekielite

2.18 Penfieldite, calomel // hausmannite, stolzite, hydrohetaerolite, hetaerolite, giekielite

2.19 Penfieldite, calomel // hausmannite, stolzite, hydrohetaerolite, hetaerolite, giekielite

2.20 Penfieldite, calomel // hausmannite, endlichite, stolzite, hydrohetaerolite, hetaerolite, giekielite

2.21 Iodyrite, penfieldite, calomel // hausmannite, endlichite, stolzite, hydrohetaerolite, hetaerolite, giekielite

2.22 Iodyrite, calomel // hausmannite, endlichite, stolzite, hydrohetaerolite, hetaerolite, giekielite

2.25 Calomel // hausmannite, schwartzembergite, ecdemite, stolzite, endlichite, hydrohetaerolite, hetaerolite, giekielite

2.27 Tapiolite, calomel // hausmannite, schwarzembergite, ecdemite, stolzite, hydrohetaerolite, hetaerolite, giekielite

2.28 Tapiolite, calomel // hausmannite, schwarzembergite, ecdemite, finnemanite, hetaerolite, giekielite

2.29 Calomel, tapiolite // hausmannite, wulfenite, schwarzembergite, ecdemite, finnemanite, hetaerolite, giekielite

2.30 Tapiolite, calomel // hausmannite, vanadinite, wulfenite, schwarzembergite, ecdemite, finnemanite, hetaerolite, giekielite

2.31 Tapiolite, calomel // hausmannite, langbanite, vanadinite, wulfenite, schwarzembergite, ecdemite, hetaerolite, giekielite

2.32 Tapiolite, calomel // hausmannite, langbanite, vanadinite, wulfenite, schwarzembergite, ecdemite, hetaerolite

2.33 Tapiolite, calomel // hausmannite, langbanite, vanadinite, lorettoite, wulfenite, schawarzembergite, hetaerolite

2.35 Tapiolite, calomel // hausmannite, langbanite, vanadinite, lorettoite, wulfenite, schwarzembergite

2.36 Wurtzite, tapiolite, calomel // hausmannite, langbanite, wulfenite, schwarzembergite

2.38 Wurtzite, tapiolite, calomel // hausmannite, wulfenite

2.40 Wurtzite, tapiolite, calomel // hausmannite, wulfenite

2.42 Wurtzite, tapiolite, calomel // hausmannite

2.46 Wurtzite, calomel // hausmannite

2.49 Wurtzite, calomel // anatase

2.51 Wurtzite, greenockite, calomel // anatase

2.53 Wurtzite, greenockite, calomel // anatase, litharge

2.56 Wurtzite, calomel // anatase, litharge

2.61 Wurtzite, rutile, calomel // litharge

2.65 Wurtzite, rutile, calomel // litharge
2.66 Rutile, calomel // litharge
2.67 // Litharge
2.7 Rutile, moissanite //
2.79 Rutile // proustite
2.88 Rutile // proustite, pyrargyrite
2.9 Rutile, cinnabar // proustite, pyrargyrite
2.94 Cinnabar // proustite, pyrargyrite, hematite
3.0 Selenium, cinnabar // proustite, pyrargyrite, hematite
3.08 Selenium, cinnabar // proustite, pyrargyrite, hematite
3.09 Selenium, cinnabar // proustite, hematite
3.22 Selenium, cinnabar // hematite
3.26 Selenium, cinnabar //
4.04 Selenium

Biaxial Minerals

Note: To the left of virgules (//) = (+); to the right = (−).

1.32 // Avogadrite
1.34 // Avogadrite, sassolite
1.39 // Mirabilite, sassolite
1.40 // Mirabilite, sassolite
1.41 Pachnolite // thomsenolite, natron, trona, sassolite
1.42 Pachnolite // thomsenolite, natron, trona, sassolite
1.43 // Kalinite, hexahydrite, epsomite, mendozite, natron, trona, sassolite
1.44 Erionite, stercorite // lecontite, wattevillite, kalinite, hexahydrite, epsomite, mendozite, natron, trona, sassolite
1.45 Taylorite, erionite, stercorite // kernite, goslarite, borax, lecontite, kalinite, hexahydrite, epsomite, gearksutite, wattevillite, sassolite, mendozite, trona
1.46 Thenardite, aluminite, picromerite, stercorite, taylorite // trona, creedite, kernite, goslarite, paraluminite, borax, mendozite, sassolite, epsomite, wattevillite, gearksutite, hexahydrite, kalinite
1.47 Fluellite, ammonioborite, boothite, pisanite, melanterite, natrolite, arduinite, alunogen, mordenite, thenardite, carnallite, tridymite, boussingaultite, lansfordite, alumi-nite, stercorite // nitrochalcite, bianchite, trona, morenosite, booth-

ite, mordenite, ptilolite, kernite, goslarite, paraluminite, borax
1.48 Ashtonite, dietrichite, misenite, boothite, pisanite, ferrierite, melanterite, natrolite, arduinite, alunogen, mordenite, thenardite, carnallite, tridymite, boussingaultite, lansfordite, picromerite, fluellite, ammonioborite, tamarugite, cyanotrichite, heulandite // nitrochalcite, bianchite, trona, stellerite, stilbite, morenosite, leonite, halotrichite, bloedite, bieberite, apjohnite, boothite, pickeringite, goslarite, clinoptilite, creedite, mordenite, ptilolite, kernite, saponite
1.49 Fluellite, ammonioborite, tamarugite, cyanotrichite, heulandite, chabazite, ashtonite, dietrichite, misenite, melanterite, natrolite, thenardite, carnallite, lansfordite, larderellite, bischofite, ulexite, chrysotile, dachiardite, kreuzbergite, arcanite // montmorillonite, inyoite, kainite, antigorite, didymolite, nitrochalcite, phillipsite, bianchite, trona, stellerite, stilbite, morenosite, vanthoffite, leonite, halotrichite, bloedite, bieberite, boothite, creedite, kernite, beidellite, artinite, uranospathite, saponite
1.50 Prosopite, uranothallite, wellsite, phillipsite, dachiardite, struvite, kreuzebergite, arcanite, fluellite, ammonioborite, tamarugite, cyano-trichite, heulandite, carnallite, lansfordite, petalite, pirssonite, mesolite, harmotome, ulexite, chrysotile // syngenite, montmorillo-nite, epistilbite, chalcanthite, inyoite, kainite, antigorite, didymolite, nitrochalcite, phillipsite, bianchite, trona, stellerite, stilbite, pholidolite, beidellite, meyerhofferite, artinite, laumontite, unranospathite, saponite
1.51 Petalite, pirssonite, larderellite, ussingite, bischofite, mesolite, harmotome, ulexite, chrysotile, prosopite, uranothallite, kreuzber-gite, fluellite, ammonioborite, heulandite, copiapite, paternoite, kaliborite, bobierrite, newberryite, faroelite, thomsonite, flagstaffite, brewsterite // scolecite, ilesite, syngenite, montmorillonite, okenite, carnegieite, leonhardite, epistilbite,

chalcanthite, inyoite, kainite, antigorite, didymolite, trona, stilbite, pholidolite, beidellite, meyerhofferite, artinite, laumontite, uranospathite, saponite

1.52 Newberryite, faroelite, thomsonite, flagstaffite, brewsterite, petalite, pirssonite, larderellite, ussingite, bischofite, mesolite, ulexite, chrysotile, uranothallite, ammonioborite, hydroboracite, kieserite, botryogen, hydromagnesite, kaliborite, chalcoalumite, spadaite, probertite, hatchettite, mascagnite, gypsum, bobierrite, felsobanyite, // chalcanthite, minasragrite, saponite, anorthoclase, orthoclase, microcline, sepiolite, scolecite, ilesite, syngenite, montmorillonite, carnegieite, okenite, laumontite, leonhardite, uransopathite, inyoite, trona, strontianite, romerite, antigorite, phlogopite, copiapite, pholidolite, luenebergite, beidellite, glauberite, meyerhofferite, artinite

1.53 Probertite, hatchettite, mascagnite, gypsum, bobierrite, felsobanyite, thomsonite, pirssonite, larderellite, ussingite, bischofite, chrysotile, uranothallite, ammonioborite, gordonite, wavellite, hydroboracite, fibroferrite, kieserite, botryogen, albite, copiapite, paternoite, hydromagnesite, kaliborite, chalcolumite, spadaite // gismondite, sulfoborite, cordierite, hyalophane, siderotil, okenite, chalcanthite, searlesite, hyalophane, minasragrite, saponite, montomorillonite, anorthoclase, orthoclase, microcline, sepiolite, trona, aragonite, witherite, strontianite, romerite, antigorite, phlogopite, lepidolite, truscottite, copiapite, mooreite, vermiculite, pholidolite, luenebergite, beidellite, glauberite, meyerhofferite, artinite

1.54 Paternoite, hydromagnesite, kaliborite, spadaite, probertite, hatchettite, bobierrite, thomsonite, pirssonite, larderellite, ussingite, chrysotile, uranothallite, ammonioborite, louderbackite, voglite, brushite, epididymite, gordonite, wavellite, hydroboracite, fibroferrite, kieserite, botryogen, albite, copiapite // brushite, mooreite, vermiculite, pholido-

lite, oligoclase, luenebergite, gismondite, sulfoborite, cordierite, hyalophane, siderotil, beidellite, okenite, glauberite, meyerhofferite, chalcanthite, artinite, searlesite, minasragrite, trona, aragonite, witherite, strontianite, kroehnkite, romerite, antigorite, jefferisite, phlogopite, polylithionite, lepidolite, edingtonite, montmorillonite, truscottite, centrallasite, copiapite, talc

1.55 Copiapite, kieserite, botryogen, paternoite, hydromagnesite, spadaite, kaliborite, hatchettite, pirsonnite, larderellite, ussingite, chrysotile, quenstedtite, metavauxite, metavariscite, louderbackite, paravauxite, andesine, vauxite, voglite, eudidymite, brushite, epididymite, gordonite, wavellite, hydroboracite, fibroferrite // jezekite, jefferisite, beryllonite, polylithionite, miloschite, lacroixite, edingtonite, montmorillonite, brushite, mooreite, vermiculite, hyalophane, pholidolite, oligoclase, luenebergite, gismondite, cordierite, meyerhofferite, chalcanthite, artinite, biotite, alurgite, pyrophanite, muscovite, kroehnkite, zinnwaldite, stilpnomelane, autunite, romerite, beidellite, antigorite, variscite, morinite, polyhalite, phlogopite, lepidolite, truscottite, centrallasite, copiapite, aragonite, witherite, strontianite, talc

1.56 Paravauxite, vauxite, bombiccite, andesine, voglite, gordonite, wavellite, hydroboracite, fibroferrite, copiapite, kieserite, botryogen, hatchettite, pirssonite, larderellite, chrysotile, szmikite, hambergite, hoernesite, tengerite, norbergite, humite, elpidite, dickite, metavauxite, labradorite, anemousite, metavariscite, louderbackite // antigorite, kaolin, variscite, anauxite, nacrite, cordierite, morinite, jezekite, jefferisite, vermiculite, polyhalite, phlogopite, beryllonite, polylithionite, miloschite, lacroixite, lepidolite, copiapite, meyerhofferite, artinite, montmorillonite, pyrophyllite, nontronite, mooreite, uranospinite, glauconite, muscovite, canbyite, kroehnkite, zinnwaldite, sphaerite, stilpnomelane, autunite, bassettite, romerite, beidellite, aragonite, witherite, strontianite, paragonite, biotite, alurgite, talc

1.57 Labradorite, metavariscite, louderbackite, paravauxite, bombiccite, gordonite, hydroboracite, fibroferrite, copiapite, kieserite, botryogen, hatchettite, pirssonite, szmikite, hambergite, kornelite, augelite, anhydrite, hoernesite, clinochlore, wagnerite, tengerite, isoclasite, norbergite, quenstedtite, gibbsite, humite, elpidite, dickite, metavauxite // eastonite, sphaerite, stilpnomelane, autunite, bassettite, englishite, hannayite, romerite, beidellite, bytownite, antigorite, kaolinite, variscite, anauxite, nacrite, vermiculite, polyhalite, phlogopite, lacroixite, lepidolite, copiapite, manganophyllite, cordierite, astrolite, montmorillonite, pyrophyllite, nontronite, mooreite, variscite, hopeite, uranospinite, celsian, glauconite, muscovite, anorthite, canbyite, kroehnkite, zinnwaldite, aragonite, witherite, strontianite, protolithionite, ganophyllite, paragonite, biotite, leucophane, johannite, alurgite, priceite, talc

1.58 Norbergite, quenstedtite, gibbsite, humite, metavauxite, metavariscite, louderbackite, bombiccite, gordonite, fibroferrite, copiapite, kieserite, botryogen, hatchettite, pirssonite, hambergite, celsian, anthophyllite, bavenite, ´zonotlite, chlorite, kornelite, sheridanite, cookeite, augelite, penninite, anhydrite, leuchtenbergite, hoernesite, clinochlore, wagnerite, tengerite, isoclasite, szmikite, johannite, vivianite // urananospinite, celsian, glauconite, muscovite, anorthite, canbyite, kroehnkite, zinnwaldite, penninite, eastonite, sphaerite, stilpnomelane, autunite, bassettite, bytownite, hannayite, variscite, romerite, vermiculite, phlogopite, amblygonite, clinochlore, astrolite, alurgite, torbernite, priceite, catapleiite, pharmacolite, talc, montmorillonite, pyrophyllite, nontronite, mooreite, variscite, hopeite, aragonite, witherite, strontianite, serpierite, protolithionite, ganophyllite, paragonite, howlite,

millisite, manganophyllite, cordierite, leucophane, johannite

1.59 Cookeite, augelite, anhydrite, leuchtenbergite, hoernesite, tengerite, norbergite, quenstedtite, gibbsite, bombiccite, gordonite, copiapite, hatchettite, fremontite, haidingerite, szmikite, cuspidine, colemanite, catapleiite, hambergite, bultfonteinite, custerite, celsian, prochlorite, wardite, anthophyllite, bavenite, zonotlite, chlorite, kornelite, sheridanite, cyanotrichite, vivianite // sphaerite, kroehnkite, anorthite, muscovite, glauconite, celsian, uranospinite, variscite, mooreite, nontronite, pyrophyllite, montmorillonite, talc, pharmacolite, catapleiite, hopeite, priceite, torbernite, alurgite, phlogopite, astrolite, clinochlore, stilpnomelane, amblygonite, johannite, leucophane, biotite, cordierite, manganophyllite, millisite, howlite, paragonite, spencerite, ganophyllite, bertrandite, chondrodite, protolithionite, herderite, meliphanite, phosphophyllite, glauconite, troegerite, roscoelite, serpierite, strontianite, witherite, aragonite

1.60 Copiapite, hoernesite, anhydrite, cookeite, kornelite, zonotlite, wardite, prochlorite, custerite, bultfonteinite, hambergite, catapleiite, colemanite, cuspidine, szmikite, johannite, amesite, vivianite, cebollite, haidingerite, fremontite, pectolite, scawtite, hydrophilite, weinschenkite, anapaite, amblygonite, monetite, cyanotrichite, chondrodite // kroehnkite, muscovite, variscite, pyrophyllite, catapleiite, nontronite, astrolite, stilpnomelane, amblygonite, johannite, leucophane, biotite, cordierite, manganophyllite, millisite, howlite, paragonite, phlogopite, spencerite, foshagite, ganophyllite, bertrandite, chondrodite, protolithionite, montebrasite, herderite, meliphanite, tremolite, phosphophyllite, glauconite, sanbornite, lehiite, ephesite, margarite, protolithionite, manganophyllite, lausenite, mariposite, troegerite, roscoelite, bementite, grandidierite, serpierite, strontianite, witherite, aragonite

1.61 Anhydrite, cookeite, kornelite, prochlorite, hambergite, catapleiite, colemanite, szmikite, johannite, amesite, vivianite, cebollite, haidingerite, fremontite, pectolite, hydrophilite, parahopeite, sklodowskite, scawtite, corundophilite, weinschenkite, topaz, aphrosiderite, anapaite, stokesite, tremolite, amblygonite, monetite, zippeite, hemimorphite, prehnite, edenite, turquois, chondrodite // muscovite, variscite, montebrasite, nontronite, stilpnomelane, johannite, howlite, paragonite, biotite, spencerite, foshagite, bertrandite, chondrodite, uranocircite, protolithionite, carpholite, hillebrandite, herderite, meliphanite, tremolite, phosphophyllite, glauconite, richterite, sanbornite, lehiite, delessite, dehrnite, ephesite, margarite, mariposite, lausenite, troegerite, roscoelite, celadonite, actinolite, bementite, manganophyllite, grandidierite, inesite, serpierite, sklodowskite, epistolite, iddingsite, liroconite, strontianite, witherite, aragonite, bementite

1.62 Kornelite, hambergite, catapleiite, szmikite, johannite, vivianite, cebollite, haidingerite, pectolite, scawtite, weinschenkite, topaz, aphrosiderite, anapaite, stokesite, tremolite, amblygonite, monetite, zippeite, hemimorphite, cyanotrichite, chondrodite, ripidolite, prehnite, edenite, turquois, churchite, afwillite, pargasite, arakawaite, celestite, scorodite, destinezite, parahopeite, guildite, humite, tilleyite, sklodowskite, clinohumite // muscovite, biotite, stilpnomelane, chondrodite, montebrasite, herderite, tremolite, phosphophyllite, glauconite, richterite, sanbornite, lehiite, delessite, uranocircite, dehrnite, ephesite, margarite, protolithionite, carpholite, lausenite, mariposite, troegerite, roscoelite, celadonite, actinolite, nontronite, anthophyllite, podolite, hastingsite, pargasite, bementite, glaucophane, wollastonite, lazulite, manganophyllite, grandidierite, inesite, gedrite, chlorite, roscherite, serpierite, sklodowskite, friedelite, epistolite, iddingsite, liroconite, cabrerite, annabergite, siderophyllite, strontianite, witherite, aragonite

1.63 Kornelite, hambergite, catapleiite, szmikite, vivianite, cebollite, haidingerite, pectolite, weinschenkite, topaz, anapaite, amblygonite, monetite, hemimorphite, cyanotrichite, chondrodite, prehnite, edenite, turquoise, churchite, afwillite, pargasite, zippeite, arakawaite, celestite, scorodite, destinezite, parahopeite, chlorite, guildite, humite, picropharmacolite, ripidolite, cummingtonite, tilleyite, sklodowskite, schizolite, clinohumite, anthophyllite, collinsite, ransomite // biotite, tremolite, richterite, lehiite, glauconite, ephesite, margarite, protolithionite, carpholite, mariposite, actinolite, bementite, glaucophane, danburite, andalusite, siderophyllite, stilpnomelane, lausenite, troegerite, roscoelite, celadonite, nontronite, anthophyllite, podolite, hastingsite, pargasite, wollastonite, lazulite, manganophyllite, arfvedsonite, holmquistite, annite, hornblende, durangite, grandidierite, inesite, gedrite, chlorite, roscherite, serpierite, sklodowskite, friedelite, epistolite, iddingsite, liroconite, datolite, cabrerite, eosphorite, annabergite, stewartite, strontianite, witherite, aragonite

1.64 Kornelite, vivianite, haidingerite, pectolite, weinschenkite, topaz, anapaite, hemimorphite, cyanotrichite, chondrodite, prehnite, turquoise, churchite, pargasite, arakawaite, scorodite, parahopeite, chlorite, edenite, guildite, humite, picropharmacolite, ripidolite, cummingtonite, tilleyite, sklodowskite, schizolite, clinohumite, barite, anthophyllite, sarcolite, mullite, collinsite, juanite, ransomite, rankinite, fairfieldite, rinkolite, loseyite, forsterite, messelite, veszelyite // richterite, lausenite, roscoelite, celadonite, actinolite, biotite, glauconite, margarite, nontronite, anthophyllite, hastingsite, pargasite, bementite, glaucophane, wollastonite, danburite, andalusite, lazulite, manganophyllite, sklodowskite, grandidierite, inesite, gedrite, chlorite, roscherite, arfvedsonite, serpierite, eckermannite, holmquistite, boehmite, daphnite, tremolite, seamanite, siderophyllite, childrenite, stilpnomelane, friedelite, crocidolite, epistolite, iddingsite, bityite, annite, liroconite, datolite, cabrerite, eosphorite, annathophyllite, anabergite, tilasite, stewartite, uranophane, symplesite, durangite, spurrite, strontianite, witherite, aragonite

1.65 Weinschenkite, anapaite, cyanotrichite, prehnite, turquoise, churchite, arakawaite, edenite, chondrodite, guildite, humite, cummingtonite, tilleyite, sklodowskite, schizolite, clinohumite, barite, pargasite, anthophyllite, sarcolite, mullite, collinsite, juanite, ransomite, rankinite, fairfieldite, rinkolite, loseyite, mosandrite, forsterite, enstatite, messelite, triplite, clinoenstatite, dickinsonite, spodumene, euclase, natrochalcite, reddingite, hiortdahlite, veszelyite, jadeite, barrandite, plancheite, leucosphenite, olivine, ludlamite // lausenite, biotite, margarite, nontronite, anthophyllite, hastingsite, wollastonite, andalusite, chlorite, serpierite, sklodowskite, eckermannite, holmquistite, boehmite, monticellite, hornblende, bementite, daphnite, tremolite, friedelite, crocidolite, epistolite, iddingsite, aphrosiderite, bityite, liroconite, datolite, cabrerite, hureaulite, eosphorite, wentzelite, anthophyllite, palaite, baldaufite, pargasite, seybertite, annabergite, brandisite, tilasite, xanthophyllite, lazulite, arfvedsonite, stewartite, seamanite, cummingtonite, thuringite, uranophane, symplesite, siderophyllite, strigovite, durangite, spurrite, childrenite, roscoelite, stilpnomelane, annite, strontianite, witherite, aragonite

1.66 Cyanotrichite, arakawaite, guildite, humite, sklodowskite, schizolite, sarcolite, collinsite, prehnite, ransomite, clinohumite, chondrodite, loseyite, mosandrite, cummingtonite, fairfieldite, forsterite, enstatite, messelite, triplite, clinoenstatite, uranochalcite, dickinsonite, spodumene, anthophyllite, natrochalcite, reddingite, hiortdahlite,

veszelyite, jadeite, barrandite, plancheite, sillimanite, leucosphenite, boracite, serandite, johnstrupite, lithiophilite, olivine, viridine, diopside, spodiosite, ludlamite, koettigite // nontronite, anthophyllite, hastingsite, chlorite, sklodowskite, monticellite, hornblende, tremolite, crocidolite, iddingsite, liroconite, datolite, tilasite, cabrerite, thuringite, ternovskite, cummingtonite, clinohedrite, soretite, gruenerite, uranophane, prochlorite, andalusite, schroeckingerite, malachite, arfvedsonite, stilpnomelane, epistolite, hureaulite, eosphorite, wentzelite, anthophyllite, palaite, baldaufite, pargasite, seybertite, annabergite, brandisite, xanthophyllite, zinkosite, childrenite, dumontite, stewartite, lazulite, seamanite, symplesite, siderophyllite, strigovite, durangite, triplite, spurrite, bustamite, biotite, roscoelite, cenosite, annite, tarbuttite, strontianite, witherite, aragonite

1.67 Guildite, prehnite, ransomite, loseyite, cummingtonite, forsterite, humite, messelite, chondrodite, euclase, natrochalcite, reddingite, spodumene, veszelyite, jadeite, triplite, enstatite, barrandite, plancheite, sillimanite, leucosphenite, forsterite, dickinsonite, boracite, serandite, johnstrupite, lithiophilite, rinkite, olivine, viridine, hinsdalite, diopside, chlorophoenicite, fillowite, clinohumite, natrophilite, spodiosite, lawsonite, diopside-jadeite, anthophyllite, ludlamite, akrochordite, hypersthene, koettigite, schefferite // hastingsite, monticellite, hornblende, epistolite, liroconite, datolite, cabrerite, annabergite, tilasite, eosphorite, ternovskite, cummingtonite, thuringite, clinohedrite, uranophane, prochlorite, andalusite, biotite, soretite, stewartite, lazulite, seamanite, symplesite, zinkosite, siderophyllite, strigovite, durangite, triplite, bustamite, kornerupine, childrenite, arfvedsonite, roscoelite, gruenerite, dumontite, iddingsite, tyuyamunite, malachite, spurrite, stilpnomelane, trichalcite, cenosite, annite, schroeckingerite, chrysotile, tarbuttite, strontianite, witherite, aragonite

1.68 Guildite, ransomite, loseyite, humite, messelite, natrochalcite, reddingite, spodumene, veszelyite, barrandite, plancheite, sillimanite, leucosphenite, forsterite, serandite, rinkite, olivine, viridine, hinsdalite, diopside, chlorophoenicite, fillowite, triplite, clinohumite, natrophilite, spodiosite, lawsonite, diopside-jadeite, anthophyllite, ludlamite, akrochordite, hypersthene, lithiophilite, pumpellyite, koettigite, schefferite, titanoelpidite, rosenbuschite, urbanite, cummingtonite, jeffersonite // epistolite, liroconite, cabrerite, annabergite, tilasite, stewartite, cummingtonite, zinkosite, symplesite, siderophyllite, andalusite, hastingsite, durangite, triplite, hornblende, spurrite, bustamite, kornerupine, biotite, soretite, childrenite, arfvedsonite, roscoelite, axinite, grunerite, dumortierite, iddingsite, schroeckingerite, chlorophoenicite, hypersthene, kaersutite, forsterite, tschermakite, olivine, tarbuttite, glaucochroite, stilpnomelane, cenosite, sincosite, annite, chrysotile, tyuyamunite, witherite, aragonite, monticellite, malachite

1.69 Ransomite, natrochalcite, veszelyite, plancheite, leucosphenite, serandite, olivine, viridine, hinsdalite, diopside, chlorophoenicite, clinohumite, spodiosite, diopside-jadeite, anthophyllite, ludlamite, reddingite, lithiophilite, pumpellyite, triplite, koettigite, schefferite, triphylite, rosenbuschite, urbanite, thulite, cummingtonite, jeffersonite, pigeonite, fowlerite, augite, barylite, neptunite, salite // cabrerite, annabergite, stewartite, symplesite, zinkosite, siderophyllite, andalusite, durangite, gruenerite, bustamite, chlorophoenicite, phosphuranylite, phosphosiderite, monticellite, malachite, soretite, roscoelite, hornblende, axinite, dumortierite, iddingsite, stilpnomelane, schroeckeringite, hypersthene, tschermakite, olivine, tarbuttite, tarapacaite, sarcopside, tyuyamunite, cenosite, sincosite, annite, chrysolite, kaersutite, forsterite, triphylite, kempite,

tinzenite, barkevikite, schoepite, tyrolite, aragonite

1.70 Ransomite, natrochalcite, veszelyite, plancheite, chlorophoenicite, clinohumite, spodiosite, ludlamite, olivine, reddingite, koettigite, schefferite, titanoelpidite, triphylite, rosenbuschite, urbanite, thulite, cummingtonite, jeffersonite, pigeonite, fowlerite, augite, barylite, zoisite, euchroite, neptunite, salite, riebeckite, gadolinite, serendibite, triplite, graftonite, astrophyllite, pumpellyite, legrandite, gerhardtite, ferrosalite, diaspore // symplesite, zinkosite, siderophyllite, bustamite, hypersthene, chlorophoenicite, forsterite, olivine, triphylite, barylite, barkevikite, gerhardtite, glaucochroite, ferrohastingsite, lavenite, phosphosiderite, stilpnomelane, gruenerite, axinite, hastingsite, hornblende, iddingsite, chrysolite, kaersutite, tschermakite, kempite, tinzenite, tarbuttite, strengite, schoepite, woehlerite, phosphuranylite, tarapacaite, aragonite, monticellite, malachite, metahewettite, tyrolite, sarcopside, tyuyamunite,

1.71 Natrochalcite, plancheite, koettigite, schefferite, rosenbuschite, urbanite, cummingtonite, jeffersonite, pigeonite, clinohumite, fowlerite, augite, euchroite, neptunite, salite, gadolinite, zoisite, serendibite, triplite, graftonite, astrophyllite, pumpellyite, strengite, legrandite, thulite, merwinite, brandtite, gerhardtite, ferrosalite, larnite, rhodonite, johannsenite, hedenbergite, adelite // gruenerite, hornblende, bustamite, hastingsite, iddingsite, hypersthene, chrysolite, kaersutite, forsterite, olivine, barylite, tarbuttite, barkevikite, gerhardtite, strengite, schoepite, glaucochroite, stilpnomelane, woehlerite, ferrohastingsite, kyanite, phosphuranylite, tarapacaite, lavenite, phosphosiderite, tyrolite, picrotephroite, sarcopside, chalcomenite, monticellite, tyuyamunite, malachite, metahewettite, hyalosiderite, adamite

1.72 Plancheite, koettigite, schefferite, clinohumite, augite, euchroite, neptunite, salite, gadolinite, zoisite, astrophyllite, pumpellyite, strengite, legrandite, thulite, merwinite, brandtite, pigeonite, gerhardtite, ferrosalite, larnite, fowlerite, rhodonite, clinozoisite, magnesium orthite, johannsenite, chloritoid, hedenbergite, adelite, diaspore, jeffersonite, homilite, titanaugite, babingtonite, roselite, ferrimolybdite // gruenerite, hornblende, iddingsite, hastingsite, olivine, gerhardtite, strengite, epidote, hydrocyanite, gageite, renardite, synadelphite, kaersutite, tyuyamunite, schoepite, glaucochroite, trimerite, tarapacaite, picrotephroite, hypersthene, sicklerite, stilpnomelane, monticellite, woehlerite, ferrohastingsite, kyanite, lavenite, phosphosiderite, tyrolite, sarcopside, adamite, landesite, chalcomenite, hyalosiderite, hodgkinsonite, malachite, metahewettite

1.73 Euchroite, neptunite, augite, astrophyllite, strengite, legrandite, thulite, pigeonite, ferrosalite, larnite, fowlerite, rhodonite, magnesium orthite, johannsenite, chloritoid, hedenbergite, adelite, diaspore, jeffersonite, homilite, titanaugite, triploidite, roselite, babingtonite, antlerite, azurite, ferrimolybdite // gruenerite, hornblende, schoepite, glaucochroite, woehlerite, trimerite, kyanite, tarapacaite, lavenite, phosphosiderite, tyrolite, picrotephroite, hypersthene, sarcopside, landesite, chalcomenite, hydrocyanite, gageite, sicklerite, hyalosiderite, renardite, thalenite, rhodonite, epidote, iddingsite, hodgkinsonite, stilpnomelane, kaersutite, monticellite, chalcosiderite, tyuyamunite, malachite, adamite, synadelphite, brochantite, metahewettite

1.74 Neptunite, augite, astrophyllite, strengite, legrandite, pigeonite, ferrosalite, fowlerite, rhodonite, johannsenite, chloritoid, hedenbergite, diaspore, jeffersonite, homilite, titanaugite, babingtonite, roselite, antlerite, ardennite, staurolite, scorodite, molengraaffite, azurite, ferrimolybdite // hornblende, schoepite, lavenite, phosphosiderite, picrotephroite, landesite, epidote, iddingsite, caracolite, aegerine,

stilpnomelane, chalcosiderite, metahewettite, hydrocyanite, gageite, sicklerite, hyalosiderite, renardite, thalenite, rhodonite, hodgkinsonite, sursassite, piemontite, kaersutite, monticellite, tyuyamunite, malachite, adamite, synadelphite, sobralite, brochantite

1.75 Augite, strengite, rhodonite, astrophyllite, hedenbergite, diaspore, jeffersonite, titanaugite, babingtonite, roselite, antlerite, ardennite, staurolite, scorodite, molengraafite, chrysoberyl, lamprophyllite, azurite, piemontite, shattuckite, ferrimolybdite // lavenite, hornblende, sicklerite, hyalosiderite, epidote, iddingsite, caracolite, aegerine, chalcosiderite, carnotite, metahewettite, hodgkinsonite, adamite, synadelphite, sobralite, sursassite, piemontite, nagatelite, leucosphenite, kaersutite, tyuyamunite, malachite, brochantite, hortonolite

1.76 Astrophyllite, ferrimolybdite, hedenbergite, strengite, antlerite, ardennite, staurolite, scorodite, molengraaffite, chrysoberyl, lamprophyllite, azurite, dewindtite, piemontite, orientite, shattuckite // hornblende, iddingsite, adamite, sobralite, caracolite, sursassite, piemontite, nagatelite, epidote, chalcosiderite, carnotite, metahewettite, aegerine, calcium larsenite, leucophoenicite, allactite, alleghenyite, roepperite, tephroite, thortveitite, acmite, kaersutite, tyuyamunite, malachite, brochantite, hortonolite

1.77 Astrophyllite, antlerite, scorodite, molengraaffite, lamprophyllite, azurite, dewindtite, piemontite, holdenite, barthite, orientite, shattuckite, olivenite, ferrimolybdite // hornblende, iddingsite, adamite, sursassite, piemontite, tephroite, carnotite, metahewettite, hewettite, nagatelite, epidote, leucophoenicite, britholite, alleghenyite, thortveitite, chalcosiderite, tyuyamunite, malachite, aegerine, calcium larsenite, hortonolite, allactite, roepperite, acmite, brochantite

1.78 Antlerite, scorodite, lamprophyllite, azurite, piemontite, holdenite, barthite, orientite, caryinite, shattuckite, beraunite, beudantite, retzian, flinkite, tephroite, olivenite, ferrimolybdite // hornblende, iddingsite, piemontite, epidote, britholite, tephroite, acmite, carnotite, hewettite, metahewettite, aegerine, leucophoenicite, allactite, alleghenyite, roepperite, thortveitite, pascoite, chalcosiderite, tyuyamunite, malachite, brochantite, hortonolite

1.79 Antlerite, scorodite, azurite, piemontite, orientite, caryinite, schattuckite, beraunite, monazite, beudantite, retzian, arseniopleite, barthite, flinkite, tephroite, olivenite, iddingsite, ferrimolybdite // hornblende, iddingsite, brochantite, hortonolite, alleghenyite, roepperite, tephroite, thortveitite, acmite, carnotite, hewettite, metahewettite, sarkinite, arsenoklase, pascoite, ferrohortonolite, hancockite, chalcosiderite, tyuyamunite, malachite, salesite,

1.80 Scorodite, azurite, piemontite, orientite, caryinite, shattuckite, beraunite, monazite, beudantite, retzian, arseniopleite, barthite, flinkite, tephroite, olivenite, gadolinite, iddingsite, ferrimolybdite // hornblende, iddingsite, brochantite, roepperite, tephroite, thortveitite, acmite, carnotite, cerussite, hewettite, metahewettite, hortonolite, sarkinite, arsenioklase, pascoite, ferrohortonolite, hancockite, higginsite, chalcosiderite, salesite, malachite, tyuyamunite

1.81 Azurite, piemontite, caryinite, shattuckite, beraunite, monazite, beaudantite, barthite, scorodite, flinkite, tephroite, olivenite, warwickite, gadolinite, iddingsite, ferrimolybdite // iddingsite, tephroite, thortveitite, acmite, manganfayalite, linarite, carnotite, cerussite, hewettite, metahewettite, sarkinite, arsenoklase, pascoite, ferrohortonolite, hancockite, higginsite, knebelite, chalcosiderite, tyuyamunite, malachite, salesite

1.82 Azurite, shattuckite, beraunite, monazite, beudantite, piemontite, barthite, flinkite, tephroite, olivenite, warwickite, gadolinite, cerite,

iddingsite, ferrimolybdite, uvanite // iddingsite, acmite, tephroite, arsenoklase, pascoite, ferrohortonolite, hancockite, carnotite, cerussite, hewettite, metahewettite, higginsite, mangan-fayalite, knebelite, linarite, fayalite, knebelite, linarite, fayalite, chalcosiderite, tyuyamunite, malachite, salesite

1.83 Azurite, monazite, piemontite, flinkite, olivenite, warwickite, iddingsite, dufrenite, ferrimolybdite, uvanite // iddingsite, pascoite, acmite, ferrohortonolite, hancockite, dietzeite, carnotite, cerussite, hewettite, metahewettite, higginsite, mangan-fayalite, fayalite, knebelite, linarite, atacamite, chalcosiderite, tyuyamunite, malachite, salesite

1.84 Azurite, monazite, olivenite, iddingsite, dufrenite, sphene, ferrimolybdite, uvanite // iddingsite, acmite, mangan-fayalite, knebelite, linarite, dietzeite, cerussite, hewettite, metahewettite, atacamite, fayalite, chalcosiderite, tyuyamunite, malachite, salesite

1.85 Monazite, olivenite, iddingsite, dufrenite, toernebohmite, uvanite, ferrimolybdite // iddingsite, higginsite, mangan-fayalite, fayalite, knebelite, linarite, dietzeite, cerussite, hewettite, metahewettite, atacamite, romeite, chalcosiderite, tyuyamunite, malachite, carnotite, salesite

1.86 Olivenite, iddingsite, dufrenite, toernebohmite, sphene, ferrimolybdite, uvanite // iddingsite, linarite, dietzeite, cerussite, hewettite, metahewettite, atacamite, fayalite, tyuyamunite, malachite, carnotite, salesite

1.87 Olivenite, dufrenite, toernebohmite, sphene, rockbridgeite, claudetite, ferrimolybdite, uvanite // atacamite, fayalite, cerussite, leadhillite, hewettite, metahewittite, tyuyamunite, malachite, carnotite, salesite

1.88 Dufrenite, toernebohmite, sphene, rockbridgeite, anglesite, claudetite, ferrimolybdite, uvanite // atacamite, fayalite, cerussite, leadhillite, hewettite, metahewettite, tyuyamunite, malachite, carnotite, salesite

1.89 Dufrenite, sphene, rockbridgeite,

anglesite, tsumebite, claudetite, ferrimolybdite, uvanite // fayalite, fersmannite, cerussite, leadhillite, hewettite, metahewettite, tyuyamunite, malachite, carnotite, salesite

1.90 Sphene, rockbridgeite, anglesite, kasolite, tsumebite, claudetite, ferrimolybdite, uvanite // fersmannite, cerussite, leadhillite, walpurgite, hewettite, metahewettite, tyuyamunite, malachite, carnotite, salesite

1.91 Sphene, kasolite, tsumebite, claudetite, feriimolybdite, uvanite // malachite, fersmannite, carnotite, cerussite, leadhillite, salesite, walpurgite, hewettite, metahewettite, tyuyamunite

1.92 Sphene, kasolite, tsumebite, claudetite, ferrimolybdite, uvanite // fersmannite, carnotite, cerussite, leadhillite, salesite, hewettite, metahewettite, lindgrenite, tyuyamunite, walpurgite

1.94 Sphene, kasolite, tsumebite, claudetite, ferrimolybdite, uvanite // fersmannite, carnotite, cerussite, leadhillite, salesite, lindgrenite, lepidocrocite tyuyamunite, walpurgite, hewettite, metahewettite

1.95 Kasolite, tsumebite, claudetite, ferrimolybdite, uvanite // salesite, alamosite, carnotite, cerussite, leadhillite, lepidocrocite, tyuyamunite, walpurgite, hewettite, metahewettite, lindgrenite

1.96 Tsumebite, claudetite, hyalotekite, sulfur, uranosphaerite, ferrimolybdite, uvanite // alamosite, cerussite, leadhillite, salesite, lindgrenite, lepidocrocite, tyuyamunite, walpurgite, hewettite, metahewettite

1.97 Claudetite, hyalotekite, sulfur, uranosphaerite, ferrimolybdite, uvanite // alamosite, cerussite, leadhillite, salesite, lindgrenite, lepidocrocite, tyuyamunite, walpurgite, hewettite, metahewettite, fiedlerite

2.00 Claudetite, sulfur, tellurite, uranosphaerite, ferrimolybdite, uvanite // cerussite, leadhillite, salesite, walpurgite, hewettite, metahewettite, lindgrenite, lepidocrocite, fiedlerite

2.01 Claudetite, sulfur, tellurite, uranosphaerite, uvanite // cerussite, leadhillite, salesite, walpurgite,

hewettite, metahewettite, lindgrenite, lepidocrocite, fiedlerite

2.02 Sulfur, tellurite, uranosphaerite, uvanite // cerussite, salesite, walpurgite, hewettite, metahewettite, lindgrenite, lepidocrocite, fiedlerite

2.05 Sulfur, tellurite, uranosphaerite, uvanite // cerussite, salesite, walpurgite, pyromorphite, hewettite, metahewettite, lepidocrocite, paralaurionite, fiedlerite

2.06 Sulfur, tellurite // pyromorphite, salesite, hewettite, metahewettite, curite, lepidocrocite, paralaurionite, fiedlerite

2.08 Sulfur, tellurite // cerussite, salesite, hewettite, metahewettite, tungstite, curite, lepidocrocite, laurionite, fiedlerite, paralaurionite

2.13 Sulfur, tellurite // mimetite, hewettite, metahewettite, tungstite, baddeleyite, curite, lepidocrocite, laurionite, paralaurionite

2.15 Sulfur, tellurite // mimetite, hewettite, metahewettite, tungstite, baddeleyite, curite, lepidocrocite, laurionite, paralaurionite

2.16 Sulfur, tellurite // chloroxiphite, hewettite, metahewettite, kleinite, tungstite, baddeleyite, lepidocrocite, laurionite, paralaurionite

2.17 Sulfur, tellurite, huebnerite // chloroxiphite, mottramite, hewettite, metahewettite, kleinite, tungstite, baddeleyite, paralaurionite, lepidocrocite

2.19 Sulfur, tellurite, tantalite, huebnerite // chloroxiphite, fervanite, descloizite, mottramite, hewettite, metahewettite, paralaurionite, kleinite, valentinite, tungstite, baddeleyite, lepidocrocite

2.20 Sulfur, tellurite, tantalite, cotunnite, huebnerite // chloroxiphite, descloizite, mottramite, fervanite, hewettite, metahewettite, valentinite, tungstite, baddeleyite, lepidocrocite, paralaurionite

2.22 Sulfur, tellurite, tantalite, cotunnite huebnerite // chloroxiphite, fervanite, descloizite, mottramite, hewettite, metahewettite, valentinite, tungstite, lepidocrocite

2.24 Sulfur, tellurite, tantalite, mendipite, cotunnite, huebnerite // chloroxiphite, descloizite, mottramite, hewettite, metahewettite, valentinite, tungstite, lepidocrocite

2.25 Sulfur, tellurite, tantalite, cotunnite, mendipite, huebnerite // chloroxiphite, schwartzembergite, descloizite, mottramite, hewettite, valentinite, tungstite, lepidocrocite

2.26 Sulfur, tellurite, tantalite, cotunnite, mendipite, huebnerite, wolframite // schwartzembergite, descloizite, mottramite, hewettite, valentinite, tungstite, lepidocrocite, goethite

2.27 Sulfur, tellurite, tantalite, mendipite, huebnerite, wolframite, raspite // schwartzembergite, descloizite, mottramite, hewettite, valentinite, lepidocrocite, goethite

2.28 Sulfur, tellurite, tantalite, mendipite, brackebuschite, huebnerite, wolframite, raspite // schwartzembergite, descloizite, mottramite, hewettite, valentinite, lepidocrocite, goethite

2.30 Sulfur, tellurite, tantalite, mendipite, nadorite, brackebuschite, huebnerite, wolframite, raspite // schwartzembergite, descloizite, mottramite, hewettite, valentinite, lepidocrocite, goethite

2.31 Sulfur, tellurite, tantalite, mendipite, nadorite, brackebuschite, huebnerite, wolframite // schwartzembergite, descloizite, mottramite, hewettite, valentinite, lepidocrocite, goethite

2.32 Sulfur, tellurite, tantalite, nadorite, brackebuschite, huebnerite, wolframite // schwartzembergite, descloizite, mottramite, hewettite, valentinite, lepidocrocite, goethite

2.34 Sulfur, tellurite, tantalite, nadorite, brackebuschite, wolframite // schwartzembergite, descloizite, hewettite, valentinite, lepidocrocite, goethite

2.35 Tellurite, nadorite, brackebuschite, wolframite // schwartzembergite, descloizite, hewettite, valentinite, lepidocrocite, goethite, terlinguaite

2.37 Montroydite, nadorite, brackebuschite, wolframite // lepidocrocite, goethite, terlinguaite

2.38 Montroydite, pseudobrookite, thoreaulite, nadorite, brackebuschite, wolframite // lepidocrocite, goethite, terlinguaite

2.40 Montroydite, pseudobrookite, stibiotantalite, nadorite, brackebuschite,

wolframite // orpiment, lepidocrocite, goethite, terlinguaite

2.41 Montroydite, stibiotantalite, pseudobrookite, derbylite, brackebuschite, wolframite // pucherite, orpiment, lepidocrocite, terlinguaite

2.42 Montroydite, stibiotantalite, pseudobrookite, derbylite, brackebuschite, wolframite // pucherite, orpiment, lepidocrocite, terlinguaite

2.46 Montroydite, stibiotantalite, derbylite, brackebuschite // pucherite, orpiment, lepidocrocite, terlinguaite

2.48 Montroydite, derbylite, brackebuschite // pucherite, orpiment, lepidocrocite, terlinguaite

2.51 Montroydite, massicot, derbylite // pucherite, koechlinite, orpiment, lepidocrocite, terlinguaite

2.54 Montroydite, massicot // koechlinite, realgar, orpiment, terlinguaite

2.58 Montroydite, massicot, brookite // koechlinite, realgar, orpiment, terlinguaite

2.65 Montroydite, massicot // koechlinite, realgar, orpiment, terlinguaite

2.70 Massicot, brookite // realgar, orpiment

2.71 Massicot // orpiment

3.02 // Orpiment

Principal sources: E. S. Larsen and H. Berman, *The Microscopic Determination of the Nonopaque Minerals,* U.S. Geological Survey Bulletin 848, 2d ed, 1934.

J. D. Dana and E. S. Dana, *System of Mineralogy,* 7th ed. (New York: Wiley), 1944-1962.

A. N. Winchell and H. Winchell, *Elements of Optical Mineralogy,* 4th ed. (New York: Wiley, 1951). Part 2, "Descriptions of Minerals."

BIREFRINGENCES OF UNIAXIAL AND BIAXIAL MINERALS

Birefringence values are often useful in quickly narrowing possible choices during identification work.

0.001 Analcime, avogadrite, cahnite, cryolite, gmelinite, leucite, mesolite, rinneite

0.002 Abukamalite, apophyllite, chabazite, chlorite, englishite, epididymite, flokite, fluocerite, gillespite, gmelinite, marialite, metatorbernite, penninite, torbernite

0.003 Apatite, cristobalite, davyne, dewindtite, eucolite, gmelinite, hyalotekite, idocrase, leuchtenbergite, merrillite, milarite, okenite, penninite, phillipsite, ptilolite, romeite

0.004 Apatite, aphrosiderite, apjohnite, arcanite, ashtonite, bloedite, carnegieite, clinozoisite, dahllite, epididymite, ferrierite, fillowite, gmelinite, leifite, mirabilite, mordenite, nepheline, phillipsite, taaffeite, tridymite, triphylite, vanthoffite, voelckerite

0.005 Aphthitalite, beryl, britholite, calcioferrite, chlorite, eudialyte, florencite, gadolinite, gehlenite, gmelinite, harmotome, harstigite, hyalophane, idocrase, kaliophilite, kaolinite, melilite, natrodavyne, orthoclase, pharmacosiderite, riebeckite, schairerite, serendibite, triphylite, triploidite, velardenite, wellsite, wilkeite, zeophyllite

0.006 Akermanite, anauxite, aphthitalite, beryl, coquimbite, cordierite, corundophilite, crocidolite, danburite, daphnite, dickite, enigmatite, eudidymite, faroelite, gmelinite, gonnardite, goyazite, mooreite, nacrite, sapphirine, stilbite, zoisite

0.007 Andesine, aphthitalite, arrojadite, beryl, cancrinite, chiolite, clinohedrite, cordierite, danburite, epidote, gmelinite, goyazite, heulandite, hillebrandite, juanite, leonite, miloschite, oligoclase, pickeringite, scolecite, uranochalcite

0.008 Anemousite, anorthoclase, aphthitalite, beryl, chlorophoenicite, chrysoberyl, coeruleolactite, cordierite, corundum, dachiardite, ekmanite, enstatite, gearksutite, gismondine, glauconite, gmelinite, goyazite, hopeite, jurupaite, labradorite, microcline, microsommite, millisite, oligoclase, orthoclase, palaite, podolite, pyromorphite, rinkolite, riversideite, svabite, tachyhydrite, thomsenolite, topaz, zoisite

0.009 Alunogen, andalusite, arseniopleite, beryl, beryllonite, bytownite, calcium larsenite, celestite, chalcoalumite, chrysoberyl, clinoenstatite, cordierite, dehrnite, deltaite, enstatite, goyazite, idocrase, labradorite, lehiite, melanterite, pachnolite, paraluminite, picropharmacolite, prosopite, pseudowavellite, quartz, rankinite, ripidolite, scapolite, sheridanite, soumansite, struvite, wardite, zoisite

0.010 Anauxite, andalusite, axinite, baldaufite, bavenite, boussingaultite, bultfonteinite, bytownite, carminite, celestite, celsian, chalcedony, chevkinite, chlorite, clinozoisite, chrysoberyl, cordierite, crandallite, daubreeite, deltaite, dennisonite, ectropite, enstatite, eosphorite, epistilbite, finnemanite, georgiadesite, goyazite, gypsum, halotrichite, hedyphane, hellandite, hugelite, hypersthene, iodyrite, koninckite, labradorite, liskeardite, lithiophilite, loewigite, manganobrucite, melanocerite, merwinite, misenite, mizzonite, montanite, nasonite, natroalunite, okenite, ottrelite, parsonsite, phillipsite, pinnoite, pyraurite, pyroxmangite, rhodonite, roselite, saponite, sepiolite, staurolite, stokesite, thuringite, topaz, torbernite, trimerite, uranopilite, wardite, zippeite

0.011 Albite, akrochordite, aluminite, andalusite, antigorite, bityite, boracite, chloritoid, chrysotile, clinochlore, cordierite, dehrnite, dumortierite, euxenite, goyazite, jezekite, laubanite, leonhardite, lewistonite, lithiophilite, pharmocolite, prochlorite, sarcolite, spodumene, stellerite, tinzenite, vauxite, velardenite, wentzelite

0.012 Akermanite, anorthite, barite, bieberite, brandisite, brushite, cordierite, cuspidine, custerite, douglasite, hardystonite, hydronepheline, hypersthene, kornerupine, kyanite, johnstrupite, laumontite, mascagnite, mendozite, morinite, mosandrite, petalite, sellaite, seybertite, staurolite, svabite, tamarugite, taylorite, xanthophyllite, zinkosite, zippeite, zonotlite

0.013 Barthite, brandtite, brewsterite, britholite, celadonite, dickinsonite, dietrichite, eastonite, eckermannite, gageite, gyrolite, hiortdahlite, hureaulite, hypersthene, jadeite, kornerupine, kyanite, lecontite, margarite, mizzonite, natrolite, natrophilite, rhodonite, soretite, ternovskite, thenardite, thomsonite, tincalconite, uranocircite, wagnerite

0.014 Augelite, barylite, bromellite, bronzite, bustamite, centrallasite, chlorite, chrysotile, crestmoreite, delessite, elpidite, epidesmine, erionite, ettringite, hydrotalcite, hypersthene, kempite, kyanite, lotrite, manandonite, manganophyllite, mendozite, mooreite, svanbergite, tourmaline

0.015 Amesite, anorthite, ardennite, buttgenbachite, didymolite, hastingsite, hydrocyanite, hypersthene, isoclasite, kyanite, landesite, leuchtenbergite, melanterite, mimetite, mullite, nagatelite, nontronite, phenakite, picromerite, pisanite, pseudowavellite, salmonsite, siderotil, spodumene, thuringite, tourmaline, wollastonite

0.016 Chlorophoenicite, daviesite, edingtonite, grothine, hedyphane, holdenite, hypersthene, kyanite, mimetite, phenakite, rinkite, sarkinite, scheelite, spodumene, tourmaline, zincite

0.017 Afwillite, anglesite, felsobanyite, glaucophane, hastingsite, hudsonite, kreuzbergite, mimetite, monticellite, scheelite, sobralite, sulfoborite, titanoelpidite, tourmaline, tremolite, yuksporite

0.018 Cyanotrichite, fairfieldite, hopeite, lacroixite, magnesium orthite, metavoltine, mimetite, pumpellyite, rinkolite, schallerite, sincosite, syngenite, tourmaline, tschermakite, willemite, zoisite

0.019 Adelite, allactite, alumian, carpholite, chalcanthite, edenite, euclase, flagstaffite, glaucophane, gerhardtite, hematolite, hinsdalite, holmquistite, howlite, kupfferite, lawsonite, loewite, meliphane, newberyite, paravauxite, pargasite, rinkolite, roscherite, swedenborgite, tourmaline, willemite

0.020 Alunite, amblygonite, ardennite, armangite, ascharite, barysilite, bassettite, becquerelite, bellite,

bialite, boleite, boothite, brazilianite, canbyite, carnotite, chalcanthite, crocidolite, dumontite, dussertite, euclase, hanksite, hannayite, homilite, jefferisite, kleinite, kupferite, lorettoite, malacon, martinite, montebrasite, newtonite, nontronite, piemontite, polyhalite, richterite, roeblingite, scapolite, scorodite, sillimanite, spadaite, spencerite, strigovite, torendrikite, tremolite, triplite, tourmaline, turanite, uvite, vashegyite, volborthite, willemite, wurtzite, zepharovichite, zeunerite, zincaluminite

0.021 Alamosite, anthophyllite, antigorite, ardennite, arfvedsonite, augite, barkevikite, bazzite, brucite, caracolite, chalcanthite, cookeite, fremontite, gedrite, gibbsite, glauberite, hastingsite, kupferite, malacon, narsarsukite, nontronite, phosphophyllite, pigeonite, scorodite, tourmaline, tremolite, truscottite, willemite, wurtzite

0.022 Anthophyllite, chalcanthite, chalcomenite, connellite, diopside-jadeite, gadolinite, glauconite, gordonite, hemimorphite, hodgkinsonite, hornblende, hydromagnesite, kupferite, malacon, mitscherlichite, montmorillonite, pargasite, phosophophyllite, plumbogummite, polylithionite, priceite, richterite, sarkinite, scawtite, scorodite, searlesite, tourmaline, tremolite, triplite, trippkeite, variscite, warwickite, wernerite, willemite, wurtzite

0.023 Amblygonite, anthophyllite, bertrandite, chalcanthite, chlorite, chrysocolla, conichalcite, edenite, homilite, jeffersonite, kupferite, larnite, lepidolite, malacon, minium, montmorillonite, nocerite, parahopeite, pargasite, phlogopite, polylithionite, retzian, scorodite, tremolite, tourmaline, voglite, willemite

0.024 Allanite, anthophyllite, autunite, chalcanthite, creedite, diopsidehedenbergite, graftonite, hornblende, kupferite, lepidolite, malacon, minium, pigeonite, renardite, scorodite, slavikite, spadaite, tourmaline, tremolite, wattevillite, willemite

0.025 Actinolite, anthophyllite, augite, barrandite, borax, chalcanthite, chondrodite, collinsite, ganophyllite, hastingsite, hedenbergite, inyoite, kupfferite, lepidolite, malacon, minium, morenosite, nontronite, ozocerite, phosphophyllite, schallerite, scorodite, seamanite, sincosite, strengite, tourmaline, tremolite, wapplerite, willemite

0.026 Amblygonite, anthophyllite, bementite, chalcanthite, chondrodite, hornblende, kupfferite, malacon, mendozite, nasonite, phosgenite, prehnite, scorodite, sphaerite, stichtite, tourmaline, tremolite, willemite, woehlerite

0.027 Astrolite, anthophyllite, chalcanthite, chondrodite, epidote, friedelite, goslarite, hastingsite, inderite, kupfferite, lehiite, leucophanite, malacon, manganophyllite, metavauxite, norbergite, scorodite, tourmaline, tremolite, uranophane, uranospinite, wavellite, willemite, zebadassite

0.028 Anthophyllite, botryogen, cancrinite, chalcanthite, chondrodite, clinohumite, colemanite, cummingtonite, epidote, epsomite, herderite, jeffersonite, johannsenite, kalinite, liskeardite, malacon, mellite, scorodite, serandite, tourmaline, tremolite, trichalcite, willemite

0.029 Aegerine-augite, anthophyllite, arsenoklasite, botryogen, carnallite, caryinite, chalcanthite, chondrodite, cummingtonite, diopside, eosphorite, epidote, friedelite, herderite, holmquistite, jadeite, kramerite, malacon, painite, phosphuranylite, rosenbuschite, salite, schefferite, schizolite, scorodite, tephroite, tourmaline, tremolite, ulexite, variscite, viridine

0.030 Anthophyllite, bementite, bianchite, botryogen, brugnatellite, catapleiite, cummingtonite, catoptrite, chloropal, chondrodite, connarite, diopside, epidote, friedelite, hatchettite, hautefeuillite, hexahydrite, hoelite, humite, koenenite, lazulite, manganophyl-

lite, mariposite, minasragrite, nontronite, paragonite, parsettensite, pigeonite, pseudoboleite, raspite, saponite, scorodite, sicklerite, stercorite, sursassite, tengerite, tourmaline, tremolite, uranopilite, uranospathite, zinnwaldite, zircon

0.031 Botryogen, catapleiite, chondrodite, epidote, friedelite, ganophyllite, grunerite, hornblende, leucophoenicite, meionite, metavariscite, monetite, reddingite, schefferite, tourmaline, urbanite, vermiculite, zircon

0.032 Bischofite, botryogen, catapleiite, chondrodite, clinohumite, dietzeite, ephesite, epidote, friedelite, glauconite, grunerite, kaersutite, leucochalcite, pectolite, reddingite, saponite, schroeckeringerite, scorodite, strengite, tourmaline, zircon

0.033 Babingtonite, biotite, bischofite, bobierrite, botryogen, catapleiite, cebollite, chondrodite, clinohumite, epidote, friedelite, grunerite, hoernesite, muscovite, prehnite, protolithionite, toernebohmite, tourmaline, zircon

0.034 Botryogen, catapleiite, chondrodite, churchite, epidote, friedelite, grunerite, kernite, muscovite, phlogopite, tephroite, tourmaline, zircon

0.035 Babingtonite, barthite, beudantite, botryogen, catapleiite, epidote, friedelite, ganomalite, grunerite, hortonolite, humite, lamprophyllite, molengraaffite, muscovite, natron, phlogopite, strengite, tilasite, tilleyite, tourmaline, zircon

0.036 Alleghenyite, ashcroftine, botryogen, catapleiite, chondrodite, epidote, grunerite, johannite, kurnakovite, lazulite, meionite, muscovite, olivine, phlogopite, spodiosite, tourmaline, tyrolite, zircon

0.037 Aegerine, botryogen, epidote, grandidierite, grunerite, hydrobiotite, louderbackite, meionite, nepouite, muscovite, olivine, orientite, phlogopite, saponite, tourmaline, zircon

0.038 Aegerine, botryogen, cenosite, epidote, euchroite, fervanite, fluoborite, fluellite, grunerite, muscovite, phlogopite, schallerite, sinhalite, tourmaline, zircon

0.039 Aegerine, beidellite, botryogen, epidote, grunerite, loseyite, nitrochalcite, paternoite, phlogopite, pyrosmalite, spurrite, thaumasite, tourmaline, uranothallite, zircon

0.040 Aegerine, alurgite, arakawaite, atelestite, bayldonite, beaverite, beraunite, biotite, botryogen, cornwallite, epidote, forsterite, fuchsite, grunerite, larsenite, ludlamite, manganostilbite, muscovite, olivine, phlogopite, plancheite, pseudobrookite, purpurite, synadelphite, tourmaline, turquoise, zircon

0.041 Aegerine, biotite, bombiccite, botryogen, childrenite, conichalcite, epidote, grunerite, muscovite, nantokite, phlogopite, piemontite, tourmaline, ussingite, zircon

0.042 Aegerine, beidellite, biotite, botryogen, epidote, fibroferrite, grunerite, hancockite, hintzeite, iddingsite, knebelite, muscovite, phlogopite, pholidolite, piemontite, pyrochroite, tourmaline, zircon

0.043 Aegerine, anhydrite, biotite, botryogen, epidote, grunerite, iddingsite, knebelite, leucosphenite, moissanite, muscovite, phlogopite, piemontite, tourmaline, zircon

0.044 Aegerine, anhydrite, biotite, botryogen, datolite, diopsideacmite, epidote, iddingsite, knebelite, ludlamite, phlogopite, piemontite, tourmaline, zircon

0.045 Acmite, aegerine, anhydrite, beidellite, biotite, botryogen, datolite, epidote, iddingsite, knebelite, lepidolite, piemontite, schoepite, tourmaline, troegerite, weinschenkite, zircon

0.046 Acmite, aegerine, biotite, botryogen, epidote, higginsite, hornblende, iddingsite, knebelite, neptunite, olivine, phosphosiderite, piemontite, roepperite, sklodowskite, tourmaline, zircon

0.047 Acmite, aegerine, anapaite, benitoite, biotite, botryogen, epidote, hydroboracite, iddingsite, knebelite, lavenite, piemontite, quenstedtite, zircon

0.048 Acmite, aegerine, biotite, botryogen, diaspore, durangite, epidote, haidingerite, iddingsite, piemontite, pyrophyllite, tephroite, zircon

0.049 Acmite, aegerine, atacamite, biotite, botryogen, durangite, epidote, glaucophane, iddingsite, monazite, piemontite, rhabdophane, zircon

0.050 Acmite, aegerine, ammoniojarosite, annabergite, biotite, bismutite, botryogen, cornetite, destinezite, duftite, durangite, endlichite, epidote, fayalite, flinkite, glaucochroite, glockerite, heterosite, hoegbomite, iddingsite, langbanite, linarite, pascoite, piemontite, talc, trigonite, zircon

0.051 Acmite, annabergite, biotite, botryogen, epidote, iddingsite, lansfordite, monazite, piemontite, zircon

0.052 Acmite, annabergite, biotite, botryogen, iddingsite, lepidomelane, siderophyllite, piemontite, zircon

0.053 Acmite, annabergite, biotite, botryogen, chloraluminite, dioptase, fersmannite, iddingsite, piemontite, spangolite, tarbuttite, zircon

0.054 Acmite, annabergite, biotite, botryogen, iddingsite, molybdophyllite, piemontite, thortveitite, vivianite, zircon

0.055 Acmite, annabergite, antlerite, astrophyllite, biotite, botryogen, dufrenite, iddingsite, kasolite, koettigite, piemontite, sarcopside, vanadinite, veszelyite, zircon

0.056 Acmite, annabergite, biotite, botryogen, iddingsite, lausenite, piemontite, quetenite, rogersite, zircon

0.057 Acmite, annabergite, biotite, botryogen, chalcophyllite, iddingsite, kroehnkite, piemontite, zircon

0.058 Acmite, annabergite, biotite, botryogen, chalcophyllite, ferrinatrite, piemontite, zircon

0.059 Acmite, annabergite, botryogen, chalcophyllite, ferrinatrite, piemontite, roemerite, zircon

0.060 Acmite, annabergite, annite, biotite, chalcophyllite, copiapite, cotunnite, derbylite, erinite, ferrinatrite, fichtelite, hemafibrite, iddingsite, legrandite, meyerhofferite, piemontite, soddyite, stewartite, taramellite, uzbekite, zircon

0.061 Anatase, annabergite, biotite, chalcophyllite, cumengeite, ferrinatrite, guildite, iddingsite, legrandite, piemontite, stibiocolumbite

0.063 Annabergite, biotite, cacoxenite, chalcophyllite, copiapite, ferrinatrite, iddingsite, kieserite, legrandite, liroconite, piemontite, serpierite, shattuckite, stibiocolumbite

0.064 Annabergite, biotite, chalcophyllite, copiapite, ferrinatrite, iddingsite, legrandite, piemontite, ransomite, stibiocolumbite

0.065 Adamite, annabergite, biotite, chalcophyllite, copiapite, ferrinatrite, iddingsite, legrandite, natrochalcite, piemontite, stibiocolumbite, trudellite

0.066 Biotite, chalcophyllite, copiapite, ferrinatrite, iddingsite, legrandite, piemontite, stibiocolumbite

0.067 Biotite, copiapite, cyanotrichite, ferrinatrite, iddingsite, legrandite, piemontite, stibiocolumbite

0.068 Artinite, biotite, copiapite, ferrinatrite, iddingsite, kaersutite, larderellite, legrandite, piemontite, symplesite, stibicolumbite

0.070 Ammonioborite, baddeleyite, biotite, cabrerite, ecdemite, hatchettite, iddingsite, kornelite, legrandite, manganotantalite, mendipite, piemontite, plancheite, purpurite, stibiocolumbite, szmikite, szomolnokite

0.071 Biotite, hambergite, iddingsite, piemontite, pirssonite, stibiocolumbite, tsumebite

0.072 Biotite, chalcosiderite, epistolite, hambergite, hornblende, iddingsite, piemontite, stibiocolumbite, stibiotantalite

0.073 Biotite, brochantite, erythrite, piemontite, stibiotantalite

0.075 Biotite, herrengrundite, stibiotantalite, szaibelyite

0.078 Arseniosiderite, biotite, margarosanite, sideronatrite, stibiotantalite

0.079 Arseniosiderite, biotite, gaylussite, stibiotantalite

0.080 Arseniosiderite, biotite, erythrosiderite, ferritungstite, goethite,

manganotantalite, mixite, penfieldite, rutherfordine, stibiotantalite

0.081 Arseniosiderite, laurionite, mixite, parisite, stibiotantalite

0.082 Arseniosiderite, mixite, natrojarosite, olivenite, stibiotantalite, sussexite

0.083 Arseniosiderite, mixite, olivenite, stibiotantalite

0.085 Alumohydrochalcite, chlormagnesite, mixite, olivenite

0.086 Dihydrite, olivenite

0.087 Griffithite, libethenite, olivenite, schultenite, stolzite

0.088 Borgstromite, olivenite

0.089 Aurichalcite, julienite, olivenite, plumbojarosite

0.090 Calciovolborthite, carphosiderite, chloroxiphite, curite, fourmarierite, lanarkite, langite, lanthanite, olivenite, wulfenite, zippeite

0.091 Caledonite, olivenite, wulfenite, zippeite

0.094 Roscoelite, wulfenite, zippeite

0.095 Becquerelite, darapskite, wulfenite, xenotime, zippeite

0.096 Cassiterite, lauterite, wulfenite, zippeite

0.097 Argentojarosite, cassiterite, wulfenite, zippeite

0.098 Cassiterite, lindackerite, wulfenite, zippeite

0.100 Amarantite, ancylite, bisbeeite, hjelmite, nadorite, pucherite, uraconite, uranosphaerite, vaterite, wulfenite, zippeite

0.101 Bastnaesite, wulfenite, zippeite

0.102 Rhomboclase, wulfenite, zippeite

0.103 Freirinite, wulfenite, zippeite

0.104 Castanite, thermonatrite, wulfenite, zippeite

0.105 Jarosite, wulfenite, zippeite

0.108 Azurite, wulfenite, zippeite

0.110 Chapmanite, chrysocolla, clarkeite, hutchinsonite, hydrozincite, matlockite, mottramite, schwartzembergite, vauquelinite, wulfenite

0.114 Nesquehonite, mottramite, wulfenite

0.115 Keilhauite, mottramite, descloizite, wulfenite

0.117 Brookite, descloizite, mottramite, wulfenite

0.119 Descloizite, mottramite, sassolite, wulfenite

0.120 Descloizite, lorenzenite, mottramite, smithite, titanite, wulfenite
0.123 Descloizite, mottramite, titanite,
wulfenite
0.127 Butlerite, descloizite, mottramite,
titanite
0.128 Descloizite, mottramite, titanite,
trona
0.130 Dawsonite, descloizite, litharge,
mottramite, rossite, stilpnomelane,
titanite
0.132 Descloizite, mottramite, teschemacherite, titanite
0.134 Descloizite, mottramite, titanite,
walpurgite
0.137 Descloizite, krausite, mottramite
0.140 Claudetite, descloizite, goethite,
leadhillite, tripuhyite
0.146 Bromlite, descloizite
0.147 Descloizite, strontianite
0.148 Descloizite, witherite
0.150 Descloizite, emmonsite, huebnerite,
hydrocerussite, koechlinite, mag-
nesioludwigite, pyrobelonite, tantalite, tapiolite, walpurgite,
wolframite
0.155 Aragonite, descloizite, tantalite,
wolframite
0.156 Descloizite, oxammite, tantalite,
wolframite
0.159 Descloizite, tantalite, whewellite,
wolframite
0.160 Descloizite, hetaerolite, tantalite,
whewellite, wolframite
0.161 Barytocalcite, descloizite, tagilite,
tantalite, tarnowitzite
0.166 Descloizite, realgar, tantalite
0.170 Ludwigite, nitromagnesite, rosasite,
tantalite, tungstite, valentinite
0.172 Calcite, niter
0.177 Plumbocalcite
0.179 Dolomite
0.180 Clinoclase, dolomite
0.183 Cordylite
0.185 Anderite
0.190 Ankerite, bismite, bismutosphaerite,
kalicinite, melanotekite
0.191 Ankerite, magnesite
0.198 Ankerite, humboldtine, magnesite
0.200 Ankerite, brackebuschite, carnotite,
hetaerolite, magnesite, massicot,
tyuyamunite
0.202 Ankerite, magnesite, tyuyamunite
0.203 Pyrargyrite, tyuyamunite
0.206 Nahcolite, tyuyamunite
0.210 Kentrolite, tyuyamunite

0.215 Molybdite, tyuyamunite
0.218 Mesitite, tyuyamunite
0.220 Rhodochrosite, trippkeite, tyuyamunite
0.228 Smithsonite, tyuyamunite
0.234 Siderite, tyuyamunite
0.240 Siderite, tyuyamunite, uvanite
0.242 Siderite, tyuyamunite
0.246 Ianthinite
0.250 Melanovanadite, sphaerocobaltite
0.251 Soda niter
0.254 Malachite
0.260 Molybdite
0.263 Durdenite
0.271 Pyrophanite
0.274 Cerussite (to 0.275)
0.280 Hematite, montroydite
0.287 Rutile
0.288 Sulfur
0.290 Manganite, sulfur
0.295 Proustite
0.300 Coccinite
0.310 Fiedlerite, hausmannite
0.320 Terlinguaite
0.347 Cinnabar
0.350 Cinnabar, crocoite, tellurite
0.351 Cinnabar
0.360 Geikielite
0.400 Cerite
0.510 Curtisite
0.530 Metahewettite
0.570 Lepidocrocite
0.580 Hewettite
0.600 Orpiment
0.683 Calomel

REFRACTIVE INDICES OF NATURAL OILS, WAXES, FATS, AND RESINS

For very complete lists, see Kanthack and Goldsmith, cited below.

Substance	Indices
Almond oil	1.45-1.47
Almond oil, bitter (benzal-dehyde	1.54-1.55
Amber oils, commercial	1.45-1.48
Anise oil	1.54-1.56
Anise seed oil	1.47-1.48
Beeswax	1.44-1.46
Bone oil	1.47
Canada balsam	1.53-1.55
Carnauba wax	1.45-1.47
Cassia oil	1.58-1.60

Substance	Indices	Substance	Indices
Castor oil	1.47-1.48	Sesame oil	1.47
Cedarwood oil	1.50-1.51	Soybean oil	1.47-1.48
Cinnamon oil	1.59-1.60	Tung oil	1.49-1.52
Clove oil	1.53	Turpentines	1.45-1.49
Cocoanut oil	1.43-1.46	Wintergreen oil	1.54
Cod liver oil	1.46-1.48		
Corn (maize) oil	1.47-1.48		
Cottonseed oil	1.45-1.48		
Eucalyptus oil	1.46-1.47		
Glycerine, pure	1.47		
Lanolin	1.48		
Lemon oil	1.47-1.48		
Linseed oil	1.47-1.49		
Neatsfoot oil	1.47		
Olive oil	1.44-1.47		
Palm oil	1.44-1.46		
Paraffin wax	1.42-1.45		
Peppermint oil	1.46-1.47		
Pine oils	1.47-1.49		
Rape seed oil	1.47-1.48		
Safflower oil	1.47-1.48		
Sandalwood oils	1.50-1.51		

The above are approximate indices only and specific oils should be tested to determine exact values before use due to considerable variation in composition. Many are strongly scented and may be objectionable on that account while others are also "drying," that is, they absorb oxygen more or less rapidly from the atmosphere and thicken to gummy consistency or develop tough elastic coatings. After use, clean off object tested with petroleum distillate, turpentine, paint brush solvent, etc.

Reference: R. Kanthack and J. N. Goldsmith, *Tables of Refractive Indices* (London: Adam Hilger, 1918-21), vol. 1, *Essential Oils;* vol. 2, *Oils, Fats and Waxes.*

MAIN TABLE OF REFRACTIVE INDEX FLUIDS

Details on properties may be found in the "Chemicals List" (p. 23). Oils, waxes, etc., appear in a following list. (*Note:* 18° C. = 64° F., 20° C. = 68° F., 24° C. = 75° F., 25° C. = 77° F.)

Chemical Name	n
Methyl alcohol [wood alcohol, methanol]	1.329 (20°) C
	1.326 (25°)
Water	1.33
Acetone	1.357 (25°)
Ethyl alcohol [grain alcohol, ethanol]	1.361 (20°)
	1.359 (25°)
Hexane	1.375 (20°)
	1.372 (25°)
Isopropyl alcohol [propanol]	1.378 (20°)
Ethyl butyrate	1.400 (20°)
	1.393 (24°)
Methyl butyrate	1.388 (20°)
Heptane	1.388 (20°)
	1.385 (25°)
Amyl acetate ["banana oil"]	1.400 (25°)
Triethyl ester phosphoric acid	1.405 (20°)
Amyl alcohol	1.410 (20°)
Ethyl valerate	1.412 (20°)
1,1-Dichloroethane	1.416 (20°)

Chemical Name	n
Dichloromethane [methylene chloride]	1.424 (20°)
Bromoethane [ethyl bromide]	1.424 (20°)
N,N-Dimethylformamide	1.427 (25°)
Diethylene glycol ["antifreeze"]	1.447 (20°)
Glycol [ethylene glycol]	1.432 (20°)
	1.429 (25°)
1,2-Dichloroethane [ethylene chloride]	1.445 (20°)
Chloroform	1.446 (20°)
	1.444 (25°)
Kerosene, variable indices	c. 1.45
1,3-Dichloropropane [trimethylene chloride]	1.449 (20°)
	1.446 (24°)
Cineole [eucalyptol]	1.459 (20°)
	1.456 (24°)
Carbon tetrachloride	1.460 (20°)
	1.459 (25°)
Cyclohexanol [hexalin]	1.465 (25°)
Mineral oil	c. 1.47-1.48
Glycerine	1.475 (20°)
	1.473 (25°)
Decalin [decahydronaphthalene]	1.481 (20°)
	1.479 (25°)
unsymm.-Tetrachlorethane	1.482 (20°)
	1.481 (24°)
symm.-Tetrachlorethane [acetylene tetrachloride]	1.494 (20°)
	1.492 (24°)
Toluene	1.496 (20°)
	1.494 (24°)
Benzene	1.498 (25°)
Pentachlorethane [pentalin]	1.503 (20°)
	1.501 (25°)
o-Xylene	1.506 (20°)
1,1-Dibromoethane	1.513 (20°)
Ethyl iodide [iodoethane]	1.513 (20°)
1,3-Dibromopropane [trimethylene bromide]	1.523 (20°)
	1.514 (24°)
Chlorobenzene	1.524 (20°)
	1.523 (24°)
Methyl salicylate [artif. oil of wintergreen]	1.537
1,2-Dibromoethane [ethylene bromide]	1.539 (20°)
	1.538 (25°)
Dibromomethane [methylene bromide]	1.542 (20°)
1,2-Dibromoethanol [*symm.*-dibromoethylene]	1.543 (20°)
Benzaldehyde [oil of bitter almonds]	1.544 (25°)
2-Nitrotoluene [*o*-nitrotoluene]	1.545 (20°)
	1.544 (25°)

Chemical Name	n
1,2-Dibromoethanol (*trans.*) [dibromoethylene]	1.551 (18°)
Hexachlor-1,3-butadiene	1.554 (20°)
Nitrobenzene	1.556 (20°)
	1.550 (25°)
2-Bromotoluene	1.557 (20°)
Bromobenzene	1.557 (25°)
Xylidine [*N,N*-Dimethylaniline]	1.558 (20°)
Benzyl benzoate	1.568 (25°)
o-Toluidine	1.573 (20°)
	1.570 (25°)
Aniline	1.583 (25°)
Bromoform	1.598 (20°)
	1.587 (25°)
Quinaldine	1.612 (20°)
Iodobenzene [monoiodobenzene]	1.620 (20°)
Cinnamaldehyde	1.62 (20°)
Quinoline	1.627 (20°)
	1.622 (24°)
unsymm.-Tetrabromoethane	1.628 (20°)
Carbon disulfide	1.628 (25°)
1-Chloronaphthalene [monochloronaphthalene]	1.633 (20°)
	1.633 (24°)
symm.-Tetrabromoethane [acetylene tetrabromide]	1.635 (20°)
1-Bromonaphthalene [monobromonaphthalene]	1.658 (20°)
Piperine + iodides, various melts	1.68-2.10
1-Iodonaphthalene [monoiodonaphthalene]	1.703 (20°)
Clerici's solution	1.705 (20°)
Methylene iodide [diiodomethane]	1.7425 (20°)
	1.738 (24°)
	1.749 (25°)
Arsenic tribromide, MP = 33° C. (91° F.)	1.78
Methylene iodide + sulfur to saturation	1.78
West's solution*	1.78-2.06
Methylene iodide + S + tetraiodoethylene	1.81
Arsenic tribromide + 10 wgt. % sulfur, melt	1.814
Methylene iodide + S + iodides†	1.868
Methylene iodide + AsS + AsBr$_3$	1.90
Sulfur + selenium, melt	1.998-2.716
Selenium + arsenic selenide, melt	2.72-3.17

* West's solution: yellow phosphorus 8 pts. by wgt. + 1 pt. sulfur + 1 pt. methylene iodide, *mixed under water* to prevent ignition of phosphorus, and gently warmed to hasten solution; see C. D. West *Amer. Mineral.* 21 (1936): 245-49. By adding methylene iodide the range becomes 1.78-2.06.

† Formula: 100 gm methylene iodide + 35 gm iodoform + 10 gm sulfur + 31 gm SnI$_4$ + 16 gm AsI$_3$ + 8 gm SbI$_3$. Warm to dissolve, filter.

PRINCIPAL REFRACTOMETRY LIQUIDS

The following are in general use because of their stability, freedom from objectionable odor, and relatively low toxicity. See table below.

Chemical name	n
1,3-Dichloropropane	1.449 (20° C.)
	1.446 (24° C.)
symm.-Tetrachlorethane	1.494 (20° C.)
	1.492 (24° C.)
Chlorobenzene	1.524 (20° C.)
	1.523 (24° C.)
Dibromomethane	1.542 (20° C.)
Bromoform	1.598 (20° C.)
	1.587 (25° C.)
1-Chloronaphthalene	1.633 (20° C.)
1-Bromonaphthalene	1.658 (20° C.)
1-Iodonaphthalene	1.703 (20° C.)
Methylene iodide	1.7425 (20° C.)
	1.738 (24° C.)
Methylene iodide + S	1.78
Methylene iodide + S + tetraiodoethylene*	1.81

* This mixture is normally supplied with purchase of a refractometer.

Poison note: Chemicals containing Cl, I, Br, Se, are potentially dangerous and contact with the skin or inhalation of vapors should be avoided, especially over prolonged periods.

Glass corrosion: Chemicals containing Br, I, As, tend to corrode refractometer prisms; clean prisms immediately after use and coat with thin layer of vaseline.

Repolishing refractometer prisms: Use small flat strips of fine-grained hardwood as maple, birch, boxwood, fruitwood, etc. Hardwood-faced plywoods, 1/8″ thickness, are excellent, dimensions of strips c. 1/4″ wide, 2″ long (0.5 x 5 cm). Moisten wood surface, apply very small dab of Linde A polishing alumina or cerium oxide, just enough to impart color to the wood; remove excess powder. Place strip *flat* on prism and move gently back and forth with light pressure (several ounces). Wipe off prism and check luster; repeat treatment as needed until iridescent corrosion film disappears. Do not use felt, cloth or any other yielding substance for polishing to avoid rounding of prism edges and emphasizing any shallow depressions which may already exist.

Clarification of liquids: Methylene iodide, and other iodides, are susceptible to decomposition due to liberation of free iodine as the liquid is exposed to light. Clarify by inserting a number of fresh, bright copper wires or strips into the solution, shaking well from time to time, and then filtering as the solution again becomes pale in color. Keep several fresh copper strips in storage container to combine with the iodine as it is liberated. Bromoform, and other liquids, may also be cleaned by shaking with fuller's earth in the proportion of about 100-150 ml with several gm of the earth. Drain off clear liquid by means of a separation funnel.

REFRACTIVE INDICES VERSUS LUSTERS

Greater reflection of light accompanies increasing refractive indices in minerals and commonly imparts characteristic lusters.

n	Luster
1.3-1.4	Poor reflections, inclined to be greasy or oily in appearance
1.5-1.8	Brightly reflective, like glass
1.6-1.9	Resinous in appearance
1.9-2.5	Very brightly reflective, adamantine, sometimes appearing as if the mineral is lightly coated with a metal film
2.5 +	Submetallic, bright luster, definitely metallic in appearance

REFLECTIVE OPTICAL EFFECTS IN MINERALS AND GEMSTONES

SHEEN. A general term used to designate bright reflections from many minute points, e.g., as from the surface of satin.

ADULARESCENCE. Bright mobile reflections from within more or less transparent feldspars, e.g., adularia, moonstone, etc. The reflective points are *not* discernible, even under fairly strong magnification.

ASTERISM. Special form of CHATOYANCY, which see below. Two or more bright lines crossing to form stars.

AVENTURESCENCE. Bright reflections from easily visible platelets of included minerals; a similar effect also occurs with discoidal separations around small inclusions.

CHATOYANCY. Reflections from a series of parallel inclusions or tubes; forms a single bright line in cabochon gems; also inclusions can be warped or wavy, as in tigereye.

IRIDESCENCE. Colored reflections resembling those observed on soap bubbles or thin films of oil on water. This term is probably best restricted to similar thin films occurring in minerals, e.g., goethite in "fire agate."

IRIS. Bright spectral colors due to diffraction of light through bands of translucent agate; a transmitted light phenomenon. Has also been applied to the reflections observed in various cracked transparent gem materials, notably rock crystal (Newton's rings).

LABRADORESCENCE. The special colored reflections, usually blue, purplish blue, green, and gold, noted in certain labradorite feldspars (Labrador, Finland, etc.).

PLAY OF COLOR. The special name for the intense pure colors observed in the precious opal and caused by diffraction from colonies of close-packed opal spherules.

SCHILLER. Bright reflections, often metallic in appearance, from minute partings, solution cavities, or platy inclusions in minerals, e.g., bronzite. Coarser silvery reflections are commonly noted in amazonite and other microcline perthite feldspars.

TYNDALL EFFECT. Scattering of light from numerous minute particles in a transparent medium, e.g., smoke particles in air. In reflected light, the effect imparts a pale blue color but in transmitted light the color observed is some shade of yellowish-brown. The term "opalescence" has been used for this effect in transparent or highly translucent minerals.

List of Minerals Displaying Special Effects

ACTINOLITE. Chatoyant, fibrous structure, usually weak.

ADULARIA. Adularescent, exsolved platelets of feldspar, weak to strong silvery sheen.

AGATE. Iris effects in certain rare banded agates, notably from Montana, Tennessee, Mexico.

ALBITE. Adularescence in silvery white and also blue, also in several colors ("peristerism") but weak.

ALMANDINE GARNET. Minute acicular inclusions, oriented, and usually confined to external zones of crystals; provides a weak to moderately strong asterism (4-ray or 6-ray).

AMBER. Aventurescent at times due to discoidal separations around inclusions giving a coarse spangled effect.

ANDALUSITE. Dark crosslike areas of inclusions occur in the variety *chiastolite*.

ANDRADITE. Chatoyancy, sometimes strong and green in hue, has been observed in crystals of brown andradite from Stanley Butte, Arizona.

ANTHOPHYLLITE. Chatoyancy, sometimes strong; somewhat metallic in luster.

APATITE. Chatoyancy observed in

some crystals and due to minute tubes parallel to the c-axis; weak to strong.

APOPHYLLITE. Schiller on basal plane, often very strong and imparting a vivid pearly luster.

ARAGONITE. Chatoyancy, weak, in some fibrous massive varieties.

BARITE. Chatoyancy, weak, in some massive fibrous varieties, notably the stalactitic material from Youlgreave, Derbyshire.

BASTITE. Schiller, often very strong with metallic bronzy luster.

BERYL. Chatoyant due to numerous minute tubes parallel to the c-axis, but very seldom strong; also observed in emerald but extremely rare.

BERYL. Asterism, due to extremely thin platelets of hematite-ilmenite forming dendritic networks along basal planes; 6-rayed stars are usually weak; general hue of cut stones brown.

BRONZITE. Named after the strong bronzy schiller commonly observed.

CALCITE. Parallel-fibrous seam material provides good chatoyant stones; "satin spar."

CASSITERITE. Weak chatoyancy observed in fibrous massive "wood tin" of Mexico and elsewhere.

CELESTITE. Poor chatoyancy from parallel-fibrous seam fillings; usually pale blue.

CERUSSITE. Chatoyancy due to parallel tubes, extremely thin and very strongly reflective.

CHALCEDONY. Commonly displays Tyndall effect in highly translucent specimens.

CHLORASTROLITE. Fairly strong chatoyancy from radiate-fibrous crystals growing in angular domains; dull olive to grayish-green.

CHRYSOBERYL. Weak to very strong chatoyancy from extremely fine parallel inclusions; also a blue adularescence in some specimens.

CORDIERITE (IOLITE). Aventurescence in some specimens due to inclusions of reddish hematite platelets; sometimes oriented and then forming a weak line or "eye."

CORUNDUM. Asterism or chatoyancy, the first forming 6-rayed stars usually; weak to strong; due to extremely fine parallel fibrous inclusions or tubes.

CORUNDUM. Schiller, generally observed on basal planes of highly impure crystals, e.g., Australia, India; sometimes the separations are large and an aventurescent effect is seen. In other specimens, the schiller varies from place to place and one type produces a crude 6-rayed figure of silvery hue upon a blue background (Australia, North Carolina).

DIOPSIDE. Chatoyancy sometimes occurs, from weak to strong, notably fine in specimens from Val Ala, Piemont, Italy, also fine from Burma.

DIOPSIDE. Aventurescence sometimes observed in Burma specimens and is due to separations around minute included crystals.

ENSTATITE. Chatoyancy, sometimes strong.

ENSTATITE. Asterism, 4-rayed stars but generally with one line of light weaker than the other.

FIBROLITE (SILLIMANITE). Chatoyancy, weak, from fibrous massive types.

GEDRITE, Chatoyancy or schiller, often with strong metallic luster.

GYPSUM. Chatoyancy of considerable brightness observed in parallel fibrous seam material; "satin spar."

HEULANDITE. Strong pearly schiller reflections from basal plane.

HYPERSTHENE. Chatoyant, sometimes strong.

LABRADORITE. Labradorescence, sometimes with scattered aventurescence due to small spangles of hematite.

LABRADORITE. Aventurescence due to numerous striplike inclusions of bright coppery-red hematite ("sunstone") in otherwise clear yellowish material from Oregon. Weak to strong.

LEPIDOLITE. Feeble aventurescence due to certain flakes reflecting light in compact granular material.

LEUCITE. Iridescence observed in some clear crystals from Alban Hills, Rome, Italy.

MICROCLINE. Schiller with resulting rather strong pearly reflections commonly observed, especially in amazonite.

MICROCLINE. Aventurescence, in amazonite, due to small spangles of hematite but rare.

MORDENITE. Weak chatoyancy in massive fibrous material.

NEPHRITE. Chatoyancy, sometimes distinct, in translucent fibrous material occurring generally as seams in ordinary nephrite (Alaska, New Zealand).

OBSIDIAN. Aventurescence due to minute striplike inclusions or partings; sometimes coarse and spangly (Mexico); at other times extremely fine and then resembling the sheeny appearance of labradorite (Oregon, California) and with somewhat similar colors.

OLIGOCLASE. Aventurescence due to spangles of hematite is sometimes very strong as in the "sunstone" of Norway.

OPAL. Play of color, sometimes very weak and hazy but also extremely brilliant. Certain opals reveal play of color only when observed via transmitted light. *Hydrophanes* are very porous precious opals which appear opaque white when desiccated but display play of color when soaked in water.

OPAL. Tyndall effect; very common in many translucent specimens.

ORTHOCLASE. Adularescence common; "moonstone."

PECTOLITE. Weak chatoyancy in compact fibrous material.

PERIDOT. Weak chatoyancy sometimes observed in specimens from Arizona and Burma.

PERIDOT. Aventurescence due to discoidal separations around minute crystals of spinel (Arizona).

QUARTZ. Chatoyancy in clear material due to tubes (Arizona, India); also reflections from silica pseudomorphs of former parallel fibrous mineral replaced by quartz, e.g., crocidolite; also weak chatoyancy, sometimes strong, observed in numerous specimens of rose quartz.

QUARTZ. Asterism sometimes observed in rose quartz.

QUARTZ. Aventurescence caused by mica inclusions in massive granular metamorphic quartz or quartzite, e.g., green (fuchsite mica) from India, yellow, golden, red, etc. (altered mica), from Ural Mountains.

QUARTZ. Chatoyancy due to foreign mineral inclusions is observed in specimens containing rutile needles, also extremely slender crystals of bright yellow goethite (misnamed "cacoxenite").

SCAPOLITE. Chatoyancy, sometimes very strong, due to tubular cavities parallel to *c*-axis; some weak chatoyancy observed in massive material from fibrous growth.

SERPENTINE. Weak chatoyancy has been observed in translucent, parallel fibrous serpentines, e.g., williamsite from Maryland, bowenite from New Zealand; very strong chatoyancy observed in opaque cross-fiber types but these may not be serpentines.

SPINEL. Asterism, very rarely observed.

SPODUMENE. Weak chatoyancy observed in some partly altered crystals of common whitish or greenish spodumene (Maine).

TOPAZ. Weak, spangly chatoyancy occurs in some prismatic crystals of Ouro Preto, Brazil, yellow-orange topaz due to numerous partings parallel to the *c*-axis.

TOURMALINE. Weak to strong chatoyancy from tubes parallel to the *c*-axis.

TOURMALINE. Weak aventurescence occurs in the brown buergerite crystals of Mexico.

TREMOLITE. Weak chatoyancy sometimes occurs.

ULEXITE. Brilliant chatoyancy in white cross-fiber seams from Boron, California. Excellent fiber-optics effect parallel to acicular crystals in "television stone."

WILLEMITE. Weak chatoyancy in impure material from Franklin, New Jersey, is rarely observed.

WILLEMITE. Aventurescence, probably due to inclusions of hematite, noted in some specimens of green willemite from Franklin, New Jersey; such inclusions are oriented and it is possible to produce a fair "eye" if a cabochon is properly cut.

WOLLASTONITE. Weak chatoyancy in massive fibrous material.

FLUORESCENCE

STOKES'S LAW. *The light waves emitted by a fluorescing substance will be longer wavelength than those used to excite the fluorescence.* The most striking and useful application of this law occurs when invisible ultraviolet (UV) light is directed toward a suitable substance which then emits longer wavelengths than those of UV, placing them in the visible portion of the spectrum and thus making the fluorescent display perceptible by the human eye. Conversely it has been found that visible light can be used to excite similar response in certain substances but the longer wavelengths emitted by the substances fall in the infrared region and are invisible to the eye.

Ultraviolet Light

Useful range: 4,000-2,000 Angstroms. Long-wave region (LW): 4,000-3,150 A. Medium-wave region (MW): 3,150-2,800 A.

Short-wave region (SW): 2,800-2,000 A. WOOD'S GLASS FILTER. A cobalt glass of very dark purplish color passing UV between 4,000A and 3,000A, with **maximum transmissibility at 3,850A** in the LW region.

MERCURY VAPOR LIGHT EMISSIONS. When mercury vapor sealed within a suitable electrical lamp is caused to glow it emits characteristic wavelengths of light in the visible region but also in the UV at 3,650A (very strong), at 3,984, 3,906, 3,654, 3,341, 3,131, 3,125, and 2,537 A (the last strong). The useful emissions for UV work are in the LW region at 3,660A and in the SW region at 2,537A, the latter requiring use of a fused quartz envelope to pass this wavelength.

ALUMINUM REFLECTORS. Polished aluminum is exceptionally effective in reflecting UV and IR with least loss.

FLUORESCENT MINERALS AND GEMSTONES

Listed by colors through the spectrum from violet through red, and through brown, tan, cream, and white. Varieties appear under the appropriate species.

Reference: For further details consult S. Gleason, *Ultraviolet Guide to Minerals* (New York: Van Nostrand Reinhold, 1960).

Abbreviations: C = commonly noted; LW = long wave; O = occasionally noted; R = rarely noted; SW = short wave ultraviolet lamp.

VIOLET. SW. Beryl (morganite, R), corundum (synth. pink, R), diamond (O), fluorite (C), hardystonite (O), margarosanite (C).

VIOLET. LW. Apatite (R), beryl (morganite, R), diamond (O), diopside (R), fluorite (C), scapolite (O).

BLUE. SW. Allophane (R), amber (O), andesine (R), anorthoclase (R), barylite (O), benitoite (C), calcite (R), celestite (O), copal (O), corundum (synth. blue, O), cuproscheelite (C), danburite (O), diamond (C), dolomite (R), dumortierite (R), fluorite (C), forsterite (R), glass (O), hydrozincite (C), manganapatite (R), quartz (amethyst, R), sassolite (O), scheelite (C), smithsonite (O), spinel (synth. blue, O)

BLUE. LW. Amber (O), anhydrite (R), calcite (R), casein plastic (C), celestite (O), danburite (O), diamond (C), dolomite (R), fluorite (C), glass (O), herderite (R), opal (O), orthoclase (moonstone, O), phosphophyllite (C), quartz (amethyst, R), turquoise (R).

BLUE-WHITE. SW. Anorthite (R), anthophyllite (R), calcite (O), dumortierite (O), epsomite (C), hanksite (C), hemimorphite (O), ivory (C), okenite (O), scheelite (C).

BLUE-WHITE. LW. Alunogen (C), brewsterite (O), brucite (C), calciothomsonite (O), danburite (O), datolite (R), hanskite (C), heulandite (R), hydromagnesite (O), ivory (C), mellite (O), nepheline (O), nesquehonite (O), opal (C), pearl (C), quartz (igneous geodal, O), sepiolite (O), witherite (C).

BLUE-GREEN. SW. Borax (O), danburite (R), pirssonite (O), wollastonite (O).

BLUE-GREEN. LW. Apophyllite (R), borax (O), pirssonite (O), wollastonite (O).

GREEN. SW. Allophane (O), amber (O), andalusite (R), andersonite (C), apatite (O), beryl (O), bolivarite (O), botryogen (R), chabazite (O), chrysoberyl (O), cuprotungstite (C), diamond (O), evansite (O), fluorite (O), glass (O), hydromagnesite (O), koksharovite (O), liebigite (C), magnesite (R), novacekite (O), opal (C), quartz (chalcedony C), rutherfordine (O), schoepite (C), smithsonite (O), spinel (synth.

yellow or green, (C), stolzite (O), variscite (O), willemite (C), witherite (R).

GREEN. LW. Adamite (C), amber (O), andersonite (C), apatite (O), beryl (emerald, O), bolivarite (O), corundophilite (O), corundum (synth. colorless, O), diamond (C), gibbsite (O), glass (O), hanksite (O), leadhillite (C), liebigite (C), margarite (O), microcline (amazonite, O), milarite (O), novacekite (O), opal (C), quartz (chrysoprase, C), rutherfordine (O), schoepite (C), serpentine (williamsite, C), spinel (synth. yellow, yellow-green, colorless, C; pale blue natural, O), variscite (O), wavellite (O), willemite (C).

GREEN-WHITE. SW. Aragonite (R), calcite (O), dolomite (O), manganapatite (R), topaz (R).

GREEN-WHITE. LW. Dolomite (O), mesolite (O), strontianite (O), topaz (R).

GREEN-YELLOW. SW. Abernathyite (C), andersonite (C), bayleyite (O), fluorite (O), gastunite (C), meta-autunite (C), metauranocircite (C), metazeunerite (O), opal (O), phlogopite (R), polylithionite (R), rabbittite (O), sabugalite (O), saleeite (C), schoepite (C), schroeckeringite (C), swartzite (C), troegerite (C), uranocircite (C), uranopilite (C), uranospinite (C), zippeite (C).

GREEN-YELLOW. LW. Abernathyite (C), andersonite (C), aphthitalite (C), autunite (C), bayleyite (O), gastunite (C), meta-autunite (C), metaurano-circite (C), metazeunerite (O), opal (hyalite, C), rabbittite (O), sabugalite (C), saleeite (C), schoepite (C), schroeckeringite (C), swartzite (C), troegerite (C), uranocircite (C), uranopilite (C), uranospinite (C), zippeite (C).

YELLOW. SW. Allingite (O), amber (C), andesine (O), anglesite (C), apatite (C), beryl (R), calcite (O), es-perite (C), chondrodite (R), cuproscheelite (C), cuprotungstite (C), diamond (C), diaspore (R), halite (O), matlockite (O), opal (C), pectolite (O), powellite (C), priceite (O), rhodizite (O), simpsonite (O),

smithsonite (O), spodumene (O), terlinguaite (O), tourmaline (Mg-types, R), trona (C), witherite (O), yttrofluorite (O), zircon (C).

YELLOW. LW. Allingite (O), amber (C), anglesite (C), apatite (O), apophyllite (O), barite (C), bronzite (R), cerussite (O), chlorapatite (C), diamond (C), fluorite (O), glass (O), greenockite (O), gypsum (C), lanarkite (O), leadhillite (C), magnesite (O), massicot (O), matlockite (O), mellite (O), opal (C), pectolite (O), periclase (R), phosgenite (C), priceite (O), pyromorphite (O), pyrophyllite (O), quartz (chalcedony, C), scapolite (C), sepiolite (O), serpentine (yellowish types, C), spodumene (O), steigerite (O), talc (O), thenardite (C), topaz (C), tremolite (O), trona (O), wernerite (C), witherite (O), yttrofluorite (O), zircon (C), zoisite (thulite (R).

YELLOW-ORANGE. Anglesite (C), manganapatite (C), wernerite (C).

ORANGE. SW. Calcite (C), clinohedrite (C), collinsite (R), corundum (colorless, C; Ceylon blue, O; Ceylon yellow, C; synth. orange, C; synth. yellow, R; synth. green, O; synth. alexandrite, O), diamond (C), dolomite (O), phosgenite (O), scapolite (O), shortite (O), sphalerite (O), svabite (O), zircon (C); zoisite (thulite, O).

ORANGE. LW. Alunite (O), amblygonite (O), ankerite (O), anthophyllite (R), apatite (O), calcite (O), calomel (R), colemanite (C), corundum (colorless, O; Ceylon blue, O; Ceylon yellow, C; synth. orange, C; synth. green, O; synth. alexandrite, O), dahllite (O), diamond (C), dolomite (O), epsomite (O), grossular (R), hambergite (R), hauyne, (O), kaemmererite (R), lapis lazuli (in spots, C), merwinite (O), metavoltine (R), mimetite (O), nosean (O), orthoclase (gem types, O), pectolite (C), petalite (O), pyrophyllite (O), scapolite (O), sodalite (massive, in spots, C; hackmanite, C), sphalerite (cleiophane, C), spinel (mauve, natural, O), spodumene (kunzite, C; Brazil pale green, C), tarbuttite (O), thenardite

(C), topaz (O), willemite (O), wulfenite (O).

ORANGE-RED. LW. Nepheline (C), sodalite (hackmanite, C).

RED. SW. Aragonite (O), beryl (nat. emerald, R; synth. emerald, C), calcite (C), chrysoberyl (alexandrite, O), corundum (ruby, pink, nat., and synth., C; Ceylon blue, O; synth. orange, C; synth. alexandrite, O); diamond (O), kyanite (R), manganoaxinite (O), marshite (R), mooreite (O), opal (R), rhodochrosite (O), rhodonite (O), spinel (red, C).

RED. LW. Anhydrite (O), aragonite (O), beryl (nat. emerald, R; synth. emerald, C), calcite (O), calomel (O), chrysoberyl (alexandrite, O), corundum (ruby, pink, nat., and synth., C; Ceylon blue, O; synth. orange, C; synth. yellow, R; synth. green, O; synth. alexandrite, O), euclase (R), gearksutite (R), hodgkinsonite (O), kyanite (R), marshite (R), opal (R), rhodonite (O), spinel (red, C; synth. blue, O), tremolite (O), willemite (R).

PINK. SW. andesine (O), apatite (O), aragonite (C), calcite (C), eucryptite (C), hauyne (O), kyanite (O), manganapatite (O), paracelsian (O), rhodochrosite (O), taeniolite (O), tremolite (O), vauxite (O).

PINK. LW. Anthophyllite (R), apatite (O), aragonite (O), benitoite (colorless cores, C), calcite (C), calomel (O), coral (C), dolomite (O), kyanite (R), lepidolite (O), leucophane (O), mesolite (O), sodalite (hackmanite, C), spodumene (kunzite, O), talc (R), tremolite (O), vauxite (O).

BROWN. SW. Amphibole (byssolite, O), colerainite (R), crocoite (R), gyrolite (R), wulfenite (O).

BROWN. LW. Amphibole (byssolite, O), chondrodite (R), crocoite (R), dahllite (O), wulfenite (O).

TAN. SW. Aragonite (O), burkeite (O), calcite (C).

TAN. LW. Amblygonite (R), anorthite (R), aragonite (O), barite (C), burkeite (O), calcite (C), lumachelle marble (C), opal (C), pyromorphite (O), quartz (chalcedony, C), scheelite (R).

CREAM. SW. Allophane (O), calcite (C), celestite (C), creedite (O), dolomite (O), lanarkite (O), parahopeite (O), spencerite (O), sulfohalite (O), taranakite (O), thorogummite (O).

CREAM. LW. Anorthite (O), barite (C), celestite (O), colemanite (C), creedite (C), dolomite (O), fluorite (C), gibbsite (O), gypsum (O), hemimorphite (O), mesolite (O), parahopeite (O), pectolite (C), petalite (O), pollucite (O), quartz (chalcedony, C), serpentine (chrysotile, O), spencerite (O), spodumene (O), strontianite (O), sulfohalite (O), talc (O), taranakite (O), thorogummite (O), topaz (C), tremolite (O), wavellite (O), witherite (C), wollastonite (C).

WHITE. SW. Albite (O), alunite (O), amber (O), anglesite (C), aphthitalite (C), aragonite (C), barite (O), calcite (C), casein plastic (C), celestite (C), copal (O). dawsonite (O), diopside (O), dolomite (O), glass (O), halite (C), ivory (C), kaolinite (C), melanophlogite (O), mellite (O), montmorillonite (O), natron (O), opal (C), petalite (O), pseudowavellite (O), quartz (chalcedony, C), scheelite (C), simpsonite (O), smithsonite (O), spinel (synth. colorless, C), stolzite (C), strontianite (C), tortoise shell (C), ulexite (C), willemite (O).

WHITE. LW. Albite (O), amber (O), amblygonite (C), analcime (O), apatite (O), aragonite (O), barite (O), bertrandite (O), calcite (C), casein plastic (C), celestite (O), cerussite (O), colemanite (C), copal (O), datolite (O), evansite (O), fluorite (O), gaylussite (O), gibbsite (O), halite (C), halloysite (O), hemimorphite (O), hydrozincite (O), ivory (C), kyanite (R), jadeite (C), laumontite (C), leucite (R), melanophlogite (O), meyerhofferite (O), opal (C), petalite (O), pickeringite (O), pollucite (O), pyrophyllite (O), quartz (chalcedony, C; igneous geodes, O), sanbornite (C), serpentine (yellowish types, C), spurrite (O), talc (O), thenardite (C), tincalconite (C), topaz (C), tortoise shell (C), tunellite (C), zircon (C).

Reference: An extensive and detailed treatment of fluorescence in minerals appears in J. De Ment, *Fluorochemistry* (Brooklyn, N.Y.: Chemical Publishing Company, 1945), pp. 420-97.

PHOSPHORESCENCE

Phosphorescence is the continued emission of light after the exciting source has been extinguished. Generally it is fleeting, lasting only a few seconds or minutes, but exceptional durations have been noted (see below). The exciting source is SW or LW ultraviolet.

Phosphorescence Noted in Minerals

Adamite—green (O).
Albite—brownish (SW).
Allophane—cream (SW).
Aluminite—white (R).
Amblygonite—pale blue (SW, LW, O).
Apatite—yellow-orange (O).
Aphthitalite—greenish-yellow (SW, C).
Aragonite—white (C).
Axinite—red (R).
Barite—cream (O).
Beryl—goshenite: blue-white; morganite: pink.
Borax—greenish, blue (C).
Brucite—blue-white (O).
Burkeite—blue (SW, LW).
Bustamite—orange.
Calcite—pink (C), blue.
Celestite—green-white (O).
Cerussite—pale blue (R).
Clinohedrite—orange (C).
Colemanite—white (C).
Dawsonite—green-white (SW).
Deweylite—pale blue (SW).
Diamond—blue (O).
Diopside—pink (R).
Dolomite—pink (R).
Elaterite—brown (O).
Fluorite—violet, blue (O).
Glauberite—blue (R).
Gypsum—white (O).
Hanksite—blue-green, cream (C).
Hydromagnesite—green (C).
Inyoite—white (SW, LW).
Kyanite—green-white.
Langbeinite—greenish-white (SW).

Lazurite—blue.
Magnesite—white (R).
Meyerhofferite—cream (SW, LW).
Natron—blue (SW).
Opal—white (C).
Pectolite—orange, yellow (C).
Phenakite—blue.
Phosgenite—red, orange (O).
Pirssonite—blue-green (SW, LW).
Quartz (chalcedony)—white (R).
Scapolite—orange-yellow (O).
Scheelite—white.
Smithsonite—green-white (R).
Sodalite—orange (hackmanite).
Sphalerite—orange (cleiophane).
Spodumene—orange (kunzite).
Strontianite—white.
Tarbuttite—orange.
Thaumasite—white (R).
Thenardite—yellow (C).
Topaz—cream (R).
Trona—blue-white (C).
Ulexite—white (C).
Wavellite—green-white (O).
Wernerite—orange-yellow (C).
Willemite—green (C).
Witherite—blue-white (O).
Wollastonite—red (C).
Zircon—blue-white.

EXCEPTIONALLY PERSISTENT PHOSPHORESCENCE

Thousands of mineral specimens examined by H. E. Millson and H. E. Millson, Jr., *J. Optical Soc. Amer.* 40, no. 7 (1950): 430-35, showed that only a relatively few phosphoresced for long periods of time after irradiation with UV (2,537A). However, *distinguishable color* could not be detected by the human eye except for short periods immediately after withdrawal of exciting source. The longest detectable color phosphorescence occurred in a radiated-massive willemite from Franklin, New Jersey, i.e., 1.5 hours. The longest visible phosphorescent duration occurred in a fluorite which continued to emit a visible phosphorescence for more than 4 years. Extremely protracted phosphorescence was also noted in other calcites, fluorites, spodumenes, wernerites, and willemites. The table below gives initial phosphorescent color noted after excitation, followed by period of persistence in hours.

Albite. Yellow-orange, 275 hrs.
Apatite. Orange, 124.
Aragonite. Yellowish-white, 80.
Beryl (goshenite). 152.
Beryl (morganite). 296.
Bustamite. 29.
Calcite. White, pink, orange; 24-4,600+.
Esperite. Yellow, 33.
Clinohedrite. Yellowish-orange, 175.
Fluorite. Violet, blue, green, orange; 36-72, 347.
Kyanite (rhaetizite). Greenish-white, 51.
Lazurite. Blue, 50.
Phenakite. Blue, 120.
Phosgenite. Orange, 58.
Scapolite-Wernerite. Gold, orange, yellow; 1,050-4,500.
Scheelite. White, 25-44.
Sodalite. White, 70.
Spodumene. Orange, 3,800.
Spodumene (kunzite). Bright orange, 69.
Tarbuttite. Orange, 57.
Willemite. Yellow-green, 27-340.
Wollastonite. Orange, 590.
Zircon. Bluish-white, 720.

INFRARED LUMINESCENT MINERALS

Infrared luminescence in the range 7,000-c. 10,000 A has been investigated by D. F. Barnes, with the following list taken from his publication. About 200,000 specimens in the U.S. National Museum were investigated for IR luminescence, of which about 1,500 specimens representing the species named below provided IR emissions after excitation with visible, violet, and/or UV light. Strong IR emissions are characteristic of species activated by chromium (e.g., corundum, beryl, spinel, jadeite, kyanite), by cadmium in the case of greenockite, and by the rare earths in such species as scheelite, fluorite, apatite, feldspars, and amphiboles.

Native elements: Diamond, sulfur, selensulfur.

Sulfides: Sphalerite, greenockite, wurtzite.

Oxides: Cuprite, montroydite, senarmontite, corundum, valentinite, cervantite, stibiconite, brucite, hydrotalcite, bauxite, diaspore, spinel, chrysoberyl (alexandrite).

Halides: Halite, marshite, fluorite, terlinguaite, matlockite, cryolithionite, cryolite, gearksutite, chiolite, creedite.

Carbonates: Calcite (also Mn-, Cu-, and Pb-calcites), magnesite, rhodochrosite, smithsonite, aragonite, strontianite, cerussite, dolomite, pirssonite, gaylussite, phosgenite, hydrocerussite, leadhillite.

Borates: Borax, probertite, ulexite, colemanite, meyerhofferite, howlite, hambergite, sussexite.

Sulfates: Barite, celestite, anglesite, anhydrite, gypsum, alunogen, lanarkite, alunite, botryogen, hanksite, crocoite.

Phosphates: Anapaite, parahopeite, amblygonite, apatite (dahllite, Mn-apatite), pyromorphite, mimetite, vanadinite, hedyphane, wavellite.

Tungstates: Scheelite, stolzite, wulfenite, cuprotungstite.

Silica: Quartz (agate, chalcedony, jasper), tridymite, cristobalite, melanophlogite, opal (cachalong, hydrophane, hyalite, opalized wood, geyserite, tabasheer).

Nesosilicates: Willemite, calcium larsenite, norbergite, leucophoenicite, andalusite (chiastolite), kyanite, topaz, grossular, andradite (demantoid), zoisite (thulite, saussurite), epidote (tawmawite), zircon, cyrtolite, alvite, sphene, axinite, howlite, tourmaline.

Sorosilicates: Hemimorphite, clinohedrite, wollastonite, pectolite, beryl (emerald, aquamarine), idocrase (californite).

Inosilicates: Sillimanite, spodumene (kunzite, hiddenite), diopside, jadeite, diallage, enstatite, bronzite, tremolite (hexagonite, chromtremolite), byssolite amphibole, actinolite, arfvedsonite, anthophyllite, serpentine (chrysotile), saponite, cerolite, deweylite, jurupaite, crestmoreite, sepiolite, iddingsite.

Phyllosilicates: Euclase, leucophane, apophyllite, talc, muscovite, lepidolite, taeniolite, xanthophyllite, cookeite, colerainite, kaolinite, montmorillonite, allophane, halloysite, gyrolite, okenite.

Tektosilicates: Nepheline, trimerite, petalite, analcime, pollucite, orthoclase, adularia, microcline (amazonite), hyalophane, albite, oligoclase, andesine, anorthite, danburite, sodalite, hauyne, scapolite, meionite, datolite, natrolite, hydronepheline, laubanite, mesolite, thomsonite, laumontite, heulandite, chabazite.

Source: David F. Barnes, *Infrared Luminescence of Minerals,* U.S. Geological Survey Bulletin 1052-C (1958).

THERMOLUMINESCENT MINERALS

Thermoluminescence is observed in complete darkness using a heat source which does not contribute visible light. In all of the specimens thermoluminescence disappears as they reach red-heat and thereafter they cannot again be reactivated. However, in certain species, temperatures below this point can be raised and lowered several times with corresponding reappearance of thermoluminescence.

Temperatures of thermoluminescence on selected specimens have been determined by Northup and Lee as follows: the figures give temperatures for first appearance of white light, first colored light, maximum brilliance, and total extinction.

Fluorite: 44° C. (111° F.), 77° C. (171° F.) greenish-white, 213° C. (415° F.) green, and 324° C. (615° F.) extinction.

Calcite: 107° C. (225° F.), 143° C. (289° F.) yellowish-white, 246° C. (475° F.) orange-yellow, and 338° C. (640° F.).

Fluorapatite: 70° C. (158° F.), 102° C. (216° F.) yellowish-white, 132° C. (270° F.) greenish-yellow, and 288° C. (550° F.).

Wernerite: 63° C. (145° F.), 91° C. (196° F.) yellowish-white, 213° C. (415° F.) greenish-yellow, and 413° C. (775° F.).

Sodalite (hackmanite): 74° C. (165° F.), 235° C. (455° F.) greenish-white, 318° C. (604° F.) yellowish-green, and 402° C. (756° F.).

Esperite: 63° C. (145° F.), 77° C. (171° F.) pale greenish-white, 98° C. (208° F.) pale greenish-white, and 124° C. (255° F.).

Source: Based on findings of F. Hegemann and H. Steinmetz, *Zentralblatt f. Min. . . .,* Jg. 1933, part A, no. 1 (1933), pp. 24-38; M. A. Northup and O. I. Lee, *J. Optical Soc. Amer.* 30, no. 5 (1940): 206-23.

The list below gives one or more colors of thermoluminescence that have been observed in the various specimens tested.

Albite: Green-white, blue-green, white, cream.

Amblygonite: Blue-white, white.

Apatite: Orange-yellow.

Aragonite: Orange-yellow.

Barite: White.

Barylite: Blue-white.

Calcite: Orange-yellow, yellow, cream, white.

Esperite: Green-white.

Cancrinite: Green-yellow.

Corundum (ruby): Pink.

Fluorapatite: Green-yellow.

Fluorite: Purplish, blue, blue-white, blue-green, green, green-white, green-yellow, orange-yellow, yellow, white.

Lepidolite: Orange-red.

Manganapatite: Yellow.

Manganpectolite: White.

Microcline (perthitic in part): Blue-white.

Oligoclase: Blue-white, white.

Pectolite: White, cream.

Phlogopite: White.

Quartz (chalcedony): White.

Quartz (smoky, rock crystal, amethyst): White.

Scapolite: Cream.

Smithsonite: Red.

Sphalerite: Blue.

Sodalite: Yellow-green.

Spodumene: Orange-yellow, yellow.

Thaumasite: White.

Topaz: Orange.

Tourmaline (some rubellite): Orange-red.

Tremolite: Blue-white.

Wernerite: Yellow, orange-yellow, green-yellow.

Willemite: Green-white.

Witherite: White.

Wollastonite: Blue-white.

Zoisite (thulite): White.

Negative results were obtained on specimens of ankerite, autunite, azurite, beryllonite, biotite, cerussite, dolomite, gypsum, hydromagnesite, lithiophyllite, magnesite, monazite, muscovite, nesquehonite, opal (hyalite), polylithionite, pyromorphite, rhodochrosite, siderite, spurrite, tourmaline (green, red, black), triphylite, and zinnwaldite.

As in nearly all examples of luminescence it must be emphasized that not all specimens of any of the species mentioned above will luminesce, and conversely, luminescence may not be confined to such species by any means.

TRIBOLUMINESCENT MINERALS

In the course of determining thermoluminescence of minerals, Northup and Lee determined triboluminescence in the species named below. It appears when minerals are ground in a mortar or scratched with a hard file in darkness, and is commonly observed when quartz varieties are sawed with a diamond blade or struck with steel in the dark. The colors of triboluminescence appear after the species name.

Albite: White (O).
Amblygonite: Blue-white, white (O).
Calcite: Faint white (R).
Fluorite: White, bluish-white, cream (C).

Lepidolite: Blue-white.
Manganapatite: Faint white.
Microcline: White (O).
Pectolite: Cream (C), white.
Quartz (chalcedony): White (C).
Quartz (rock crystal): White (C), yellow.
Quartz (rose): Yellow (C).
Sphalerite: Orange (C), white, cream, yellow.
Willemite: Green-white, white.
Wollastonite: White.

Reference: M. A. Northup and O. I. Lee, *J. Optical Soc. Amer.* 30, no. 5 (1940); 206-23.

The following list of triboluminescent minerals is from Lindener. The question marks indicate reported triboluminescence not confirmed by Lindener.

Adularia	Biotite
Aeschynite	Boracite
Albite	Borax
Andalusite	Calcite
Andesine	Cancrinite
Anhydrite	Cerussite
Ankerite	Chiolite
Anorthite	Chrysoberyl
Apophyllite	Clinochlore
Aragonite	Clinohedrite
Asbestos (chrysotile?)	Colemanite
Barytocalcite	Corundum
Bertrandite	Cryolite
Beryl	Cryolithionite

Danburite	Pectolite
Davyne	Petalite
Diamond	Pharmacolite
Diopside	Pharmacosiderite
Dolomite	Phenakite
Edenite	Phlogopite
Eudidymite	Prehnite
Euphyllite	Prosopite
Fluorapatite	Proustite (?)
Fluorite	Pyrargyrite (?)
Galena	Quartz
Gaylussite	Ralstonite
Glauberite	Rhodochrosite
Gypsum	Sanidine
Halite	Scolecite
Hemimorphite	Serpentine
Kyanite	Sillimanite
Labradorite	Sodalite
Langbeinite	Sphalerite
Lazurite	Sphene
Lepidolite	Spinel
Leucite	Spodumene
Leucophane	Stannite
Magnesite	Stolzite
Marialite	Strontianite
Margarite	Struvite
Meionite	Sulfur (alpha)
Melinophane	Tetrahedrite (?)
Microcline	Thomsonite
Microsommite	Topaz
Mizzonite	Tourmaline (colored)
Muscovite	Tremolite-actinolite
Natrolite	Willemite
Nepheline	Witherite (?)
Nephrite	Wollastonite
Oligoclase	Wulfenite
Opal	Zircon

Note: No tantalates or niobates were triboluminescent.
Source: B. Lindener, "Über die Tribolumines-cenz der Mineralien," *Bull. Acad. Sci. St. Petersb.* (1910), pp. 999-1022.

X-RAY FLUORESCENCE

The numbers in the below list refer to Keilhack's system of measuring intensity of fluorescence on a scale from 0 to 64, with the last being extremely brilliant.

Sources: Identified by the letters "W" for R. Webster, *Gems* (London, 1970), pp. 766-67; "A" for A. E. Alexander, *Gemmologist* 15, no. 177 (1946): 49; and "K" for K. Keilhack *Zeitschrift d. Deutsch. geolog. Gesellschaft*, Jg. 1898 (1898), pp. 131-36, all of which extracts or articles concern the X-ray fluorescence of minerals and/or gemstones.

Adularia: 26 (K).

Amblygonite: 12 (K); green (W).

Andalusite (green): faint (A).

Anglesite: 25 (K).

Anhydrite: 5 (K).

Anorthite: 2 (K).

Apatite: Yellow, 14-43 (K).

Aragonite: 5 (K).

Autunite: 18 (K).

Benitoite: Blue (W).

Beryl (morganite): Red (W); dull to bright (A).

Beryl (emerald): Red (W).

Beryl (synth. emerald): Red (W).

Beryllonite: Blue (W).

Calcite: 32 (K); Orange (W).

Cassiterite: Yellow (W).

Cerargyrite: 27 (K).

Cerussite: 32 (K).

Corundum (ruby, nat. or synth.): Red (W); brilliant (A).

Corundum (pink, nat. or synth.): Red (W).

Corundum (Ceylon blue): Red (W); bright (A).

Corundum (Siam blue, some): Faint (A).

Corundum (Ceylon yellow): Orange (W).

Corundum (synth. blue): Blue (W).

Corundum (synth. yellow): Violet, some (W).

Corundum (synth. orange): Red (W).

Corundum (synth. green): Orange (W).

Corundum (synth. alexandrite): Orange or red (W).

Corundum (synth. colorless): Orange or some violet (W).

Danburite: Violet (W).

Diamond: Blue, white, yellow, or green (W); brown diamond-12, colorless diamond-18 (K); medium to brilliant (A).

Diopside: 1 (K); yellow (W).

Fluorite: Blue or violet (W); 4-64, green (K).

Glass: Some, green or blue (W).

Glauberite: 17 (K).

Halite: 29 (K).

Hemimorphite: 16 (K).

Hydrogrossular ("Transvaal jade"): Orange (W).

Jadeite (green): Medium to bright (A).

Kyanite: Blue (W).

Labradorite: 4 (K).

Lanarkite: 25 (K).

Lapis Lazuli: Blue or yellow (W).

Leadhillite: 14 (K).

Matlockite: 26 (K).

Microcline (amazonite): Medium to bright (A).

Opal: Green, some (W).

Orthoclase: 5 (K).

Orthoclase: (moonstone): Blue (W); dull, medium (A).

Orthoclase (yellow): Faint (A).

Pearl (freshwater): Yellow (W).

Pearl (cultured): Yellow (W).

Petalite: Orange (W).

Phenakite: Blue (W).

Phosgenite: 19 (K).

Prehnite: 20 (K).

Pyromorphite: 9 (K).

Quartz (rock crystal): Faint (A).

Quartz (rose): Medium (A).

Rhodizite: Yellow or green (W).

Rhodolite: Faint (A).

Sanidine: 6 (K).

Scapolite: Orange, white, or violet (W).

Scheelite: Blue (W, K); 60 (K).

Sinhalite (pale yellow): Orange (W).

Sodalite: Yellow (in spots, W), or blue (W).

Spinel (red): Red (W); dark red none (A).

Spinel (light red): Faint (A).

Spinel (blue): Faint (A).

Spinel (green): Faint (A).

Spinel (synth. blue): Blue or some red (W).

Spinel (synth. green): Red (W).

Spinel (synth. yellow-green): Green (W).

Spinel (synth. yellow): Green (W).

Spinel (synth. colorless): Green or some blue (W).

Spodumene (kunzite): Orange (W).

Stolzite: 5 (K).

Strontianite: 3 (K).

Sylvite: 25 (K).

Taaffeite: Green (W).

Topaz (blue gem): Medium (A); topaz generally is blue, green, or orange (W); intensity 0-10 (K).

Tourmaline (pink): Violet (W); pale blue fl. (A).

Tourmaline (Elba): 0-7 (K).

Tremolite: 5 (K).

Willemite: Green (W).

Witherite: 2 (K).

Wollastonite: 50 (K).

Wulfenite: 5 (K).

Zircon: Yellow, blue, or violet (W); 8-39 (K); medium to brilliant (A).

Zoisite (thulite): Red (W).

Index